D1314826

LOGICAL FOUNDATIONS OF MATHEMATICS FOR BEHAVIORAL SCIENTISTS

LOGICAL FOUNDATIONS OF MATHEMATICS FOR BEHAVIORAL SCIENTISTS

ABRAHAM S. LUCHINS

Department of Psychology
State University of New York at Albany

EDITH H. LUCHINS

Department of Mathematics
Rensselaer Polytechnic Institute

HOLT, RINEHART AND WINSTON, INC.

New York · Chicago · San Francisco · Toronto · London

Passages from *Productive Thinking* by Max Wertheimer copyright 1945 by Max Wertheimer. Reprinted with the permission of Harper & Row, Publishers, Inc.

Passages from *The Nature of Mathematics* by Max Black (1934, 1950) by permission and Routledge and Kegan Paul Ltd.

Passages from *A Source Book of Gestalt Psychology* edited by Willis D. Ellis (1938) by permission of Harcourt, Brace & World, Inc. and Routledge and Kegan Paul Ltd.

Passages from "Formal Analysis and the Language of Behavior Theory" by William W. Rozeboom in *Current Issues in the Philosophy of Science* edited by Herbert Feigl and Grover Maxwell (1961) by permission of Holt, Rinehart and Winston, Inc.

Passages from *Contemporary Ethical Theories* by Thomas E. Hill (1950) by permission of The Macmillan Company.

Passages from *Out of My Later Years* by Albert Einstein (1950) by permission of the Estate of Albert Einstein.

In Memory of
Morris Aaron Luchins
1880–1959

Preface

During the past two decades, we have collaborated on research and publications that relate the behavioral sciences to mathematics. Time and time again we have encountered points of contact between the behavioral sciences and foundational issues of mathematics. This book explores such contacts. It seems to us that certain foundational issues in mathematics have their counterparts in psychological issues. Moreover, knowledge of various foundational viewpoints and major issues in mathematics may prove helpful in the attempts to develop foundations for the behavioral sciences. Furthermore, foundational and philosophical controversies in mathematics pose some problems that behavioral scientists may help to solve. Such problems take on added importance in light of the growing interchange between mathematics and the behavioral sciences and the increased interest among behavioral scientists in the fields of mathematics and philosophy of science. In its description of the foundations of mathematics, the book emphasizes (but does not restrict itself to) aspects that may interest behavioral scientists, particularly psychologists.

Parts of the book have been used by the psychologist-author for courses in the history and systems of psychology, doctrines of man in the behavioral sciences, and methodology and foundations of clinical psychology. Some chapters were used by the mathematician-author for lectures in a metamathematics course and a number-systems course that were given to upperclassmen and graduate students, some of whom were teachers of secondary school mathematics. *Logical Foundations of Mathematics for Behavioral Scientists* can be an aid to students of the behavioral sciences, to mathematics teachers and teachers-in-training, and to those taking courses in the philosophy of mathematics where an interdisciplinary approach is desired. This book also lends itself to use in courses or seminars in the foundations, philosophy, or methodology of science. We hope that it will also be of interest to the nonprofessional, general reader, since the material is presented so that it can be understood in the main by those who have not had formal courses in psychology, mathematics, or philosophy.

The chapters need not be read in the order in which they are presented. It is advisable first to read the introductory chapter, which surveys the book, and then to read the rest in the order of one's interests and concern. A reader may not want to become involved with the concept of number at the onset, and he may, after the introduction, turn to the foundational schools. In the course of reading, he may become curious about the number concept and turn back to earlier chapters. It is even possible to read and understand the chapters on psychological implications before the corresponding chapters on mathematics, to read the chapter on formalism and psychology before the chapters on formalism, or to read the chapter on intuitionism and psychology before the chapters on intuitionism. In view of the possibility that the reader may want to skip around, we tried to keep each chapter self-contained, even to the extent of, at times, repeating concepts and ideas.

This book was influenced by the work of mathematicians, philosophers, and psychologists from ancient times to the present. We want here to acknowledge in a general way our indebtedness to those whose thinking on foundational matters has influenced us, whether or not their writings are included in the bibliography. We are grateful to the writers and their publishers who granted us permission to quote from their publications. We want to thank the following authors whose stimulating texts have been used extensively herein: Yehoshua Bar-Hillel, Richard Courant, Abraham A. Fraenkel, Arend Heyting, Stephen C. Kleene, Herbert Robbins, J. Barkley Rosser, Alfred Tarski, Friedrich Waismann, and Raymond L. Wilder.

It is a pleasure to thank our respective departments and chairmen for having in so many ways facilitated the preparation of this text. We want to thank Margaret A. Tooley and Barbara Tilley for their efficient typing. Our children, David, Daniel, Jeremy, Anne, and Joseph, helped with clerical tasks during the years of preparation for the book. Finally, we are grateful to the staff of Holt, Rinehart and Winston for their encouragement and assistance.

Albany, New York　　　　　　　　　　　　　　　　　A. S. L.
Troy, New York　　　　　　　　　　　　　　　　　　E. H. L.

July 1965

Contents

CHAPTER 1

Introduction

Mathematics in Psychology

The application of mathematics to psychology has been relatively limited until recent years. The limitations have been both with respect to the kinds of mathematics used and the areas of psychology to which they were applied. Mathematics has been applied mainly to so-called experimental psychology (Boring, 1961) and to certain aspects of tests and measurements. Psychologists, generally speaking, have sought in mathematics for ways of quantifying their findings and of testing the statistical significance of their data and hypotheses; for these purposes they turned to classical statistics. To some extent, such limitations still exist. Luce (1964, pp. 364–365) points out that "huge portions of both academic and applied psychology are essentially free from mathematical inroads" and that much of psychology "has not been seriously influenced by any mathematical developments other than classical statistics."

In recent years psychologists have increased their actual and attempted use of mathematics, along with their skill in its applications. Miller, editing a volume of readings on the use of mathematics by psychologists, writes that the "mathematical maturity and competence of psychologists has improved over the years" (1964, p. 1) and that "most of mathematical psychology has developed in the past thirty years" (p. 2). Marx and Hillex (1964, p. 345) believe that psychology is undergoing a revolution in its point of view due to the influence of modern mathematics and engineering. Mathematics is not confined now to tests of statistical significance. There is a growing sophistication in the use of mathematical statistics as psychologists estimate the parameters of models and theories and measure "goodness-of-fit" to the data (Bush, 1963). Psychologists make use of mathematical methods, concepts, and systems which transcend the bounds of classical statistics and impinge on measure theory, probability theory, calculus, algebra, geometry, and other branches of mathematics. Some of these branches have been applied directly, and others indirectly, for their suggestive values or as analogies. An example of the latter is Kurt Lewin's (1936) drawing of analogies from topology for topological psychology. Another example is the use of set theory and group theory to represent the structure of thought processes by Piaget (see 1949, 1953). Geometries, such as projective, Euclidean, and even non-Euclidean geometries, have been used in studies of visual perception (Gibson, 1950; Luneburg, 1947). Probability theory, especially Markov chains and stochastic processes, have been applied to psycholinguistics and to learning theory (Bush and Mosteller, 1955). Matrix algebra is utilized in tests and measurements, as in factor analysis applied to the study of personality (Thurstone, 1947; Horst, 1963). Graph theory is used by social and industrial psychologists to study group structure and group processes (Cartwright and Harary, 1956; Haire, 1959). Game theory has been used in psychophysics, decision making, judgment (Thrall and Coombs, 1954; Galanter, 1963; Restle, 1961), and in learning (Simon, 1956). Likewise, information theory has been used in learning and perception (Attneave, 1959). Cybernetics has been adapted to problems of learning and perception (Miller, Galanter, and Pribram, 1960; Rosenblatt, 1958). Symbolic logic has been used as a model in social behavior (George, 1959), in neurophysiology (McCulloch and Pitts, 1943), and in computer simulation of human behavior (Newell and Simon, 1963). Mathematical computer and programming theories have been used in system development applied to man-machine systems in industry and in the military (Gagné, 1962).

The above is a sample of the variety of mathematics used in contemporary psychology. There is more communication between psychologists and mathematicians and more interest in the development of mathematics suitable for the behavioral sciences (Kemeny, 1959b). Some psychologists are intrigued by the possibility that a breakthrough in psychology will come via mathematics. It is, therefore, not surprising that elementary statistics, which a few years ago sufficed for the mathematical knowledge required of a psychology graduate student, is no longer adequate. No student of psychology can be expected to be proficient in, or even acquainted with, all the mathematical theories and methods used in psychology. But he is generally expected to have more mathematical knowledge and maturity than his counterpart of a generation ago.

Foundations of Mathematics
in Psychology

Despite the diversity of mathematical areas being explored for their immediate and suggestive values to psychology, one area remains virtually untapped: foundations of mathematics (sometimes called metamathematics or philosophy of mathematics). There are several reasons for psychologists to study this area and to explore its implications for psychology.

1. In keeping with the greater mathematical background expected of the psychology student, he should also be acquainted with different foundational issues and viewpoints toward the mathematics he is learning and applying. The most common justification for the psychologist to learn mathematics is that mathematics contains powerful tools to deal with psychological data. But we dare to hope that the psychologist is interested in the mystery of mathematics as well as its power, in its problems as well as its tools, in its philosophy and foundations as well as its techniques and applications. Understanding mathematics as an intellectual discipline, rather than as a collection of techniques, skills, and formulas, would seem to require some familiarity with the foundations of mathematics.

If knowledge of the foundations of mathematics becomes more widespread and arouses interest in the philosophical and "humanistic" aspects of mathematics, it can help to dispel some of the fears that the mathematization of psychology must inevitably cause psychology to become mechanical or mechanized and thus "dehumanized." There is a rather prevalent view that science in general tends to be mechanized and dehumanized. A proponent of an extreme version of this viewpoint writes that mechanization "is at the same time the great advantage and the gravest peril of the new science, and of the civilization directed and represented by it . . . in order to obtain quite abundant results it is not even necessary to have rigorous notions of their meaning and foundation" (Ortega y Gasset, *The Revolt of the Masses*, cited in Dubos, 1961, p. 146). While not agreeing that "the modern scientist is thoroughly dehumanized, with no horizon beyond his specialized techniques," Dubos does believe that scientists show some tendency to be "mechanical and unconcerned with philosophical and truly intellectual problems" (p. 148). He suggests, therefore, that scientists return to social philosophy, pointing out that "scientists in the ancient world were more concerned with philosophy than technology" (p. 100). Dubos also thinks that in "most cases the illusion of understanding comes from a failure to examine the philosophical basis of one's professional knowledge" (p. 102).

Knowledge of the philosophical issues involved in the foundations of mathematics may possibly make the psychologist more prone to examine the philosophical issues involved in his own and other sciences. We shall see that foundational issues in mathematics are paralleled in other modern sciences and can be traced back to ancient philosophy. As Dubos notes, "ancient philosophers perceived the central core of many problems of modern science [and] their formulations of these problems present great similarities to our own" (p. 128). For example, bearing on the problem of the continuum to which we shall turn shortly, Dubos wrote:

It is a remarkable fact that, in their efforts to formulate the central problems of modern science, experimenters as well as theoreticians tend to phrase their questions in the form of alternatives which, formally at least, resemble those considered by ancient philosophers. A large part of the history of science, for example, appears to continue the debate begun several millennia ago between the proponents of the continuum and the atomicists . . . mathematical, physical, and chemical theories offer, of course, many illustrations of the endless debate between atomicists and partisans of the continuum. (Dubos, 1961, p. 126)

2. Mathematics has had several "foundational crises" and indeed has been in the throes of such a crisis during all of the twentieth century. Psychology, in its own search for foundations, may garner suggestions from what mathematics has experienced in this search. Foundations of mathematics can suggest germinal ideas, problems and issues that arise in attempts to formalize and systematize a discipline. Some of the concepts and issues at the crux of the foundational crises in mathematics have counterparts, as we shall see, in psychological concepts and issues.

3. Reflecting different ways of meeting the foundational crises are the three major schools of foundational thought in mathematics, often designated as logicism, intuitionism, and formalism. It would be farfetched to claim that these three schools have exact parallels in psychological thoughts. Nonetheless, there are some similarities between these mathematical schools and various approaches to psychology. The logicists, who seek to reduce mathematics to logic, may be compared to psychologists who are interested in the logic or language of psychology and to the reductionists who consider that psychology should be reduced to a more basic discipline or that certain branches of psychology (for example, clinical psychology) should be reduced to "more fundamental" aspects of psychology (for example, learning theory). The formalists, who seek to abstract content out of an informal mathematical theory and to concentrate on the remaining form or structure, may be compared to psychologists who stress formalization of theories or who are concerned with form rather than content or who consider that experimental form or design is at least as important as the content of the experiment. The mathematical intuitionists, who stress the need for intuitively clear concepts and methods, may be compared to psychologists who stress intuitive conceptions and the internal frame of reference, ranging from the introspectionists of past years to the phenomenologists and existentialists of today.

4. Psychologists sometimes are embarrassed that they are "parasites on mathematics" (Luce, 1964, p. 376), and they fear that it will be a long time before they are able to contribute to mathematics. Yet the foundations of mathematics seems to be one area to which psychologists can presently contribute. Mathematicians themselves recognize that psy-

chological factors influence various foundational philosophies as well as views on specific issues (for example, whether or not to accept the axiom of choice). Moreover, some concepts and tenets of foundational views invite psychological investigation; for example, the intuitionists' belief that the concept of natural numbers can serve as a fundamental concept, that this concept need not be reduced to simpler concepts, and that it is so intuitively clear that it can be understood by even the young child. Psychologists have already contributed to concepts and topics that figure prominently in foundations of mathematics, such as number, structure, language, logic, intuition, perception of time, space, motion, thinking, problem solving, and creativity. A challenging task, in the direction of which we take only a small step in this text, is to present, from existing psychological literature, examples relevant to foundations of mathematics. Finally, as we shall see, this area offers new research problems for the psychologist.

Brief Overview of the Book

Following this introductory chapter, Chapter 2 describes the various foundational crises in mathematics. Paradoxes or antinomies are among the problems that gave rise to the crises. Many of the problems pertain to continuity and to a continuum—such as the straight line considered as an unbroken stretch—and hinge on the relationship between the continuous and the discrete.

> *Bridging the abyss between the domains of discreteness and of continuity . . .* is certainly a central problem of the foundation of mathematics. . . . To understand the nature of the problem one should stress the fundamental differences between the *discrete, qualitative, individual* nature of *number* in the "combinatorial" domain of *counting* (arithmetic) and the *continuous, quantitative, homogeneous* nature of *space* in the "analytical" domain of *measuring* (geometry). Every integer differs from every other in characteristic individual properties comparable to the differences between human beings, while the continuum appears as an amorphous pulp of points each of which is interchangeable with each other. . . . Bridging the abyss between these two heterogeneous domains is not only the central but also the oldest problem in foundation of mathematics and in the related philosophical fields. (Fraenkel and Bar-Hillel, 1958, p. 198)

We consider problems concerning continuity and the continuum relevant to psychology. A case could be made that attempts in psychology to quantify and measure, important as they are, involve the danger of distorting the qualitative, individual nature of human beings and their responses (analogous to the representation of different integers by indistinguishable points). More specifically, the second chapter notes that psychologists are faced with the problems of whether or not certain processes (for example, learning processes) are continuous; whether continuous or discontinuous classifications are more adequate for certain descriptions of phenomena (for instance, personality or social behavior); and how to justify the assumption that what they are dealing with is in the nature of a continuum or that it lends itself to mathematical methods based on continuity.

Intimately related to continuity and the continum are the concepts of infinity, time, space, and motion. They are at the heart of Zeno's paradoxes, which form part of the first foundational crisis in mathematics. Chapter 2 also discusses the roles of infinity, time, space, and motion in mathematics, philosophy, and psychology.

The present foundational crisis has revealed the extent of controversy over such fundamental concepts as number and set. Chapter 3 deals with the so-called natural, or counting, numbers 1, 2, 3, $\cdots$. After discussing the problems of the meaning of number, it outlines an axiomatic development of the natural numbers and portrays the extension of the number concept to rational numbers and then to real numbers and then to complex numbers. Chapter 4 explains various kinds of hypercomplex numbers. An arithmetic of infinity, concerned with infinite sets and infinite, or *transfinite*, cardinal numbers is developed in the fifth chapter.

These early chapters do not spell out the significance of the various number concepts to psychology. In part this is because later chapters touch on the relevance of some number concepts to psychology, but mainly this is because we still do not know how various kinds of numbers can be applied in psychology. Yet, number is certainly a central concept in mathematical psychology. Indeed, to "mathematize" psychology has usually been tantamount to the introduction and manipulation of numbers. Of course, there are branches of mathematics that are not directly concerned with numbers and such "nonnumerical" mathematics has begun to be used in psychology (Cartwright and Harary, 1958; Kemeny, 1959b). While the use in psychology of nonnumerical mathematics may be expected to increase, it is likely that many of the mathematical models used in psychology will continue to involve numbers, as they have in the past. The numbers may be part of a composite notion as, for example, a vector (in contrast to a scalar), which involves not only a number to represent its length but also a direction. Vectors have been used in psychology (and not only in so-called vector psychology) to represent forces such as tensions, attractions, repulsions, and so on. The vectors may be interpreted as elements in a space (for example, Euclidean geometric, or vector, space), which is itself regarded as a continuum. Yet most problems that occur in psychology do not come garbed in numbers, vectors, and space. In contrast to physics, "social sciences may be characterized by the fact that in most of their problems numerical measurements seem to be absent and considerations of space are irrelevant" (Kemeny, 1959b, p. 578). Thus, unlike many problems in physics where measurements and numbers seem to fit readily, in psychology the problem may be to decide whether numbers should be introduced and how they can be introduced with some real justification. In other words, "that the variables can be represented by numbers or vectors . . . we take for granted in much of physics, but for psychology and the other social and behavioral sciences one of the most perplexing problems is how to introduce numbers in a meaningful way" (Luce, 1964, p. 366). Knowledge of different conceptions of the nature of number and of the many different extensions and kinds of numbers, finite and infinite, which the text surveys, may help the psychologist to decide which of the numbers, if any, is suitable for his particular problem. Psychologists have tended to represent variables by integers or rational numbers and only occasionally by irrational numbers. In the main psychologists have been restricted to real numbers, and other kinds of numbers have had only limited utilization. It will be of interest to explore the relevance to psychology of various kinds of numbers; for example, complex numbers, including pure imaginary numbers, have many applications in physics and the exploration of their applicability to psychology seems worthwhile. It is also instructive to go beyond complex numbers and consider the applicability of hypercomplex numbers such as the quaternions, matrices, and the algebraic ideals. Matrices have been used in psychology, but they have not generally been regarded as numbers. Yet the number concept has been extended to include matrices that have many (but not all) of the properties of natural numbers. In addition to the investigation of the domain of applicability of various numbers, it is of interest to consider whether the number concept itself can be further extended to meet the needs of psychology, just as it was extended to meet certain needs in mathematics. Here is an area calling for the cooperation of mathematicians and psychologists.

Chapters 6 to 14 present information on the three major foundational schools in mathematics. Historical predecessors of each of these schools are surveyed and basic tenets are delineated. This is followed by an evaluative chapter and then by a chapter that explores some relationships between the foundational school and psychology.

The three mathematical schools have diverse views on the nature of logic and on its relationship to mathematical thinking. Psychology also contains diverse views on this relationship, ranging from the belief that thinking takes place in accordance with the laws of traditional logic to the belief that traditional logic does not adequately portray productive thinking or mathematical thinking. Chapter 15 is concerned with the relationship of logic to inquiry, discovery, and validity, and the roles played in thinking by various logical operators. We examine the thesis that the conclusions of a logically valid argument are implicit in the premises. There is discussion of so-called thinking machines, which have been used by both psychologists and mathematical logicians to study thinking.

Truth has been inextricably linked with logic even in those systems which at first glance may seem to be free of philosophical shackles. The troublesome problem of truth creeps into mathematics—ironic since mathematics has been characterized (by Bertrand Russell) as the science in which we know not what we are talking about nor whether what we are saying is true. Psychologists, despite attempts to remain aloof from problems of truth, have done some research but much remains to be done. Chapter 16 focuses on some conceptions of truth and validity in mathematics, philosophy, and science. We discuss various characterizations of tautologies and of analytic and synthetic statements, and we consider factors, including cultural factors, that influence the characterizations. This chapter merely spots the surface but hopes to encourage a deeper concern with the problems of truth.

Chapter 17 is concerned with reductionism, a term applied to two releated approaches. One approach tries to study or explain a complex whole in terms of its parts or elements. This approach is illustrated in certain methods of analysis that have been widely used in psychology and other sciences and have led to controversies dubbed as whole versus parts, holistic versus atomistic, or macroscopic versus microscopic. The chapter examines these controversies. Reductionism has also been applied to the attempt to "reduce" one discipline to another or, more precisely, to reduce the concepts and propositions of one discipline to those of another discipline. Reductionism is illustrated by the logicists' attempts to reduce mathematics to logic. It is also illustrated by the trend in psychology to reduce it to a "more fundamental" discipline such as biology or physics. We find it instructive to turn to foundations of physics both because of the relevance to "physicalism" in psychology—the trend to reduce it to physics—and for intrinsic and suggestive value. The chapter sketches some of the attempts to develop foundations for physics via classical mechanics, the special and general theories of relativity, and quantum theory. One motivation for reductionism is the principle of parsimony (also known as *scientific economy* or *Occam's razor*) and we therefore consider the role played by parsimony in mathematics and psychology. Another motivation that is examined is the desire to achieve, through reductionism, a unity of the sciences or a unified language for science. The chapter ends with a proposal for a reinterpretation of reductionism.

The final chapter gives us the opportunity to express our own views on the philosophy and foundations of psychology. Psychology, once eager to divorce itself from philosophy, has in recent years returned to philosophy, particularly to the philosophy of science, in attempts to seek answers to some of its foundational dilemmas.

Finally, it should be noted that there are various shades of belief within each school of foundational thought. Moreover, many mathematicians do not consider themselves to belong to one or another school. In the words of R. L. Wilder:

> Probably the great majority of mathematicians spend little, if any, time speculating on the question of membership in a "school of thought." They are either too busy doing research at the higher levels of their fields, or (in many cases) disdainful of such a question.
>
> Nor is this so-called division into "schools" even to be considered a decomposition of the relatively small body of mathematicians and philosophers who make research in the foundations their main occupation. They, too, are usually found to have their differing shades of individual opinion. Rather, it represents an attempt at classification of *thought tendencies*. It may be impossible to say of a given mathematician that he accepts the "logistic thesis" or is a "formalist"—he may lean to a little of both! (1952, p. 230)

We hope that the reader will have leaned a little to each of the various foundational schools of mathematics by the time he completes the book and will share our belief that all the approaches have the possibility of being fruitful. This belief influenced us to the extent that we explored and presented the three major schools rather than limit our text to one school. We believe that there are dangers in a one-sided introduction to a discipline. These are effectively stated by the mathematician and logician Evert W. Beth, who maintains that an introductory course in symbolic logic should acquaint the student with various methods of deduction and various conceptions of logic. He warns that a one-sided introduction to logic may foster a dogmatic attitude in which other conceptions seem less sound or more obscure and that "later on it is extremely difficult to overcome the bad effects of a narrow-minded initiation" (1962, p. xii). Believing that this can be the case, we have tried to avoid a narrow initation. It is up to the reader to decide whether or not he will accept one viewpoint and reject the rest, reject or be indifferent to all of them, or be able and willing to entertain features of various approaches, as done, for example, by mathematicians with a predilection for formalism who try to utilize methods and concepts acceptable to intuitionists while adhering to the logical rigor and axiomatic development stressed by the logicists.

CHAPTER 2

Foundational Crises
and Problems

Psychologists are sometimes embarrassed by the unsettled state of their discipline and by the variety of opinions regarding the foundations of psychology. One sometimes hears voiced the wish that psychology were as settled as mathematics and had as little diversity of opinion with regard to foundations. Yet, turning to mathematics to view the state of affairs of its foundations, we find considerable diversity of viewpoints. Indeed, about the only unanimity is with regard to the belief that mathematics is currently in the throes of a crisis in its foundations. The current foundational crisis in mathematics is often referred to as *the third crisis*. The first crisis is considered to have taken place when Pythagoras, in the fifth century B.C., discovered that there were line segments whose lengths could not be expressed as the ratio of two whole numbers. In other words, no rational numbers corresponded to the lengths. To Pythagoras and his disciples, who believed that whole numbers ruled the universe, this was a startling finding. Legend has it that they tried to suppress the information, lest it discredit mathematicians in the eyes of the public.

Also regarded as forming part of the first foundational crisis are various paradoxes (or arguments) that have been attributed to Zeno (or Zenon) from the Greek city of Elea in Italy. Common to these paradoxes is the assumption that an infinite number of acts cannot be carried out in a finite time or, otherwise put, that a finite magnitude cannot be constructed out of infinitely small parts. For example, Achilles, having once given the tortoise a head start in a race, could never hope to overtake the slow-moving creature because, to get to the place where the tortoise was, Achilles would first have to cover $\frac{1}{2}$ of that distance, and before that $\frac{1}{4}$ of the distance, and before that $\frac{1}{8}$ of the distance, and so on and so on. And how could he perform this infinite number of acts in a finite amount of time? Zeno's paradoxes are sometimes considered to have been "resolved" by the mathematical notion, clearly formulated in the nineteenth century, that some infinite series converge. An infinite series is said to converge if

10

the "partial sums," obtained by considering the sum of the first n terms of the series (n a natural number or positive integer), and then the sum of the first $n + 1$ terms, and then the sum of the first $n + 2$ terms, and so on, approach closer and closer to a fixed (finite) number, or, more succinctly, if the partial sums have a finite limit. In particular, the infinite series $1 + \frac{1}{2} + \frac{1}{4} + \frac{1}{8} + \cdots$ (arising in the paradox of Achilles and the tortoise) converges to 2. We shall return to consideration of Zeno's paradoxes.

The second crisis in the foundations occurred in the beginning of the nineteenth century when it was realized that the calculus rested on a very questionable foundation and that there was little justification for the treatment of differential quotients and infinitesimals. In the eighteenth century, investigations of the differential and integral calculus had "soared extraordinarily, one brilliant discovery following another in the realm of pure analysis as well as in the domain of their applications . . . . In odd contrast to this series of wonderful discoveries was the obscurity that spread over the foundations" (Waismann, 1959, p. ix). This obscurity was gradually removed, due in large part to the introduction of the use of limits instead of unjustified manipulation of infinitesimals, the study of the real number system, which is a foundation for the calculus, and the increasing stress on careful definitions and rigorous proofs.

It seemed that at last mathematical rigor had been attained and a secure foundation laid for mathematics, at least for the discipline of mathematical analysis, which includes the calculus. This seemed all the more certain when analysis was "arithmetized" in the sense that it was based on integers and finite or infinite sets of integers. So secure seemed the foundations that as eminent a mathematician as Poincaré could in 1900 tell the international congress of mathematicians that mathematics has been "arithmetized" and that "absolute rigor" had been attained in mathematics.

But all was not as settled as this picture suggested. Although analysis might have been based on integers and on infinite sets of integers, these infinite sets apparently were not secure enough to serve as a foundation. It was just about the time of Poincaré's claim of "absolute rigor" that there appeared symptoms of what has come to be known as the third foundational crisis in mathematics. These symptoms were connected with a discipline known as the theory of sets or set theory, which originated largely due to the efforts of Georg Cantor. Cantor's set theory, which he formulated starting about 1875, may be considered as the first formal attempt to deal mathematically with the idea of the infinite. What Cantor did essentially was to develop an "arithmetic" of infinite quantities by introducing the concepts of equality, greater, and less, for infinite sets. In so doing he "corralled the infinite for mathematics" (Reid, 1959, p. 62). His view of an infinite set as something that could be handled like a number, as "something consummated," as something actual or completed rather than in the process of becoming, was startling to many mathematicians including Cantor himself. In fact, Cantor frankly admitted that he was led to this view of the infinite much against his will and that it was opposed to traditions that were dear to him. For almost two decades Cantor's ideas met with indifference, distrust, and even rejection and ridicule. Many mathematicians objected to the vagueness of the general concept of set. Nonetheless, Cantor's ideas won acceptance and, before the nineteenth century ended, they were widely utilized by mathematicians and became the basis of mathematical analysis. It was therefore all the more startling when it was found, at just about the turn of the century, that this set theory apparently had contradictions, or paradoxes or antinomies (conflicts of ideas), in it. Famous among these antinomies is one formulated by Bertrand Russell (1902), to which we now turn.

Some Antinomies or Paradoxes

By way of introduction to Russell's antinomy, note that a set or collection of objects may or may not have the character of these objects. For example, a group of horses is not a horse and a group of people is not a person. But in some cases a set of objects does have the character of the objects. For example, a set of numbers may itself be a number. As another example, the set of all sets may be considered to be a set. In other words, a set may or may not be a member of itself. Thus, the set of all horses is not a member of itself whereas the set of all sets is a member of itself. Consider now the set, denoted by S, of all sets that are not members of themselves. Is S a member of itself or not? Suppose S is a member of itself; then (by definition of S) S is not a member of itself. Suppose S is not a member of itself; then (by definition of S) it is a member of S. Hence we arrive at the contradiction that S is a member of S if and only if S is not a member of S. This is known as *Russell's antinomy* and is an example of a set-theoretic antinomy.

That this antinomy is not peculiar to set theory or to mathematics can be seen in the following reformulation. Call a property or concept *impredicable* if it does not apply to itself. Thus, the property of being green is impredicable since it is not itself green, whereas the property of being abstract, being itself abstract, does apply to itself and is not impredicable. Consider the property of being impredicable. Is it impredicable or not? If impredicable is impredicable then it applies to itself and hence is not impredicable. On the other hand, if impredicable is not impredicable then it does not apply to itself and hence (by definition) is impredicable. Thus we arrive at the contradiction that impredicable is impredicable if and only if it is not impredicable.

As another example, call an adjective *heterological* if it does not have the same property that it refers to. "English" and "polysyllabic" are English adjectives that are not heterological. "Long," "hot," "red" (unless the latter happens to be written or printed in red), are heterological as are most adjectives. It can be shown that the adjective heterological is heterological if and only if it is not heterological.

The famous "paradox" involving a village barber may be known to the reader. Consider the inhabitant of a village (denote him by A) who shaves all and only those inhabitants of a village who do not shave themselves. It can then be shown, through the same kind of reasoning as in the previous paradoxes, that if A exists there arises the contradiction that A shaves A if and only if A does not shave A. This apparent paradox can be resolved by concluding from the contradiction that A does not exist.

As a similar illustration, consider the chief (or high priest) of a tribe who makes sacrifices for those and only those members of the tribe who do not make sacrifices for themselves. Does he make a sacrifice for himself? If he does, then he does not; and if he does not, then he does. Again such an apparent paradox can be resolved by concluding that such a chief (or priest) does not exist.

Can a similar procedure be followed to resolve the other paradoxes? It would seem to go against common sense to claim that the set of all sets that are not members of themselves does not exist or that such adjectives as impredicable or heterological do not exist. Nonetheless, in their efforts to eliminate some of the known antinomies, mathematicians have restricted the meaning of the word *set* so that a set may not be a member of itself (thus ruling out the definition of the set of all sets and Russell's antinomy). And some logicians have restricted the kind of concepts permitted in their system of logic so that concepts such as impredicable and heterological are eliminated.

Another well-known antinomy concerns a liar. For example, suppose a person says, "This statement I am now making is a lie." Is the quoted statement true or false? It can be shown that it can be neither, without involving a contradiction.

Several riddles also hinge on such paradoxes (Kleene, 1952). A famous one is the "dilemma of the crocodile" wherein a crocodile, who has stolen a baby, promises the baby's mother to return the child, if the mother guesses whether or not the crocodile will return the child. Suppose that the mother guesses that the crocodile will not return the child. What should the crocodile do?

A similar riddle concerns the man, captured by cannibals, who is told by them that he may make a statement and, if his statement is true, he will be boiled and if it is false, he will be roasted. What should the man say? If he says, "I will be roasted," what should the cannibals do? It can be shown that the statement, "I will be roasted" is true if and only if it is false.

All these paradoxes, as well as many other antinomies that have been discovered, have in common what might be called a self-referential feature. In all these antinomies the characterization or definition of a particular entity depends on a set or totality to which the particular entity belongs. For example, the concept of a set being a member of itself is a self-referential concept. Doubts about the status and permissibility of such concepts were already expressed in the Middle Ages. But a clear proposal to eliminate such concepts seems to have been first made in the twentieth century. Russell, who, like Poincaré, believed that the source of the antinomies was this self-referential feature, formulated a "vicious circle" principle, according to which no object determined by a condition that refers to a totality should belong to this totality. Acceptance of this principle apparently eliminates the antinomies but, unfortunately, it also eliminates all self-referential concepts. Such concepts are useful in everyday language, for example, the youngest member of the family, the brightest child in the class, the highest-scoring man on the team. Moreover, many scientific disciplines, including classical analysis and other branches of mathematics, contain such concepts, for example, the surface with the maximum area, the shortest distance between two points. Indeed, there has not yet been found a way of retaining all of classical mathematics without introducing self-referential concepts.

In short, attempts to eliminate the antinomies of set theory tend to eliminate parts of mathematics. Moreover, even when it seems that some restriction suffices to eliminate the known antinomies, it is not known whether other antinomies or contradictions are retained. Furthermore, focusing attention on the antinomies has spotlighted the divergence of viewpoints on supposedly fundamental concepts of mathematics and it has been this divergence and uncertainty which, as much as the antinomies, testified to the insecure nature of the foundations of mathematics.

> More than the mere appearance of antinomies in the basis of set theory, and thereby of analysis, it is the fact that the various attempts to overcome these antinomies . . . revealed a fargoing and surprising divergence of opinions and conceptions on the most fundamental mathematical notions, such as set and number themselves, which induces us to speak of the *third foundational crisis* that mathematics is still undergoing. (Fraenkel and Bar-Hillel, 1958, p. 15)

Relationships among Foundational Crises

The three foundational crises in mathematics are not unrelated and distinct. The problems that are symptomatic of a given crisis are themselves related and several common threads run through the various crises and the intervening periods. Consider, for example, the relationships between the two major symptoms of the first crisis: (1) Zeno's paradoxes and (2) the discovery by the Pythagoreans of lengths to which no rational numbers corresponded. This discovery, which meant that there were points on the line to which rational numbers could not be assigned, underscored the difficulty of characterizing the straight line, or linear continuum, which is continuous, in terms of points or numbers, which are discrete. The Pythagoreans were interested in this problem as well as in the more general problem of whether the universe (including time, space, and matter) was continuous or discrete. We shall see that Zeno's paradoxes are pertinent to the nature of the linear continuum and to problems of continuity and infinity as they pertain to space, time, and motion. For example, motion in Zeno's arguments is regarded as involving the traversing of an infinite number of points, and a fundamental problem that arises is whether or not this can be done in a finite amount of time.

These problems of continuity, of infinity, of the nature of motion, of the nature of the linear continuum, of the characterization of lengths that are not rational numbers reoccur, in one guise or another, in the second foundational crisis in mathematics, which centered on the calculus. Motion was the first problem dealt with in the calculus. We shall see that efforts to characterize continuous motion mathematically led to the introduction of static conceptions of motion and of such related concepts as approach, converge, limit, and continuity. Such static concepts help to resolve the difficulties underlying Zeno's paradoxes but they fail to portray the dynamic nature of motion. In short, problems of motion were common to both the first and second foundational crises. Moreover, the second crisis showed the need for more careful formulations of what is meant by the terms *infinitely small* and *infinitely large;* thus, problems of infinity also were a common link between the first and second crises. Furthermore, the second crisis stimulated efforts to lay a more secure foundation for the calculus. These efforts included examination of the real number system, which is a foundation for the calculus, and led to careful characterization, by such mathematicians as Cauchy, Weierstrass, Dedekind, and Cantor, of real numbers, particularly irrational numbers (real numbers which are not the ratio of two whole numbers), and of the linear continuum. In the characterization of the linear continuum, it is assumed that to each point on the line there corresponds a real number, and, conversely, so that the "gaps" on the line, discovered by the Pythagoreans, are no longer without number correspondents. In short, further common links between the first and second foundational crises are the problems of the characterization of irrational numbers and the linear continuum.

These problems are still controversial issues and form part of the third foundational crisis in mathematics. The various foundational schools, we shall see, differ in their characterizations of real numbers, particularly irrational numbers, and the linear continuum. The very problems that troubled the Pythagoreans and Zeno twenty-five centuries ago and were fought out again centuries later in attempts to lay a rigorous foundation for the calculus are still unresolved issues. Moreover, the concept of infinity, which figured prominently in the first and second crises, is a central concept in the current crisis. Infinite sets are at the core of the paradoxes that are symptomatic of the current crisis. Infinite sets are also involved in the axiom of choice, which has been a controversial issue for over half a century. One formulation of this axiom is as follows: Given an *infinite* collection of mutually disjoint nonempty sets (no two sets have any elements in common), there exists a set that contains exactly one element from each of the sets. What is meant by existence of sets and numbers, as well as the general problem of what is meant by *existence* in mathematics, receives different answers from the various foundational schools.

We see that paradoxes or antinomies have figured in both the first and third foundational crises. Some paradoxes have been eliminated by careful definition of the concepts of limit and continuity and by restrictions on the kinds of sets permitted in mathematics. But mathematics still has paradoxes. Ironically, attempts to lay a careful foundation for certain parts of mathematics have sometimes introduced paradoxes. For example, the assumption that there is a one-to-one correspondence between points on the line and real numbers (an assumption that was made explicit in the classical characterizations of the linear continuum offered following the second foundational crisis) led to paradoxes. To assume that a real number corresponds to every point on the line is, in effect, to assume that there is a measure for every length. The branch of mathematics known as measure theory, or the theory of point-sets (Halmos, 1950), is rich in paradoxes. An example is the Banach-Tarski paradox. Banach and Tarski (1924) proved that it is possible to "disassemble," point by point, a solid unit sphere (such as a solid ball with a radius of length 1) into a finite number of pieces (that five pieces will suffice was shown by Robinson, 1947) and then reassemble the pieces, point by point, into two solid spheres, each the same size as the original sphere. This paradox (in which the axiom of choice is used) illustrates that mathematical conceptions may not fit our conceptions of reality. It also suggests that perhaps the notion of size or measure in point-set theory is quite different from our common-sense conception or that perhaps no measure can be assigned to the points of the sphere. This paradox and others in the theory have been described as steps "on a logical path to which mathematics committed itself when it accepted the idea that there is a measure for every length— a real number, rational or irrational, for every point on the number line" (Reid, 1959, p. 159).

To eliminate the Banach-Tarski paradox one might change the assumption that to every point there corresponds a real number or to every length a measure, or one might decide not to use the axiom of choice or decide that the points of a sphere cannot be measured or introduce certain changes in the concept of measure. But each alternative has repercussions on measurement and other parts of mathematics, and each alternative limits various areas of mathematical knowledge (for example, we do not know how to get certain results without the axiom of choice) and does not guarantee that all paradoxes are eliminated from mathematics. Incidentally, there are some suggestions here for psychologists and other scientists who are concerned with measurement. It is of interest to examine the concepts of measurement that the scientist uses, to study how a particular concept affects the outcome of measurement, and to consider certain changes in the concepts of measurement and their possible consequences. Are there certain data or phenomena that are not measurable under one conception of measure but would be measurable or could have a measure assigned to them under a different conception of measure?

We have tried to establish the thesis of intrarelations and interrelations among the various foundational crises. In particular, the problem of the linear continuum and the general problem of the characterization of the continuous in terms of the discrete run through all three foundational crises.

Continuity and Discreteness

Many of the problems that gave rise to the crises in mathematics may be formulated as aspects of one problem: How to bridge the gap between the continuous and the discrete. We shall see that attempts to solve this problem generally invoke the concept of infinity. The problems of whether or not space and time are continuous, are infinitely divisible, and have infinite extent have been central in philosophical discussions from ancient times to the present. Certain difficulties or antinomies arise because we seem compelled to conceive of space and time both as continuous and as discontinuous, both as finite and as infinite. For example, time is regarded as continuous, in the naïve sense of being uninterrupted, having no gaps or jumps or separations, no discrete parts, but only a single connectedness. Yet the present moment serves to separate the time that is past from the time in the future. Time is divided into hours and minutes and seconds that can be further subdivided into finer and finer subdivisions so that time seems to be infinitely divisible. Is time infinitely divisible? Moreover, does time have infinite extent? One point of view is that time has infinite extent at both ends; that it has no beginning and no end, akin to the sequence of signed integers $\cdots -3, -2, -1, 0, +1, +2, +3, \cdots$. Another point of view is that time will go on indefinitely but that it had a definite beginning, so that it is infinite at only one end akin to the sequence of natural numbers, 1, 2, 3, · · · . Still other views exist, for example, time is finite at both ends. Just as for time, there are also different views concerning the continuity, divisibility, and extent of space and of matter. For example, are they infinitely divisible or do we ultimately reach certain "points" or "particles" that are indivisible?

The straight line seems to typify the notion of continuity. "The prototype of all ideas which meet these specifications [of continuity in the sense of something uninterrupted, something singly connected] is the line and especially the straight line which in our mind is endowed with this continuity *par excellence*" (Dantzig, 1956, p. 169). The name *continuum*, or, more precisely, *linear continuum*, is applied in mathematics to the straight line in order to suggest its continuous nature. But a point on the line or a number associated with the point is discrete. How can the continuous be characterized in terms of the discrete? Starting with points or numbers, how can we arrive at the linear continuum? This problem has received different answers from the different foundational schools. It has been said that various attitudes in the foundations of mathematics may be classified "according to the kind of 'continuum' they admit" (Fraenkel and Bar-Hillel, 1958, p. 247). In particular, intuitionistic conceptions of the continuum differ from classical conceptions.

The problem of characterizing the linear continuum was already a difficulty at the time of the first foundational crisis. It was a major problem for the Pythagoreans. Pythagoras and his followers, searching as were other Greek philosophers for the common substrate of all things, believed that the answer was number, by which they meant whole or natural numbers. But they ran into difficulties when they discovered that there were lengths that could not be measured by whole numbers or by their ratios. They were aware that this meant that there were incommensurable lengths. No matter how small a unit of measurement is taken, it does not go into such lengths a whole number of times. To resolve this difficulty, the Pythagoreans appealed to the notion of a *monad*, a unit of measurement so small that it was itself without measure. They regarded the monad as the common or universal unit of measurement. "The universal common measure had to shrink to a smallness indeed beyond measure, and yet it had to remain a unit: a kind of *actual infinitesimal*. Such is the new monad" (de Santillana, 1961, p. 96). The Pythagoreans conceived of the monad as having no magnitude but as having a position on the straight line, which they considered to be composed of infinitely many monads.

Other Greek philosophers disagreed with the view that monads were the common substrate of all things and that the line was infinitely divisible. In particular, Parmenides of Elea and his disciple Zeno regarded continuity as the common substrate and maintained that the universe, including the straight line, was continuous and not infinitely divisible. Against the notion of a monad or infinitesimal, Zeno argued in a manner that led Aristotle to call him the inventor of dialectics. Either a monad has magnitude or it does not, Zeno contended. If it has no magnitude, then another magnitude added to it will still have no magnitude, since nothing added to nothing yields nothing. No matter how many monads are added together, Zeno continued, the sum will still have zero magnitude. Hence the infinitely many monads that are supposed to compose a line segment (for example, one inch in length) will have zero magnitude so that the line segment will have zero magnitude, which is a contradiction. Zeno reasoned further that if a monad has magnitude, then infinitely many monads will have infinite magnitude, so that the afore-mentioned line segment will have infinite length, which again is a contradiction. He concluded that the line segment is not divisible into infinitely many parts or monads and similarly that the line is not infinitely divisible.

There were still other views among Greek philosophers of the nature of the continuum. Anaxagoras believed that the universe is continuous but that it is also infinitely divisible into what might be called actual infinitesimals. He held that there is not *a least* to the small but always *a smaller*. A contrary doctrine—that there are ultimate particles or "atoms," indivisibles that cannot be further divided—was the atomic doctrine formulated by Leucippus and later developed by Democritus and Epicurus.

In brief, among the ancient Greek philosophers there were various beliefs concerning the nature of the universe in general (including time, space, and matter) and the straight line in particular—continuous and not infinitely divisible, continuous and infinitely divisible, made up of ultimate indivisibles.

Parmenides' doctrine of a continuous, uninterrupted, unchanging world led him to conclude that in reality there is no change. There can be no beginnings or endings, for these would involve interruptions, discontinuities between *being* and *not being*. Parmenides apparently equated the notions of not being with empty space or a void and being with pure geometric space or a space-filling mass. He held that there cannot be empty space and that the notion of not being is nonsensical, that it is not (that is, does not exist) and can not be thought. It is senseless to say that something does not exist and it is impossible to think or believe in nothing or not being as something which exists. What is (exists) is in contact with what is—there is no void between—so that the universe is wholly continuous and unchanging. If it seems otherwise to us, it is because our senses deceive us. If it seems to us that things change and move, it is because our senses mislead us. In particular, motion, as all change, is merely an appearance and not a reality, an illusion of the senses. Sheer sense impressions do not give knowledge of the real world. This can be obtained only through thought, reasoning, or logic. In effect, Parmenides

denied the reality of the phenomenal world and maintained that only
through reasoning can we get to know the world of reality.

In contrast to Parmenides' views are those of Greek philosophers such
as Leucippus who accepted the notion of a void and Heraclitus who held
that there is nothing fixed, that everything changes, and that motion is
primary.

Zeno's Paradoxes

The paradoxes or arguments of Zeno of Elea epitomize many of the
difficulties implicit in various conceptions of time, motion, space, and, in
particular, of the straight line or linear continuum. Zeno's arguments,
Russell has said, have been the basis for almost every theory of space,
time, and infinity that has been constructed from his day to our own. It
is therefore worthwhile to reflect on Zeno's arguments in detail. We know
of them from Plato and from Aristotle. The latter described them and
attempted to cope with them in his *Physica*. There are four arguments,
which are known respectively as *The Dichotomy*, *Achilles*, *The Arrow*, and
The Stadium. Only the first three need concern us here.

1. *The Dichotomy*. Motion is not possible since in order to cover a certain
distance one must first cover half of that distance, and before this half of that
half or one quarter of the original distance, and before this one half of the one
quarter or one eighth of the distance, and so on. But this means an infinite number of spaces must be covered and, Zeno concluded, this cannot be done in finite
time.

2. *Achilles*. If the tortoise has a headstart, then Achilles can never overtake
him, since by the time Achilles gets to the tortoise's starting point, the tortoise
will be at a further point, and by the time Achilles gets to that point, the tortoise
will be still further, and so on, so that the slower tortoise will always be ahead
of Achilles.

3. *The Arrow*. At any given instant, the head of the flying arrow is at a particular point in space. Since it is at rest there it cannot be in motion then. But,
at every instant it is at rest at some point in space and therefore is motionless.

Centuries of speculations have centered on Zeno's intentions. Was he
trying to disprove the reality of motion? Some writers claim that this was
Zeno's motive. Others believe that he accepted the reality of motion and
did not need an exasperated Diogenes to demonstrate to him its reality by
walking about. It is sometimes said that Zeno could not possibly have
refuted the existence of motion. What is overlooked is the distinction
that Parmenides and Zeno made between the phenomenal world, or the
world of the senses, on the one hand, and the world of reality, on the
other. Motion as a sense impression was not being denied, but motion
could not occur in the real world because the real world is free of contradictions, whereas the assumption of the existence of motion leads to

contradictions as Zeno's arguments demonstrate. Some writers believe that Zeno used the arguments to point out deep-rooted incongruencies in our conceptions of motion, time, space, and, in particular, the linear continuum. Whether or not this was his primary motive, the arguments have certainly served this purpose.

The first two arguments are sometimes interpreted as opposed to the belief that matter is infinitely divisible and, in particular, that the line is made up of infinitely many points. The last two arguments are thought to be opposed to the belief that matter is finitely divisible and particularly that the line is made up of a finite number of points. But if matter in general—and the straight line in particular—is neither infinitely nor finitely divisible, then it is not divisible at all and the only alternative is that it is a continuum as Parmenides had maintained.

The argument about Achilles has also been interpreted to mean that whenever Achilles is at a point in the interval which he has to traverse, the tortoise is at a corresponding point in the shorter interval which he has to traverse. When Achilles gets to another point, the tortoise also has gotten to another point, so that there is a one-to-one correspondence between the two sets of points. But this would mean that there are "as many" points in one interval as in the other. Surely a shorter line segment cannot have as many points as a longer one! The fallacy of this last statement was suggested by Galileo when he pointed out the one-to-one correspondence between the natural numbers and their squares, that is, between n and n^2, even though the squares constitute a proper part (not all) of the natural numbers. The one-to-one correspondence was used by Cantor to develop his concept of cardinal number. Two sets have the same cardinal number if their elements can be put into one-to-one correspondence. Hence, the longer line segment has the same cardinal number as the shorter segment. Thus, the Achilles argument may be resolved by noting that the one-to-one correspondence between the points of the two intervals does not constitute a contradiction, and Achilles can overtake the tortoise.

Many attempts have been made to resolve Zeno's paradoxes. One answer to *The Dichotomy* is that if space is infinitely divisible so is time; if there are infinitely many spaces or points on the line segment to be traversed, there are infinitely many instances of time in which to do so. This is the answer with which Aristotle sought to dispose of the first two arguments. Some attempted answers point to Zeno's fallacious conception of the "sum" of an infinite series. The argument concerning Achilles may be regarded as giving rise to the series $1 + \frac{1}{2} + \frac{1}{4} + \frac{1}{8} + \cdots$, which Zeno concluded must have an infinite sum but which is now known to "converge" to 2 in the sense that if sufficiently many terms are taken in the series, the resulting "partial sum" of the infinite series can be made as close to 2 as desired, that is, differing from 2 by less than any preassigned positive number. It is in this sense that we talk of a "sum" of an infinite series. Hence the above series is said to converge to 2 or to have the sum of 2 rather than the infinite sum that Zeno suggested. The assumption that an infinite series of positive terms has an infinite sum is also found in Zeno's reasoning about the monads; he concludes that if a monad has any magnitude, then infinitely many would have infinite magnitude.

Another answer to Zeno's arguments is that matter is indefinitely divisible, not in the sense that there actually exist infinitely many parts but in the sense that no matter how far we divide, there is nothing in the nature of spatial or temporal properties to prevent us from dividing further. Thus it is not an actual or existing infinity but a potential infinity of parts.

The argument about the arrow notes that the arrow head occupies a definite point in space at a given time and since it is at rest there, it is not in motion. The supposition is that it cannot at the same time be in motion and also be motionless, that is, at rest. However, the mathematical conception of motion, which was an outgrowth of the calculus, is that of an infinite succession of states of rest so that in this respect "mathematics reduces dynamics to a branch of statics" (Dantzig, 1956, p. 129). Motion was the first problem dealt with by the calculus and this conception of it evolved in attempts to put the calculus—and in particular the notions of infinitesimal and limit—on a rigorous basis. From this point of view, the answer to Zeno's *Arrow* is that the arrow is in motion, considered as an infinite succession of states of rest. But of course we ordinarily do not think of motion as a succession of states of rest nor do we perceive it as such. The mathematical notion does not fit the phenomenal notion. This is also the case for other mathematical notions that pertain to the world about us. For example, the mathematical notions of a point (as having no magnitude or dimension) and of a line (as having only one dimension and being of infinite extent) are idealizations that do not correspond to anything we can see in the world about us. Mathematical terms are not images of our phenomenal world, and when physicists use these terms they too are not portraying the phenomenal world. "In accepting a mathematical description of nature, physicists have been forced to abandon the ordinary world of our experience, the world of sense perceptions" (Barnett, 1957, p. 18). In this respect physicists and mathematical physicists resemble Parmenides, Zeno, and their historical successors.

One answer to Zeno's paradoxes is that the mathematical notions of time, motion, point, and line do not have to correspond to either their "counterparts" in a phenomenal or behavioral world or to counterparts in any real or empirical world. In other words, the mathematical notions may be divorced from, and need not necessarily reflect on the nature or existence of, objects or processes in the phenomenal world or in any world of reality.

Another answer to Zeno's paradoxes is that motion is a continuous process and cannot be understood by enumeration of every step or phase since it involves an infinite series of steps. But we can characterize or define the series of steps by a formula for its terms, without listing each term. More generally, Zeno's arguments seem to assume that something is real or can be understood only if we can give a list, an enumeration, or an inventory of its parts. This is not possible when we are dealing with a continuous process or an infinite series or any infinite whole. For example, an infinite series can be understood through the law that defines or characterizes the series, but it is not possible to enumerate all its terms. A line may be defined as a certain infinite set of points but it cannot be constructed by adding point to point. In other words, the line contains infinitely many points but it cannot be constructed through the synthesis of its points. This distinction may be the clue to resolving Zeno's paradoxes and related antinomies.

> Thus it is contended that the notion of a whole as "made up of parts" involves a confusion between the notion of a whole as *containing* its parts, and a whole as *arrived at* by the successive enumeration and synthesis of its parts. . . . There is no paradox in knowing an infinite whole, once we rid ourselves of the notion that to know means to take a *successive inventory* of the content. (Perry, 1916, p. 104)

Incidentally, these words might have been said by Max Wertheimer or other Gestalt psychologists as applicable to wholes, whether they are considered finite or infinite. The Gestalt thesis is that while a whole contains its parts, there are wholes (*Gestalten*) that cannot be understood merely through the enumeration, synthesis, or study of their parts in isolation.

The paradoxes suggested by Zeno's arguments and by related antinomies may be indicative, not of contradictions in motion or space, but of inadequacies in our attempt to conceptualize them. If, for example, our conceptualization of the process whereby Achilles overtakes the tortoise is such that we conclude that he does not overtake it, then we can decide, with Parmenides, that our senses deceive us and that a faster runner can never overtake a slower one who has a headstart and that in reality motion does not exist. Or we can decide that our conceptualization of the process of motion or of the nature of the space traversed may have deceived us.

It seems advisable to separate the nature of motion from the nature of the space in which it occurs. For example, how Achilles and the tortoise move may have to be separated from the nature of the space they traverse. Implied in Zeno's arguments is the conception of continuous motion in a continuous space. But modern physics conceives of the idea of continuous motion in a discontinuous space.

Alfred North Whitehead, for example, considers that Zeno's paradoxes can be resolved by the introduction of discontinuities. He notes that the physical sciences in the late nineteenth century were established on a basis that presupposed the idea of continuity, but that quantum physics requires "some theory of discontinuous existence" (1948, p. 124). For example, the orbit of an electron can be considered "as a series of detached positions, and not as a continuous line" (p. 124). With regard to time, there is no need to conceive of time as "atomic in the sense that all patterns must be realised in the same successive durations" (p. 125). Instead time can be considered to have discontinuous existence. Whitehead maintains that "if this concept of temporalisation as a successive realisation of epochal durations be adopted, the difficulty of Zeno is evaded" (pp. 125–126).

As a final example of philosophical views that have been used in attempts to resolve Zeno's paradoxes, we mention the philosophy of Hegel. Hegel conceived of reality as involving a dynamic process of becoming. He held that traditional logic, because of its static nature, is not suitable to portray this process. Instead he proposed a logic involving a dialectical process where a thesis by its very coming into existence engenders an antithesis. The clash between the thesis and its antithesis results in a synthesis from which there arises a new thesis, which in turn engenders an antithesis, and so on. Another way of wording this is to say that *being* passes into *nonbeing* (corresponding to a process of decay), or *nothing*, and nonbeing, or nothing, passes into being (corresponding to a process of origination). The process of becoming includes both being and nonbeing, or nothing. In traditional logic it constitutes a contradiction to say that something is both being and nonbeing, or nothing, that it is both A and not-A; but this is not so in Hegelian logic where A changes into not-A so that A is both A and not-A and they are in this sense the same even though they are different. Herein lies the answer, Hegel believed, to paradoxes about changes such as Zeno's.

> Change was a puzzle to the old logic (e.g., Zeno's), precisely because it saw that the concept of Becoming involves both Being and Nothing. To change, A must be both A and not-A. If it remains sheerly A, it does not change; if it is sheerly B, it is not A that changed. Hegel believed he had found the key that resolves this paradox. Every concept (not just the concept of Being) falls into contradiction when considered in isolation, and *every* contradiction is resolved by a synthesis (like that of Becoming) only to fall into a new contradiction when considered in isolation in its turn. Thought is thus a continuously expanding process of resolving contradictions by seeking even larger wholes in which they are included. (Jones, 1952, p. 875)

In other words, Hegel says that the concept of becoming, regarded as involving a synthesis of both being and nonbeing, makes the concept of change intelligible and resolves the puzzles about change. However, as Jones points out (p. 877), Zeno's puzzle is not resolved; Hegel simply said that it was resolved. One still is left with a disguised form of the puzzle of change, dressed up in terms of becoming which includes being and nothing. There is still the puzzle of how being can change to nonbeing or vice versa and how being and nonbeing can be different and also the same. In short, Zeno's paradoxes are not satisfactorily solved by Hegel s philosophy. At most, they are replaced by other paradoxes.

Motion and the Calculus

Horror infiniti (fear of the infinite) persisted in mathematics from Zeno's time until about the seventeenth century. Kepler has been described as "the first of the seventeenth-century mathematicians to make use of methods that involved the idea of 'infinity' that had been banished from mathematics ever since the time of Zeno" (Hooper, 1948, p. 206). Basing his procedure on Archimedes' work, Kepler found the volume of the contents of a wine cask by means of what later came to be called *infinitesimals*. Kepler, as well as Fermat with his work on tangents to a curve (that laid the foundation for derivatives to a curve at a given point), and Cavalieri with his work on "indivisibles," all helped to pave the way for the development of the calculus by Newton and Leibniz. Although Newton spoke of "fluxions" and Leibniz of "infinitesimals," we shall use only the latter term. In that very productive mathematical age, infinitesimals were treated rather carelessly, at least not with a rigor sufficient for our day or even sufficient to satisfy some contemporaries of Newton and Leibniz. Infinitesimals were arbitrarily treated at times as variables and at other times as constants, at times as having finite magnitude and at other times as having an infinitesimally small magnitude or no magnitude. The objections that Zeno raised against the monads and against the infinite divisibility of the line could equally well have been raised against this treatment of the infinitesimals. Indeed, critics of the calculus, including the astute nonmathematician Bishop Berkeley (see Hooper, 1948, pp. 321–322), pointed to the illogical reasoning in the use of the infinitesimals and the difficulties to which they led.

Attempts to clarify the notion of infinitesimal and to put the calculus on a more rigorous basis were confronted with the problem of motion. For example, one definition of an infinitesimal is that it is a variable that approaches zero or tends to zero or, otherwise expressed, has zero as a limit. But the notion of approaching or of tending to a value is but a veiled reference to motion. The variable is moving; it is getting closer and closer to a stipulated point. Moreover, in the calculus it is assumed that the nature of this motion is continuous in the sense that the variable assumes every value in the interval in which the motion occurs or hits every point and does so in the order in which the points occur on the real line. But conceivably such continuous motion or continuous variation need not occur. The variable might not vary continuously in that it does not assume all values in a given interval but, for example, assumes only rational values and not irrational ones so that there are gaps in its path, points in the interval that are not within its domain of variation. Or the variable might assume all values in the interval but not in their order of magnitude so that it does not hit the points in succession but skips around and yet eventually covers every point in the interval. There should be ways of distinguishing among such modes of motion and, in particular, a way of mathematically characterizing *continuous variation*. But how can we describe mathematically that the variable moves through all the points on an interval in succession? We cannot talk about it going from one point to the next point since there is no next point. Between any two points there is another point; that is, between any two real numbers there is another real number. Even between any two rational numbers there is another rational number (for example, their arithmetic average).

The concept of limit does not evade these difficulties since a variable x is said to have a constant c as a limit if x can be made to approach as close as desired to c through continuous variation. This still does not answer the question of how to characterize mathematically the notion of continuous variation. Moreover, it also raises the question of how to characterize mathematically the notion of "as close as desired."

In attempts to deal with these questions, in the nineteenth century the mathematician Cauchy proposed a definition of limit which is still in use today. Let x be a real variable, that is, one to which only real numbers may be assigned as values. Then x is said to have the real number c as its limit if, given any positive number whatsoever, the absolute value of the difference between x and c can be made less than the given number. Let the arbitrary positive number be designated by ϵ; then x has c as its limit if $|x - c| < \epsilon$. Let us say what this means in several equivalent ways. The notation $|x - c|$, read "the absolute value of x minus c," means that the numerical or unsigned value of $x - c$ is less than ϵ. If $x - c$ is positive, then $x - c$ is less than ϵ; if $x - c$ is negative, then $-(x - c)$, the negative of $x - c$, is less than ϵ; if $x - c = 0$, then its absolute value is 0, which is certainly less than a positive number ϵ. If $x - c < \epsilon$, then $x - \epsilon < c$; if $-(x - c) < \epsilon$, then $-x + c < \epsilon$ or $c < x + \epsilon$. Combining the two inequalities, we get $x - \epsilon < c < x + \epsilon$. This means that the variable x can be brought within ϵ (or a distance of ϵ) of c. In other words, there is an interval of length 2ϵ, with its center at c, such that every point in the interval (with the possible exception of c) belongs to the domain of x (that is, can be assigned as a value to x). We may picture a gate of length 2ϵ, and know that every point within the gate (except possibly c) belongs to the domain of x. For a different ϵ, a different size "gate" or interval may have to be chosen. Since any positive number may be chosen, no matter how small, x can be brought as close as desired to c. In particular, to say that an infinitesimal is a variable that has 0 as a limit means that $c = 0$ so that for any $\epsilon > 0$, $|x - c| = |x - 0| = |x| < \epsilon$ or $-\epsilon < x < \epsilon$. This means that an infinitesimal can be made less than any preassigned positive number or, in other words, can be brought as close to 0 as desired.

Cauchy gave a similar definition of limit for a function of a real variable. Let x be a real variable and f a single-valued function of x which assumes only real values; that is, $f(x)$ is a real number for a given value of x. In other words, the domain and the range of x consist of real numbers. Then $f(x)$ is said to have the limit L (L a real number), or to approach L or to converge to L, as x approaches c, if for any positive number ϵ, there is a positive number δ such that for all x which lie in the interval $|x - c| < \delta$, it is the case that $|f(x) - L| < \epsilon$. This means that given an $\epsilon > 0$, some $\delta > 0$ can be found such that for all x in the interval $x - \delta < c < x + \delta$, with the possible exception of c itself, it is the case that $f(x) - \epsilon < L < f(x) + \epsilon$. In other words, given an $\epsilon > 0$, some $\delta > 0$ can be found such that for all x within δ distance of c (except possibly the point c itself) the corresponding $f(x)$ is within ϵ distance of L. This definition amounts to replacing the interval that occurred when we were dealing with only the variable x (the one-dimensional case) with a rectangle of base 2δ and height 2ϵ. In other words, the "gate" now is rectangular in shape.

Finally, $f(x)$ is said to be continuous at c if $f(x)$ has a limit L at c and, moreover, the limit $L = f(c)$. This means that the point c (at which the limit exists), which was allowed as an exception above is no longer an exception. Since $L = f(c)$, $|f(c) - L| = 0$ which is certainly less than any positive ϵ. In short, $f(x)$ is continuous at c if it has a limit there which equals the value of f at c.

Returning to Cauchy's definition of limit, let us note that no mention is made of motion or approach or of "tending to" a particular value. His is a static definition which does not include the dynamic concept of motion or approach. Similarly, the definition of a continuous function is a static one. There is no mention of motion or continuous motion.

Cauchy's achievement was to realize that, as far as the mathematical concepts are concerned, any reference to a prior intuitive idea of continuous motion may and even must be omitted. . . . This [Cauchy's] definition is *static;* it does not presuppose the intuitive idea of motion. On the contrary, only such a static definition makes possible a precise mathematical analysis of continuous motion in time, and disposes of Zeno's paradoxes as far as mathematical science is concerned. . . . Whether this definition corresponds satisfactorily with the intuitive "dynamic" notion of approach is a question of the same sort as whether the axioms of geometry provide a satisfactory description of the intuitive concept of space. Both formulations leave out something that is real to the intuition, but they provide an adequate mathematical framework for expressing our knowledge of these concepts. (Courant and Robbins, 1941, p. 306)

In short, mathematical rigor has been attained at the cost of losing the dynamics characteristic of our everyday conception of motion.

Philosophical Problems of Time, Space, and Motion

As already mentioned, we know of Zeno's paradoxes from Plato and Aristotle. Unlike Zeno and Parmenides, Plato did not consider the phenomenal world as unreal but claimed that we cannot fully comprehend it through our ideas or our intelligence. "[It] is not to be forgotten that the Eleatic [Parmenides] denied the reality of the world of phenomenon, while Plato denied only that it could be known scientifically, i.e., through conceptions" (Windelband, 1958, p. 130n). Plato considered that the world of the senses is an intimation of an external world. This is seen in the famous allegory of the cave dwellers who, because they are chained so that they face the wall of the cave and cannot turn around to look outside, can see only the shadows cast on the wall by the objects and events outside. Due to ignorance, the cave dwellers may confuse the shadows with the reality outside. But through proper training (formal discipline), they can learn to distinguish between shadow and substance and learn to seek the reality, the organization, structure, or pattern that the shadows reflect. In other words, although they are still physically chained so that they see only the shadows, the mental development they achieve through certain education can help them to comprehend the substance that the shadows reflect. Thus Plato's writings may be interpreted to mean that sense impressions yield clues to reality if one is freed from the bondage of the immediate sensation and its stimulus.

Plato had much more to say about the world of ideas, the only realm about which we can have true knowledge, than about the phenomenal world or the corporeal world of nature about which we have only the knowledge derived from our untrustworthy senses. He wrote a scientific dialogue, *Timaeus*, which is named after a Pythagorean. Plato is believed to have met Pythagoras and to have acquired from members of this school his knowledge of mathematics and astronomy. These helped Plato to link the world of ideas with the phenomenal world. "Mathematics taught what was eternal in the earthly and perceived the supersensual in the material, while astronomy turned the gaze . . . to those mysterious celestial bodies . . . whose movements are ordered by number and measure and can be comprehended by the thinking mind" (Zeller, 1955, p. 163).

The world of the senses is described in the *Timaeus* as a world of happenings or becomings. Since whatever becomes is the product of an agent, there is an artisan or creator who makes this world. The model or archetype that the creator uses, is exact, eternal, and unchanging, but its copy, the world of the senses, is variable and changeable. Plato stresses that discourse about the model can be exact and final, as is the object it deals with, whereas discourse about its copy must be approximate, tentative, and subject to correction. Hence, "in metaphysics and mathematics there can be finality; in the natural sciences we have to be content with approximate and tentative results, though our business is to make our approximations as accurate as we can" (Taylor, 1936, p. 441).

Time and the world began together, the dialogue points out, with the creator making both of them. In order to make the model as nearly eternal as could be, the creator "devised a 'moving image of eternity,' which he called *time*. Time is to eternity as number is to unity; its absolutely uniform flow is an imperfect mirroring of the self-sameness of eternity, and time is the characteristic form of the sensible [the world of the senses]" (Taylor, 1936, p. 446). The sun and other heavenly bodies with uniform motions provide means of measuring time.

Another concept in the *Timaeus* is that of the "receptacle," or "matrix," in which the becoming takes place. Some writers interpret this as not-being, noting that Plato "denies it any form of being, but not its existence" (Zeller, 1955, p. 164). This would mean that, in contrast to Parmenides and Zeno, Plato assumed not-being in addition to being. There are some differences in interpretation as to whether this "receptacle" is changing or nonchanging. For example, Zeller describes it as everchanging (p. 164) and Taylor as permanent, the self-same under all processes of change (1936, p. 456). The dialogue also refers to it as a sort of space or place. Some writers interpret this to mean space while others take it to mean the substance that fills space; some interpret it as empty space, or "nothing," whereas others refute this interpretation (compare Windelband, 1958, p. 129 and Zeller, 1955, p. 165). Windelband has said that space refers to the "unlimited" out of which phenomena are formed through a process of "limitation" in which they take on mathematical shape or form in an attempt to imitate the pure forms of the realm of ideas (1958, p. 129). In any event, there seems to be agreement that the space, whether it be regarded as the material out of which the creator makes things or the space in which they are made, is itself without form or structure, but the objects that are constructed (in it or of it) have definite geometric shape.

In general, the *Timaeus* provides the principles of a science of nature that is largely geometrical. Physical or corporeal bodies are regarded as mathematical structures. Five distinct types of regular solids are recognized. The cube is considered to be appropriate to earth, the pyramid or tetrahedron to fire, the octahedron to air, and the icosahedron to water. There is also the dodecahedron, with twelve pentagons as its faces, which is regarded as the design underlying the universe as a whole. Each of the first four solids is considered to be composed of, or reducible to, certain triangles. These are the ultimate elements, themselves indivisible, akin to Democritus' atomic forms. Whereas Democritus considered that movements are the resultants of the accidental, lawless motions of the individual atoms, Plato considered that the universe as a whole is in ordered, lawful motion and that every particular motion is derived from this.

Aristotle, who contributed to virtually every field except mathematics, offered a less mathematical description of the universe than did Plato. Indeed, Aristotle has been said to have had an antimathematical bias and to have believed that there is a more natural, more sensible way than mathematics to derive understanding of the universe, a way that does more justice to the individual nature of things. Aristotle regarded mind as primary and as giving us the most immediate contact with the reality of the universe, which he considered to be finite in extent. Aristotle started from things or objects and focused the mind on them in attempts to understand their particular nature. Whereas objects were mathematical in nature to Plato (the mathematical or geometrical forms that arose as limitations of empty space), to Aristotle objects were not geometrical or mathematical in nature but were qualitative substances. Space to Aristotle was only the boundary between an object and the objects that surrounded it and not something occupied by all objects or something fundamental out of which all objects emerged.

Focusing on a particular thing or object, Aristotle asked: What is it and what is it to be? What is its potential and its purpose? Instead of asking what the object is composed of or how it operates, as a modern scientist might, he asked what its mode of being is and what it is to become. He was interested in distinguishing among various modes of being and various potentialities and in doing justice to the individual character, the uniqueness (essence) of the particular thing. For such ends, he found mathematics inadequate and therefore veered away from it.

Aristotle considered that each thing has the potential of actualizing or fulfilling itself and that each being acts as if it were realizing a complete form of itself out of an amorphous beginning, like the oak tree develops out of the embryonic tree in the acorn. In this process there is purpose, striving, and direction, so that, for example, the stone strives toward the center of the earth and the fire aims toward the heavens. There are basically two kinds of changes, that by which something comes into being and grows and achieves its potential and that by which it passes away or decays, generating in the process another thing that grows and then decays. All of nature may be characterized as change or motion that takes place in an orderly, lawful manner. What we call motion was a special case to Aristotle, which he considered terrestial or local motion. Motion or movement in general may be characterized as "the act of being in potency in so far as it has not reached its full actualization or unfolding" (de Santillana, 1961, p. 217).

Note that Aristotle was concerned with *why* motion occurs. It occurs because potentiality is being transformed into actuality. Perhaps not until the time of Galileo do we find the complete abandonment of the *why* of motion and its replacement with the *how* of motion. With Aristotle and the scholastic philosophers who followed him, the *"why* of motion had been the object of study and the study had proceeded in qualitative and substantive terms; with Galileo now it is the *how* of motion that becomes the object of analysis, and that by the method of exact mathematics" (Burtt, 1955, p. 91). Like Parmenides, Galileo assumed that it is only through reason that we can know the real world. But reason to Galileo meant mathematical reasoning. Like Plato, he regarded space as mathematical or geometrical space. But whereas Plato saw the world filled with mathematical forms about whose motion he had relatively little to say, to Galileo the world consisted of matter which was in motion. He subjected the process to mathematical study which in turn made the concepts of space and time more important than they had been to Aristotle or to Plato. Mathematics was the key that opened the secrets of the universe, for Galileo considered that the "book of nature is written in mathematical characters" (de Santillana, 1961, p. 212). What did not lend itself to mathematical treatment was regarded as less important, less objective or as secondary and subjective. Those properties of an external object which do not lend themselves to mathematical treatment, Galileo decided, do not actually belong to the object but are ascribed to it by the observer. In Galileo's words (translated by Burtt, 1955, p. 88), "many affections which are reputed to be qualities residing in the external object, have truly no other existence than in us, and without us are nothing else than names." In this category he placed tastes, odors, sounds, and other such properties that "demanded other than size, figure, number, and slow or rapid motion . . . if the ears, the tongue, and the nostrils were taken away, the figures, the numbers, and the motions would indeed remain, but not the odors nor the tastes nor the sounds, which, without the living animal, I do not believe are anything else than names" (p. 88). In short, the properties capable of mathematical representation would remain even if the observer were removed whereas the other properties are ascribed to the object by the observer. In this distinction between objective and subjective, or primary and secondary, qualities, Galileo was following the doctrine of the Greek Democritus who wrote: "Sweet and bitter, cold and warm as well as all colors, all these things exist but in opinion and not in reality; what really exists are unchangeable particles, atoms, and their motions in empty space" (cited in Barnett,

1957, p. 18). This thesis was strongly affirmed by the English philosopher John Locke, who promulgated the doctrine of primary and secondary qualities. He distinguished sharply between primary, or real, properties such as shape, motion, and other geometric properties, which were considered to reside or be inherent in the external object itself and secondary, or subjective, qualities, including tastes, colors, and sounds, which were attributed to the object by the observer. It is difficult to overestimate the influence on philosophy and psychology of the primary-secondary doctrine and of the view so clearly expressed by Galileo that what is capable of mathematical treatment is primary and real and what is not must be secondary and subjective. A case can be made that this doctrine runs like a central theme through psychology (especially experimental psychology), influencing the choice of topics and of means by which to study them. The so-called tertiary properties such as sentiments, experience of emotions, feelings, and values have also been distinguished. These tertiary properties are even more subjective and less primary than the secondary qualities, less capable of mathematical representation, and concomitantly, throughout much of the history of psychology, less suitable for scientific study. Some psychologists have criticized this threefold classification of properties and the implied hierarchical ordering. This has led some to reject the scientific approach to psychology, but others, for example, the Gestalt psychologists, have attempted to study the tertiary qualities (Wertheimer, 1935; Köhler, 1938a; Wolff, 1943). More recently there have been attempts to apply mathematical measurements to tertiary qualities (compare Hochberg, 1964 and Attneave, 1959). But even in contemporary psychology there are echoes of Democritus', Galileo's, and Locke's distinctions among primary, secondary, and tertiary qualities, between the objective and the subjective, and between that which lends itself to mathematical treatment and that which does not.

In Galileo's views there were attempts to eliminate the observer, to regard man as less important or less primary than nature, which can be reduced to mathematical study. Galileo departed radically from hoary traditions. Common to Plato, Aristotle, and even such materialists as Democritus, and common to many Greek, Roman, and medieval philosophers, was a belief that man was primary. This view Galileo rejected.

> Till the time of Galileo it had always been taken for granted that man and nature were both integral parts of a larger whole, in which man's place was the more fundamental. . . . *Now, in the course of translating this distinction of primary and secondary into terms suited to the new mathematical interpretation of nature, we have the first stage in the reading of man quite out of the real and primary realm.* Obviously man was not a subject suited to mathematical study. . . . Hence the real world must be the world outside of man. . . . Man begins to appear for the first time in the history of thought as an irrelevant spectator and insignificant effect of the great mathematical system which is the substance of reality. (Burtt, 1955, pp. 89–90)

This diminishing importance of man's place is illustrated in the role played by the concept of time in Galileo's work as compared to earlier occidental systems of thought. For example, the medieval philosophers, under the influence of Aristotle, thought of time, or the temporal process, as a transformation of potentiality into actuality, of the present drawing the future into itself.

> That this sounds absurd to our ears is because we have followed Galileo and banished man, with his memory and purpose, out of the real world. Consequently time seems to us nothing but a measurable continuum. . . . To such a view it is impossible to regard the temporal movement as the absorption of the future into the actual or present, for there really is nothing actual. All is becoming. We are forced to view the movement of time as passing *from* the past *into* the future, the present being merely that moving limit between the two. Time as something *lived* we have banished from our metaphysics. (Burtt, 1955, p. 95)

Time, as a measurable continuum, can be represented by a straight line and symbolized by a numerical variable t. There would seem to be no room here for man, the nonmeasurable.

The distinction that Galileo suggested between primary and secondary qualities was sharpened in Descartes' dualism (also referred to as the Cartesian dualism after the Latinized version of Descartes). The sharp distinction that the inventor of analytic geometry drew between the primary mathematical realm and the secondary realm of man set the stage for the famous mind-body problem. Descartes maintained that the so-called secondary qualities, such as color, smell, taste, and pain, cannot even be conceived as existing outside of one's mind. To say, for instance, that one sees color or feels pain is tantamount to saying that one does not know, or is completely ignorant of, what he saw or felt. Whatever is not mathematical, or depends on thought, belongs to the realm of mind; whatever belongs to the realm of bodies is mathematical. Even more than Galileo, Descartes accepted the view that the universe is mathematical in nature and that mathematics can unlock its secrets.

A more empirical view was taken by Newton who hoped that the universe was mathematical and that existing mathematics would suffice to reveal its principles. Unlike Galileo and Descartes, he did not assume that this must be the case. But he seems to have accepted Descartes' dualism and the distinction between primary and secondary qualities. "In Newton the Cartesian metaphysics finally overthrew Aristotelianism and became the predominant world-view of modern times" (Burtt, 1955, p. 239).

Newton's thought centered on the phenomena of motion, which he studied through a combination of mathematical and experimental methods. Fundamental concepts in his system included space and time. He distinguished between absolute and relative time, space and place, and motion. Absolute time is true mathematical time, sometimes called *duration*, which constitutes a homogeneous, infinite continuum. Relative time, which is apparent or vulgar time commonly used in place of absolute time, is some external measure of duration through motion, such as a minute, hour, or day. Absolute space is true mathematical space and is homogeneous, infinite, and immovable. Relative space, which is vulgarly, or commonly, used instead of absolute space, is an external measure of duration through motion such as the distance between discernible objects. Thus, relative time and space depend on distinctions between objects and events discernible to the senses, whereas absolute time and space are independent of external objects and are not accessible to observation of the senses. Place is that part of space which a body occupies, and place is considered absolute or relative according to whether the space is regarded as absolute or relative. Finally, absolute motion is the transfer of a body from one absolute place to another absolute place, and relative motion is the transfer from one relative place to another. Not satisfactorily answered were the problems of how we distinguish between absolute and relative motion and between absolute and relative time and space. Actually, Newton's system raised new problems concerning time, space, and motion and did not satisfactorily answer the old problems. It is interesting that Leibniz, who was Newton's contender for the honor of "inventing" the calculus, disagreed vehemently with his views on time, space, and motion. Leibniz maintained that there were not absolute objective space, time, and motion but that these along with color, light, heat, and shape, were mere apparent qualities, qualities with no reality independent of our senses.

In this sketchy outline we skip to Kant who, in order to resolve the antinomies of time and space, assumed that man has a priori intuitions of time and space. He maintained that these are not empirical concepts derived from experience but are prior to experience. Space, for example, is considered to be a necessary a priori representation, a pure intuition. We must have some conception of space before we can experience objects in space. Kant went on to conclude that geometry (Euclidean) consists of a priori truths about space. The discovery of non-Euclidean geometries is usually interpreted to reveal the error of Kant's assumption that space is an a priori intuition. However, it is possible to maintain Kant's assumption and to regard the different geometries as different ways through which a mind may apprehend, or order, space.

> Though it seems clear that Kant was mistaken in believing that such-and-such specific forms of spatial putting together are a priori, it does not follow that he was mistaken about space being a form of the mind's apprehension of its world. Space might be a mode of ordering contributed by the mind and the various geometries might be accounts of the various possible types of such ordering. (Jones, 1952, p. 825)

Likewise time was regarded by Kant as a pure form of intuition, as a way of putting together experienced order, except that it is a temporal rather than a spatial order. The mathematical intuitionists accept Kant's conception of the a priori nature of time but reject his conception of the a priori nature of space.

Twentieth century philosophy is marked by diversity of views on space and time and on their relationship to mathematics. For example, Whitehead, in the rational tradition of Platonism, believes that mathematical truths (such as those about space and time) portray objectively real patterns. Russell, on the other hand, though Whitehead's collaborator in the *Principia Mathematica,* is far apart from him philosophically. Russell maintains that mathematics does not portray objectively real patterns or truths about the universe but is a language for analyzing propositions.

Einstein carried further the notion that space and time are merely forms of intuition dependent on our senses, a notion which we saw in Parmenides, Leibniz, and Kant.

> [Einstein showed] that even space and time are forms of intuition, which can no more be divorced from consciousness than can our concepts of color, shape, or size. Space has no objective reality except as an order or arrangement of the objects we perceive in it, and time has no independent existence apart from the order of events by which we measure it. (Barnett, 1957, p. 19)

In Einstein's theories, fields and field properties play the roles that particles, masses, and their properties played in Newton's theories. For example, the gravitational laws may be regarded as describing certain field properties of the space-time continuum.

The universe in Einstein's theories is not regarded as Euclidean in nature but is considered to be better represented in terms of Riemann's non-Euclidean geometry. Space is not considered to be infinite, but to be finite, which represents a return to Aristotle's views. However, space is not only regarded as finite but also as unbounded. The analogy has been offered to a sphere, with the three-dimensional universe related to the four-dimensional space-time continuum as the two-dimensional surface of a sphere is related to space. In other words, the universe may be considered as the four-dimensional counterpart of a spherical surface.

Quantum physics offers quite a different conception of space and time than field theory. For example, absolute time, prominent in Newton's theory and discarded in relativity theory, re-enters the scene in quantum theory. Discontinuity plays a central role. Carried to their ultimate conclusions, the methods of quantum physics would call for the "elimination of continuous functions from physics" (Einstein, 1950, p. 92) and hence call for the abandonment of the space-time continuum. Quantum physics differs from both Newton's mechanics and from field theories, such as Einstein's relativity theory, in that it does not use a space-time model of nature; it does not offer a mathematical representation of an event as it happens in space and time but instead gives statistical or probability distributions.

Not only in physics but in biology and other sciences discontinuities have come to the fore, with a corresponding demand for a mathematics capable of dealing with the discontinuous and the discrete. For example, the genetic biology introduced by Gregor Mendel in 1866 and rediscovered in 1900 involves probability distributions of large numbers of genetic units, making for a kind of quantum theory in genetics (Margenau, 1950, p. 454).

> Mendelism introduces serious mathematics into biology—the kind of mathematics, involving statistics, probability, permutations and combinations, which deals with discrete objects in large numbers. This is different from the mathematics of continuous change, which grew up in the service of Newtonian physics. Mendelism, with its distinct and indestructible genetic units, ranks philosophically with the atomic, kinetic, and Quantum theories, in suggesting an ultimately discontinuous nature. Ironically, the mathematics of continuity has begun to acquire sound logical foundations just as science is beginning to have less use for it. (Hull, 1959, p. 304)

Psychological Problems of Time, Space, and Motion

We have seen that the problems of space and time, once primarily philosophical problems, have also become of interest to the natural sciences. Similarly, these problems are of concern to psychologists, particularly those in the field of perception. Some psychologists take the position that perception of space and time is an outgrowth of experience, that it is learned, whereas others assume that it is primarily intuitive, or prior to experience (like Kant's a priori), or due to so-called autochthonous factors. This difference involves the controversy of nativism versus empiricism. For example, that we perceive space as three-dimensional, even though the retinal image is two-dimensional, has been interpreted by the so-called empiricists as due to learning, or experience, but by the nativists as due to innate or unlearned factors. Gestalt psychological views are sometimes reinterpreted in terms of the empiricism-nativism controversy (compare Koffka, 1935, for a rejection of the nativistic position and Postman, 1963, for rejecting Koffka's rejection and insisting that Koffka and other Gestalt psychologists have to be nativists).

The controversy is still a lively and interesting one (compare Hochberg, 1964 and Walk and Gibson, 1963). There is, perhaps, some danger that it may become a philosophical rut, bogging down research, or a sterile rather than fruitful issue. We feel that it may be worthwhile to consider space and time from viewpoints other than the empiricism-nativism issue.

The psychological problem of the nature of motion is also of considerable interest. Corresponding to a static conception of motion in mathematics, there are theories in psychology that treat motion as static, rather than dynamic. One theory is that motion consists of a series or sum of static events, such as a succession of sensations on the retina of the eye. Motion itself is not perceived. What is sensed is the effect of the stimulation of the individual points on the retina. Because of one's past experience, one infers that something moved. Thus some psychologists (as some philosophers) claim that motion is not a primary experience but a secondary experience, that it is an epiphenomenon, or appearance.

It was Wertheimer's experiment on the phi phenomenon that helped to launch the revolt against the assumption that motion can be understood as a sum of static sensations. This experiment, and other experiments on perception, were used to oppose the thesis that one's experience is only made up of static sensations. Instead it was hypothesized that there are true dynamic experiences, of which motion is an example, that these can best be understood as dynamic processes (dynamic in the phenomenal or behavioral world and in the neurophysiological realm) and not as an "and-summation" or synthesis of static sensations.

Continuity, so important in mathematics, is also of concern in psychology. A popular use of the term is in the continuity-discontinuity controversy in learning theory. Is learning a rather continuous process, gradually built up, or does it occur suddenly, discontinuously, rather independently of previous trials and errors? Different answers to this question are sometimes used to characterize the differences between stimulus-response, or S-R, theories of learning (supporting a continuous view of learning) and cognitive theories of learning (supporting a discontinuous view). It might be pointed out, however, that the S-R versus cognitive theory does not coincide with the continuity-discontinuity dichotomy. For example, Gestalt psychologists are generally regarded as holding a cognitive theory of learning and yet they do not say that all learning is discontinuous, not even the so-called insightful kind (Koffka, 1935). Nor do they say that all learning is independent of past experience. But neither do they say that all learning is continuous. They recognize that learning may be of one kind or another and are interested in determining the conditions under which each occurs (Koffka, 1935; Luchins and Luchins, 1959).

Some of the statistical procedures and other mathematical procedures employed in psychology are based on assumptions of continuity. For example, the statistics may be based on the assumption that the trait or behavior under analysis is continuously distributed. Moreover, the statistical procedures may be suitable for a population of responses or people that approaches infinity rather than for the finite sample used. In general, the mathematics may be suitable only under continuity conditions, which do not prevail in the psychological situation where the concern usually is with the discrete rather than with the continuous. A mathematical psychologist has noted that "the continuous mathematics of classical analysis is not particularly well suited to the discreteness of most psychological experiments" (Luce, 1964, p. 366). Although some progress has been made in the development of statistical methods suitable for discrete data, continuity often is the prerequisite for the mathematics used for analysis and discussion of psychological experiments and data. It is important to consider whether the mathematics is valid for the particular case to which it is applied and what the effects are of the deviation between the prevailing conditions and those which are prerequisites for the mathematics.

In the light of our discussion of space, time, continuity, and related concepts, we would like to raise some problems that suggested themselves for research for psychology. Investigations are needed to ascertain the various conceptualizations of time and of space, of continuity and of discontinuity, of discreteness and of nondiscreteness held by people in everyday life. Just how are these words used? Developmental and epistemological studies, such as those done by Piaget, are needed in these areas as well as analyses of primitive peoples' conceptions. Do these conceptions (space, time, continuity) manifest themselves early in life? Do they change with age? Are there cultural differences and differences related to modes of language and thought patterns? For example, what happens to children's conceptions of space and time as they get older? Do children conceive of space as having infinite extent, infinite divisibility? Do adults? Can children or adults conceive of space as finite and unbounded? Do they think of space as a big ball that encloses everything? (It is of interest to ask a person to think of two balls, one twice as large as the other, and to ask him to compare the *number* of points on the surfaces of the two balls.) How do children and adults conceive of a point, of a line? Do they think of a point as a dot or as the intersection of two lines? Do they think of a line as composed of infinitely many points or dots or as one continuous, undivided structure? Experiments may be performed in which a series of points or dots are presented and the number of dots increased or the distance between dots decreased in order to see when the subjects will report it as a line. Are there differences among subjects of different ages, educational, cultural, and intellectual backgrounds? In what way are they the same? Or one might think of a "line with gaps" in it and let the size and/or the number of gaps be decreased in order to see when a line or line segment will be reported. Here we are touching on laws of organization and other organizational features with which Gestalt psychology is concerned.

Research is also needed on awareness of continuity and discontinuity and on the developmental, intellectual, social, and cultural factors that maximize or minimize such awareness. Awareness of contradictions is a related area of research (see Luchins and Luchins, 1964c). Specific problems are to investigate reactions to paradoxes such as Zeno's paradoxes or the Banach-Tarski paradox. For example, under what conditions are individuals aware that a paradox or contradiction is involved in Zeno's arguments? What is the naïve reaction to them in their classical, symbolic, or modern form? What can be done to enhance or lessen this awareness? How do individuals react to various attempts to resolve the paradoxes? We completed such a study recently and found that what is logically a paradox may not seem so to subjects. Some high school students and even college students do not seem to be aware of paradoxes, do not detect them when asked, and see no problem involved when the paradoxes are pointed out.

The Continuum in Science

It is often said that modern science, particularly physics, has less interest in continuity than it once had or than mathematics still has. "Modern physics has largely lost interest in, and sensitivity to, the conceptual delicacies of the continuum problem [whether or not matter is continuous] while mathematics, perpetuating the curiosity of ancient Greece, is appropriately aware of them and is finding ways for dealing with old paradoxes" (Margenau, 1950, p. 194). Moreover, quantum physics centers on discontinuities. Nonetheless, continua and continuous methods are still of interest in physics. This is especially true of such branches of physics as electromagnetic field theory and the mechanics of continuum. The latter "treats matter as a continuum while admitting at the same time its atomic structure" (p. 195). It is not unusual in physics and in other sciences (including psychology) to have, on the one hand, a phenomenon recognized as discrete but treated by methods appropriate for continuous phenomena or, on the other hand, recognized as continuous but treated as if it were discrete. An example of the latter is found in the study of eigen values—also called characteristic roots, proper values, spectral values, latent roots (just what these are is unimportant in the present context but the interested reader might refer to Hille and Phillips, 1957; Hoffman and Kunze, 1961). There are many mathematical procedures available for dealing with eigen values when they are discrete or scattered. But the physicist sometimes has a problem that involves a continuum of eigen values (a "line," or "block," of eigen values) and he may cope with this problem by assuming that the eigen values are discrete, that they are scattered or have gaps between them.

It is interesting to speculate what would be the consequences to mathematics and to the sciences if the number line were not a continuum, if there were gaps in it; if, for example, irrational numbers had not been invented to fill the gaps which are left after rational numbers are assigned to points on the line. It is sometimes said, but probably in jest, that physicists would not know the difference; or, if they did, they would not care. One reason for the remark may be that, as already mentioned, physicists are generally believed to have less interest in continuum problems than mathematicians. Another reason is that physicists, as other scientists, are often interested in approximations rather than in exact figures and any irrational number can be approximated as closely as desired by rational numbers. Hence, for purposes of approximation rational numbers suffice and the number line might just as well have gaps in it corresponding to nonrational points. Nonetheless, in many contexts in physics and other sciences use is made of irrational numbers, such as π and e and $\sqrt{2}$, and it is important to know that there are no gaps in the number line, that to every point or length there corresponds a real number. In short, it is important, not only for mathematics but also for the sciences, to have an adequate characterization of the number line, one which depicts it as a continuum.

It has been said (but, as we shall see, not quite accurately) that the distinguishing characteristics of a continuum are that it has infinite extent and that the interval between any two points can be divided into infinitely many small parts. But these definitions are not sufficient, since they are also characteristics of the set of rational points, or the points on the line that correspond to rational numbers. This set, too, has infinite extent and between any two rational numbers there are infinitely many rational numbers so that the interval between any two rational points can be divided into infinitely many small parts. Thus these two characteristics do not distinguish between the linear continuum and the "rational line" with gaps in it corresponding to irrational numbers.

In an attempt to characterize the linear continuum, let us first look naïvely at its properties. We have often said that the line is infinite in extent, that is, it is unbounded at both ends. In other words, there is no point that is to the left of all the other points on the line and no point that is to the right of all the other points on the line. If we associate a number with each point, then to say that the continuum is infinite means that it is unbounded in the sense that there is no "smallest" number and that there is no "largest" number.

To make these concepts more precise we use the notion of a simple (linear, total) ordering. Let S be a set and let $x \in S$ mean that x is an element of S. Let R be a binary relation on S (one that relates two elements). Then R is said to be a simple ordering for S, and S is said to be a simply ordered system with respect to R, if the following properties hold:

1. For any $x, y \in S$, one and only one of the following holds: either $x = y$ or xRy or yRx (trichotomy).
2. If xRy and yRz, then xRz for $x, y, z \in S$ (transitivity).

It is customary to denote the ordering relation by the symbol $<$ (read "less than"). Hence the two axioms that characterize a simple ordering may be reworded as follows:

1. For any x, $y \in S$, one and only one of the following holds: either $x = y$ or $x < y$ or $y < x$ (trichotomy).
2. If $x < y$ and $y < z$, then $x < z$ for x, y, $z \in S$ (transitivity).

In short, the system consisting of S under $<$, denoted by $(S, <)$, is a simply ordered system if these two axioms hold. It is readily seen that the relation "is to the left of" is a simple ordering for the set of points on the line and that the relation "is less than" is a simple ordering for the set of real numbers.

It is assumed that to every point on the line there corresponds a unique, real number, and conversely. Moreover, it is assumed that this one-to-one correspondence preserves a simple ordering. Thus, if a point p is to the left of a point q then the real number r_p which corresponds to p is less than the real number r_q which corresponds to q; that is, if $p < q$, then $r_p < r_q$. The assumption that there is a one-to-one order preserving correspondence between the points on the line and the real numbers is sometimes referred to as Cantor's axiom.

In viewing the line naïvely we saw that it was unbounded and that it had no smallest point or number (and likewise no largest one). In terms of a simply ordered set, this property can be worded as follows: There is no smallest element in the continuum: there is no element x in the set such that $x < y$ for all $y \neq x$ in the set. (In contrast, every nonempty set of natural numbers or positive integers has a smallest element; this is called the well-ordering property.) Likewise there is no largest element in the continuum: there is no element z in the set such that $y < z$ for all $y \neq z$ in the set. In short, one necessary property of the continuum is that it is unbounded in the sense that it has neither a largest nor a smallest element.

Let us again take a naïve look at the line to see another property. Between any two points there is another point; between any two real numbers another real number. The term "between" may be described in terms of the simple order relation. If $p < q$ (where p and q are points on the line and $<$ denotes "to the left of") then there is a point s on the line such that $p < s$ and $s < q$ or, combining these by the transitivity property, $p < s < q$. A similar formulation may be given in terms of real numbers; if $b < d$, then there is a real number c such that $b < c$ and $c < d$ or $b < c < d$. The property that between any two elements of the set there is another element of the set is called the denseness property and a simply ordered set with this property is dense. In short, a set S is "dense," or "densely ordered," if: it is simply ordered; x, $y \in S$, $x < y$, then there is $z \in S$ such that $x < z$ and $z < y$.

To summarize, we have dealt with two properties of the line:

1. It is simply ordered and indeed densely ordered.
2. It is unbounded, having no largest or smallest element.

These are necessary properties for the linear continuum. But they are not sufficient properties; they do not adequately characterize the line. For example, these two properties also hold for the set of rational numbers. They too are simply ordered with respect to the usual meaning of "less than" and indeed densely ordered since between any two rational numbers there is another rational number, for example, their arithmetic average. Moreover, the rational numbers are unbounded since there is no smallest or largest rational number. Thus these two properties do not serve to distinguish the real numbers from the rational numbers or to distinguish the linear continuum from the line-with-gaps.

In an attempt to get properties which are sufficient to characterize the continuum we turn to a definition of real numbers. There are many definitions of real numbers, such as definitions offered by Weierstrass, Cauchy, Cantor, and Dedekind. Here we shall consider the latter's.

Dedekind's continuum

A Dedekind cut is a separation of the rational numbers into two non-empty sets such that every element in one subset is less than any element of the other subset. The notion of a cut may be applied to any simply ordered system, not necessarily the rationals and not necessarily densely ordered. The term Dedekind cut is sometimes (but not universally) reserved for cuts applied to the rational numbers and the unmodified term cut for other cuts. A cut is a separation of a simply ordered system $(S, <)$, into two nonempty subsets, A and B, such that S consists of A and B, and $a < b$ for every $a \in A$ and $b \in B$. The cut may be designated as $[A,B]$ and A called the lower and B the upper segment of the cut (a segment is sometimes referred to as a part or section). Thus, a cut may be made in the set of all integers under the usual ordering; for example, A may designate the set of all integers less than 2 and B may designate the set of all integers greater than or equal to 2.

A real number may be defined as a lower segment of a Dedekind cut (for the rational numbers) where the lower segment has no greatest element. The upper segment may or may not have a least element. For example, the set of all rational numbers less than 2 is a lower segment of a Dedekind cut; the rational number 2 is the least element of the corresponding upper segment. Another real number is defined by the lower segment which consists of the rational numbers that are negative or 0, or, if positive, have the property that their square is less than 2; the corresponding upper segment does not have a least element since there is no rational number that yields 2 when squared. The real number defined by a Dedekind cut may be identified with the least element of the upper segment, if such an element exists, and in this case the number is called rational. If such an element does not exist, then the real number is called irrational. Thus in the first example, where 2 is the least element of the upper segment, the real number defined by the cut may be identified with the rational number 2; in the second example, the real number, denoted by $\sqrt{2}$, is irrational.

We have seen that when a cut is made in the rational numbers, the upper segment may or may not have a least element. However, if a cut is made in the real numbers, and the lower segment does not have a greatest element, then the upper segment must have a least element which may be rational or irrational. For example, the set of all real numbers each of which is less than $\sqrt{2}$ constitutes the lower segment of a cut in the real numbers; the upper segment has the real number $\sqrt{2}$ as its least element. This property that each upper segment has a least element is taken as an axiom for a continuum, known as the Dedekind axiom. This axiom is sometimes stated as follows: For each cut of a continuum, the lower segment has a greatest element or the upper segment a least element. However, since the lower and upper segments of a cut are complements (their union is the whole set S), it suffices to deal with only one of them. We choose to deal with lower segments (but could just as well have chosen upper segments). More precisely, a lower segment of a cut is defined as a subset A of a simply ordered set S with the following properties:

1. A is not empty and $S - A$ (S minus A, the complement of A) is not empty.
2. If $x \in A$ and $y \in S, y < x$ then $y \in A$ (that is, every element of S which is less than an element of A belongs to A).
3. If $x \in A$, then there exists $y \in A$ such that $x < y$ (hence A has no greatest element).

The Dedekind axiom then asserts that $S - A$ has a least element, that is, there exists $z \in S - A$ such that for every $s \in S - A, s \neq z$, it is the case that $z < s$.

Combining the two necessary properties of a continuum which we listed previously with the Dedekind cut axiom, we get the following conditions which are necessary for a system $(S, <)$ to be a continuum.

1. S is simply ordered and densely ordered.
2. S is unbounded, having no largest or smallest element.
3. The Dedekind axiom: For each cut of S, the upper segment has a least element.

These are sometimes taken as the axioms for a continuum or, as it may be called, a continuously ordered system (Feferman, 1964, p. 227). Note that this set of axioms does distinguish between the rational numbers and the real numbers since the former, although satisfying the first

two axioms, do not satisfy the Dedekind cut axiom. Note also that the
set of all integers, under the usual ordering, satisfies the axiom about
unboundedness and also the Dedekind axiom, but not the first axiom
since, although simply ordered, it is not densely ordered but is, of course,
a discrete series. The set of points in a closed interval on the line, for
example, between 0 and 1 inclusive (that is, the set of all real numbers x
such that $0 \leq x \leq 1$), satisfies both the density axiom and the Dedekind
axiom but not the unboundedness axiom. Such a set may be called a
bounded continuum.

It is of interest that there are systems other than the linear continuum
which satisfy the axioms for a continuum. For example, the set of points
(x, y) in a square may be assigned the following ordering: the ordered
pair (x_1, y_1) is less than the ordered pair (x_2, y_2) if $x_1 < x_2$ or, in case
$x_1 = x_2$, if $y_1 < y_2$; two points are equal if their x components and their
y components are equal. It can be shown that under this ordering the set
of points is densely ordered and obeys the Dedekind axiom (Huntington,
1955, p. 45; Wilder, 1952, p. 137). This is an example of a two-dimensional
continuum (bounded in case the points on the boundary of the square
are included). A two-dimensional continuum can be put into one-to-one
correspondence with the linear continuum but not in such a way as to
preserve the order relations. That a one-to-one correspondence is possible
means that they have the same cardinal number. That this correspondence cannot preserve the simple ordering means that the two-dimensional
and the linear continuum do not have the same order type (a generalization of ordinal number); two simply ordered sets are said to have the
same order type if there exists a one-to-one order-preserving correspondence between them and otherwise, to have different order types (Hobson,
1957, p. 216).

Just as a two-dimensional continuum satisfies the postulates for a continuum, so does an n-dimensional continuum. For example (Huntington,
1955, p. 60), consider the set of all n-tuples of real numbers $(x_1, x_2, \cdots ,$
$x_n)$ where x_1 may be any real number and each of $x_2, \cdots , x_n$ lies between 0 and 1 inclusive; the set may be ordered by the magnitude of the
first components or, if these are equal, by the magnitude of the second
component, or, if both of these are equal, by the magnitude of the third,
and so on, with two elements considered equal if all n respective components are equal. An n-dimensional continuum can be put into one-to-
one correspondence with the linear continuum (and therefore they have
the same cardinal number) but the correspondence cannot be order preserving (and therefore they have different order types).

In short, there are systems which obey the axioms for a continuum
but do not have the same order type as the linear continuum. In order
to have a set of axioms that characterize the linear continuum and not
any continuum of a different order type, the density axiom may be re-

placed by a stronger axiom, one which implies—but is not implied by—the density property. This is known as the linearity axiom or the separability axiom and may be worded as follows for a simply ordered set S: The set S contains a nonempty, enumerable subset such that between any two elements of S there is an element of the subset. The key word here is the word *enumerable*, a set which can be put into one-to-one correspondence with the natural numbers. Between any two real numbers there is a rational number and the set of rational numbers is enumerable. But in the case of the two-dimensional continuum consisting of the points in the square, there cannot be a subset of the kind required by the linearity axiom since such a subset would contain elements corresponding to every point of the base, $0 < y < 1$, and therefore would have a cardinal number c which is greater than that of the natural numbers; in other words the subset cannot be enumerable (Huntington, 1955; Wilder, 1952).

More generally, for a continuum of dimension higher than the first the subset called for by the linearity axiom cannot be enumerable. Thus we finally have a set of axioms that characterize the linear continuum and may be summarized as follows:

1. Linearity axiom.
2. Unboundedness axiom.
3. Dedekind axiom.

Clearly the linearity axiom implies the density axiom since it requires that between any two points there be another point (density property) and further requires that these "between" points form an enumerable set. Thus the new set of axioms has imposed a further condition on the axioms for a continuum, yielding the axioms for a linear continuum. If the axiom on unboundedness is removed, the remaining axioms characterize a bounded linear continuum, such as a closed interval of the real line (an interval with its end points or extreme points).

Cauchy's continuum

The characterization of the continuum can also be based on definitions of the real numbers other than the Dedekind cut. Real numbers may be considered as limits of sequences of rational numbers, as was done by Cauchy. For example, the sequence 1.4, 1.41, 1.414, $\cdots$ can be chosen to have $\sqrt{2}$ as its limit in the sense that the terms of the sequence can be made to approximate as close as we wish to $\sqrt{2}$ or, otherwise expressed, that the difference between $\sqrt{2}$ and the terms of the sequence can be made arbitrarily small if we go out far enough in the sequence. More precisely, the sequence of real numbers $\{x_k\} = (x_1, x_2, x_3, \cdots)$ is said to have the real number L as its limit if for each positive rational number ϵ there is some natural number n such that $|x_k - L| < \epsilon$ for all natural numbers $k \geq n$. It is easy to show that if a sequence has a limit, then the limit is unique. A sequence with a limit is called a convergent (Cauchy, fundamental) sequence. The sequence 1, 0, 1, 0, $\cdots$ is an example of a sequence that is not convergent.

The same real number is the limit of more than one sequence of rational numbers. For example, 2 is the limit of the sequence 2, 2, 2, $\cdots$ and also of the sequences 1, 1.9, 1.99, 1.999, $\cdots$ and 1.9, 2.1, 1.99, 2.01, 1.999, 2.001, $\cdots$. Similarly, $\sqrt{2}$ is the limit not only of sequences such as that mentioned in the previous paragraph which approximate $\sqrt{2}$ from below (starting with terms that are less than $\sqrt{2}$ and gradually get larger) as well as of sequences that approximate $\sqrt{2}$ from above (starting with terms that are larger than $\sqrt{2}$ and gradually get smaller) as well as of sequences that alternate above and below $\sqrt{2}$. We may consider the set of all sequences of rational numbers which have $\sqrt{2}$ as a limit and use this set to characterize $\sqrt{2}$. More generally, convergent sequences may be separated into "equivalence classes" with two sequences belonging to the same class if and only if they have the same real number as a limit. Otherwise expressed, the two convergent sequences of rational numbers $\{x_k\}$ and $\{y_k\}$ belong to the same equivalence class if and only if the limit of $|x_k - y_k|$ is 0 for k sufficiently far out in the series, that is, as k approaches infinity. A real number may be defined as the limit of sequences of rational numbers or as the equivalence class of such sequences. This definition can be used as the basis of a characterization of the continuum (Feferman, 1964).

Cantor's continuum

Cantor offered still another approach to the definition of the continuum. He was interested not only in the linear or one-dimensional continuum but also in n-dimensional continua, n being any natural number. Cantor referred to the discussions of the continuum concept by Leucippus, Democritus, Aristotle, and other philosophers. He emphasized that "we cannot begin in this determination [of the continuum], with the conception of time or that of space, for these conceptions can only be clearly explained by means of a continuity-conception which must, of course, be independent of them" (Jourdian, 1952, p. 71). Assuming the real numbers to be given, he started with the space of all ordered n-tuples $(x_1, x_2, \cdots, x_n)$ where the x_k may be any real number. Such an n-tuple was called an arithmetical point of the space which was itself designated by G_n. The distance between two points $x = (x_1, x_2, \cdots, x_n)$ and $y = (y_1, y_2, \cdots, y_n)$ was denoted by

$$d(x, y) = \sqrt{(x_1 - y_1)^2 + \cdots + (x_n - y_n)^2}$$

The problem was to determine whether or not a given subset of the space G_n was a continuum. For this purpose Cantor introduced concepts of perfect and of connex. To define these concepts we need the notions of a neighborhood of a point in G_n and of a limit point (also called cluster point and accumulation point). A neighborhood of radius r or an r-neighborhood of a point p consists of all points q in G_n such that $d(p, q) < r$. For instance, if $n = 1$ so that the points lie on a line, then an r-neighborhood is the set of all points in an interval (line segment) of length $2r$ with its center at p, where the end points of the interval are not included. If $n = 2$, then an r-neighborhood is the set of all points in the interior of the circle with center at p and radius r. A point p is called a limit point of a subset S of G_n if every neighborhood of p contains a point q of S other than p. The point p may or may not be a member of S. For example, a real number p, whether or not it is rational, is a limit point of the set of all rational numbers since every neighborhood of p (an interval centered at p) contains rational numbers other than p. However, if S is the set of all natural numbers, then any real number (for example, 2 or $\frac{1}{2}$ or $\sqrt{2}$) is not a limit point of S since there are neighborhoods about p (such as a neighborhood of diameter $\frac{1}{3}$ about 2) which do not contain any natural numbers (that is, do not contain any points of S). If every limit point of S is a point of S, then S is called closed. For example, the set of real numbers is closed since every limit point of it is a real number and belongs to S; but the set of rational numbers is not closed since there are limit points of this set which are irrational numbers and therefore do not belong to the set. To take another illustration, the interior of a circle is not closed since it does not contain its limit points (the boundary or circumference of the circle); the interior of the circle together with its boundary constitutes a closed set. If every point of S is a limit point of S, then S is called *dense in itself* (not to be confused with the term *dense* introduced earlier which is sometimes called *dense everywhere*). A set which is both closed and dense in itself is called a perfect set. The real numbers are perfect but not the rational numbers. Cantor gave an example of a set that is both closed and dense in itself, and hence is perfect, and yet is not dense in the sense of being everywhere dense. This is the so-called Cantor, or middle third, set (Cantor, 1952; Rudin, 1953, p. 34). Huntington (1955, p. 50) gives as an example of a set that is perfect but not dense, the set of all real numbers in the interval from 0 to 3 inclusive with the real numbers between 1 and 2 omitted; this omission does not allow the set to be dense since there are not real numbers between every two numbers of the set.

Cantor calls a set connex if between any two points p and q of the set, there exist two points t_1 and t_2 of the set such that the distance between t_1 and t_2 is as small as we please. Similarly, there are two points in the set which are between t_1 and t_2 and whose distance is arbitrarily small, and so on. This property of connexity holds, in particular, for the real numbers, since an infinite series of real numbers lies between two given real numbers. Hence the property of connexity for the set of real numbers may be expressed by saying that the set is dense.

Cantor noted that these two conditions of *perfect* and *connex* are the necessary and sufficient characteristics of a continuum. He characterized a linear continuum as a set that is perfect (closed and dense in itself) and has the linearity property: It contains an enumerable subset such that between any two elements of the set there is an element of the subset. The reader may recall that the linearity property was also used in the characterization of the linear continuum, which was founded on a definition of real numbers in terms of Dedekind cuts.

Equivalence of classical conceptions

Cantor's definition of real numbers can be shown to be equivalent to Dedekind's definition (Hobson, 1957, pp. 40–42). The equivalence is established by showing that every convergent sequence of rational numbers uniquely defines a Dedekind cut in the rational numbers and conversely, that any number defined by a segment of a Dedekind cut can be represented by a convergent sequence of rational numbers.

The real numbers, as defined by Dedekind or Cantor, leave no gaps on the line; there is no room for more numbers. Thus, acceptance of these definitions of the real numbers in effect assures the continuity of the line. But this involves an assumption as to the nature of the line and the nature of the real numbers, as Dedekind himself recognized:

> The assumption of this property of the line [continuity as defined by the existence of real numbers] is nothing else than an axiom by which we attribute to the line its continuity, by which we find continuity in the line. If space has at all a real existence it is *not* necessary for it to be continuous; many of its properties would remain the same even were it discontinuous. And if we knew for certain that space was discontinuous there would be nothing to prevent us, in case we so desired, from filling up its gaps, in thought, and thus making it continuous; this filling up would consist in a creation of new point-individuals and would have to be effected in accordance with the above principle [through the definition of real numbers]. (Dedekind, 1901, p. 12; originally published 1872)

The Continuum and Foundational Schools | The logicists' continuum

The various foundational schools differ in their approaches to the real numbers and to the continuum. Logicists accept, with some modifications, the Dedekind-cut definition of real numbers. For example, Russell (1919) defines a real number as the class of all the rational numbers less than it.

Russell is well aware of the difficulties and even contradictions provoked by Dedekind's definition. The essential difficulty is that a real number is defined as an infinite set (of rational numbers) bringing in its wake all the difficulties surrounding the "actual infinite" in mathematics. These difficulties are not avoided by defining a real number as the limit of an infinite sequence of rational numbers or as an equivalence class of rational numbers, which is again an infinite set, or as an unending decimal, which is but a notation for an infinite set. There is also the danger of a "vicious circle" principle, as Russell pointed out, in reference to Dedekind's definition. This is also a danger in definitions involving infinite sequence of rational numbers. For example, a real number may be defined as the *limit* of a sequence of rational numbers; but the very definition of the concept of limit may presuppose the existence of real numbers. Logicists have sought to meet various difficulties concerning the real numbers but have not been entirely successful, and they admit that their attempts are largely in the nature of *ad hoc* remedies. For example, to deal with real numbers logicists appeal to the axioms of infinity and reducibility, axioms with which they themselves are not satisfied. (More will be said about these axioms in Chapter 6 on logicism.)

The formalists' continuum

Formalists regard actual infinities, such as those involved in the classical definitions of real numbers, as "ideal" elements that may be appended to the finite, constructible elements of mathematics. The resulting system is studied as a formal, axiomatic system with the goal of ascertaining if it is consistent, complete, and categorical (where categorical means that all sets of objects that satisfy the axiom system are isomorphic). The fate of these goals of establishing the consistency, completeness, and categoricalness of axiomatic mathematical systems is the central concern of Chapter 9 on formalism. Hilbert (1956) defines continuity of the number line by noting that an axiom system for the real numbers is satisfied by no set of objects that includes the real numbers as a proper subset. Hence, if the set of points on the line is considered as a set that satisfies the axioms for the real numbers, and if the points are considered to correspond to the real numbers, then there are no points left over to which other objects (other numbers) must be assigned; therefore there are no gaps or breaks in the number line and it is continuous.

The intuitionists' continuum

Intuitionists object to classical definitions of real numbers on the grounds that they involve the actual infinite (treating an infinite set—for example, the set of all rational numbers less than a certain number or the set of all Cauchy sequences with a certain limit—as if it were a completed whole). Another objection is that the classical methods talk about the existence of real numbers but do not provide means for constructing all of them. Intuitionists reject the classical approach to real numbers and the concomitant conceptions of the continuum. They offer, instead, new definitions of real numbers and new approaches to the continuum. Just as there are several equivalent classical definitions of real numbers, so there are several equivalent intuitionistic definitions (Brouwer, 1918–1919; Heyting, 1935, 1952).

One of the earliest attempts at a constructive definition of real numbers and of the continuum was by Weyl (1918) who started with a criticism of Dedekind's approach. Weyl's approach is not, strictly speaking, intuitionistic and has been described as *semi-intuitionistic*. Unlike the intuitionists, Weyl was willing to accept the infinite sequence of natural numbers as a mathematical object. He regarded this sequence and "the concept of existence" which refers to the natural numbers as basal to all mathematical constructions (Weyl, 1918, p. 37).

Weyl's approach has features of the logistic approach. Somewhat analogous to Russell's theory of types, Weyl introduced different levels of relations. The first level consists of the natural numbers and of relations between them; the second level of relations whose variables are partly natural numbers and partly relations of the first level. Relations of the third level are those in which there occur variable relations of the second level, and so on (Becker, 1954, p. 341; Körner, 1960, p. 151).

By using only a finite number of principles of construction and by means of a certain restricted calculus of propositional functions, Weyl succeeded in defining a set of real numbers with many but not all of the properties of the classical continuum. The "Weyl numbers" are dense in the line; that is, every interval contains infinitely many of these numbers. But there are points on the classical line which are not defined by the Weyl procedure (no Weyl numbers correspond to them) and these gaps are dense in the classical line. Certain basic theorems about the classical real numbers are not able to be proved by Weyl. For example, in classical theory it is shown that every nonempty set of real numbers which has an upper bound (that is, a real number $x \geq y$ for every y in the set) has a least upper bound (an upper bound x for the set such that $x \leq z$ for any upper bound z of the set). Thus a set of Weyl numbers with an upper bound need not have a least upper bound. Of course, in the classical theory this theorem on least upper bounds involves a "vicious circle" or "impredicative definitions" (Kleene, 1952, p. 43) which Weyl avoided.

The Weyl continuum, although adequate for the early stages of mathematical analysis (for example, elementary differential and integral calculus), is inadequate for more advanced analysis (for example, Lebesgue integration). Weyl (1918, p. 71) admits that his continuum does not reflect the continuum of pure intuition or perception which he thinks is more adequately reflected by Brouwer's mathematics. Later he abandoned his own conception of the continuum for Brouwer's conception.

Brouwer (1924) characterizes a real number by a "closing down" process involving successively smaller intervals, one lying inside the other. These are called "nests of intervals," or "nested intervals." We may think of a nest as "a sequence of intervals each lying inside the previous one and contracting indefinitely in length; and each such nest picks out a real number from the continuum" (Black, 1959, p. 197). The process corresponds to the approximation process in measurement and amounts to saying that given any natural number n, the value of the real number is determined with an error of less than $1/n$. The successive intervals may be chosen in accordance with a stipulated rule (*Gesetz*) or may be arbitrarily chosen, yielding what Brouwer calls a free-choice sequence (compare this to Heyting, 1956, p. 33) but should be chosen to yield a nest of intervals.

Although each nest of intervals characterizes a real number, there are real numbers in the classical sense that cannot be characterized by a nest and therefore are not admissible as intuitionistic real numbers. If the Brouwer continuum is regarded as including all the intuitionistic real numbers or the nested intervals, then there are classical real numbers that are not in the Brouwer continuum. This continuum is not to be regarded as a completed totality or an actual infinity but, as it has been variously described, as a medium of free growth or free development or free becoming, since the real numbers are not all given at the start but must be developed as through a nest of intervals.

There is an essential difference between Brouwer's continuum and the classical continuum. In the latter the point is a basic concept and it is regarded as a *member* of the continuum. In Brouwer's continuum a basic concept is an interval which is itself continuous and is a proper subset or part of the continuum. "The conception of the continuum as an aggregate of existing *points* (members) . . . is replaced [in Brouwer's continuum] by an aggregate of *parts* which are partially overlapping and each of which is continuous itself. Instead of the membership relation the part-whole relation becomes fundamental" (Fraenkel and Bar-Hillel, 1958, pp. 249–250).

Heyting (1956) offers an intuitionistic definition of real numbers which stems from revisions of Cantor's approach. He calls a sequence $\{a_n\}$ of rational numbers a Cauchy sequence if for every natural number k we can find a natural number $n = n(k)$, such that $|a_{n+p} - a_n| < 1/k$ for every natural number p. It is not enough to say that n exists; we must be able to find n or to give a rule for constructing it. Some Cauchy sequences in the classical sense are not Cauchy sequences in the intuitionistic sense. For example (Heyting, 1956, p. 16), let $b = \{b_n\}$ be defined as follows: If the sequence 0 1 2 3 4 5 6 7 8 9 occurs in the decimal expansion of π, and if the nth digit after the decimal point represents the 9 of the first such sequence, then let $b_n = 1$; in every other case let $b_n = 2^{-n} = 1/2^n$. Now b differs from $a = \{a_n\}$, where $a_n = 2^{-n}$, in only one term, and since a is a classical Cauchy sequence so is b. However, although a is an intuitionistic Cauchy sequence, b is not. So long as it is not known whether a sequence 0 1 2 3 4 5 6 7 8 9 occurs in π, we are not able to find n such that $|b_{n+p} - b_n| < 1/2$ for every p and therefore the intuitionistic criterion for a Cauchy sequence is not satisfied.

An intuitionistic Cauchy sequence of rational numbers is called a *real number-generator*. Two real number-generators, $a = \{a_n\}$ and $b = \{b_n\}$, are said to be identical, denoted by $a \equiv b$, if $a_n = b_n$ for every n. Two real number-generators, $a = \{a_n\}$ and $b = \{b_n\}$, are said to coincide, denoted by $a = b$, if for every k we can find $n = n(k)$ such that $|a_{n+p} - b_{n+p}| < 1/k$ for every p. Classically no distinction is made between these relations of identity and coinciding. For example the sequences $\{2\}$ and $\{1.9, 1.99, 1.999, 1.9999, \cdots\}$ coincide but are not identical intuitionistically.

The real number-generators that coincide with a given number-generator form a set or more exactly, a *species* which is a set defined by a characteristic property of its elements. This set or species is called a real number. If r is a real number and the real number-generator b is one of its members, then it is said that b represents r and also that b coincides with r. All real numbers form a set or species which is the (one-dimensional) continuum.

Whitehead's continuum compared to the intuitionistic continuum

It is of interest that a philosophical notion, Whitehead's *extensional continuum*, has been compared with Brouwer's intuitionistic continuum (Mays, 1962). The extensive or extensional continuum, a key concept in Whitehead's philosophical thought, refers to an abstract structure or logical scheme that is considered to pervade all experiences. Whitehead characterizes the concept in terms of a set of postulates and describes it as a "one relational complex in which all potential objectifications find their niche" (1929, p. 91). This relational complex is considered to underlie the whole world, past, present, and future.

Relating it to the mathematical continuum, Whitehead notes: "The notion of a 'continuum' involves both the property of indefinite divisibility and the property of unbounded extension. There are always entities beyond entities" (p. 91). "The extensive continuum is 'real' because it expresses a fact derived from the actual world and concerning the contemporary actual world," with actual entities or events said to "atomize the continuum" (p. 92). The extensive continuum itself is characterized in terms of part-whole relationships, overlapping of regions, and so on.

> [Whitehead] expressly tells us that the extensive continuum is a complex of entities united by the various allied relationships of whole to part, or of overlapping and contact, and other derivative relationships. . . . It is clear from Whitehead's conception of the extensive continuum as exhibiting the properties of the inclusion, over-lap and contact of regions, that he has not the classical mathematical continuum in mind. It is in any case difficult to see how he could conceive it as a closely packed infinite series of points, since he regards points as derivative from these extensive relationships. In this respect his position would seem in some ways to resemble the mathematical intuitionist's notion of the continuum, where the fundamental relationship is taken to be that of part and whole. (Mays, 1962, p. 112)

What Mays has in mind here is the mathematical continuum of Brouwer in which, as we saw, a real number is defined in terms of a sequence of nested intervals. The intervals are proper subsets or parts of other intervals and of the continuum.

Criticizing Whitehead's description of the extensive continuum as real, as concerning the actual world, and as atomized by actual facts, Mays asks how the extensive continuum, if it is a system of logical relations, can be a matter of actual fact or actual occurrence. Mays argues that logical entities and contingent facts have different properties and ought not to be confused. He also distinguishes between experimental continuity which refers "to the fact that the perceptual field is given as a connected whole which cannot be split up into ultimate simple parts" and mathematical continuity which "deals precisely with such elements, i.e., an infinite collection of individuals arranged in a certain order" (1962, p. 112). He seems to be suggesting that Whitehead may be confusing the two. Moreover, he is admittedly skeptical about the assumptions that logic can serve as a model for direct experience and that the universe may be regarded as a logical system (pp. 13, 113). Both assumptions seem to underlie Whitehead's account of the extensive continuum.

The Continuum in Psychology

The assumption that a continuum is involved is implicit or explicit in several concepts and areas of psychology. For example, Kurt Lewin (1936) pointed out that the tendency to characterize phenomena in terms of gradients or continuous classifications instead of dichotomous classifications is a distinguishing characteristic of what he called the Galilean approach to science as compared to the Aristotelian approach. Not only Lewin's field theory but many other systematic approaches in psychology tend to reject dichotomous classifications in favor of gradients. In general, whenever gradients or measurements of psychological phenomena are proposed, it is assumed that what is being measured has the nature of a continuum. "Modern science . . . has forced us to recognize that no question of science can have meaning unless it involves a problem of measurement along a scale whose order is that of the continuum" (Churchman, 1948, p. vii).

The dimension of the psychological continuum may be considered to be greater than 1. For example, n factors yielded by factor analysis have been interpreted as lying in an n-dimensional space or continuum. "Most of the psychometric techniques postulate that the subjects can be represented as points in a Euclidean vector space" (Luce, 1964, p. 373). Such a space is a continuum.

The many attempts to measure thinking and intelligence have been regarded as presupposing an n-dimensional continuum.

> Observe that thinking is a continuum, an n-dimensional continuum. This notion is certainly not new, for it has existed since man first compared his mental abilities with another man's and it is implicit in all of the positive arguments on machine intelligence. Psychologists long ago developed "intelligence quotient" as a yardstick in this continuum, and their concept of "factors" is indicative of the n-dimensionality of the continuum of intelligence. The use of the one-dimensional "I.Q." is obviously an oversimplification of reality. Although the concept of an n-dimensional continuum for intelligence is not new, and although it is implicit in many discussions of artificial intelligence, it is rarely stated explicitly. (Armer, 1963, p. 390)

It seems to us to be of value for psychologists to survey their literature in order to discover the implicit and explicit uses therein of the notions of continuum and continuity. In what areas, and for what kinds of concepts and problems, are continua and continuity assumed, and for which are they not assumed? What are the theoretical and practical (technological) consequences of the use of continua as opposed to dichotomous or other noncontinuous classifications of phenomena? What happens to concepts, ideas, methods, research designs, mathematical models, techniques, and their applications, as a result of a shift from discontinuous to continuous classifications? For example, what have been the consequences in theory and practice of conceptualizing mental illness in terms of a continuum of "abnormal behavior" instead of the use of a dichotomous classification of normal and abnormal types of people? What have been the consequences of dealing with personality, not in terms of types or dichotomies such as introvert-extrovert, but in terms of some continuous classification, such as a trait theory based on a multifactor conceptualization? Have there been areas that have gone from continuous to dichotomous classification? If so, what are the reasons for the change? Are certain problems or difficulties peculiar to or attendant on the use of continuous or discontinuous classifications? Moreover, what are the effects of a change in the dimension of the assumed continuum; for example, a change from a one-factor theory of learning to a dual-factor or multifactor theory? What happens when there exist both continuous and discontinuous conceptions, for example, as in the continuity-discontinuity controversy about the nature of learning?

It is also of interest to compare the notions of continuum, continuity, and discontinuity as used in psychology, with their mathematical counterparts. What kinds of mathematical models tend to be associated with these terms? Do the so-called psychological continua satisfy any of the axiom sets for a mathematical continuum? For a given psychological continuum, which of the properties of a mathematical continuum hold and which do not? Are any of these properties assumed or utilized in the discussion or treatment of the psychological continuum? Are any of the properties of mathematical continuity or discontinuity assumed or utilized with reference to the corresponding psychological concepts?

Numbers and Sets

The present foundational crisis in mathematics has highlighted the lack of agreement concerning such basic concepts as *number* and *set*. Let us focus on these concepts and on some controversies that they have aroused.

The Natural Numbers

The natural or whole numbers 1, 2, 3, · · · seem so "natural," as their name suggests, that they have long been taken for granted as something given or pre-existing rather than an invention of mathematicians. The nineteenth century mathematician Kronecker reportedly said, "The whole numbers were made by the good Lord; everything else is the work of man." But even as Kronecker spoke, mathematicians were asking penetrating questions concerning the natural numbers. Among them was Frege (1960, first published 1884) who examined views of the concept of number. It is of interest that many of these views are still prevalent today. For example, Frege discussed the opinion that a natural number is an *idea;* and a recent text notes: "The first point we would make is that a number is an idea; it exists in the mind only" (Hayden and Finan, 1961, p. 36). This conception was severely criticized by Frege as making number a private, subjective matter that can vary from person to person, since an idea may mean different things to different people. "If the number two were an idea, then it would have straight away to be private to me only. Another man's idea is, *ex vi termini,* another idea" (Frege, 1960, p. 37). There might be as many ideas of *two* as there are people, including unconscious or latent ideas. Yet the number *two*, Frege wrote, is objective and should have a common meaning, not one that varies from person to person. Moreover, if number were an idea, it would be doubtful that there existed infinitely many numbers or that certain large numbers existed. For example, there might exist no idea, in any being, to answer to the symbol 17^{17}, so this would be an empty symbol and not correspond to any number. Furthermore, number as an idea would fall into the psychological rather than the mathematical realm. "If number were an idea, then arithmetic would be psychology. But arithmetic is no more psychology than, say, astronomy is. Astronomy is concerned, not with ideas of the planets, but with the planets themselves, and by the same token the objects of arithmetic are not ideas either" (Frege, 1960, p. 37). It would be strange indeed, Frege contended, if the most exact of all the sciences had to seek support from psychology. And yet, this would have to be the case, he insisted, if number were an idea.

Another conception of number is that it constitutes an abstraction from empirical objects, a property of external objects which is on a level with the properties of shape and color. A criticism of this notion is that we are free to vary the "number" of an object more than its shape or color. For example, we may think of the Iliad as one poem or as twenty-four books or as some large number of verses (Frege, 1960, p. 28). To deny that number is a property of external objects is not to say that number is subjective. The botanist makes as objective a statement when he gives the number of petals of a flower as when he describes its color or shape.

A related conception of number is that it is a characteristic property of an agglomeration of things; it is the manner in which the agglomeration is made up of parts or may be separated into parts. But, we are free to vary the way in which we separate an agglomeration into parts. Thus, a pile of straws may be separated into two piles or ten piles or into as many piles as there are single straws or into even more piles by cutting each straw into halves or into thirds or into more parts. Moreover, is an agglomeration of 100 pieces of straw made up of parts, or able to be separated into parts, in the same way as an agglomeration of 100 stars or 100 grains of sand?

What may be regarded as a critique of the last two conceptions of number is the thesis that number is more pervasive than such properties of objects and agglomerations as color or shape or divisibility. Everything, both material and immaterial, so this thesis asserts, can be numbered. This view was held by Leibniz who regarded number as going beyond material or physical properties, and as being metaphysical in nature. Leibniz conceived of *one* as the number of the Creator of the universe and *zero* as the number of the void out of which He created it, with *one* and *zero* generating all the whole numbers.

Various conceptions of number start with *one* or a unit and consider that all the other natural numbers can be reached through successive addition of units. What is meant by *one* or a *unit*? *One* or *oneness* is sometimes defined as that which is characteristic of every object whatsoever. How can it make sense, Frege asked, to ascribe *one* to every object?

To do so makes the concept so extensive in its scope as to lose the particularity or specificity required of a definition. Frege also raised the question of whether units are identical with each other and with *one*. If they are, then it makes no more sense to speak of units than it does to speak of *ones*. The term *unit* masks—but does not eliminate—difficulties that we encounter in dealing with *ones*. Thus it is said that *one* and *one* and *one* are *three;* but the set consisting of *one* and *one* and *one* consists only of *one*, that is, its only member is *one*. Clearly, the use of *and* in the expression "*one* and *one* and *one* are *three*" differs from its use when applied to members of a set or to collections of symbols. What then is the meaning of *and* or *plus* when applied to units or *ones*? Frege concluded that this question also has not been answered satisfactorily.

That attempts to define number have not been satisfactory does not mean that the concept is inherently incapable of definition. What troubled Frege was not only the lack of a precise definition but also the lack of agreement on the nature of the concept. There is no agreement on whether number refers to an idea or to a property of objects or to a chalk mark or to a pencil stroke, and so on. In short, it is a foggy and hazy concept. "How can a science which bases its claim to fame precisely on being as definite and accurate as possible repose on a concept as hazy as this is." (Frege, 1960, p. 41).

In an attempt to clarify the concept, Frege offered a definition of natural number in 1879 which was given independently by Russell in 1901. Known as the Frege-Russell definition, and accepted by logicism, it involves the concepts of *set* and *cardinal number*. Two sets are said to have the same cardinal number if there exists a one-to-one correspondence between them. The cardinal number of a given set is defined as the set of all sets that have the same cardinal number as the given set. For example, *two* is the cardinal number of all sets of pairs. This definition of number also has been criticized. The "set of all sets" which occurs in it can lead to contradictions, or antinomies, as we saw in the previous chapter, and this possibility is not eliminated by limiting it to the set of all sets that can be put into one-to-one correspondence with a given set. Indeed, as Wilder (1952, p. 100) points out, the inclusion of the words "all sets" in this definition is sufficient to create an uneasy feeling in someone familiar with the set-theoretic antinomies. Of course, when Frege proposed the definition he was not aware of this antinomy. When informed of it by Russell, he recognized its crushing effect on his years of efforts to secure the foundations of arithmetic. The second volume of Frege's *Grundgesetze* (1903) concludes with this admission: "A scientist can hardly encounter anything more undesirable than having the foundation collapse just as his work is completed. A letter from Mr. Bertrand Russell placed me in this position just as this work was all but through the press." With this, Frege suspended any further work on the foundations of arithmetic.

As already noted, the Frege-Russell definition of natural number, whatever its shortcomings, is accepted in logicism. The definition is unacceptable in intuitionism on grounds that will become clearer to us in a later chapter. For example, the definition refers to the existence of a one-to-one correspondence without requiring the actual construction of the correspondence, and it treats the set of all sets that are in one-to-one correspondence with a given set (a set that may include infinitely many elements) as a completed totality rather than as "potentially infinite." Intuitionists do not attempt a precise definition of numbers. In the spirit of Kronecker, they consider natural numbers as given before mathematics starts, as premathematical. Heyting, a leading spokesman for intuitionism, writes: "Mathematics begins after the concepts of natural numbers and of equality between natural numbers have been formed" (1956, p. 15). The natural numbers are regarded as so intuitively clear that they can be understood even by young children and can serve as a foundation on which to build mathematics.

> Children in the elementary school understand what the natural numbers are and they accept the fact that the sequence of natural numbers can be indefinitely continued. . . . This elementary notion of natural numbers, familiar to every thinking creature, is fundamental in intuitionistic mathematics. . . . We contend that it is sufficiently clear to build mathematics upon. (Heyting, 1956, p. 7)

Although intuitionists do not consider it necessary to reduce the concept of natural number to simpler concepts, they recognize two notions as the source of the natural numbers. One is that in perceiving an object we conceive of an entity by a process of abstraction from the particular qualities of the perceived object. Another notion is the possibility of indefinitely repeating the conception of an entity. In short, intuitionists consider that the two sources of the concept of natural number are the notion of an abstract entity and the notion of an indefinite repetition or of a sequence of the entities. It seems to us that these underlying sources of the natural numbers bring the intuitionistic conception close to the notion that a natural number is an idea or that it is a property abstracted from external objects. In particular, the conception seems close to the notions that *one* is that which is common to every object and that every natural number can be expressed as *one* and *one* and *one*, and so on, that is, by the repetition of *ones* (abstract entities). Frege's criticisms of the latter notion therefore seem applicable to the intuitionistic conception of natural number.

Such criticisms as well as the dangers that peril the logicists' definition of number would seem to be avoided by the formalists. They regard natural number as an undefined concept subject to certain axioms, such as the set of axioms offered by Peano (1894–1908). We shall consider Peano's axioms shortly. Suffice it to say here that the formalists' treatment of natural number has also met with criticism. For example, Waismann (1959) criticizes formalists for not attempting to clarify the concept of number. He also notes that the Peano axioms do not uniquely characterize the set of natural numbers since other sets of objects also satisfy these axioms (a point which will be elaborated in the next section).

In short, even as "natural" a concept as natural number has been and is a matter of controversy. Neither logicism nor intuitionism nor formalism has offered a conceptualization that is generally acceptable.

Axiomatic Development
of Natural Numbers

Peano's axioms involve the undefined concept of natural number, a specific natural number called *one* or 1 (which tells us that the set of natural numbers is not empty, that it has a member), and also the function of the successor of a natural number. The successor operation, which may be regarded intuitively as the addition of one, may be denoted by ' (read "prime") so that the successor of a natural number n is denoted by n'. It is assumed implicity (without being explicitly stated as an axiom) that the successor function is single-valued in the sense that for every natural number n there exists *one and only one* natural number n' which is its successor. (Note that this is a converse of axiom 3 below.) The Peano axioms may be worded as follows:

1. 1 is a natural number.
2. The successor of a natural number is a natural number.
3. There are no two natural numbers with the same successor.
4. 1 is not the successor of any natural number.
5. (Axiom of mathematical induction.) If a set of natural numbers contains 1 and contains the successor of each of its members, then it contains all the natural numbers.

Let N designate the set of natural numbers and let $\in$ designate set membership, so that $n \in N$ means that n is a member of N (n belongs to N). Let $\subset$ denote set inclusion so that $S \subset N$ means that S is a subset of the natural number, that is, $S \subset N$ means that if $s \in S$, then $s \in N$. Then Peano's axioms may be reworded as follows:

1. $1 \in N$
2. If $n \in N$, then $n' \in N$.
3. If $n' = m'$, then $n = m$.
4. For every $n \in N$, $n' \neq 1$.
5. Let $S \subset N$. If $1 \in S$, and if $n \in S$ implies $n' \in S$, then $S = N$.

(It should be noted that some writers regard *zero* or 0 as a natural number whereas others do not, but regard it is a whole number or unsigned integer. If 0 is included in the natural numbers, then the above axioms have to be modified by replacing 1 wherever it occurs with 0. This affects axioms 1, 4, and 5; for example, axiom 1 becomes $0 \in N$ and axiom 4 becomes for every $n \in N$, $n' \neq 0$. The successor operation remains unchanged, still meaning intuitively the addition of 1 which may be designated as $0'$.)

In the axiomatic development of the natural numbers, addition and multiplication are defined in terms of the successor operation. Addition, denoted by $+$, is defined as a (single-valued) function on the natural numbers which has the following properties for every $n, m \in N$.

1. $n + m \in N$.
2. $n + 1 = n'$.
3. $n + m' = (n + m)'$.

Property 1 is the closure property which states that addition of two natural numbers again yields a natural number. (On the other hand, subtraction does not have the closure property since subtraction of two natural numbers may, for example, yield a negative number.) Property 2 characterizes addition in terms of the successor operation. The left-hand side of property 3 may be written as $n + m' = n + (m + 1)$ by property 2 which allows us to substitute $m + 1$ for m'. Similarly, the right-hand side of property 3 may be written as $(n + m)' = (n + m) + 1$. Hence property 3 may be rewritten as $n + (m + 1) = (n + m) + 1$. It tells us that the parentheses may be rearranged so that the numbers are grouped or associated differently and yet the results of addition are the same. Property 3 is an illustration of what is known as the associative property of addition: For any natural numbers $n, m,$ and k, $n + (m + k) = (n + m) + k$. The associative property may be obtained as a theorem by using the defining properties of addition and Peano's axioms. In particular the proof appeals to the axiom of mathematical induction and is therefore a *proof by induction*. It is instructive to consider the proof in detail. Let S be the set of all natural numbers s for which $n + (m + s) = (n + m) + s$ for every $n, m \in N$. The first three steps of the proof below establish that $1 \in S$. Steps 4 through 8 establish that if $j \in S$, then $j' \in S$. Hence by axiom 5, the axiom of mathematical induction, $S = N$, that is, the associative property of addition is established for all natural numbers, as follows:

THEOREM $n + (m + k) = (n + m) + k$ for all natural numbers $n, m,$ and k.
PROOF By induction on k.

STEPS	REASONS
1. $n + (m + 1) = n + m'$	By property 2 of addition
2. $\quad\quad\quad = (n + m)'$	By property 3 of addition
3. $\quad\quad\quad = (n + m) + 1$	By properties 1 and 2
4. Assume that for $j \in N$, $\quad n + (m + j) = (n + m) + j$	Hypothesis for mathematical induction
5. $n + (m + j') = n + (m + j)'$	By property 3
6. $\quad\quad\quad = (n + (m + j))'$	By properties 1 and 3
7. $\quad\quad\quad = ((n + m) + j)'$	By step 4
8. $\quad\quad\quad = (n + m) + j'$	By properties 1 and 3
9. Hence $n + (m + k) = (n + m) + k$	By axiom of mathematical induction

Similarly, it can be shown by induction on j that $1 + j = j + 1$ for all $j \in N$. By induction on k it can then be shown that for all $k, j \in N$, $k + j = j + k$, which is called the commutative property of addition.

The operation of multiplication of natural numbers, which may be written as $n \cdot m$ or as nm is defined as a (single-valued) function on N with the following properties for every $n, m \in N$.

1. $n \cdot m \in N$.
2. $n \cdot 1 = n$.
3. $n \cdot k' = n \cdot k + n$.

Property 1 is the closure property. Property 2 tells us that 1 acts as the identity under multiplication in the sense that when it multiplies a natural number n it leaves it unchanged or identical. Property 3 may be thought of as $n \cdot k' = n(k + 1) = n \cdot k + n \cdot 1 = n \cdot k + n$ by property 2. The expression $n(k + 1) = n \cdot k + n \cdot 1$ illustrates the distributive property for multiplication: For all n, m, k in N, $n(m + k) = n \cdot m + n \cdot k$, which asserts that multiplication distributes over addition. The distributive property can be established by induction. Similarly, induction can be used to establish the associative property of multiplication— $(m \cdot n)k = m(n \cdot k)$—and the commutative property of multiplication— $m \cdot n = n \cdot m$.

An order relationship among natural numbers is defined in terms of addition: j is said to be less than k, $j < k$, if there exists a natural number, call it m, such that $j + m = k$. Many interesting theorems can be proved about the order relationship as well as theorems that relate order to addition and to multiplication (Landau, 1960). These include the "trichotomy" theorem which states that for any natural numbers n and m, one and only one of the following holds: $n < m$ or $m < n$ or $n = m$. The cancellation laws for addition and multiplication can be proved: if $j + n = k + n$, then $j = k$; if $j \cdot n = k \cdot n$, then $j = k$. It can be proved that $j < k$ if and only if $j + n < k + n$ and $j \cdot n < k \cdot n$ for every $n \in N$. It can be proved that there are no natural numbers between n and its successor $n' = n + 1$. This is known as the lack of density property. Moreover, it can be proved that every nonempty subset of natural numbers has a smallest element, call it k, smallest in the sense that every element of the subset is less than or equal to k. This theorem is known as the well-ordering principle.

In short, many properties of the natural numbers are derived from Peano's axiom system. We shall see that some but not all of the properties hold for various extensions of the natural numbers.

Peano apparently assumed that we have an intuitive idea of what is meant by a natural number, by the natural number 1, and by the successor of a natural number. Yet each of these terms is capable of various meanings or interpretations. This was pointed out by Russell (1919) who gave some interesting examples.

1. Let the successor operation refer to the addition of *two* to a number. There results the sequence of odd numbers 1, 3, 5, · · · . If natural numbers are taken to mean the odd numbers, then all of Peano's axioms are satisfied.

2. Let 1 refer to the number *two* and the successor operation to the addition of *two*. There results the sequence of even numbers, 2, 4, 6, · · · . If natural numbers are interpreted to mean the even numbers, then all of Peano's axioms are satisfied.

3. Let 1 stand for any specified natural number m (for instance, 100 or 101 or 1000) and let the natural numbers refer to all such numbers from m onward, including m. There results the sequence $m, m + 1, m + 2, · · ·$, which satisfies Peano's axiom system.

4. Let the successor of a number refer to half of that number. There results the sequence 1, $\frac{1}{2}$, $\frac{1}{4}$, · · · . If the natural numbers are interpreted as referring to these numbers, then again Peano's axiom system is satisfied.

Shall we say that 1, $\frac{1}{2}$, $\frac{1}{4}$, · · · constitutes the natural number sequence? More generally, shall we call any object that satisfies Peano's axioms a natural number? Opposition to this viewpoint has been based on the use of numbers as a means of communication.

> For example, in saying, "There are only 5 regular solids," I want to assert a true proposition unambiguously. However, it is impossible to attach a definite meaning to this statement if "5" is a mere counter which can be interpreted in the most varied ways. On adopting such a standpoint, we would no longer be able to distinguish the two communications, "There are 5 regular solids" and "There are 105 regular solids." Thus . . . the very sense of the number statement is allowed to escape. (Waismann, 1959, p. 105)

In other words, the symbol 5 has a very different meaning if the natural numbers are given their customary interpretation than if they are interpreted to mean all the natural numbers from 101 onward, so that 1 denotes 101, 5 denotes 105, and so on.

Citing various examples of interpretations of Peano's axioms, Waismann concludes: "These examples show that the axioms do not characterize the concept of number series . . . Peano's system of axioms can be interpreted in an infinity of distinct ways" (pp. 104–105). Yet, Kleene (1952) draws apparently contradictory conclusions. Although also citing various interpretations of Peano's axioms, Kleene concludes that these axioms do characterize and indeed uniquely characterize the natural numbers, "that exactly one abstract system satisfies these [Peano's] axioms, namely the natural numbers" (p. 27).

How does it happen that such apparently different conclusions are drawn? It seems to us that the answer hinges on the notion of isomorphism. Let an interpretation (a model or representation) of Peano's axioms be called a Peano system. It has been proved that all Peano systems are isomorphic, "which shows that there is essentially only one Peano system" (Feferman, 1964, p. 70). To say that two Peano systems S and T are isomorphic means that there exists a correspondence between them which has the following properties. Firstly, the correspondence is one-to-one in the sense that every element of S corresponds to exactly one element of T and every element of T to exactly one element of S. Secondly, the 1 of S corresponds to the 1 of T. Thirdly, the successor operation is preserved under the correspondence in the sense that if s and t correspond to each other, then s' and t' must also correspond. For example, there is a correspondence between the set of odd numbers and the set of even numbers (each of which can serve as a model of Peano's axioms) in which 1 corresponds to 2 which serves as the 1 in the even numbers, and which has the property that if an odd number corresponds to an even number, then their successors also correspond to each other. It can be proved that the various operations (for example, addition, multiplication, and order relationship) are preserved under the isomorphism between two Peano systems S and T; for example, if s_1, s_2 belong to S, and their correspondents in T are denoted as t_1, t_2, then $s_1 + s_2$ corresponds to $t_1 + t_2$.

In short, the conclusions that Peano's axioms uniquely characterize the natural numbers and that there is only one abstract system which satisfies these axioms rest on the recognition that all interpretations of these axioms are isomorphic. The apparently contrary conclusions focus on the differences among the interpretations. That two interpretations or models or systems are isomorphic does not make them identical. For example, the interpretation in which successor means "half of" so that the resulting sequence is 1, $\frac{1}{2}$, $\frac{1}{4}$, $\frac{1}{8}$, $\cdots$ is certainly not identical with the usual interpretation of the natural number sequence or with an interpretation which yields all the natural numbers from 101 onward. Abstractly all these interpretations are "identical" in the sense that they are isomorphic but concretely they are very different.

In general, given an axiom system, either there exists no set of objects that satisfies it, in which case the axiom system is *vacuous*, or there exists a set (or sets) of objects that satisfy the axiom system, which is then called nonvacuous. If the various interpretations are all isomorphic, the axiom system is *categorical*. If there are nonisomorphic interpretations, the axiom system is *noncategorical*, or *ambiguous*. We say more about categorical and noncategorical axiom systems in the chapters on formalism. Using this terminology, we can say that Peano's axiom system is categorical since all interpretations of it are abstractly identical in the sense of being isomorphic or, as sometimes worded, all interpretations of it are identical up to an isomorphism.

We should not leave Peano's axioms without referring to the number of axioms involved. The axiom of mathematical induction may be regarded as an axiom schema rather than a specific axiom since every time another set S is involved, another specific axiom results. This point can be clarified if we reword the axiom of mathematical induction as follows: Let P be a property that holds for 1, and if it holds for the natural number n it also holds for the successor of n; then P holds for all natural numbers. For each P, a specific axiom results. Thus the axiom of mathematical induction can give rise to infinitely many specific axioms. Is it possible to characterize the natural numbers by omitting the axiom of mathematical induction and allowing only a finite number of specific axioms? Skolem (1933) showed that this could not be done. When the natural numbers constitute a model of an abstract system with a finite number of specific axioms, the resulting axiom system is noncategorical in the sense that there are models of it that are not isomorphic to the natural numbers. In short, it is not possible to characterize the natural number uniquely or categorically by using a finite number of axioms, no matter how large this number may be. This point is referred to in Chapter 9.

Extensions of the Natural Numbers

We have seen that, since the end of the last century, there has been controversy concerning the natural numbers. Centuries before there were disputes over various extensions of the number concept. Development of the number system furnishes dramatic illustrations that concepts had to struggle for acceptance and that some are still subject to controversy.

Consider negative numbers, which high school students now handle with nonchalance. The distrust with which such numbers were viewed is revealed in the names applied to them in about the fifteenth century: *absurd numbers* and *fictitious numbers*. "The idea of a negative number struggled for recognition for centuries and was received with great reluctance as late as the early years of the 17th century, even by mathematicians" (Richardson, 1941, p. 89). A similar struggle was faced by the idea that zero or that a fraction constitutes a number. "Today, when we deal with such numbers as a matter of course, it is hard to believe that as late as the seventeenth century they were not generally credited with the same legitimacy as the positive integers, and that they were used, when necessary, with a certain amount of doubt and trepidation" (Courant and Robbins, 1941, p. 56).

The number concept has been extended in a manner that preserves many of the rules and properties of the original concept. This is in line with what has been called the principle of permanence of form, or permanence of the calculating rules. This principle states that in the extension of a concept that direction is to be chosen which leaves the properties unchanged or as intact as possible. "This principle of permanence is not a statement whose validity may be questioned; instead it is, so to speak, a guiding principle for the formation of concepts" (Waismann, 1959, p. 27). In line with this principle, the concept of number is extended from the natural numbers in such a manner as to retain many of the properties of these numbers. For example, operations with negative integers, zero, and fractions are introduced so that they obey the so-called laws of arithmetic that hold for the natural numbers—namely, the commutative and associative properties of addition and multiplication and the distributive property. These properties, observable in experiences with natural numbers, can be obtained as theorems, we have seen, in axiomatic development of these numbers from Peano's axioms.

In line with the axiomatic approach, the number concept can be extended by introducing various sets of natural numbers with operations on the sets defined so that analogues of certain axioms and theorems for the natural numbers also hold for the extended number concepts (Landau, 1960; Feferman, 1964; Haag, 1964). This approach is of interest, although it is not the manner in which numbers were extended historically. We illustrate the approach for fractions and rational numbers and other extensions of the natural numbers.

Rational Numbers

A (positive of unsigned) fraction can be introduced as a pair of natural numbers which may be written as (a, b) where (a, b) is distinguished from (b, a). Since the order in which the natural numbers occur in the pair is taken into account, this is referred to as an ordered pair. The couple (a, b) may be thought of as a/b. The definition of equality of these ordered pairs, definitions of addition, of multiplication, and of order (what it means for a fraction to be greater or less than another) are chosen with an eye to preserving rules that hold in the system of natural numbers. For example, (a, b) is defined to be equal to (c, d) if and only if $a = c$ and $b = d$; (a, b) is defined as less than (c, d) if and only if $ad < cb$; $(a, b) + (c, d)$ is defined as equal to $(ad + bc, bd)$, and $(a, b) \cdot (c, d)$ is defined as equal to (ac, bd). Under such definitions the addition of fractions can be shown to have in common with the addition of natural numbers the property of *closure*: addition of two fractions yields a fraction, just as addition of two natural numbers yields a natural number; the *commutative* property: the order of addition is immaterial, so that $p + q = q + p$; and the *associative* property: $[p + q] + r = p + [q + r]$, where p, q, and r are fractions. Similar properties hold for multiplication of fractions, just as they do for natural numbers. Moreover, multiplication is distributive over addition for both kinds of numbers, that is,

$$p \cdot (q + r) = p \cdot q + p \cdot r$$

A rational number may be defined as the set of all fractions that are similar to a given fraction, where a fraction p/q is said to be similar to m/n if and only if $pn = mq$. For example, the set of all fractions similar to $\frac{1}{2}$ may be considered as the rational number $\frac{1}{2}$ and may be denoted as the set of all a/b such that a/b is similar to $\frac{1}{2}$ or, more briefly, as [1, 2]. The rational number [k, 1], that is, the rational number whose second member is 1, may be shown to have many of the properties of the natural number k. In fact, the subset of the rational numbers which consists of [k, 1], where k ranges over the natural numbers, can be shown to be isomorphic to the set of natural numbers in the following sense. There is a one-to-one correspondence between these rational numbers and the natural numbers, with [k, 1] and k correspondents, which preserves the operations of taking a successor of a number (adding 1 to k or adding [1, 1] to [k, 1]) and, more generally, preserves the operations of addition, multiplication, less than, and so on. It can be shown that axioms and definitions for the natural numbers are theorems for the subset of the rational numbers which consists of [k, 1], where k ranges over the natural numbers. The rational number, [k, 1] may therefore be considered as identified with the corresponding natural number k. Thus the rational numbers may be regarded as an extension of the natural numbers.

In a manner similar to that in which positive or unsigned fractions were introduced, positive and negative integers may be introduced as sets of natural numbers (which now may be regarded as including 0). This may be done by introducing an ordered pair (a, b), which may be thought of as $a + -b$ or as $a - b$. Under suitably chosen definitions for equality, order, addition, multiplication, and so on, the new concept can be shown to follow many of the rules that hold in the system of natural numbers. The definitions differ from those introduced for fractions. Thus (a, b) is defined as equal to (c, d) if $a + d = c + b$; $(a, b) + (e, f)$ is defined as $(a + e, b + f)$; (a, b) is defined as less than (c, d) if $a + d < c + b$, and so on. Addition can be shown to have the property of closure as well as the commutative and associative properties. Moreover, a subset of these integers can be shown to be isomorphic with the system of natural numbers. For example, the natural number 1 is identified with the positive integer $+1$ or the unsigned integer 1. Fractions (positive, negative, and 0) may be introduced as ordered pairs of integers, analogous to the manner in which positive or unsigned fractions are introduced as ordered pairs of natural numbers. And rational numbers (positive, negative, and 0) may be introduced as sets of fractions, with a subset of the rational numbers isomorphic to and identifiable with the system of integers.

Why not simply regard a fraction as a rational number? The difficulty is that, for example, the "rational numbers" $\frac{1}{1}$, $\frac{2}{2}$, $\frac{3}{3}$, $\frac{4}{4}$, and so on would then all correspond to the natural number 1 and to the unit length on a line. Similarly, the "rational numbers" $\frac{1}{2}$, $\frac{2}{4}$, $\frac{3}{6}$, $\frac{4}{8}$, and so on, would all correspond to the point on the line equal to one half of the unit length. For many purposes it is more convenient to have only one number correspond to a point on a line. What we may do is think of $\frac{1}{2}$ as somehow "equal" to $\frac{2}{4}$ and to $\frac{3}{6}$ and to $\frac{4}{8}$, and so on. But this is essentially what is done in thinking of a rational number as the set that consists of $\frac{1}{2}$, $\frac{2}{4}$, $\frac{3}{6}$, $\frac{4}{8}$, and so on, that is, the set of fractions similar to $\frac{1}{2}$. Ordinarily we speak of a fraction as a rational number, with the tacit understanding that fractions that are similar to each other are regarded as "equal." With this understanding we may in turn speak of a rational number as one that can be expressed as the ratio of two integers.

Irrational Numbers

Intuitively, it might seem that the rational numbers should suffice to correspond to all the points on a line. Yet there are points on the line to which no rational number corresponds. In other words, the length from the origin or 0 point to the point in question cannot be expressed as a rational number or as the ratio of two lengths. The existence of such lengths seems to have been known by the Greek philosopher Pythagoras and his disciples. Such a length may be described as incommensurate with the unit length, that is, as having no measure in common with it. For if there were a common measure, suppose that it went into the length in question m times and into the unit length n times; then the measure could be represented by the number $1/n$ and the length by m/n, which would contradict the idea that the length cannot be expressed as the ratio of two integers. In particular, Pythagoras seems to have been aware that the diagonal of a square whose sides are exactly one unit in length is incommensurate with the unit length. "The most astonishing aspect of this fact is that . . . no matter how finely the inches of a ruler are divided into equal parts, it is impossible for both ends of the diagonal to coincide simultaneously with marks on the ruler" (Hull, 1959, p. 30). The discovery of incommensurate lengths seems to have greatly disturbed Pythagoras, perhaps because it suggested an inadequacy in the ability of whole numbers to describe the universe and violated his philosophy that (whole) number ruled the universe. Indeed, Pythagoras and his followers tried unsuccessfully to suppress the discovery.

There is a simple proof that the square root of 2 cannot be expressed as the ratio of two integers. Suppose that there exist such numbers a and b with $(a/b)^2 = 2$. If a and b have any factors in common, divide through by these factors (that is, reduce to lowest terms), getting $a/b = p/q$ where p and q are integers having no natural number in common other than 1. Now, $(p/q)^2 = 2$ yields $p^2/q^2 = 2$ or $p^2 = 2q^2$. Since q is an integer, so is q^2, and therefore p^2 is an even number (since it is equal to 2 times an integer). Then p must be even, since if it were odd, p^2 would be odd. To see this, suppose p is odd, so that $p = 2m + 1$, where m is an integer; then $p^2 = (2m + 1)^2 = (2m)^2 + 4m + 1 = 4m^2 + 4m + 1 = 2(2m^2 + 2m) + 1 = 2s + 1$ where s is the integer $2m^2 + 2m$, so that p^2 would be odd. Since p is even, $p = 2n$, n some natural number. Inserting this in $p^2 = 2q^2$, we get $(2n)^2 = 2q^2$ or $4n^2 = 2q^2$ or $2n^2 = q^2$. Hence q^2 is even and by the same reasoning as before, q is even. Thus p and q have the common factor 2 which contradicts the supposition that they have no factor in common other than 1. In short, the assumption that the square root of 2 can be expressed as the ratio of two integers led to a contradiction.

The square root of 2 is not the only quantity that is incapable of being expressed as a rational number, that is, as the ratio of two integers. This is also the case for the square root of 3 and for the cube root and fourth root of 2 and 3, and, in fact, for the nth root of any number which is itself not the nth power of a rational number. Since these quantities are not rational they may be referred to as irrational. It was not until the sixteenth century that the number concept was broadened to include irrational quantities. Irrational numbers make it possible to extract the root of any positive number.

It is of interest that irrational numbers are, in a sense, more plentiful than the rational numbers. If every rational number is multiplied by an irrational number, such as the square root of 2, the results are all irrational numbers. Still other irrational numbers result if the rational numbers are multiplied by the square root of 3. All the rational numbers can be placed in one-to-one correspondence with the natural numbers, whereas a proper subset of the irrationals (for instance, those obtained by multiplying the rationals by the square root of 2) can be placed in a one-to-one correspondence with the natural numbers. In other words, such a correspondence exhausts the rational numbers but not the irrational numbers. If we think of the rational and irrational numbers marked off as lengths on a line, starting from an origin and using the same unit, then in a sense more lengths or more points correspond to irrational numbers than to rational numbers. And yet, as we saw, it took some sixteen hundred years after the Pythagoreans knew of the existence of lengths that did not correspond to rational numbers, before the concept of irrational number was introduced.

Real Numbers

It was not until the second half of the nineteenth century that a theory of irrational numbers was developed on a fairly rigorous basis. This was done as part of an attempt to establish an adequate theory of real numbers, where real numbers consist of both the rational numbers and the irrational numbers. Dedekind introduced the definition of positive real number as a "cut," which is a certain set of rational numbers. If the set of all positive rational numbers is denoted by R, then a cut (more exactly, a Dedekind cut) may be characterized as the set C, where C is a non-empty, proper subset of R with the property that every member of C is smaller than every member of R which is not in C and with the further property that C has no largest member. In other words, C is a cut if and only if it has the following properties:

1. C is a subset of R, that is, every member of C is a member of R.
2. C is not empty, that is, at least one positive rational number is a member of C.
3. C is proper, that is, there is a member of R which is not in C.
4. Each member of C is smaller than each member in the complement of C, where the complement is the set consisting of elements which are in R but not in C.
5. C does not have a largest member, that is, for any member r in C there is some member s in C, such that $r < s$.

If the complement of C has a smallest element, then C is considered a rational cut, and otherwise an irrational cut. A rational cut may be thought of as (or identified with) a rational number and an irrational cut as an irrational number.

This method of introducing real numbers, although acceptable to many mathematicians, is not acceptable to some. In particular, the intuitionists object to Dedekind's method as well as to other classical methods of introducing real numbers on the grounds that they treat infinite sets (of positive rational numbers) as if they were completed entities. Instead, as we saw in Chapter 2, intuitionists have proposed other methods of introducing real numbers, including irrational numbers. Thus we see that the concepts of irrational number and real number are still matters of controversy.

Complex Numbers

Although the real-number domain is adequate to represent lengths, to represent all points on a line, yet not one of its members can solve as simple an equation as $x^2 + 1 = 0$. In order to have a "number" which solves such an equation, mathematicians extended the number domain to include the square root of -1, which may be represented by the symbol i, and other imaginary numbers. Complex numbers are of the form $a + bi$ where a and b are real numbers, so that for $b = 0$ the complex number system yields the real number system and for $a = 0$ it yields the "pure" imaginary numbers. The name *imaginary* attests to the uneasiness with which such numbers were first greeted in some quarters. Indeed, such numbers were introduced "without the approval, and even against the desires of individual mathematicians" (Klein, 1932, p. 56) and were treated with suspicion as late as the middle of the nineteenth century.

Suspicion of the complex numbers was somewhat allayed by a geometric interpretation of them. The complex number $a + bi$ may be associated with the point in the plane that has (a, b) as its coordinates, that is, that has a as its x coordinate and b as its y coordinate. Conversely, the point in the plane with coordinates (p, q) may be associated with the complex number $p + qi$. Thus there is a one-to-one correspondence between the complex numbers and the points in the plane. Or one may associate the complex number $a + bi$ with the vector in the plane which starts at the origin and terminates at the point with coordinates (a, b). Hence a one-to-one correspondence can be established between complex numbers and such vectors.

Complex numbers can also be introduced as ordered pairs of real numbers, with the pair (a, b) corresponding to $a + bi$. Two pairs (a, b) and (c, d) are defined to be equal if and only if $a = c$ and $b = d$. The sum of (a, b) and (c, d) is defined to be $(a + c, b + d)$ and their product is defined as $(ac - bd, ad + bc)$. It can be verified that these operations (like the operations of addition and multiplication for natural numbers) have the properties of commutativity, associativity, and the distributive property of multiplication with respect to addition.

These definitions of operations with the complex numbers can be better understood if we regard $a + bi$ as if it were the polynomial $a + bx$, where a and b are real numbers. Two polynomials $a + bx$ and $c + dx$ are equal if $a = c$ and $b = d$. Analogously, two complex numbers $a + bi = (a, b)$ and $c + di = (c, d)$ are defined to be equal if $a = c$ and $b = d$. Two polynomials $a + bx$ and $c + dx$ have the sum $a + c + bx + dx = a + c + (b + d)x$. Correspondingly, two complex numbers $a + bi = (a, b)$ and $(c + di) = (c, d)$ are said to have the sum $a + c + (b + d)i = (a + c, b + d)$. The product of two polynomials $a + bx$ and $c + dx$ is $ac + bcx + adx + bdx^2$. Letting $x = i$, we get $x^2 = -1$ since i is a square root of -1. Hence the product of $a + bx$ and $c + dx$ may be written as $ac + bcx + adx - bd = ac - bd + (ad + bc)x$. Analogously the product of two complex numbers is defined to be $(ac - bd) + (ad + bc)i$.

Algebraic and Transcendental Numbers

The classification which we now consider cuts across the distinction between real and complex numbers or between rational and irrational numbers. A complex number (which may be real) is said to be algebraic if it is the root of at least one polynomial equation with rational coefficients. In other words, it satisfies an equation of the form $a_n x^n +$

$a_{n-1}x^{n-1} + \cdots + a_1x + a_0 = 0$, where n is a natural number and the a's are rational numbers (ratios of integers). Such an equation can be "cleared of fractions" through multiplication by the greatest common denominator of the coefficients, so that the resulting equation has integer coefficients. Hence an equivalent definition of an algebraic number is that it is a complex number that satisfies a polynomial equation with integer coefficients. For example, the complex number i is algebraic since it satisfies $x^2 + 1 = 0$. A complex number which is not algebraic is said to be transcendental. The name is due to Euler who considered that such numbers "transcend" the power of algebraic methods.

A real number which is rational is necessarily algebraic. For a rational number can be represented as a/b, where a and b are integers. Let $x = a/b$ so that $bx = a$ and the number satisfies the equation $bx - a = 0$. Thus the equation satisfied by a rational number is of degree $n = 1$. An algebraic number may therefore be regarded as a generalization of a rational number, where the degree of the equation is not restricted to be one.

An irrational number may or may not be algebraic. For example, $\sqrt{2}$ satisfies the equation $x^2 - 2 = 0$. Irrational numbers that are transcendental are, in a sense, more numerous than those that are algebraic. This conclusion follows from the finding that the algebraic numbers can be put into one-to-one correspondence with the natural numbers and hence the algebraic numbers are countable (enumerable, denumerable). For a proof see p. 95 of this text or Courant and Robbins, 1941, p. 103; Niven, 1961, p. 125; Haag, 1964, p. 137. Since the real numbers are not countable, there must be some real numbers that are not algebraic, that is, which are transcendental. In particular, since the irrational numbers are not countable, some of them must be transcendental. For if all irrational numbers were algebraic, they would be countable, since a subset of a countable set is itself countable. In short, the set of real numbers which is not countable, contains a countable subset, the set of rational numbers, which constitutes a proper subset of another countable set, the real algebraic numbers, leaving an uncountable number of real transcendental numbers.

Despite the plentifulness of transcendental numbers, the transcendental nature of any given number has been difficult to prove. The transcendency of e ($e = 2.71828 \cdots$), the base of the natural logarithms, was proved by Hermite in 1873. Using a variation of Hermite's method, Lindemann in 1882 showed the transcendency of π ($\pi = 3.14159 \cdots$), the ratio of the circumference of a circle to its diameter. Since π is a real number it must be irrational, for if it were rational it would be algebraic. Lindemann's proof not only answered the long-standing problem of whether or not π is irrational but also led to a decision concerning the ancient Greek construction problem of squaring the circle. This problem was to construct, by means of compass and straight edge only, a square which has the same area as a given circle. Since a circle with radius r has its area equal to πr^2, this amounts to constructing a square whose side has length $\sqrt{\pi}\, r$. Since we may take r to be one, the problem amounts to constructing, with compass and straight edge only, a line segment with length $\sqrt{\pi}$. It can be shown that this construction is possible if and only if π is so constructible which in turn is possible if and only π is algebraic (Courant and Robbins, 1941, pp. 104, 140). Thus Lindemann's proof that π is transcendental yielded the nonsolvability of this classical construction problem.

It was not until the present century that the theory of transcendental numbers "was formulated as a theory having its own special methods and a sufficient supply of solved problems" (Gelfond, 1960, p. vii). An interesting problem concerning transcendental numbers, which has since been solved, was proposed by Hilbert in 1900 to the international congress of mathematicians when he listed over twenty unsolved mathematical problems. The seventh "Hilbert problem" was to ascertain whether $2^{\sqrt{2}}$ is transcendental or even irrational. This problem was solved in the 1930s by Siegel and a more general problem was solved by the Russian Gelfond and independently by Siegel's student, Schneider. The Gelfond-Schneider theorem, as it is called, shows the transcendency of a^b, where a is an algebraic number different from 0 or 1, and b is an irrational algebraic number. If a is 0 or 1 or b is rational, then a^b is algebraic. In particular, $2^{\sqrt{2}}$ is transcendental and hence irrational. The Gelfond-Schneider theorem also shows the transcendency of other numbers, such as the common logarithm of 2 (to the base 10). For we may write $a^b = 10^{\log 2} = 2$, so that if log 2 were an irrational algebraic number, 2 would have to be transcendental whereas it is certainly algebraic. Then the alternatives are that log 2, a real number, is a rational algebraic number or that it is not algebraic. But log 2 cannot be rational (see Niven, 1961, p. 70), for if log 2 can be written as a/b, a and b integers, we may take a and b to be positive integers, since log 2 is positive. Hence $2 = 10^{\log 2} = 10^{a/b}$ or $2^b = 10^a = (5 \cdot 2)^a = 5^a 2^a$ by rules of exponents. Since a is a positive integer, 5 is a factor of 5^a and therefore a factor of $5^a 2^a$ which equals 2^b. But 5 cannot be a factor of 2^b since this is a contradiction to the fundamental theorem of arithmetic which states that every natural number other than 1 can be factored into primes only in one way, except for the order of the primes. In short, the supposition that log 2 is rational led to the conclusion that the prime 5 is a factor of the natural number 2^b in which the only prime factor is 2. This contradiction to the fundamental theorem of arithmetic rules out the possibility that log 2 is rational. Since the possibility that it is algebraic but irrational was ruled out by the Gelfond-Schneider theorem, it follows that log 2 is transcendental. More generally, this theorem has been used to show the transcendency of log r, where r is rational and log r is irrational.

Beyond the Complex
Numbers

One motivation for extending the number system is the search for roots for equations. For example, $2x - 3 = 0$ has no root in the natural number system but has a root in the rational number system; $x^2 + 1 = 0$ has no root among the real numbers but has a root in the complex number system. Given a polynomial equation with real or complex coefficients, will it be necessary to extend the concept of number beyond the complex numbers in order that the equation have a root? The fundamental theorem of algebra assures us that this is not necessary, that every polynomial equation with real or complex coefficients has at least one root among the complex numbers (which may of course be a real number). Indeed, the equation has as many roots among the complex numbers as its degree (its highest exponent), provided that a root is counted as often as its multiplicity, for example, a double root is counted twice. Thus if the desire to ensure that such equations have roots was the only motivation for extending the number concept, it would not be necessary to go further than the complex numbers. But it is not the only motivation and the number concept has been extended beyond the complex numbers to what have been called hypercomplex numbers.

Quaternions

Quaternions, an example of hypercomplex numbers or hypernumbers, were devised by Hamilton, a physicist and mathematician, in the nineteenth century (Bell, 1951; Birkhoff and MacLane, 1944). Analogous to the manner in which the complex numbers may be obtained by adjoining to the real numbers a square root of -1, either $+i$ or $-i$, so the quaternions may be obtained by adjoining to the complex numbers a square root of -1 other than $+i$ or $-i$. Denote this square root by j. It is not possible that j is a complex number since by the fundamental theorem of algebra the equation $x^2 = -1$ has exactly two roots among the complex numbers and these are given by $+i$ and $-i$. Instead j is introduced as a new square root of -1, subject to the rule that $(a + bi)j = j(a - bi)$ where a and b are real numbers. In other words, the basic rules of multiplication are:

$$j^2 = -1 \qquad \text{and} \qquad \alpha j = j\bar{\alpha}$$

where $\alpha = a + bi$ is a complex number and $\bar{\alpha} = a - bi$ is its conjugate. For example, $ij = j(-i) = -ji \neq ji$. Note that this multiplication is not commutative. If ij is designated as k, then k is also a square root of -1 since $k^2 = (ij)^2 = (ij)(ij) = i(ji)j = i(-ij)j = i \cdot -i(j \cdot j) = -i^2 \cdot j^2 = -(-1)(-1) = -1$. Use has been made here of the associative property of multiplication which does hold even though the commutative property does not. Similarly, the basic rules of multiplication yield the following "table of multiplication":

$$i^2 = j^2 = k^2 = -1$$

$$ij = -ji = k \qquad jk = -kj = i \qquad ki = -ik = j$$

Let i, j, and k, in this order, be thought of as arranged in a circle (cyclic order). Then multiplication of two of them yields the third, provided that the cyclic order is maintained in the sense that i comes before j, j before k, k before i, and that once we start around the circle, we do not skip any of the quantities. Multiplication of two of i, j, and k yields the negative of the third if the cyclic order is not maintained. Thus, $ij = k$ and $jk = i$ and $ki = j$ since each of these products maintains the cyclic order. But $ji = -k$, $kj = -i$, and $ik = -j$ since the cyclic order is not maintained. A quaternion, or more precisely a real quaternion, has the form $a + bi + cj + dk$, where a, b, c, and d are real numbers. If a is thought of as $a \cdot 1$ then the quaternion may be represented by the ordered quadruple of real numbers (a, b, c, d) where a is the coefficient or component of 1, b the coefficient or component of i, and so on. For example, the quaternion j may be represented by $(0, 0, 1, 0)$. That quaternions can be represented by an ordered *quadruple* is what led Hamilton to name them as he did. This representation is analogous to the representation of a complex number $a + bi$ by the ordered pair of real numbers (a, b). In fact, to have consistent terminology one might call a real number a singleton or a 1-tple, a complex number a pair or couple or 2-tple, a number represented by an ordered triple of real numbers (a, b, c) (for example, a vector in three-dimensional space) a triple or 3-tple, and a quaternion a 4-tple. This could be generalized to "numbers" represented by 5 or 6 or any number n of ordered real numbers or even to a "number" represented by infinitely many real numbers $(n_1, n_2, n_3, \cdots)$.

To return to quaternions, we note that two quaternions are considered equal if and only if their corresponding components are equal, that is, if the numbers in the same position in the two ordered quadruples are equal. Quaternions are added by adding their corresponding components. For example, if $q_1 = a_1 + b_1 i + c_1 j + d_1 k$ and $q_2 = a_2 + b_2 i + c_2 j + d_2 k$, then

$$q_1 + q_2 = (a_1 + a_2) + (b_1 + b_2)i + (c_1 + c_2)j + (d_1 + d_2)k$$
$$= (a_1 + a_2, b_1 + b_2, c_1 + c_2, d_1 + d_2)$$

To multiply a quaternion by a real number r, one multiplies each component by r (scalar multiplication). Two quaternions are multiplied by use of the basic rules or the table of multiplication for i, j, and k and the associative and distributive laws. Thus,

$$q_1 q_2 = (a_1 a_2 - b_1 b_2 - c_1 c_2 - d_1 d_2, a_1 b_2 + b_1 a_2 + c_1 d_2 - d_1 c_2, a_1 c_2 - b_1 d_2$$
$$+ c_1 a_2 + d_1 b_2, a_1 d_2 + b_1 c_2 - c_1 b_2 + d_1 a_2)$$

For example, $ij = (0, 1, 0, 0) \cdot (0, 0, 1, 0) = (0, 0, 0, 1) = k$.

Hamilton would have liked to regard quaternions as numbers and the rules of equality, addition, scalar multiplication, and multiplication as the rules of an arithmetic or algebra of quaternions. However, he was troubled by the failure of the commutative property of multiplication of quaternions. Was this property not a characteristic of numbers? In other words, in order that quaternions be regarded as numbers, was it not necessary that their multiplication be commutative? For some fifteen years he puzzled over how to overcome the difficulties. While out walking he suddenly hit on the solution: Discard the commutative property of multiplication even though it holds for the natural numbers and for all previous extensions of them. Numbers need not have the commutative property of multiplication! So struck was Hamilton by this discovery that he carved on the bridge on which he was walking the date, October 16, 1843, and the equations which defined multiplication of the quaternions. Thus were created the first noncommutative numbers and the first noncommutative arithmetic or algebra. It should be emphasized that the quaternions, under the operations of addition and multiplication, obey all the so-called laws of arithmetic except the commutative law of multiplication. Quaternions have been further generalized by having the quadruple of numbers (a, b, c, d) consist of complex numbers rather than real numbers. Moreover, algebras have been developed in which even the associative law of multiplication does not hold and which are therefore known as nonassociative algebras. "Perhaps quaternion algebra was something of a Declaration of Independence, for it freed algebra for all time from the tyranny of the natural numbers and their natural laws" (Reid, 1959, p. 38).

A complex number (a, b) may be regarded as a special case of a quaternion (a, b, c, d) when $c = d = 0$. Similarly a real number may be regarded as a special case of a complex number when $b = 0$. Thus, quaternions may be regarded as extensions of complex numbers which in turn are extensions of real numbers. Correspondingly, the arithmetic of quaternions is an extension of the arithmetic of complex numbers. When $c = d = 0$, all the rules in the arithmetic of quaternions reduce to rules in the arithmetic of complex numbers.

Hamilton was led to devise quaternions by his interest in rotation of vectors in space. The $\mathbf{i}$, $\mathbf{j}$, $\mathbf{k}$ may be interpreted as the unit vectors (vectors each of length one) along the x, y, and z axis respectively. A vector in three dimensional space can be described in terms of its components in the x, y, and z directions. The quaternion (a, b, c, d) may be regarded as $a + \mathbf{v}$ where $\mathbf{v}$ is the vector $b\mathbf{i} + c\mathbf{j} + d\mathbf{k}$. A "pure quaternion," one for which a is 0, may be identified with a vector in three-dimensional space. This is analogous to the identification of the complex number $a + b\mathbf{i}$ with a vector in the plane which starts at the origin and terminates at the point with coordinates (a, b). If q_1 and q_2 are pure quaternions (first component 0), then their product is $(0, b_1, c_1, d_1)(0, b_2, c_2, d_2) = (-b_1b_2 - c_1c_2 - d_1d_2, c_1d_2 - d_1c_2, d_1b_2 - b_1d_2, b_1c_2 - c_1b_2)$. The "pure part" of a quaternion $a + b\mathbf{i} + c\mathbf{j} + d\mathbf{k}$ is $b\mathbf{i} + c\mathbf{j} + d\mathbf{k}$ which may be regarded as a vector $\mathbf{v}$. The "pure part" of the above product is called the vector product (or outer product or crossproduct) and is usually denoted by $\times$.

$$(b_1, c_1, d_1) \times (b_2, c_2, d_2) = (c_1d_2 - d_1c_2, d_1b_2 - b_1d_2, b_1c_2 - c_1b_2)$$

The vector product is not commutative. It can be shown that it is anticommutative in the sense that $\mathbf{v}_1 \times \mathbf{v}_2 = -\mathbf{v}_2 \times \mathbf{v}_1$. Moreover, the vector product is not associative, that is, $\mathbf{v}_1 \times (\mathbf{v}_2 \times \mathbf{v}_3)$ does not necessarily equal $(\mathbf{v}_1 \times \mathbf{v}_2) \times \mathbf{v}_3$ (Olmsted, 1961, p. 560). The vector product can be expressed in terms of the multiplication of pure quaternions and conversely. In fact, it has been shown (Eberlein, 1963) that under a suitable definition of multiplication of vectors in three-dimensional space, the product of any two of these vectors yields a quaternion and conversely, every quaternion is such a product. Hamilton had hoped that the algebra of quaternions would be suitable for physics, particularly for mechanics and optics. Quaternions were widely used in three-dimensional vector analysis by physicists during the latter half of the nineteenth century but fell into disuse in physics thereafter, to be briefly revived in the 1920s when it was found that some of the equations of quantum mechanics (for example, Dirac's equation) could be expressed in terms of quaternions. Although quaternions did not attain the popularity and usefulness in physics that Hamilton had hoped for, they enlarged the mathematical horizon by constituting an extension of the number concept that paved the way for still other extensions of number, arithmetic, and algebra.

Matrices

Important extensions of number and of algebra which came after the quaternions include matrices, introduced by Cayley in 1858, and the corresponding matrix algebra. A matrix is an array of elements, arranged in (horizontal) rows and (vertical) columns. An n by m matrix is one with n rows and m columns. For our purposes we may restrict ourselves to a "square" matrix where $n = m$, and we may take the elements in the array to be real or complex numbers. Matrices are subject to certain rules of equality, addition, and multiplication which yield a matrix algebra (Andree, 1959; Birkhoff and MacLane, 1944; Reid, 1959). Two n by n matrices are defined to be equal if and only if corresponding elements (occupying the corresponding position) are equal. For example, the 2 by 2 matrices

$$\begin{bmatrix} a & b \\ c & d \end{bmatrix} \quad \begin{bmatrix} e & f \\ g & h \end{bmatrix}$$

are equal if and only if $a = e$, $b = f$, $c = g$, and $d = h$. Two n by n matrices are added by adding corresponding elements. Thus the sum of the above 2 by 2 matrices is another 2 by 2 matrix:

$$\begin{bmatrix} a + e & b + f \\ c + g & d + h \end{bmatrix}$$

To multiply a matrix by a real or complex number (scalar multiplication) one multiplies each element by this number. For example, if α is a complex number,

$$\alpha \cdot \begin{bmatrix} a & b \\ c & d \end{bmatrix} = \begin{bmatrix} \alpha a & \alpha b \\ \alpha c & \alpha d \end{bmatrix}$$

Multiplication of two n by n matrices, call them A and B, follows a "row by column" rule. To obtain the element in the resulting (product) matrix AB which is in the rth row and in the tth column, one considers the rth row in A and the tth column in B, multiplies "corresponding" elements (the first element in the rth row of A by the first element in the tth column of B, the second element in the rth row of A by the second element in the tth column of B, and so on) and adds the products; this sum of these products yields the element in the rth row and tth column of AB. For example:

$$\begin{bmatrix} a & b \\ c & d \end{bmatrix} \cdot \begin{bmatrix} e & f \\ g & h \end{bmatrix} = \begin{bmatrix} ae + bg & af + bh \\ ce + dg & cf + dh \end{bmatrix}$$

This matrix multiplication, like the multiplication of quaternions, is associative but not commutative. For example,

$$\begin{bmatrix} 1 & 2 \\ 3 & 4 \end{bmatrix} \cdot \begin{bmatrix} 5 & 6 \\ 7 & 8 \end{bmatrix} = \begin{bmatrix} 1\cdot5+2\cdot7 & 1\cdot6+2\cdot8 \\ 3\cdot5+4\cdot7 & 3\cdot6+4\cdot8 \end{bmatrix} = \begin{bmatrix} 19 & 22 \\ 43 & 50 \end{bmatrix}$$

whereas

$$\begin{bmatrix} 5 & 6 \\ 7 & 8 \end{bmatrix} \cdot \begin{bmatrix} 1 & 2 \\ 3 & 4 \end{bmatrix} = \begin{bmatrix} 5\cdot1+6\cdot3 & 5\cdot2+6\cdot4 \\ 7\cdot1+8\cdot3 & 7\cdot2+8\cdot4 \end{bmatrix} = \begin{bmatrix} 23 & 34 \\ 31 & 46 \end{bmatrix}$$

Similarly,

$$\begin{bmatrix} 0 & -2 \\ 0 & 1 \end{bmatrix} \cdot \begin{bmatrix} 4 & 8 \\ -2 & -4 \end{bmatrix} = \begin{bmatrix} 4 & 8 \\ -2 & -4 \end{bmatrix}$$

whereas

$$\begin{bmatrix} 4 & 8 \\ -2 & -4 \end{bmatrix} \cdot \begin{bmatrix} 0 & -2 \\ 0 & 1 \end{bmatrix} = \begin{bmatrix} 0 & 0 \\ 0 & 0 \end{bmatrix}$$

The last matrix, in which each entry is 0, is known as the *zero matrix* and designated as 0. The last illustration indicates that there are nonzero divisors of zero among matrices in the sense that AB may equal zero when neither A nor B is the zero matrix. Nonzero divisors of zero do not exist among the real or complex numbers or among the real quaternions; that is, in each of these systems of numbers a product of two numbers is zero if and only if at least one of the numbers is zero. However, among the quaternions with complex coefficients there are nonzero divisors of zero.

Square matrices with real or complex numbers as entries, under the rules of equality, addition, and multiplication given previously, obey all the so-called laws of arithmetic except the commutative law of multiplication. In this respect they are like the real quaternions. Indeed, real quaternions may be regarded as certain 2 by 2 matrices. The quaternion $(a, b, c, d) = a + bi + cj + dk$ may be identified with the matrix

$$\begin{bmatrix} \alpha & \beta \\ -\bar{\beta} & \bar{\alpha} \end{bmatrix}$$

where $\alpha = a + bi, \beta = c + di$ and $\bar{\alpha}$ and $\bar{\beta}$ are the complex conjugates of α and β respectively, that is, $\bar{\alpha} = a - bi$ and $\bar{\beta} = c - di$. In particular, $i = (0, 1, 0, 0)$, $j = (0, 0, 1, 0)$, and $k = (0, 0, 0, 1)$ are identified with the matrices

$$\begin{bmatrix} \sqrt{-1} & 0 \\ 0 & -\sqrt{-1} \end{bmatrix} \quad \begin{bmatrix} 0 & 1 \\ -1 & 0 \end{bmatrix} \quad \text{and} \quad \begin{bmatrix} 0 & \sqrt{-1} \\ \sqrt{-1} & 0 \end{bmatrix}$$

For example, for i, $b = 1$ and $a = c = d = 0$ so that $\alpha = a + bi = i = \sqrt{-1}$ and $\beta = c + di = 0$; $\bar{\alpha} = a - bi = -i = -\sqrt{-1}$ and $\bar{\beta} = 0$; and therefore

$$\begin{bmatrix} \alpha & \beta \\ -\bar{\beta} & \bar{\alpha} \end{bmatrix} = \begin{bmatrix} \sqrt{-1} & 0 \\ 0 & -\sqrt{-1} \end{bmatrix}$$

Similarly, for j, $a = b = d = 0$ and $c = 1$ so that $\alpha = a + bi = 0$, $\beta = c + di = 1$, $\bar{\alpha} = 0$ and $\bar{\beta} = 1$, which yields

$$\begin{bmatrix} 0 & 1 \\ -1 & 0 \end{bmatrix}$$

as the matrix identified with j. The "scalar matrix"

$$\begin{bmatrix} r & 0 \\ 0 & r \end{bmatrix}$$

where r is any real number may be identified with r. This is in keeping with the definition of scalar multiplication since if c_1, c_2, c_3, c_4 designate any complex numbers, then

$$r \begin{bmatrix} c_1 & c_2 \\ c_3 & c_4 \end{bmatrix} = \begin{bmatrix} rc_1 & rc_2 \\ rc_3 & rc_4 \end{bmatrix} = \begin{bmatrix} r & 0 \\ 0 & r \end{bmatrix} \begin{bmatrix} c_1 & c_2 \\ c_3 & c_4 \end{bmatrix}$$

$$= \begin{bmatrix} c_1 & c_2 \\ c_3 & c_4 \end{bmatrix} \begin{bmatrix} r & 0 \\ 0 & r \end{bmatrix} = \begin{bmatrix} c_1 & c_2 \\ c_3 & c_4 \end{bmatrix} r$$

By carrying out the indicated matrix multiplication and addition, one can verify that if $\alpha = a + bi$, $\beta = c + di$, then

$$\begin{bmatrix} \alpha & \beta \\ -\bar{\beta} & \bar{\alpha} \end{bmatrix} = \begin{bmatrix} a & 0 \\ 0 & a \end{bmatrix} \begin{bmatrix} 1 & 0 \\ 0 & 1 \end{bmatrix} + \begin{bmatrix} b & 0 \\ 0 & b \end{bmatrix} \begin{bmatrix} \sqrt{-1} & 0 \\ 0 & -\sqrt{-1} \end{bmatrix}$$

$$+ \begin{bmatrix} c & 0 \\ 0 & c \end{bmatrix} \begin{bmatrix} 0 & 1 \\ -1 & 0 \end{bmatrix} + \begin{bmatrix} \alpha & 0 \\ 0 & \alpha \end{bmatrix} \begin{bmatrix} 0 & \sqrt{-1} \\ \sqrt{-1} & 0 \end{bmatrix}$$

$$= a \cdot 1 + b \cdot i + c \cdot j + d \cdot k$$

In the last step each matrix has been identified with a corresponding quaternion.

If quaternion algebra has not quite lived up to its inventor's hopes for it, matrix algebra has undoubtedly surpassed any dreams Cayley may have had concerning its popularity and usefulness. Quite aside from being an important branch of algebra, matrix algebra has been used in other branches of mathematics and in other disciplines, including the physical, biological, and social sciences.

> Modern physics uses matric [matrix] theory in quantum mechanics and in the study of atomic and crystal structure. . . . *Multiple Factor Analysis* by Thurstone uses matric methods in modern psychology. The study of electrical networks, oscillation theory, damped vibrations, circuit analysis, and many other branches of engineering and physical sciences are simplified by the use of matric methods. The biological sciences (particularly in studies of growth problems and of heredity) as well as sociology, economics, and industrial management also use matric methods in modern research. (Andree, 1959, p. 129)

Noting that the "widespread utility of matrices stems from their unusual method of multiplication in which each element of the product matrix is obtained through the interaction of several elements of the original matrices" (p. 106), Andree cites specific examples including some of the following. The Pauli matrices, which are 2 by 2 matrices that include the quaternions i, j, and k, are employed in the study of electron spin in quantum mechanics Matrices are used to solve systems of equations (sometimes many equations in many unknowns) which arise in industrial research, for example, in oil refineries and in steel mills. Diffusion studies in physics, chemistry, and geology make use of matrix methods, particularly in statistical and probability studies that involve what are known as Markov chains (Bharucha-Reid, 1960). Differential equations that arise in the study of stress and structure and other problems in aerodynamics are solved by matrix methods (Frazer, Duncan, and Collar, 1938). Matrices are used in computations concerning rocket and projectile flights at the Naval Ordnance Testing Station and other defense installations. Matrix methods have been adapted for use with modern computers, the so-called electric brains.

In psychology and other social sciences, matrix theory is used not only in factor analysis but also in the other major types of analysis such as multiple regression analysis and analysis of variance. A recent text by a psychologist is devoted entirely to matrix algebra for behavioral scientists (Horst, 1963).

Some Algebraic Structures

We pause now in our survey of numbers to consider the nature of the structure of various systems of numbers. The system of natural numbers has the properties that it is closed under addition and multiplication, with each operation associative and commutative. With respect to each operation this system is called a commutative semigroup. A semigroup is a system that consists of a set of elements together with an operation on two of the elements (hence called a binary operation) such that the operation is closed and associative. If the operation is denoted by $\oplus$ (it may stand for addition or multiplication or some other binary operation) then the properties of a semigroup may be formulated as follows. A set of elements S constitutes a semigroup with respect to a binary operation $\oplus$ if for every s, t, u in S:

1. $s \oplus t \in S$.
2. $s \oplus (t \oplus u) = (s \oplus t) \oplus u$.

It is a commutative semigroup if a further property holds

3. $s \oplus t = t \oplus s$.

An identity element with respect to $\oplus$ is an element, call it e, with the property that for every s in S

   4. $s \oplus e = e \oplus s = s$.

Thus the identity element leaves s identical or unchanged. For example, 1 is the identity element under multiplication for the natural numbers. Under addition the natural numbers lack an identity unless 0 is adjoined; $0 + n = n + 0 = 0$ so 0 is an identity under addition. A semigroup with an identity is called a *monoid*. In other words, a monoid is a set of elements that satisfies properties 1 and 2 and that contains an element that satisfies property 4. If property 3 is also satisfied, then it is a commutative monoid. Thus the set of natural numbers is a commutative monoid under multiplication. The set of natural numbers with 0 adjoined is a commutative monoid under both addition and multiplication.

An element a in S is said to have an inverse with respect to the operation $\oplus$ if there exists an element in S, call it a', such that

   5. $a \oplus a' = a' \oplus a = e$.

Here e is the identity of S with respect to $\oplus$. For example, in the set of all integers, positive, negative, and zero, the inverse of an element a with respect to addition is $-a$ since $a + (-a) = 0$ and 0 is the additive identity with respect to addition. But a does not have an inverse with respect to multiplication unless a happens to be $+1$ or -1 (in which case it is its own inverse) since $a \cdot a' = 1$ means that $a' = 1/a$, the reciprocal of a. Thus we would have to enlarge the number system to the rationals to ensure an inverse with respect to multiplication for an arbitrary natural number a different from 0 (since $1/0$ is not defined). In short, to ensure that a natural number a has an inverse with respect to addition (additive inverse) requires enlargement of the number system to the set of all integers. To ensure that every natural number different from 0 has an inverse with respect to multiplication requires still further extension of the number system to the rationals.

Turning now to the very important concept of a *group*, we note that a set of elements S is a group with respect to the binary operation $\oplus$ if S is a monoid and every s in S has an inverse with respect to $\oplus$. In other words, S is a group with respect to $\oplus$ if it satisfies properties 1, 2, 4, and 5. It is a commutative group with respect to $\oplus$ if it also satisfies property 3. Thus the set of all integers constitutes a group under addition. The set of all rational numbers constitutes a group under addition while this set, with 0 excluded, constitutes a group under multiplication.

Another important algebraic structure is that of ring. A set of elements S is a ring if it is a commutative group with respect to addition and a semigroup with respect to multiplication and satisfies the two distributive laws for every r, s, t, in S:

   6. $r(s + t) = rs + rt$.
   7. $(s + t)r = sr + tr$.

A ring is called commutative if its multiplication operation is commutative. A ring is said to have an identity if it has an identity with respect to multiplication. Examples of rings are the set of all integers, the sets of rational numbers, of real numbers, of complex numbers, of quaternions, of all 2 by 2 matrices, of all n by n matrices, and of all algebraic numbers. Each of these has an identity under multiplication. An example of a ring without an identity under multiplication is the ring of all even integers: $0, \pm 2, \pm 4, \pm 6 \cdots$.

A ring is called an *integral domain* if it has the property that if the product of two of its elements is 0, then at least one of these elements must be 0. In other words it has the following property:

8. If $st = 0$ then $s = 0$ or $t = 0$.

If for an element s of a ring R, there exists $t \neq 0$ in R such that $st = 0$ or $ts = 0$ then s is called a left zero-divisor or a right zero-divisor, respectively. Thus an integral domain has the property that it has no left or right zero-divisors other than 0.

The prototype of an integral domain is the ring of all integers. Other examples of integral domains are the rings of all rational numbers, of all real numbers, and of all complex numbers. The ring of matrices is not an integral domain since the product of two matrices A and B may be 0 even though neither A nor B is the zero matrix.

The reader should be forewarned that the terminology of *integral domain* is not uniform. While some writers use the definition cited here (for example, Jacobson, 1951), others require that in addition to satisfying property 8, an integral domain must have more than one element, must have a commutative multiplication, and an identity with respect to multiplication (for example, McCoy, 1960). In terms of this definition, the lack of commutativity of multiplication bars the ring of all quaternions from being an integral domain and the lack of an identity does the same for the ring of all even integers even though each meets the requirements of the definition we adopted. Other writers (for example, Birkhoff and MacLane, 1944) cite commutativity and all the other requirements just mentioned except property 8 for which they substitute the cancellation laws: if $s \neq 0$ and $st = sr$ or $ts = rs$ then $t = r$, that is, a nonzero element may be cancelled. Property 8 is equivalent to the cancellation laws. For suppose the cancellation laws hold; if $s \neq 0$ and $st = 0$, then $st = 0 = s \cdot 0$ and by the cancellation law $t = 0$, which yields property 8. Conversely suppose property 8 holds; $s \neq 0$ and $st = sr$, then $st - sr = 0$ and by the distributive property which holds in all rings $s(t - r) = 0$ so that by property 8, $t - r = 0$ or $t = r$ which gives us one of the cancellation laws. Similarly property 8 implies that if $s \neq 0$ and $ts = rs$ then $t = r$. In short, the cancellation laws imply that there are no nonzero divisors of 0 and conversely.

We have assumed implicitly that a set designated as a semigroup or group or ring and so on, is not an empty set, that at least one element belongs to the set. If a ring has only one element, that element must be 0 since a ring is a group under addition and therefore must have an identity under addition. In order that a ring have a nonzero element it must therefore have more than one element. Integral domains, in particular, are of little interest unless they contain a nonzero element. This accounts for the stipulation, in some definitions of integral domain, that it must contain more than one element. Following Jacobson (1951), we choose to bring this stipulation into the definition of a division ring to which we now turn.

A ring is called a division ring if it contains more than one element and the set of all its nonzero elements (that is, the set with 0 excluded) constitutes a group under the operation of multiplication of the ring. This means that a division ring has an identity with respect to multiplication and each element other than 0 has an inverse with respect to multiplication. Hence in addition to the other properties of a ring, a division ring R satisfies the following two properties:

9. There exists an e, such that $e \cdot r = r \cdot e = r$ for each $r \in R$.
10. For each $r \neq 0 \in R$, there exists $r' \in R$ such that $rr' = r'r = e$.

The r' can be shown to be unique. For each $r \neq 0$ there is one and only one element with the property of r' since if r'' also has this property, then $r' = r''$ since

$$r' = er' = (r''r)r' = r''(rr') = r''e = r''$$

In effect, property 10 indicates that a unique multiplicative inverse or "reciprocal" exists for every nonzero element of a division ring. In such a ring, division is always possible except for division by 0, if $r \div s$ is interpreted to mean $r \cdot s'$ where s' is the multiplicative inverse or "reciprocal" of s. Hence the name *division ring*. A division ring is also called a *quasifield* or a *skew-field*. A division ring is called a *field* if its multiplication is commutative. Examples of division rings are the rings of all rational numbers, of all real numbers, all complex numbers, all algebraic numbers, and all quaternions. All these examples except the quaternions also constitute fields.

For a division ring the cancellation laws must hold. For suppose $s \neq 0$ and $sr = st$; then $s'(sr) = s'(st)$ and $s'(sr) = (s's)r = er = r = s'(st) = (s's)t = et = t$ so that $r = t$. Similarly in a division ring if $s \neq 0$ and $rs = ts$, then $r = t$, so that a nonzero element may be cancelled. We saw that the cancellation laws imply that there are no nonzero divisors of zero. Hence a division ring is necessarily an integral domain (under the definition we accepted) and a field is necessarily an integral domain under the other definitions cited. The converse is not the case since an integral domain need not be a division ring or a field. For example, the ring of all integers is an integral domain but not a division ring or a field since multiplicative inverses are lacking.

In summary, the very important algebraic structure known as a field is a system consisting of a set S with more than one element, together with two binary operations referred to as addition and multiplication, which satisfy the following where r, s, t denote any elements of S; 0 and 1 denote the additive and multiplicative identities, respectively; and $-r$ and r^{-1} denote the additive and multiplicative inverses of r respectively.

1. $r + s \in S$.
2. $(r + s) + t = r + (s + t)$.
3. $0 + r = r + 0 = r$.
4. $r + (-r) = (-r) + r = 0$.
5. $r + s = s + r$.
6. $r \cdot s \in S$.
7. $(r \cdot s) \cdot t = r \cdot (s \cdot t)$.
8. $1 \cdot r = r \cdot 1 = r$.
9. For $r \neq 0$, $r \cdot r^{-1} = r^{-1} \cdot r = 1$.
10. $r \cdot s = s \cdot r$.
11. $r(s + t) = r \cdot s + r \cdot t$,
    $(s + t)r = sr + t \cdot r$.

A system which satisfies these properties with the possible exception of property 10 is known as a division ring. Properties 1 to 5, together with 6, 7, and 11, characterize a ring; it is commutative if it satisfies property 10, and has an identity if it satisfies property 8. Properties 1 to 4 characterize a group under addition with property 5 making it a commutative (or *abelian*) group. Properties 6 to 10 characterize a group under multiplication with property 10 making it a commutative group. Property 11 gives the distributive laws that relate multiplication and addition; of course, if property 10 holds it is not necessary to give both the left distributive law $r(s + t) = rs + rt$ and the other, the right distributive law, since they coincide for commutative rings. In brief, a field is a set that is a commutative group under addition, whose nonzero elements constitute a commutative group under multiplication, and whose elements satisfy the distributive laws.

Still Other Numbers

Other interesting numbers are the *ideals* which were by-products of the study of algebraic numbers. Ideals were introduced by Kummer in 1847 and generalized by Dedekind in 1871. Bell (1951, pp. 222, 243) considers Kummer's creation of "a totally new species of number, which he called *ideal*" as comparable in importance to the invention of non-Euclidean geometry and he considers that "Dedekind's 'ideals,' which replace numbers, stand out as one of the memorable landmarks of the nineteenth century."

To define an ideal let us first recall that a ring R is a system consisting of a set of elements and two operations, called addition and multiplication, such that R is a commutative group under addition, multiplication in R is closed and associative, and both distributive laws hold. For example, R might be the ring of all integers or all rational numbers or all real numbers or all complex numbers or all quaternions or all 2 by 2 matrices or all n by n matrices.

A set S of elements in R is called an *ideal* in R if the difference of every pair of elements in S is also in S and if S is closed under multiplication by elements in R. In other words, a subset S of the ring R is an ideal in R if and only if for every s, $t \in S$ and every $r \in R$:

1. $s + (-t) = s - t \in S$.
2. $rs \in S$.
3. $sr \in S$.

If properties 1 and 2 hold, S is called a *left ideal* in R (closed under multiplication on the left by elements of R). If properties 1 and 3 hold, S is called a *right ideal*. If all three properties hold, S is both a left and right ideal and hence a two-sided ideal which is usually referred to simply as an ideal. If a is in an ideal, then so, by property 1, is 0, which is $a - a$, and so is $-a$ which is $0 - a$. If a and b are in an ideal, then so are $a + b = a - (-b)$ and sa and as, for any s in the ideal. It follows that the ideal is a *subring* in the sense that it is itself a ring under the operations of the ring R (McCoy, 1960, p. 26).

As an illustration of an ideal, consider the ring of all integers and the set of all multiples of 10, that is, the set consisting of 0, ± 10, ± 20, ± 30, and so on. Clearly the set is an ideal since the difference of any two multiples of 10 is again a multiple of 10 and since a multiple of a multiple of 10 is itself a multiple of 10. Similarly the set of all multiples of any integer n constitutes an ideal in the ring of all integers since if k and j are integers, then $k - j$ is an integer and $kn - jn = (k - j)n$ is a multiple of n and $jn = nj$ is a multiple of n. Each of these is an example of what is called a *principal ideal*, which has the property that each of its members can be expressed as $rf + nf$ where f is a fixed element, r any element of the ring R, and n any integer. If R has an identity element under multiplication, then nf need not be specifically mentioned since it is included as an rf for r equal to n times the identity element; for example, if n is 3 and e denotes the identity element under multiplication, then $n \cdot e = e + e + e$, and if n is -3, then $-3 \cdot e = 3(-e) = (-e) + (-e) + (-e)$, with each sum in R by the closure property for addition.

As an example of a left ideal, take R to be the ring of all 2 by 2 matrices with real numbers as components, and S the set of all matrices of the type

$$\begin{bmatrix} 0 & a \\ 0 & b \end{bmatrix}$$

where a and b are not fixed but may be any real numbers. The difference of two matrices in S is a matrix in S (subtract corresponding components). Let r be any matrix in R and s any matrix in S; then rs equals

$$\begin{bmatrix} c & d \\ f & g \end{bmatrix}\begin{bmatrix} 0 & a \\ 0 & b \end{bmatrix} = \begin{bmatrix} 0 & ca + db \\ 0 & fa + gb \end{bmatrix}$$

and hence rs belongs to S. Thus S is a left ideal. But it is not a right ideal since

$$\begin{bmatrix} 0 & a \\ 0 & b \end{bmatrix}\begin{bmatrix} c & d \\ f & g \end{bmatrix} = \begin{bmatrix} af & ag \\ bf & bg \end{bmatrix}$$

and af and bf need not be 0 so that sr need not belong to S.

Kummer developed an arithmetic or algebra for ideals in certain fields (recall that a field is a fortiori a ring). Dedekind generalized it to an arithmetic of ideals in any algebraic field. The sum of two ideals S and T in a ring R is defined as the set of all elements of R of the form $s + t$, where s belongs to S and t to T. The sum, which may be denoted by $S + T$, is readily shown to be an ideal in R. Moreover this addition of ideals can be shown to be associative and commutative. The product of S and T, denoted by ST, is defined to consist of all finite sums of products st, where s belongs to S and t to T; that is, ST consists of elements of the form

$$s_1t_1 + s_2t_2 + \cdots + s_nt_n$$

where $s_i \in S$, $t_i \in T$, and n may be any natural number. The product is an ideal in R. This multiplication is associative and it is commutative when R is commutative. There are still other ways of constructing ideals from the given ideals S and T. For example, the intersection of S and T, the set of all elements which belong both to S and to T, usually denoted by $S \cap T$, is an ideal in R.

Not only addition and multiplication but even division has been defined for ideals. This is based on set-inclusion (one ideal included as a subset of the other) which has many of the properties of divisibility among numbers. To illustrate the definition, let us consider the ring of integers and (3) and (12) the principal ideals generated by 3 and 12, respectively, that is, the set of all multiples of 3 and of 12, respectively. Note that $(12) \subset (3)$ since $12 = 3 \cdot 4$ so that 12 belongs to (3) and hence (12) is contained in (3). But (3) is not contained in (12) since, for example, ± 3 and ± 6 do not belong to (12). In short $(12) \subset (3)$ while 12 is a multiple of 3, or 3 is a factor, or divisor, of 12. This suggested the following definition for principal ideals in the ring of integers: (m) is said to be a factor or divisor of (n) if $(n) \subset (m)$. Note that the "larger" or more inclusive is defined to be a factor of or to divide the "smaller" or less inclusive, which is quite the reverse of divisibility among integers. This definition was generalized to any ideals S and T of a ring R by defining S to divide T or to be a factor of T if $T \subset S$. Again note the reversal of the relationship that holds among natural numbers. The notion of a prime number (a natural number other than 1 that has only itself and 1 as factors) has been generalized to prime ideals. There is a counterpart for ideals of the fundamental theorem of arithmetic that asserts that a natural number can be factored into a product of primes in a unique manner (except for the order in which the primes are written). In short, there is a highly developed algebra of ideals (Birkhoff and MacLane, 1944; McCoy, 1948). Since about 1920 there has been increasing interest in the study of ideals. Ideals have turned out to be very significant in many branches of algebra, particularly in the study of algebraic structures. For example, it can be shown that a division ring has no left ideal other than the "improper" ideal which consist of the whole ring or only of 0 and, if a ring with a multiplicative identity other than 0 has no proper left ideals, then it must be a division ring (Jacobson, 1951, p. 77).

CHAPTER 5

Infinite Sets
and Transfinite Numbers

Mathematicians have long been aware of the difficulties involved in dealing with the infinite. Ever since Zeno of Elea, a pupil of Parmenides, posed his paradoxes, it was recognized that their crux lay in the conceptualization of the infinite. For example, the paradox of Achilles and the tortoise may be said to rest on the conception of motion as involving an infinite number of steps to be carried out in a finite amount of time. The Greeks seemed to be extremely wary of the infinite and sought to avoid dealing with it in their mathematics. One wonders whether this may have influenced them to adhere to geometry rather than to develop an "infinitesimal calculus." True, there were a few Greek mathematicians who were precursors of the calculus. Eudoxus (408–355 B.C.) computed areas and volumes by a "method of exhaustion" which, in effect, exhausted the "whole" under investigation by considering it to be subdivided into smaller and smaller parts. Aside from matters of rigor, Eudoxus' method bears striking similarities to methods now used in the integral calculus where, for example, the area of a region is obtained as the "limit of the sum" of parts into which the region is considered to be subdivided, as the number of parts increases to infinity (gets larger than any preassigned real number) while the size or area of the parts tends to zero (gets smaller than any preassigned positive number). Archimedes (287–212 B.C.) also used a "method of exhaustion" to find areas and volumes. It is of interest that he did not make his method public. Not until twenty centuries later was a letter uncovered in which Archimedes confided his method to a friend, Eratosthenes, a librarian at Alexandria, Egypt. The translation of this letter (Heath, 1912) makes fascinating reading. One wonders whether Archimedes' apparent reluctance to publicize his method of exhaustion was because it involved what might be called "infinitely many" quantities that are "infinitely small."

The calculus of the eighteenth century brought infinity into mathematics, mainly in the form of a "potential infinity" rather than "actual infinity," or "completed infinity." For example, we speak of the limit $\sqrt[n]{n}$ as n approaches infinity, but this exemplifies potential infinity, since n assumes only finite values. To say that n approaches infinity is a convenient way of saying that the values n assumes may be larger than any preassigned number. In contrast, the set of all natural numbers consists of infinitely many elements and is an example of an actual or completed infinity rather than potential infinity. Actual infinity sometimes crept into mathematics without being explicitly recognized as such. For example, Dedekind defined a real number in terms of sets of infinitely many rational numbers, each such set exemplifying an actual or completed infinity. While mathematicians of the eighteenth and nineteenth centuries were generally willing to use the concept of potential infinity, if only as a convenient manner of speaking—a *façon de parler*—they were reluctant to admit an actual or completed infinity into mathematics. Let religion or philosophy deal with actual infinity, but not mathematics! The eminent mathematician Gauss expressed the prevalent attitude of his time when, in 1831, he warned against "the use of infinite magnitude as if it were something finished; such use is not admissable in mathematics" (1863). This attitude prevailed some fifty years later when Georg Cantor attempted to develop a mathematics of infinite magnitudes and infinite sets. He was led to do so almost against his wishes (and surprisingly enough as an outcome of his study of derivatives and trigonometric series) since the introduction of infinite sets and infinite numbers into mathematics was counter to his training and to mathematical views of infinity and of number. One wonders whether the distrust, ridicule, and rejection of his ideas by many of his colleagues may have contributed to the mental illness which Cantor suffered intermittently.

A strange property of infinite sets was noted by Galileo in 1638. This property was that the natural numbers could be placed in one-to-one correspondence with a part of themselves, the squares of natural numbers:

$$1 \quad 2 \quad 3 \quad \cdots \quad n \quad \cdots$$

$$2 \quad 4 \quad 9 \quad \cdots \quad n^2 \quad \cdots$$

Galileo presented this in the course of a dialogue in which one of the characters, when asked how he would resolve this difficulty, concluded:

> I see no other decision that it may admit, but to say, that all Numbers are infinite; Squares are infinite; and that neither is the multitude of Squares less than all Numbers, nor this greater than that; and in conclusion, that the Attributes of Equality, Majority and Minority have no place in Infinities, but only in terminate quantities. . . . (from Bell, 1951, p. 400)

But Cantor accepted this "paradox" of a one-to-one correspondence between an infinite set and a proper subset of itself. He built upon it to found an arithmetic of infinite quantities with attributes of equality (equivalence), majority (greater than), and minority (less than). Nonetheless, as we shall see, this arithmetic of infinite, or transfinite, number does lead to other paradoxes—a fact Cantor himself discovered.

Cardinal Numbers

Cantor's arithmetic of infinite or so-called transfinite numbers was part of his theory of sets (*Mengenlehre* or *Mannichfaltigkeitslehre* variously translated as theory of sets, aggregates, manifolds, ensembles, classes, or collections). By a set, Cantor meant "any collection into a single whole of definite well-distinguished objects of our intuition or of our thought" (1952; originally published in 1895). Thus Cantor required that a set be well defined in the sense that a rule stipulates exactly which elements belong to the set and which do not. His theory refers to both a finite set, consisting of a finite number of elements, and an infinite set. If S is a subset of T (that is, if every element of S is an element of T), and if S and T are finite sets, then S and T have the same (natural) *number* of elements if either of the following conditions holds:

1. T is a subset of S and hence $S = T$.
2. There is a one-to-one (biunique) correspondence between S and T—that is, a correspondence in which each element of S corresponds to one and only one element of T, and, conversely, each element of T corresponds to one and only one element of S.

Cantor recognized that in the generalization of natural (finite) numbers to infinite numbers, he could not preserve both of these properties. "All so-called proofs of the impossibility of infinite numbers," he warned, "begin by attributing to the numbers in question all the properties of finite numbers, whereas the infinite numbers, if they are to be thinkable in any form, must constitute quite a new kind of number" (1952, p. 74). For this new kind of number, Cantor drew on property 2—the one-to-one correspondence which is so fundamental a notion in counting. He defined two sets as equivalent (*aequivalent*) "if it is possible to put them, by some law, in such a relation to one another that to every element of each one of them corresponds one and only one element of the other" (p. 86). In symbols, if M is equivalent to N, we write $M \sim N$. This relation has the properties required of an equivalence relation: reflexive, symmetric, and transitive. The relation is reflexive since clearly a set can be put in one-to-one correspondence with itself so that $M \sim M$. It is symmetric since if $M \sim N$, then $N \sim M$. Finally, the relation is transitive since if $M \sim N$ and $N \sim S$, then $M \sim S$.

With every set or aggregate M, Cantor associated its cardinal number (*Cardinalzahl*) or power (*Machtigkeit*) as "the general concept which, by means of our active faculty of thought arises from the aggregate M when we make abstraction of the nature of its various elements m and of the order in which they are given" (p. 86). In other words, the concept of cardinal number abstracts from (that is, does not take into account) both the nature of the elements and the order in which they occur, so that it involves a double process of abstraction. Cantor employed a suggestive notation for the result of this double act of abstraction, denoting the power or cardinal number of the set M by $\bar{\bar{M}}$ (p. 86). (In contrast, when one abstracts only from the nature of the elements but takes the order of the elements into account there results Cantor's concept of an *ordinal* which for certain sets M he designated by $\bar{M}$.) Since a single element m of M, "if we abstract from its nature, becomes a 'unit,' the cardinal number [of M] is a definite aggregate composed of units, and this number has existence in our mind as an intellectual image or projection of the given aggregate M" (p. 86). A fundamental theorem in Cantor's work is that two sets have the same cardinal number if and only if they are equivalent, or symbolically expressed, if $M \sim N$, then $\bar{\bar{M}} = \bar{\bar{N}}$ and conversely. This is sometimes taken as the definition of cardinal number, characterized as an object common to all sets which are equivalent to a given set. Some mathematicians, including Frege and Russell, characterize the cardinal number of a set M as the set of all sets equivalent to M. Other mathematicians, including von Neumann (1928), characterize it as a particular set in the set of sets equivalent to M.

The cardinal number of a finite set is called a *finite cardinal* and that of an infinite set is called an *infinite*, or *transfinite*, cardinal number. Thus the concept of cardinal number, which Cantor regarded as the most fundamental in his theory, may be considered a generalization of natural number, since finite cardinal numbers may be identified with natural numbers. For example, if each of two sets contains three elements, then the sets are equivalent and have the same cardinal number, which may be identified with the natural number 3. The set of all natural numbers and of all sets equivalent to this set have the same cardinal number, which Cantor designated by $\aleph_0$ (aleph zero), which of course is a transfinite cardinal number.

An infinite set may have the same cardinal number as a proper subset of itself. For example, as previously noted, Galileo pointed out that the natural numbers can be placed in one-to-one correspondence with a proper subset, the squares of natural numbers:

1	2	3	$\cdots$	n	$\cdots$
2	4	9	$\cdots$	n^2	$\cdots$

Similarly, the natural numbers can be placed in one-to-one correspondence with another subset of themselves, the even numbers:

1	2	3	$\cdots$	n	$\cdots$
2	4	6	$\cdots$	$2n$	$\cdots$

In Cantor's terminology, these three sets are equivalent and have the same cardinal number $\aleph_0$. But this seems contrary to the intuitive notion that a whole is greater than a (proper) part of itself and therefore should have a larger number associated with it. Cantor claimed that "there is no contradiction when, as often happens with infinite aggregates, two aggregates of which one is a part of the other have the same cardinal number. I regard the non-recognition of this fact as the principal obstacle to the introduction of infinite numbers" (1952, p. 75). While a finite set cannot be put in one-to-one correspondence with a proper part of itself, an infinite set can. Indeed, just this distinction was advanced by Dedekind (1888) as the basis of definitions of infinite and finite sets: A set is infinite if it can be placed in one-to-one correspondence with a proper subset of itself, and otherwise it is finite.

In short, an infinite set S may be "more" or "greater" than T in the sense that it includes T as a proper subset of itself and yet S and T may have the same cardinal number. Cantor's ingenious approach to an arithmetic of infinite numbers involved a definition of "greater than" for cardinal numbers, not in terms of set inclusion, but in terms of one-to-one correspondence. If there is a subset N_1 of N such that $N_1 \sim M$, and if there is no subset of M which is equivalent to N, then $\bar{\bar{N}}$ is said to be greater than $\bar{\bar{M}}$, expressed symbolically as $\bar{\bar{N}} > \bar{\bar{M}}$. It was proved, by Schröder in 1896 and independently by Bernstein in 1898 that if M is equivalent to a subset of N, and N is equivalent to a subset of M, then M and N are equivalent. Conjectured by Cantor and proved by an appeal to the axiom of choice, is the *comparability theorem* of cardinal numbers, which is a generalization of the *law of trichotomy* for natural numbers. The comparability theorem states that for any two cardinal numbers $\bar{\bar{M}}$ and $\bar{\bar{N}}$, one and only one of the following relations prevails: either $\bar{\bar{M}} = \bar{\bar{N}}$ or $\bar{\bar{M}} > \bar{\bar{N}}$ or $\bar{\bar{N}} > \bar{\bar{M}}$. A notion of "less than" for cardinal numbers may be defined in terms of "greater than," with $\bar{\bar{N}}$ less than $\bar{\bar{M}}$ if and only if $\bar{\bar{M}}$ is greater than $\bar{\bar{N}}$ or, in symbols, $\bar{\bar{N}} < \bar{\bar{M}}$ if and only if $\bar{\bar{M}} > \bar{\bar{N}}$. The above theorem may therefore be reworded to say that one and only one of these relations holds: either $\bar{\bar{M}} = \bar{\bar{N}}$ or $\bar{\bar{M}} > \bar{\bar{N}}$ or $\bar{\bar{M}} < \bar{\bar{N}}$.

To illustrate, let N be the set of natural numbers and let S be any set consisting of just three elements. Then there is a proper subset of N which is equivalent to S but not conversely. Therefore $\bar{\bar{S}} < \bar{\bar{N}}$ or $3 < \aleph_0$. More generally, $n < \aleph_0$ for any natural number n.

A set which is equivalent to the set of all natural numbers is said to be enumerable (or denumerable or countable). We have seen that the set of even numbers and the set of squares of natural numbers is enumerable. Each of these is a subset of the natural numbers. It turns out that there are "supersets" of the natural numbers, sets which contain the natural numbers as a proper subset, which are also enumerable. For example, the set of all signed integers is enumerable. This can be seen by prefacing the list of natural numbers by 0 and by preceding each n in the list by $-n$.

There results the single sequence

$$0, -1, +1, -2, +2, -3, +3, \cdots, -n, +n, \cdots$$

This sequence, as any single sequence of distinct elements, can be put in one-to-one correspondence with the natural numbers by letting the first element in the sequence correspond to 1, the second to 2, and so on. What is a somewhat more surprising result is that the set of all rational numbers is also enumerable, that is, has the cardinal number $\aleph_0$. One way of establishing this is to first show that the unsigned rational numbers constitute an enumerable set. Let n/d represent such a rational number where n and d are natural numbers. We obtain a single sequence of these rational numbers, by listing them in order according to increasing sum of numerator and denominator $n + d$, and ordering them, for a fixed $n + d$, according to increasing numerators. For example, list first those unsigned rationals for which $n + d = 2$ (namely, 1/1), then all those for which $n + d = 3$ (namely, 1/2, 2/1 which are listed according to increasing numerators), then those for which $n + d = 4$ (1/3, 2/2, 3/1), then those for which $n + d = 5$ (1/4, 2/3, 3/2, 4/1), and so on. From this enumeration, eliminate any number that is equal in value to a preceding one. (Or, to begin with, we might have restricted ourselves to rationals that were reduced to lowest terms.) Thus the distinct (unsigned) rational numbers may be enumerated in a single sequence:

$$\frac{1}{1}, \frac{1}{2}, \frac{2}{1}, \frac{1}{3}, \frac{2}{2}, \frac{3}{1}, \cdots$$

As previously noted, this sequence, as any single sequence of distinct elements, may be placed in a one-to-one correspondence with the natural numbers by letting the first element in the sequence correspond to 1, the second to 2, and so on. Thus the unsigned rationals are enumerable.

To show that all rational numbers are enumerable, we adopt the procedure used in showing that all integers are enumerable. If the single sequence of unsigned rationals is preceded by $0/1 = 0$, and if every term n/d in the sequence is preceded by $-n/d$, then the resulting sequence contains all the signed rational numbers: positive, negative, and zero. This sequence too can be placed in one-to-one correspondence with the natural numbers. Thus the set of all the rational numbers has $\aleph_0$ as its cardinal number. This result is somewhat surprising. If the rational numbers are considered to correspond to points on a straight line, then such points are *dense* in the sense that between any two rationals there is another rational. In contrast, the natural numbers correspond to isolated points, since between two consecutive natural numbers there is no natural number. Another way of conceptualizing the vast difference between the rational numbers and the natural numbers is to realize that there are infinitely many rational numbers in any interval between two distinct points on the line, regardless of how small the interval, whereas there are intervals on the line without any natural numbers, for example, the interval between 2 and 3 excluding the end points of the interval. Yet the rational numbers have the same cardinal number as the natural numbers.

We have seen that the rational numbers are enumerable. Even more remarkable is Cantor's discovery that the real algebraic numbers, which contain the rational numbers as a proper subset, are also enumerable. Recall that such a number is a real number which satisfies an algebraic equation of the form

$$a_n x^n + a_{n-1} x^{n-1} + \cdots + a_1 x + a_0 = 0$$

where the coefficients are integers with $a_n \neq 0$ and the exponents are natural numbers. Thus a rational number is a special case of a real algebraic number (namely, one that satisfies the displayed equation when $n = 1$). One way of enumerating the real algebraic numbers is to associate with each such equation a natural number H, characterized as the equation's height or index, which may be defined as follows:

$$H = |a_n| + |a_{n-1}| + \cdots + |a_1| + |a_0| + n$$

Enumerate the Hs by increasing magnitude. For each natural number there are at most a finite number of equations of the displayed form which have it as their height. For example, no such equation has 1 as its height; $x = 0$ is the only equation that has 2 as its height; and $x + 1 = 0$, $x - 1 = 0$, $x^2 = 0$, and $2x = 0$ are the only equations that have 3 as their height. The fundamental theorem of algebra guarantees that each equation of the first displayed form can have at most n roots. The roots may be real or complex but we discard all those that are not real. Associate with each H the real roots of those equations which have H as their height. Thus a given value of H has associated with it a finite number of real algebraic numbers (arising from a finite number of equations each with a finite number of roots). Enumerate the real algebraic numbers associated with a fixed H in order of increasing magnitude but discard any numbers that have already been associated with an H of lower value. In short, we have an enumeration of real algebraic numbers according to increasing magnitude of the Hs with which they are associated and, for a fixed H, according to increasing magnitude of those numbers associated with H which have not already been enumerated. Thus there results a single sequence of numbers which therefore is in one-to-one correspondence with the natural numbers. But this sequence must contain all real algebraic numbers since each such number is a root of an equation of the first displayed form and consequently was associated with some H. Hence the set of all real algebraic numbers has the same cardinal number $\aleph_0$ as the set of natural numbers.

Addition and multiplication
of cardinal numbers

The definition of addition of cardinal numbers refers to *disjoint sets*—sets that have no elements in common—and to the union of sets. If S and T are sets, then their union, which may be denoted by $S \cup T$, refers to the set that consists of elements in either set. The sum of the cardinal numbers of two disjoint sets S and T is defined as the cardinal number of the union of S and T, expressed symbolically as $\bar{S} + \bar{T} = \overline{S \cup T}$. To see the need for disjoint sets, let $S = \{a, b, c\}$ and let $T = \{c, d\}$; then $S \cup T = \{a, b, c, d\}$ and $\bar{S} = 3$, $\bar{T} = 2$, and $\overline{S \cup T} = 4$, so that $\bar{S} + \bar{T} \neq \overline{S \cup T}$. However, if S and T are disjoint, for example, if $S = \{a, b, c\}$ and $T = \{d, e\}$, then $S \cup T = \{a, b, c, d, e\}$ and $\bar{S} + \bar{T} = 3 + 2 = 5 = \overline{S \cup T}$. The definition does not rule out the addition of a cardinal number to itself but it does require that there be enough distinct elements so that the number can be represented by disjoint sets. For example, if $S = \{a, b, c\}$ and $T = \{d, e, f\}$, then $S \cup T = \{a, b, c, d, e, f\}$ yielding $3 + 3 = 6$. To take another example, to add $\aleph_0$ to $\aleph_0$ each is taken to be the cardinal number of a set, say, of $S = \{a_1, a_2, \cdots, a_n, \cdots\}$ and of $T = \{b_1, b_2, \cdots, b_n, \cdots\}$ where the a's are distinct, the b's are distinct, and no a equals any b. It is possible to enumerate the elements of $S \cup T$, for example,

$$a_1, b_1, a_2, b_2, a_3, b_3, \cdots, a_n, b_n, \cdots$$

so that $S \cup T$ has the cardinal number $\aleph_0$. Hence $\aleph_0 + \aleph_0 = \aleph_0$. If n is any natural number, then $n + \aleph_0 = \aleph_0$ since the listing of the elements of an enumerable set T may be preceded by the listing of the elements of a set S which is disjoint from T and which contains exactly n elements. For example, if n is 3, then

$$a_1, a_2, a_3, b_1, b_2, b_3, b_4, \cdots, b_n, \cdots$$

would be a suitable enumeration of distinct elements.

By definition, the addition of two cardinal numbers is a cardinal number so that the closure property holds. It is readily established that the commutative and associative properties also hold, since the order of the elements is not taken into account in the concept of cardinal number. Thus if S, T, and U are disjoint sets,

$$\bar{S} + \bar{T} = \bar{T} + \bar{S} \qquad \text{and} \qquad (\bar{S} + \bar{T}) + \bar{U} = \bar{S} + (\bar{T} + \bar{U})$$

Because the associative property holds, parentheses need not be included in addition since $\bar{S} + \bar{T} + \bar{U}$ is a well-defined sum; the expression can have only one meaning. In particular, $\aleph_0 + \aleph_0 + \aleph_0 = \aleph_0$.

The definition of multiplication depends on the "Cartesian product" or "binding" of two sets M and N, denoted by $M \times N$, which is the set made up of all pairs (m, n) where $m \in M$ and $n \in N$. The product of $\bar{M}$ and $\bar{N}$ is defined as the cardinal number of $M \times N$.

$$\bar{M} \cdot \bar{N} = \overline{M \times N}$$

Cantor established that the commutative and associative properties hold and also the distributive law

$$\bar{M} \cdot (\bar{N} + \bar{U}) = \bar{M} \cdot \bar{N} + \bar{M} \cdot \bar{U}$$

More Infinities

It is easy to be lulled into the belief that every infinite set is enumerable and that $\aleph_0$ is the only transfinite cardinal number. But Cantor proved the important theorem that the set of real numbers is not enumerable. One way of proving this remarkable theorem is to think of every real number expressed as a nonterminating decimal (for example, $\frac{1}{2}$ may be written as $0.5000 \cdots$ or as $0.4999 \cdots$). Assume that an enumeration has been obtained of all the real numbers. The proof consists of showing that a real number r can be constructed that will not be in the enumerated list. This yields a contradiction to the supposition that all the real numbers are enumerated. (This indirect proof or proof by *reductio ad absurdum* would not be acceptable to intuitionists who have their own theory of cardinal numbers.)

Suppose that the enumeration of all the real numbers is as follows:

$$
\begin{array}{llll}
n_1 \cdot a_{11} & a_{12} & a_{13} & \cdots \\
n_2 \cdot a_{21} & a_{22} & a_{23} & \cdots \\
n_3 \cdot a_{31} & a_{32} & a_{33} & \cdots \\
\cdot & \cdot & \cdot & \cdot \\
\cdot & \cdot & \cdot & \cdot \\
\cdot & \cdot & \cdot & \cdot \\
n_n \cdot a_{n1} & a_{n2} & a_{n3} & \cdots \\
\cdot & \cdot & \cdot & \cdot \\
\cdot & \cdot & \cdot & \cdot \\
\cdot & \cdot & \cdot & \cdot \\
\end{array}
$$

Here the n represents the integral part of the number, the subscript of the n represents the place or position of the number in the enumeration, and the a's represent the digits in the decimal portion of the number. To construct r, the real number not in the enumeration, we concentrate on its decimal portion. For the first digit in the decimal portion of r we select any digit other than a_{11} (the first digit in the decimal part of the first number in the enumeration) but here and elsewhere in r we agree not to choose 0 or 9 in order to avoid ambiguity (for example, between 0.5000 · · · and 0.4999 · · ·). For example, if $a_{11} \neq 6$ we choose 6 and if $a_{11} = 6$ we choose 7 for the first digit. For the second digit in the decimal portion of r we select any digit other than a_{22} (the second digit in the decimal part of the second number in the enumeration) except 0 or 9. We continue in this way, selecting for the kth decimal place of r any number other than a_{kk} (the kth number in the enumeration) except 0 or 9. Now the resulting number cannot be one of those in the enumeration since it differs in at least one place from each number in the enumeration. But a decimal expansion represents a real number. Therefore r is a real number which is not in the enumerated list of real numbers. This contradicts the assumption that the enumeration contained all real numbers.

If the decimal portions of the numbers in the enumeration constitute the entries in a matrix, then a_{11}, a_{22}, a_{33}, a_{kk}, · · · are the diagonal entries; hence the name *diagonal procedure* for the construction used in this proof. A diagonal procedure is an important tool in proofs concerning infinite sets.

This proof also yields the result that the real numbers between 0 and 1 are not enumerable. The only modification is that each n in the supposed enumeration is taken to be 0. In other words, if the real numbers between 0 and 1, expressed in decimal notation, were enumerable, then an enumeration of them could be taken as in the above but with each n equal to 0. An r could be constructed as before, with the integral part of n equal to 0. This r would not be in the enumeration even though it is a real number between 0 and 1, thus contradicting the supposition that the enumeration included all such real numbers. A similar proof also shows that the set of real numbers in any finite interval is not enumerable.

The cardinal number of the set of all real numbers is usually designated by $\aleph_1$ or by C (for continuum, the linear continuum represented by the real line). All the conditions hold which indicate that the cardinal number of the natural numbers is less than that of the real numbers, since the former are equivalent to a proper subset of the real numbers (namely, the natural numbers) but the real numbers, since they are not enumerable, cannot be equivalent to the natural numbers or any subset of them. Hence: $\aleph_0 < \aleph_1$.

The famous continuum problem asks whether there is any cardinal number between these two or whether, as the subscripts suggest, $\aleph_1$ is the first cardinal number larger than $\aleph_0$. In other words, the continuum problem asks whether $\aleph_1$, or C, the "power of the continuum," is the next largest transfinite cardinal number or whether there is an intervening cardinal. The so-called continuum hypothesis asserts that no cardinals intervene between the power of the natural numbers and the power of the continuum. Cantor conjectured this hypothesis and made many attempts to prove it. It has still not been proved. It is known to be related to the axiom of choice, with Cohen's recent paper (1963) throwing light on this relationship. The generalized continuum problem asks whether $\aleph_{n+1}$ is the next largest number after $\aleph_n$ and the generalized continuum hypothesis conjectures that this is the case. But we are getting ahead of ourselves since so far $\aleph_0$ and $\aleph_1$ are the only transfinite cardinals we have mentioned. Soon, we shall introduce other transfinite cardinal numbers.

In 1874, Cantor published proofs of the theorems that the set of real numbers is not enumerable and that the set of real algebraic numbers is enumerable. It follows that the set of those real numbers which are not algebraic—the so-called transcendental numbers—cannot be enumerable. Suppose that the transcendental numbers were enumerable; since the real algebraic numbers are enumerable, the set of real numbers would be the union of two enumerable sets and hence enumerable. In other words, if R represents the set of real numbers, A the set of real algebraic numbers, and T the set of real numbers that are nonalgebraic or transcendental, then $R = A \cup T$ and therefore $\bar{\bar{R}} = \bar{\bar{A}} + \bar{\bar{T}} = \aleph_0 + \bar{\bar{T}}$. If $\bar{\bar{T}} = \aleph_0$ then $\bar{\bar{R}} = \aleph_0$. But Cantor showed that the real numbers are not enumerable. Thus we were led to a contradiction by the supposition that the transcendental numbers are enumerable.

Similar reasoning leads to the conclusion that the irrational numbers are not enumerable. The real numbers are the union of the rational and irrational numbers, and we have seen that the rational numbers are enumerable. Hence, if the irrational numbers were enumerable, the cardinal number of the real numbers would be $\aleph_0 + \aleph_0 = \aleph_0$ which is not the case.

The above can be interpreted as proving the "existence" of transcendental and irrational numbers. Since the real algebraic numbers are enumerable and the real numbers are not, there must exist real numbers other than the algebraic ones; call them the real transcendental numbers. Similarly, since the rational numbers are enumerable and the real numbers are not, there must exist real numbers other than the rational ones; call them the real irrational numbers. Such indirect existence proofs are not acceptable to intuitionists, since the proofs do not indicate how to construct the transcendental or irrational numbers.

Each of the sets of irrational numbers and of real transcendental numbers can be shown to be equivalent to the set of real numbers. To show this, we first establish a general theorem that every infinite set has an enumerable subset. The proof uses the axiom of choice.

Theorem. Every infinite set has an enumerable subset.

Proof. Let S be an infinite set. Then S cannot be an empty set or it would have the cardinal number 0 and not be an infinite set. Choose any element from S and call it s_1. The set S without s_1, designated by $S - s_1$, cannot be empty or else S would have had only one element and would not be infinite. Choose an element from $S - s_1$ and call it s_2. Then choose an element in the set that remains when s_1 and s_2 are removed from S and call it s_3. Continuing in this fashion, we obtain the infinite sequence $s_1, s_2, s_3, \cdots$ which is an infinite subset of S that is enumerable.

In other words, this theorem means that every infinite set has a subset that is equivalent to the set of natural numbers. But then those conditions are met which indicate that any transfinite cardinal number must be greater than or equal to $\aleph_0$. Thus, $\aleph_0$ is the "first," or smallest, transfinite or infinite number. Now applying this theorem to the irrational numbers, which are not enumerable, we conclude that its cardinal number is greater than $\aleph_0$. Similarly, the cardinal number of the transcendental numbers is greater than $\aleph_0$.

To show that each of the sets of irrational numbers and of transcendental numbers has the same cardinal number as the set of real numbers we shall establish and use a theorem concerning the cardinal number of the union or sum of two sets, one of which is enumerable and the other infinite but not necessarily enumerable.

Theorem. If T is an infinite set and S an enumerable set, then $T \cup S$ has the same cardinal number as T.

Proof. By the previous theorem, T has an enumerable subset which we denote by T'. Designating $T - T'$ by T'' we have

$$T = (T - T') \cup T' = T'' \cup T'$$

where T'' and T' are disjoint sets. Hence,

$$T \cup S = (T'' \cup T') \cup S = T'' \cup (T' \cup S)$$

by the associative property for the operation of set union. Now, T' was chosen to be enumerable and S was given as enumerable, so that $T' \cup S$ is enumerable. Therefore, there is a one-to-one correspondence between the elements of T' and those of $T' \cup S$. Using this correspondence together with the identity correspondence under which the elements of T'' correspond to themselves, we get a one-to-one correspondence between the elements of T and those of $T \cup S$. In other words, since T'' and T' are disjoint sets, we may combine the correspondence under which T' is associated with $T' \cup S$ and the identity correspondence of T'' to itself to obtain a one-to-one correspondence between $T = T'' \cup T'$ and $T \cup S = T'' \cup (T' \cup S)$. Thus, adjoining an enumerable set to an infinite set does not change its cardinal number.

Applying this theorem to the set of real transcendental numbers T and to the set of real algebraic numbers A, which is enumerable, we know that $T \cup A$ has the same cardinal number as T. But $T \cup A$ is the set of real numbers. Hence, T has the cardinal number of the real numbers. Similarly, the irrational numbers are shown to have the same cardinal number as the real numbers.

We have seen that the set of real numbers in the interval between

0 and 1 is not enumerable. This set can be shown to be in one-to-one correspondence with all the real numbers and also with all the real numbers in a finite (not empty) interval. For example, a one-to-one correspondence between the points in the interval between 0 and 1 and the points say, between 0 and 3 may be obtained by imagining the smaller interval drawn in the plane parallel and above the larger interval; projecting from a common point above both intervals, as in the figure, leads to a one-to-one correspondence between the points in the two intervals.

If each point is considered to correspond to a unique real number, this may be interpreted as yielding a one-to-one correspondence between the real numbers in the two intervals. (See Courant and Robbins, 1941, p. 82 for a diagram illustrating the one-to-one correspondence between the points on a finite interval and on a whole straight line and Fraenkel, 1961, pp. 49–50, for other approaches to the proof.) In short, the set of real numbers in any finite nonempty interval has the same cardinal number as the set of all real numbers.

Even more contrary to intuition is the theorem that the points in the plane have the same cardinal number as the points on the real line. In other words, the two-dimensional continuum has the same cardinal number C as the linear or one-dimensional continuum. So surprised was Cantor by this theorem, which he proved in about 1878 after several years of attempting to disprove it, that he wrote to Dedekind: "Je le vois, mais je ne le crois pas." (Fraenkel, 1961, p. 103 has an account of the history of the theorem.) To prove the theorem, it is sufficient to show that the set of points in the unit interval, the interval between 0 and 1, can be put in one-to-one correspondence with the set of those points of the plane which lie in the unit square defined by the equations $0 \leq x \leq 1$ and $0 \leq y \leq 1$, since the former set is equivalent to the set of all points on the whole straight line and the latter set can be shown to be equivalent to the set of all points in the plane. A rather rough outline of the proof is as follows. (See Wilder, 1952, p. 87 or Fraenkel, 1961, p. 102 for details.) Let (x, y) designate a point of the square where x and y are real numbers which may be written in nonterminating decimal form as

$$x = 0 \cdot a_1 a_2 a_3 \cdots$$

$$y = 0 \cdot b_1 b_2 b_3 \cdots$$

To (x, y) we let correspond the point on the unit interval which is represented by the following real number

$$r(x, y) = 0 \cdot a_1 b_1 a_2 b_2 a_3 b_3 \cdots$$

Here the digits of the decimal expansions of x and y have been interlaced. The argument is reversible so that $r(x, y)$ corresponds to (x, y) and, more generally, any real number of the form $0 \cdot c_1 c_2 c_3 \cdots$ can be made to correspond to a unique ordered pair $x = (c_1, c_3, c_5, \cdots)$ and $y = (c_2, c_4, c_6, \cdots)$. In a similar manner, the points in three-dimensional space can be made to correspond to a unique point on the line and vice versa. For example, let a point in the unit cube, $0 \leq x \leq 1$, $0 \leq y \leq 1$, $0 \leq z \leq 1$, be represented by (x, y, z) where the nonterminating decimal expansion of the three coordinates are

$$x = 0 \cdot a_1 a_2 a_3 \cdots$$

$$y = 0 \cdot b_1 b_2 b_3 \cdots$$

$$z = 0 \cdot c_1 c_2 c_3 \cdots$$

To (x, y, z) we let correspond the point on the unit interval which is represented by the real number

$$r(x, y, z) = 0 \cdot a_1 b_1 c_1 a_2 b_2 c_2 a_3 b_3 c_3 \cdots$$

Similarly, a one-to-one correspondence can be established between, on the one hand, the points on the line, and, on the other hand, the points in n-dimensional space or in a "Euclidean space" with dimension $\aleph_0$. In other words, continua or "spaces" of dimensions 1, 2, 3, $\cdots$, n, and even $\aleph_0$, each has the same cardinal number: C or $\aleph_1$. Clearly, the notion of cardinal number does not preserve differences in dimensionality. This result, surprising to Cantor and to other mathematicians, led to a penetrating analysis of the concepts of dimensionality and of cardinal number. In brief, the concept of dimension takes into account both the "number" and the order or position of the points whereas the cardinal number involves a one-to-one correspondence which is not continuous and does not preserve the relative order of the points.

Still More Infinities

One may wonder whether $\aleph_1$ is the largest of the cardinal numbers. However, Cantor showed how to obtain larger and larger cardinal numbers so that the sequence of cardinals, like the sequence of natural numbers, is unending. Start with any set S, finite or infinite, and consider the set of all subsets of S. For example, if S consists of the three elements a, b, c, then the subsets of S are S itself, the empty set which has no elements, the sets (a, b), (a, c), and (b, c), and the unit sets made up of only one element (a), (b), and (c). Thus the set of all subsets of S contains 8 or 2^3 members. Similarly, if a finite set has n elements, then the set of all its subsets has 2^n members. More generally, if the cardinal number of a set is α, then the cardinal number of all its subsets is 2^α. One way of seeing this is to associate with each subset of a set S a representing (single-valued) function f with domain S and with range the set consisting of 0 and 1, where for $s \in S$, $f(s) = 1$ if s belongs to the subset, and $f(s) = 0$ if s does not belong to the subset. Thus, sequences of 0s and 1s result which differ for different subsets. For example, let S again be the set (a, b, c), with the elements considered in this order. Then the representing function for S is given by the sequence 1, 1, 1 since a, b, and c all belong to S; the representing function for the empty set is given by the sequence 0, 0, 0 since none of the elements belongs to the empty set; the representing function for the subset (a, c) is given by 1, 0, 1; the representing functions for (a) and for (b) are given by 1, 0, 0, and by 0, 1, 0, respectively, and so on. In short, the representing function for a subset has 1 or 0 in the first position in the sequence depending on whether a does or does not belong to the subset, and similarly, the second position depends on b, and the third on c. Each subset gives rise to a representing function or sequence of 0s and 1s, and, conversely, each possible three-term sequence of 0s and 1s correspond to a subset so that there is a one-to-one correspondence between the subsets of (a, b, c) and the sequences. Given three positions to fill, there are 2^3 permutations of 0 and 1 and therefore 2^3 possible sequences which correspond to 2^3 subsets. If a set has n elements, then, fixing on an order for the elements, we find that there are 2^n possible sequences of 0s and 1s and therefore 2^n subsets of the set of n elements.

Consider now the set of natural numbers in their usual order. Corresponding to a subset is the representing function which may be taken to be a nonterminating sequence of 0s and 1s. For example, the subset consisting only of 2 and 3 corresponds to the sequence 0, 1, 1, 0, 0, 0, $\cdots$ with all 0s following the two 1s; the subset consisting of the even numbers corresponds to 0, 1, 0, 1, . . . , and so on with 0 and 1 alternating. Since each position in the nonterminating sequence can be filled by 0 or 1, there are $2^{\aleph_0}$ possible sequences and therefore $2^{\aleph_0}$ subsets of the natural numbers.

Incidentally, it can be shown that $2^{\aleph_0}$ equals $\aleph_1$, the cardinal number of the set of real numbers. Perhaps the best way to establish this is to represent a real number, not by a decimal expansion, but in terms of the binary scale or base which uses only the digits 0 and 1. For example, when the decimal base, the base of 10, is used, 111.011 means $1(10^2) + 1(10^1) +$ $1(10^0) + 0(10^{-1}) + 1(10^{-2}) + 1(10^{-3})$ which equals $100 + 10 + 1$ (since $10^0 = 1) + 0 + \frac{1}{100} + \frac{1}{1000}$ but when the binary base, the base 2, is used, it means $1(2^2) + 1(2^1) + 1(2^0) + 0(2^{-1}) + 1(2^{-2}) + 1(2^{-3}) =$ $4 + 2 + 1 + 0 + \frac{1}{4} + \frac{1}{8} = 7\frac{3}{8}$. The binary scale is of considerable practical value and is used in many computers and also is of theoretical value as, for example, in simplifying the present proof. If the binary base is employed, every real number can be written as an infinite sequence of 0s and 1s. For example, 6 can be written as $110.000 \cdots$ and $\frac{1}{2}$ can be written as $0.1000 \cdots$. Thus, every real number written in the binary base corresponds to a nonterminating sequence of 0s and 1s and vice versa. Hence, the set of all real numbers is equivalent to the set of such sequences. But we have seen that the latter set is equivalent to the set of all subsets of the natural numbers. Therefore, the set of all real numbers is equivalent to the set of all subsets of the natural numbers. Their cardinal numbers are, therefore, equal, yielding the promised result that $2^{\aleph_0}$ equals $\aleph_1$.

We might also mention here that 2 with an exponent that is a cardinal number is a special case of exponentiation of cardinal numbers. Cantor dealt with α^β where α and β are both cardinal numbers. As a prelude to this concept, he introduced the notion of a *covering* of a set S with a set T. By such a covering, denoted by S/T, he meant the set of all single-valued functions with domain S and range T, that is, the set of all functions $f(s)$ with $s \in S$ and $f(s) \in T$. The cardinal number of the covering S/T was taken as the definition of the cardinal number of T exponentiated by the cardinal number of S or expressed symbolically

$$\overline{S/T} = \overline{\overline{T}}^{\overline{\overline{s}}}$$

For example, if S has 3 elements and T has 4 elements, then S/T has $4^3 = 64$ as its cardinal number, that is, it has 64 elements. If T has 2 elements, then S/T has 2^α as its cardinal number, where α is the cardinal number of S. Thus, the representing functions that we discussed before are special cases of the functions in a covering. The usual laws of exponents can be shown to hold for exponentiation of cardinal numbers, so that if a, b, and c are cardinal numbers

$$a^b \cdot a^c = a^{b+c}$$

$$(a^b)^c = a^{b \cdot c}$$

$$a^b \cdot c^b = (a \cdot c)^b$$

Let us return now to consideration of 2^α where α is a cardinal number. If α is equal to n, a natural number, then clearly $n < 2^n$. Analogously, it can be proved that $\alpha < 2^\alpha$ so that, for example $\aleph_0 < 2^{\aleph_0} = \aleph_1$. The basic idea of the proof is to assume that a one-to-one correspondence has been established between the elements of a set M and the members of the set of all its subsets, and then to show that there is a subset of M which is not involved in this correspondence. Let the subset of M which is assigned to a given element m of M under the assumed correspondence be designated as S_m. Now, either m is a member of S_m or m is not a member of S_m. Let B denote the subset of M which consists of all those elements m of M which are not members of the subsets S_m to which they correspond. To what element of M does the subset B correspond? The set B cannot be any of the S_m since it differs from each S_m by at least the element m; that is, if a given m belongs to B, then it does not belong to S_m and, conversely, if it belongs to S_m, then it does not belong to B. Thus, the assumed correspondence between the elements of M and its subsets did not include B; hence, a contradiction has been established to the supposition that it is possible to have such a correspondence. But, it is possible to establish a one-to-one correspondence between the set M and a proper part of the set of all its subsets, namely, between an element m of M and the unit subset (m): the subset consisting only of m. Hence, all the conditions hold which allow us to assert that the cardinal number of M is less than that of the set of all its subsets:

$$\bar{\bar{M}} < 2^{\bar{\bar{M}}}$$

Similarly, the set of all the subsets of M gives rise to the set of all *its* subsets which in turn has a larger cardinal number yielding

$$2^{\bar{\bar{M}}} < 2^{2^{\bar{\bar{M}}}}$$

and so on. Starting, for example, with $\aleph_0$, we get a sequence of cardinal numbers $\aleph_0 < 2^{\aleph_0} = \aleph_1 < 2^{\aleph_1}$ which we designate as $\aleph_2$ and $\aleph_2 < 2^{\aleph_2}$ which we designate by $\aleph_3$. In short, there arises an unending sequence of greater and greater transfinite cardinals: $\aleph_0, \aleph_1, \aleph_2, \cdots$.

But even this sequence does not end the possibility of cardinal numbers. It can be shown that there is a cardinal number which is greater than any of the $\aleph$s in this sequence. More generally, if $M_1, M_2, M_3, \cdots$ is an infinite sequence of sets such that the cardinal number of each M_k is greater than that of its predecessors, then we will show that there is a cardinal number greater than that of each M_k (Sierpiński, 1950b, p. 88). To this end, consider the set M whose elements are the sets M_k, and designate by S the union or sum of M. In other words, the sum S is the set of all elements each of which belongs to some M_k. Since each M_k is a subset of S, it is readily established, by the reasoning we used above, that $M_k \leq \bar{\bar{S}}$ for each M_k. Suppose $M_k = \bar{\bar{S}}$ for some M_k. Since M_{k+1} has a greater cardinal number than M_k, it follows that M_{k+1} has a greater cardinal number than S, which is a contradiction. Hence, $M_k < \bar{\bar{S}}$ for each M_k. In other words, S has a greater cardinal number than each M_k.

If S is the sum or union of the sets having $\aleph_0, \aleph_1, \aleph_2, \cdots$ as their cardinal numbers, then S has a greater cardinal number than each of the $\aleph$s in the sequence. Designate the cardinal number of S by $\aleph_{\omega_0}$ and consider the set of all subsets of S whose cardinal number is $2^{\aleph_{\omega_0}}$ which is greater than $\aleph_{\omega_0}$. Denote $2^{\aleph_{\omega_0}}$ by $\aleph_{\omega_1}$. Thus, just as $\aleph_0$ was used to start an unending sequence of greater and greater transfinite numbers, so can $\aleph_{\omega_0}$:

$$\aleph_{\omega_0}, \aleph_{\omega_1}, \aleph_{\omega_2}, \cdots$$

Consider now the sum of the set whose elements have the $\aleph$s in this sequence as their cardinal numbers. This sum must have a cardinal number greater than any of these $\aleph$s and it can be used to start a new unending sequence of increasingly greater transfinite numbers. Thus, there is no end to the infinity of infinities.

But a price is paid for this inexhaustible store of infinities. Paradoxes arise from the unending sequences of increasingly larger infinities. For example, let S be the set of all (well-defined) sets and consider the set of all subsets of S which we will designate by $\mathfrak{U}S$ ($\mathfrak{U}$ for the German word for subset, *Untermenge*). Now, according to what we have just said, $\mathfrak{U}S$ has a larger cardinal number than has S. But since S is the set of all sets, it must in particular contain all the sets which are members of $\mathfrak{U}S$; that is, $\mathfrak{U}S \subset S$. Therefore, a one-to-one correspondence can be established between $\mathfrak{U}S$ and a part of S. But this makes it impossible for $\mathfrak{U}S$ to have a greater cardinal number than S. This paradox, known as Cantor's paradox, was discovered by him in 1899; it has a counterpart in Cantor's theory of transfinite ordinals, known as the Burali-Forti paradox, published by Cesare Burali-Forti in 1897 but already known by Cantor in 1895 (Fraenkel, 1961, p. 202).

Evaluation

The discovery of the described paradoxes and other paradoxes involving infinite numbers may make one wonder whether there was perhaps a germ of truth in Galileo's dialogue (which did not necessarily represent Galileo's own views) when it was said that the attributes of equality, majority, and minority have no place in infinities but only in terminate quantities (Bell, 1951, p. 400). On the other hand, there are paradoxes in mathematics other than those involving infinite numbers. It has been said that Cantor, "in the opinion of the majority of 20th century mathematicians, has succeeded in the task of bestowing legitimacy upon infinitely great magnitude" (Fraenkel, 1961, p. 1). If this legitimacy is tainted by paradoxes and by indirect and nonconstructive proofs unacceptable to certain mathematicians, there is the consolation that the same taints may portions of mathematics which do not pertain to the transfinite numbers

It is essentially Cantor's notion of a finite cardinal number that Frege used in his treatment of the natural numbers and that Russell adopted as his definition of a finite cardinal number. Cantor believed that the principles underlying "the theory of the actually infinite or transfinite cardinal numbers . . . afford also the most natural, shortest, and most rigorous foundation for the theory of finite numbers" (1952, p. 98). But while the logicists apparently agree here with Cantor, the formalists and intuitionists prefer other approaches to the finite or natural numbers.

Cantor's theory of cardinal number was incorporated in the *Principia Mathematica* of Whitehead and Russell (1910), with additional principles added to avoid the known contradictions or antinomies to which the theory gives rise. But the additional principles "are neither obviously nor demonstrably logical in any accepted sense of the term [and] have, and are generally agreed to have, the character of *ad hoc* remedies" (Körner, 1962, p. 66). Our chapters on logicism deal with such principles. The intuitionists reject much of Cantor's theory of transfinite numbers and develop their own theory of cardinal numbers. The formalists refuse to abandon Cantor's transfinite mathematics. Instead they have tried to take Cantor's naïve theory and put it on a more formal basis. Hilbert distinguished between the "concrete" or real notions of finite mathematics and the "ideal" notions of infinite or transfinite mathematics, and maintained that it is permissible to adjoin the ideal notions to the real ones as long as the resulting system remains consistent. But this plan was dealt a death blow by Gödel's results, which show that it is not possible to prove the consistency of a completely formalized arithmetic by "finite" methods. (Our chapters on formalism have a more detailed account of the "ideal" notions and of the attempts to prove the consistency of formalized arithmetic.)

Three main philosophical attitudes toward the concept of an actual infinity may be described as finitism, transfinitism, and methodological transfinitism.

> Finitists such as Aristotle, Gauss, and the older and new intuitionists, deny all "real" content or even "intelligibility" to such mathematical notions as are not characteristic either of finite aggregates or at most of potentially infinite, i.e., growing but never completed, aggregates. (Those among them who do not admit even the conception of potentially infinite aggregates might be called "strict finitists.") Transfinitists such as Cantor and his followers ascribe the same reality and intelligibility to transfinite as to finite concepts. Methodological transfinitists, in particular Hilbert, admit transfinite concepts into mathematical theories without according them full "ontological" status. They are admitted because they are useful for such purposes as the simplification and unification of mathematical theories. (Körner, 1962, p. 111)
>
> The historical importance of the "naïve" transfinite mathematics, created by Cantor and incorporated almost wholly into *Principia Mathematica*, can hardly be overestimated; for without it the less naïve theories would have had little to analyze, to be critical of, to reconstruct. (p. 62)

CHAPTER 6

Logicism

The Logistic Thesis

Of the three major schools of thought in foundations of mathematics—logicism, intuitionism, and formalism—it is the first which is probably the best known, due in part to the fame of the school's *magnum opus*, the *Principia Mathematica* (1910–1913) of Alfred North Whitehead and Bertrand Russell. The chief aim of the school of logicism is to establish the so-called logistic thesis—that is, to show that all concepts of mathematics can be defined in terms of concepts of logic and that all theorems of mathematics can be proved solely on the basis of logical principles. There are, as might be expected, considerable differences of opinion as to the importance of this aim. What is more surprising is that there are also considerable differences of opinion as to whether or not this aim has already been achieved and, hence, whether mathematics has been developed from logic, founded on logic, or reduced to logic. Let us sample the variety of opinions regarding this question.

Diverse views on logistic thesis

Bertrand Russell writes that the development of pure mathematics from logic was set forth in detail in *Principia Mathematica* by Whitehead and himself (1945). Russell maintains that, while historically mathematics and logic were once distinct disciplines, it has now become almost impossible to draw a line of demarcation between the two fields, so that, in fact, now the two are one. There are those who endorse this view and who, like the philosopher-mathematician, John G. Kemeny (1959a, pp. 20–21), refer to "the identity of the two fields" and claim that in the *Principia Mathematica* "Mathematics is shown to be no more than highly developed Logic."

At the other extreme are those who claim that mathematics and logic are not one and the same, and that it has not even yet been shown that mathematics is a branch of logic or that mathematics can be founded on logic. It is sometimes added that it is rather pointless to attempt to found mathematics on logic or to reduce mathematics to logic. A representative of this point of view is Friedrich Waismann, who believes that mathematics "is not a branch of logic, but completely autonomous . . . The belief that mathematics is more seriously founded if it is reduced to logic is, on the whole, only a misunderstanding" (1959, p. 118).

It is of interest to contrast Russell's views on the relationship between mathematics and logic with those of another philosopher-mathematician, Charles Sanders Peirce, whom some consider to be the greatest philosopher America has produced (see White, 1955). Peirce wrote: "It does not seem to me that mathematics depends in any way upon logic" (1933, p. 189). He pointed out that, on the contrary, logic cannot possibly solve its problems without much use of mathematics and that all of formal logic is "merely mathematics applied to logic." He therefore questioned the validity of the contention that mathematics is a branch of logic.

In between the view that mathematics has been reduced to logic and the view that it has not been so reduced is the view that certain branches of mathematics have been reduced to logic and others have not. For example, it is sometimes stated that the *Principia Mathematica*, by reducing to logic a set of axioms for the natural numbers, thereby reduced arithmetic, algebra, and analysis to logic, but did not reduce to logic the so-called nonarithmetical parts of mathematics, such as geometry, topology, and abstract algebra. This is the view taken by Carl Hempel, who notes that, although it was possible in the case of arithmetic to define the customary meaning of the undefined or primitive concepts in the axioms "in terms of purely logical concepts," an "analogous procedure is not applicable to those disciplines which are not outgrowths of arithmetic" (1953, p. 236). In particular, he believes that an analogous procedure is not available for geometry, topology, and abstract algebra, examples of mathematical disciplines "which are not outgrowths of arithmetic and thus of logic" (p. 235). On the other hand, the logician Willard Quine, who holds that "mathematics reduces to logic" (1951a, p. 5), sees that for geometry "a method of reduction to logic is ready at hand" (p. 279) and that each of topology and abstract algebra "fits into the general structure of logic" (p. 279).

To summarize: We are told that mathematics reduces to logic, is a branch of logic, or is identical with logic. But we are also told that mathematics has not been or even cannot be reduced to logic. In between are the views that some but not all branches of mathematics have been reduced or can be reduced to logic, with some differences of opinions as to just which branches have been or can be so reduced.

Consequences of logistic thesis

There are diverse views on the relationship between mathematics and logic. But what actually is the relationship between mathematics and logic? This problem is of concern to other scholars besides mathematicians and logicians. It is of considerable interest to philosophers, particularly those concerned with the philosophy of science. In fact, the thesis that mathematics has been reduced to logic is pivotal for certain schools of philosophical thought. Logical positivism, it has been said, considers that *Principia Mathematica* succeeded in reducing all mathematics to logic and uses this thesis as a basis for classifying together mathematical and logical propositions (as tautologies or as analytic statements). Discussing logical positivism, White writes: "It was maintained that because the *Principia* had reduced all of mathematics to logic, and because all of logic was what Wittgenstein called tautologous, it followed that all mathematical truths are analytic in this Wittgenstein sense" (1955, p. 208). Moreover, the *Principia* serves logical positivists as a model upon which to pattern their philosophical inquiries. As White words it, logical positivism accepts "the belief that philosophy should press forward in the tradition of *Principia Mathematica*. Philosophy was to do for other concepts and disciplines what that system had accomplished for logic and mathematics" (1955, p. 205). This belief is related to the logical positivist's conviction that all of philosophy is—or should be—nothing but the logic of science. If the *Principia* did not succeed in reducing mathematics to logic, if indeed, as some insist, mathematics cannot be reduced to logic, then basic tenets of logical positivism are in need of revision.

Thus, the relationship between mathematics and logic and just what it is that the *Principia* has shown with regard to this relationship both have far-reaching consequences. They have consequences for every science, since every science makes use of mathematics and of logic. In particular, they have consequences for psychology, especially in view of the utilization in psychology of mathematical and of logical models. Mathematical models have, for example, been used in learning theory (Bush and Mosteller, 1951, 1955; Estes, 1950). Logical structures, such as the propositional, or sentential, calculus and the functional, or predicate, calculus have been used as models for systems of neurons in the nervous system and as models of social behavior (McCulloch and Pitts, 1943; George, 1956, 1959). Mathematical structures (such as lattices, rings, groups, fields, abstract algebras, and various topological structures), may also be used as models. But, if mathematics has actually been founded on logic or has been reduced to logic, then logical models should suffice while mathematical models should not be necessary, since they should be expressible in terms of logic. F. H. George, in a report on models and theory in social psychology, notes that various logical calculi "are open to use in science, and will, if the logical foundations of mathematics can be believed, lead to the whole of mathematics" (1959, p. 314). There are other recent reports in psychology and sociology which accept as a fact that the whole of mathematics *has* been founded on logic. Moreover, this "fact" has even been incorporated into, or served as an analogy for, approaches to psychology and other behavioral sciences.

Hence it seems entirely fitting that we should concern ourselves with the relationship between mathematics and logic, with whether the former has been founded on the latter or reduced to the latter, and with how it happens that there are such diverse and apparently conflicting views with respect to the relationship. As a background for a study of these problems, it will be helpful to have a brief survey of the work done by logicists and their forerunners. It is to such a survey that we now turn.

Historical Overview

Logicism may in a sense be traced back as far as Aristotle (384–322 B.C.), the originator of the discipline of logic or, more exactly, of so-called traditional Aristotelian logic. It is true that the logic used in most writings on logicism involves extensive revision of Aristotelian logic. It has been said that traditional Aristotelian logic constitutes only a fragment of the new logic, "a fragment moreover which, from the point of view of the requirements of other sciences, and of mathematics in particular, is entirely insignificant" (Tarski, 1946, p. 19). Nonetheless, any discipline that emphasizes logic inevitably owes some debt to Aristotle.

Logicism makes use of a logical discipline to which mathematicians contributed and to which they are still contributing. As Wilder words it, in talking about the movement of mathematicians toward the study of logic: "And, whereas logic was traditionally a cut-and-dried rehash of the work of Aristotle—with great concentration on the syllogism, etc.—it has today become a live and growing field of investigation, known under the name of *symbolic logic* or *mathematical logic*" (1952, p. 56). It is symbolic or mathematical logic that is used in logistic writings.

Although it would be foolhardy to try to condense into a few phrases the radical differences between symbolic, or mathematical, logic and traditional Aristotelian logic, some of the chief differences can be outlined. Symbolic logic is not confined to the predicate-subject form of a statement that predominated in Aristotelian logic. It is not even confined to statements or to the calculus of statements (also called sentences, or propositions) but includes other logical calculi, such as the predicate calculus (also called functional calculus) which deals with functions of variables, and with the number-theoretical calculus which is based on relations between numbers. Modern logic makes use of the axiomatic-deductive method, which is believed to date back to Pythagoras (about 500 B.C.) and comes to us from Euclid (300 B.C.) whose geometric treatise, Euclid's *Elements*, has been said to have had the greatest circulation of any book with the exception of the Bible. A characteristic property of symbolic logic, as the name suggests, is its reliance on abstract symbolic notation and on manipulation of these symbols. Abstract symbols are used not only for propositions or propositional forms but also for the relationships between them. Abstract symbols, which revolutionized algebraic notation and manipulation when applied to algebra by Vieta (about 1591) and others, likewise revolutionized logic. It is its utilization of abstract symbols and formal manipulation of them that has helped modern mathematics to advance in power. Similarly, logic was helped to advance far beyond the Aristotelian level as it received symbolic treatment under the hands of such mathematicians and philosophers as Leibniz, De Morgan, Boole, Peirce, and Schröder. We shall refer to their work in the next section. Finally, modern logic does not confine itself to the syllogistic inference so popular in traditional Aristotelian logic, but considers other forms of inferences which come closer to the kinds of deductive inferences widely used in mathematics. It has been said that the most serious defect in the classical tradition of logic "extending from Aristotle in the fourth century B.C. to Leibniz in the seventeenth century . . . was the failure to relate logic as the theory of inference to the kind of deductive reasonings that are continually used in mathematics" (Suppes, 1957, p. xv). Although the desirability of relating mathematics and logic was recognized in the seventeenth century, it was not until the latter half of the last century that this was systematically carried through, primarily due to the efforts of Frege, Peano, Russell, and others to whose work we shall subsequently refer. Only in recent years—within the last four decades—has symbolic logic reached the stage of what has been called a theory of inference adequate for most of mathematics and the empirical sciences (p. xvi). Contributing prominently to these developments have been David Hilbert, Kurt Gödel, and Alfred Tarski. Many of the recent developments in symbolic logic were stimulated more by the formalistic movement than by logicism, indicating how difficult it is to draw a sharp line between the influences of the foundational schools. That symbolic logic is a thriving and changing discipline is attested to by the number of recent texts in the field, the many summaries of reports of new developments presented at the 1957 summer institute for symbolic logic (at Cornell University), and the many contributions that appear in the *Journal of Symbolic Logic*, which has been in existence for about a quarter of a century.

Forerunners of logicism

We shall now backtrack to deal briefly with the work of contributors to the development of symbolic or mathematical logic who may be regarded as the forerunners of the logistic movement. The philosopher and mathematician G. W. Leibniz (1646–1716) conceived of logic as the discipline basic to all sciences. He recognized the value of abstract symbols in logic and he developed a system of symbols known as a calculus of reasoning (*calculus ratiocinator*). Although Leibniz is sometimes credited with creating symbolic logic, it would probably be more accurate to say that he helped to lay the groundwork for its development. Systematic development of symbolic, or mathematical, logic did not take place until almost two centuries later in the work of the English mathematician, George Boole (1815–1864). Boole, whose major work was *An Investigation of the Laws of Thought* (1854), developed so-called Boolean algebras, which include the algebra of logic. Other important contributors to the algebra of logic were the English logician Augustus De Morgan (1806–1871), whose chief work was *Formal Logic* (1847); the American logician and philosopher Charles Sanders Peirce (1839–1914), originator of the method of truth tables that are widely used in logic; and the German Ernst Schröder (1841–1902), who gave a comprehensive treatment of the subject in his *Vorlesungen über die Algebra der Logik* (1890–1905).

Forerunners of the logistic movement also include the German mathematician Karl Weierstrass (1815–1897), who was influential in the movement to "arithmetize" mathematics—that is, to reduce it to the study of properties of integers. One should also mention the German mathematician and philosopher Richard Dedekind (1831–1916), who devised a method (Dedekind "cut") for defining real numbers, and hence, in particular, irrational numbers in terms of rational numbers. Since a rational number can be considered as an ordered pair of integers—for example, ⅔ as the pair (2, 3) and ³⁄₂ as the pair (3, 2)—Dedekind's methods offer a means of defining real numbers in terms of sets of integers. Dedekind exerted profound influence on both the logical and philosophical analyses of the foundations of mathematics, particularly with his essays on numbers: *Stetigkeit und irrational Zahlen* (1872) and *Was sind und was sollen die Zahlen?* (1888).

Early logicists

Logicism is deeply indebted to the German logician Gottlob Frege (1848–1925), "who, without doubt, was the greatest logician of the 19th century" (Tarski, 1946, p. 19n). It is in his work (1879) that there occurs the first presentation of a sentential calculus (calculus of sentences or calculus of propositions), now considered a primary and indispensable part of mathematical logic. Frege devoted more than a score of years to reduce arithmetic to logic, with results described in *Die Grundlagen der Arithmetik* (1884) and *Grundgesetze der Arithmetik* (1893–1903). We shall subsequently have more to say about Frege. Here it is of interest to note that Frege's books were virtually unknown until rediscovered by Russell, who brought them to the attention of mathematicians and logicians. It is of interest that the logistic thesis is also referred to as the Frege-Russell thesis.

Any historical account of logicism should include the Italian mathematician Guiseppe Peano (1858–1932) and his school (*Formulaire de Mathématiques*, 1895–1905), who are responsible for extensive research in symbolic logic that resulted in the expression of a number of mathematical theorems in logical symbolism and in the axiomatic treatment of the natural numbers. It was Peano's system of axioms for the natural numbers that the *Principia Mathematica* sought to reduce to logic.

With Peano there ends what has been called the first period of the logicism movement. The second period reaches its peak in both Russell's *Principles of Mathematics*, originally published in 1903 and essentially a philosophical discussion of the logistic thesis, and in the *Principia Mathematica*, purportedly a proof of the thesis.

Principia Mathematica

We have already noted that Frege devoted years of his life in efforts to reduce arithmetic to logic. Yet he was not entirely successful. After a decade of work, he was putting the finishing touches on his *chef-d'ôevre* (the second volume of *Grundgesetze*) when he received a letter that revealed that one of his syllogisms led to an antinomy that indicated a weakness both in set theory and in logic. It was Russell who wrote that now-famous letter. In his appendix to this work, Frege admitted that its foundations had been shaken by Russell's antinomy. So upset was Frege by the antinomy and its consequences that he suspended further attempts to reduce arithmetic to logic.

Russell considers that it follows from Frege's work that arithmetic— and indeed pure mathematics in general—is a prolongation of deductive logic. Yet quite a different interpretation has been given to Frege's work (Fraenkel and Bar-Hillel, 1958). It has been said that even if Frege had been successful in reducing arithmetic to logic, even if no antinomies were involved, it would not have meant that other parts of mathematics, such as analysis, were thereby reduced to logic. It is true that analysis was already spoken of as "arithmetized" in Frege's days; but the so-called arithmetization of analysis reduced it not only to integers but also to finite sets of integers and to infinite sets of integers. For example, the real, irrational number π may be represented by an infinite sequence of integers, $3.14159 \cdot \cdot \cdot$; $\pi/4$ by the infinite sum of rational numbers (ordered pairs of integers)

$$1/1 - 1/3 + 1/5 - 1/7 + 1/9 - 1/11 + \cdot \cdot \cdot$$

and $\pi/2$ by the infinite product of rational numbers

$$2/1 \cdot 2/3 \cdot 4/5 \cdot 6/5 \cdot 6/7 \cdot 8/7 \cdot 8/9 \cdot \cdot \cdot \cdot$$

Hence, to found analysis on logic it was necessary to reduce to logic not only a theory of integers but also a theory of finite and infinite sets of integers and perhaps a general theory of sets. The latter was one of the tasks undertaken in the *Principia Mathematica*. But, in order to introduce infinite sets and to account for classical analysis, Russell and Whitehead found it necessary to introduce axioms that have been the hub of considerable controversy and that are sometimes regarded as outside the domain of logic. We discuss these axioms as well as other aspects of the *Principia Mathematica* in the next chapter.

Evaluation of Logicism

Controversial Axioms | Axiom of infinity

In order to allow for infinite sets, such as infinite sets of natural numbers, Russell and Whitehead introduced an axiom of infinity. This axiom asserts that there exist infinitely many "individuals." ("Individuals" are elements or entities belonging to the lowest level in a postulated hierarchy of types and orders; these need not concern us here, but will be briefly alluded to when the axiom of reducibility is discussed.) We may consider that the axiom of infinity in effect asserts that there exist infinitely many objects.

It may help us to understand why such an axiom was introduced if we consider Peano's axioms for the natural numbers. These axioms may be worded as follows, with number referring to natural number (which is here taken to include 0):

P1. 0 is a number.
P2. The successor of any number is a number—that is, if n is a number, then $n + 1$ is a number.
P3. There are no two numbers with the same successor.
P4. 0 is not the successor of any number.
P5. Mathematical induction: A property of 0, which is a property of the successor of every number with this property, is a property of every number.

P5 may also be formulated as follows: If P is a property such that (a) P belongs to 0, and (b) whenever P belongs to a number P also belongs to its successor, then P belongs to every number.

It can readily be seen that P3, taken together with P1 and P2, implies that the (natural) numbers constitute an infinite set. This helps to explain why the axiom of infinity was introduced. But let us pursue the matter further.

The concept of natural number may be reduced to concepts of logic by defining it as a class of classes (essentially Frege's definition). Thus 0 may be defined as the class of all null classes (where a null, or empty, class is a class with no members), 1 as the class of all unit classes (classes with one member each), 2 as the class of all couples, 3 as the class of all triads, and so on. The concept of successor may be reduced to concepts of logic by basing it on a process of adding to a class of n elements some element not in that class.

Now, if natural number and successor are given the meanings that they customarily have in arithmetic, then it would be highly desirable that, under this interpretation of the terms, Peano's axioms would constitute true propositions. But what about P3? Suppose that there existed only a finite number of elements (things, individuals), say, 9 elements. Then 10, defined as $9 + 1$ would constitute a null class (empty set, set with no elements). Similarly, 11, defined as $10 + 1$, would constitute a null class, and so on, so that 10 and all subsequent natural numbers would be identical. But this means that P3 would not be true. Moreover, numbers that mathematicians consider to be distinct would be identical. To avoid such "an arithmetical catastrophe" (Waismann 1959, p. 115), the axiom of infinity was introduced.

One of the criticisms raised against this axiom is that it represents a statement about the world—namely, that there exist infinitely many objects in it—and hence has an empirical character. The axiom thereby introduces an empirical element into mathematics, whereas a characteristic of mathematics is that its propositions are devoid of empirical content. Moreover, as Waismann points out, "the structure of the whole of arithmetic now depends essentially on the truth of this axiom," whereas there is not the slightest reason for believing in its truth and, worse yet, there is no way of reaching a decision regarding its truth, so that the introduction of the axiom of infinity has the effect of basing arithmetic on a hypothesis which can never be verified but must remain "eternally uncertain" (1959, pp. 115–116). Körner notes that the axiom admits of no empirical falsification or confirmation and he criticizes the logicistic "illegitimate conflation" of mathematical and empirical concepts (1962, pp. 61–62).

In all fairness to Russell and Whitehead, it should be pointed out that they hesitated to accept the axiom of infinity as an axiom of logic. They were, as Fraenkel and Bar-Hillel (1958, p. 165) put it, "very reluctant about taking this step," since they were disturbed by the recognition that the content of the axiom had a "factual look," with not only its logicality but even its truth in doubt. One of the interpretations suggested for the term "individual" in *Principia Mathematica* is *that of the ultimate particles or elements of which the universe is composed.* The axiom of infinity, although it is couched in logical terms, thus seems to pose the question of whether the universe is composed of a finite or infinite number of ultimate particles, the answer to which can perhaps be attempted by physics, but not by mathematics and logic. Nonetheless, if Peano's axioms were to be true in their customary interpretation, if infinite sets were to be introduced, and if mathematical theorems in whose derivation the axiom of infinity was used were to be shown to be theorems of logic, then it seemed necessary to accept this axiom as an axiom of logic. In short, if mathematics was to be "reduced" to logic then logic seemingly would have to include the axiom of infinity.

Axiom of choice

Russell and Whitehead also use the axiom of choice, which they call the multiplicative axiom. This axiom may be formulated as follows: Given a class of disjoint (mutually exclusive) classes, none of which is the null, or empty, class, then there exists a class composed of exactly one element from each class and of no other elements. The axiom seems not to have been explicitly formulated until 1904. Since then it has engendered more discussion and controversy than any other axiom, with the possible exception of Euclid's axiom of parallels, introduced more than 2000 years earlier.

As we shall see later, intuitionists place considerable restrictions on the use of this axiom and object to some of its applications in mathematical proofs. Many mathematicians who have little sympathy with intuitionists are also somewhat distrustful of the axiom. Even some mathematicians who use the axiom when they see no other alternative prefer to avoid its use whenever possible. It is noteworthy that the axiom has been invoked in proofs of some rather paradoxical results—for example, the Banach-Tarski paradox (1924). Cries of "illegitimate" and "meaningless" have been raised against the axiom. Aside from the intuitionistic point of view, the attack and defense of the axiom seem to have been influenced more by emotional, or psychological, factors and practical reasons (it is expedient to have the axiom) than by logical reasons or arguments of principle. (See Fraenkel and Bar-Hillel, 1958, p. 74 for a discussion of this point.) Much time and effort have gone into proofs that the axiom of choice is equivalent to (implies and is implied by) other statements that may be easier for mathematicians to accept (Rubin and Rubin, 1963). Nonetheless, the axiom is still highly controversial. "Even today, a number of first-rate mathematicians . . . have not essentially changed their distrustful attitude" toward it (Fraenkel and Bar-Hillel, 1958, p. 77). To introduce it as an axiom into a system of logic does not *eliminate* the distrust and controversy, but *transfers* them to the system of logic.

Russell and Whitehead were themselves uneasy about the axiom of choice (multiplicative axiom) and "could not persuade themselves to treat it as a logical truth on a par with the other logical axioms" (p. 165).

Nonetheless, if those parts of classical mathematics whose derivation needed the axiom of choice were to be "reduced" to logic, then it seemed that this axiom had to be considered a part of logic. The axiom of choice (as well as the axiom of infinity) is often included in axiom systems for set theory. If set theory is regarded as part of logic or reducible to logic—which is a moot issue (see Benacerraf and Putnam, 1964, p. 10)—then the axiom of choice may be considered as part of logic or as reducible to logic. In 1938, Kurt Gödel established the important result that the axiom of choice is consistent with the other axioms of various systems of set theory. This means that the axiom of choice is compatible with the other axioms, that it does not introduce inconsistencies. Hence, the axiom of choice cannot be disproved within these axiom systems.

In 1963, Paul Cohen provided an answer to a long-standing conjecture about the independence of the axiom of choice. He proved this axiom to be independent of the other axioms in a certain system of set theory by constructing a model that satisfied the other axioms in the system but not the axiom of choice. This means that it is not possible logically to derive or to prove the axiom of choice from the other axioms in the system; or else the model, which satisfies the other axioms, would also satisfy the axiom of choice. Thus, just as the parallel-line axiom is independent of the other axioms of Euclidean geometry, so the axiom of choice is independent of the axioms in a certain system of set theory.

In brief, Gödel's results established the impossibility of *disproving* and Cohen's results established the impossibility of *proving* the axiom of choice within a particular axiom system for set theory.

Axiom of reducibility

The statement of this axiom involves the concept of a hierarchy of types, the full delineation of which involves technicalities unimportant for this particular presentation. One reason for the introduction of this hierarchy along with a hierarchy of orders within a type was to guard against antinomies, such as antinomies of set theory. The axiom of reducibility postulates that there exist propositional functions of lowest type (type 1) that are formally equivalent to a propositional function of any (higher) type. In other words, for a propositional function of any type, there is said to exist an equivalent propositional function of lowest type. One of the functions of the axiom is to ensure that there are sufficiently many propositional functions to be put in one-to-one correspondence with the real numbers.

The justification given by Russell and Whitehead for the axiom of reducibility in the first edition of the *Principia Mathematica* was essentially that it seemed to be needed for certain results, that it led to these

results, and that it seemed to lead to no other results. Despite such a
pragmatic justification, they were apparently uneasy about this axiom
In the introduction to the second edition of the *Principia Mathematica*
they wrote that "clearly it is not the sort of axiom with which we car
rest content." Various attempts have been made to reduce mathematics
to logic without an axiom of reducibility (by Ramsey, 1931, and others)
But these efforts do not seem to be entirely successful and some of them
have been criticized (for example, by Black, 1934) on the grounds that
they involve fallacious proofs. The axiom itself has been criticized on the
grounds that there is a lack of evidence for it, that it is difficult to verify
its truth or falsity, and that it is even difficult to understand what it
means. Black (1934) presented a summary of these and other criticisms
of the axiom of reducibility as well as a survey and critical evaluation
of attempts to dispense with it. It is sometimes said that Russell postulated the principle of reducibility because there seemed to be no means of
proving it and that, when in trouble, he invoked the axiom as a *deus ex
machina* much as someone else in trouble might invoke the name of God
or other theological concepts.

General criticisms of
controversial axioms

In summary, the axioms of infinity, choice, and reducibility are highly
controversial. Aside from criticisms specific to each of these axioms, there
are criticisms common to all three, including the following:

1. The truth (or falsity) of these axioms is in doubt.
2. They do not belong to the domain of logic.

It may seem that the argument in 1 is irrelevant. Why be concerned
with the truth or falsity of the axioms? Why not treat them simply as
hypothetical statements? Yet a case can be made in support of 1. In the
logic of the *Principia Mathematica* a false proposition implies *every* proposition, whether it is true or false (that is, if P is false, then P implies
any Q). This is because the nature of logical implication, known as *material implication*, which is accepted in the *Principia Mathematica* (and in
many systems of logic) is such that an implication, P implies Q, holds
whenever P is false or whenever Q is true. "A feature of the Russell
Whitehead system, often called 'paradoxical,' is . . . that a false proposition implies every proposition" (Wilder, 1952, p. 219).

Therefore there is a need to be concerned with the truth or falsity of
the axioms introduced in the *Principia Mathematica* since if a false proposition P were introduced as an axiom we would have to accept that P
implies Q, regardless of whether the proposition Q is true or false. In
other words, if a false proposition were introduced as an axiom, any

proposition at all could be deduced from it. Moreover, Russell and Whitehead are themselves concerned with the truth or falsity of the axioms and deductions from them. For example, in the *Principia Mathematica* (Vol. 1, pp. 55–60) it is stated that a reason for accepting the axiom of reducibility is "that many other propositions which are nearly indubitable can be deduced from it, and that no equally plausible way is known by which these propositions could be true if the axiom were false, and nothing which is probably false can be deduced from it." As Black pointed out, the validity of the first part of the quotation is questionable since, in the logic of *Principia Mathematica*, "all the 'indubitable' propositions could very well be deduced from the axiom if it happened to be false; and the remainder of the quotation tries to justify expediency by an appeal to the truth of unverified hypotheses" (1934, p. 113).

Russell and Whitehead have "an attitude which believes that selected axioms are obviously true and for that reason cannot lead to contradictions" (p. 141). Yet it would be difficult to support the claim that the three axioms we have discussed are obviously true or intuitively evident. Indeed, as we saw, the authors of *Principia Mathematica* are well aware of the problematic and controversial status of these axioms.

Let us now consider the criticism formulated in 2—namely, that the axioms of infinity, choice, and reducibility are not part of logic. Even the strongest adherent of logicism would agree that these axioms are not part of traditional logic but might contend that they can be considered as additions to or extension of traditional logic, since they can be expressed in purely logical terms (Hempel, 1953, p. 158). It is sometimes maintained that the logic used in *Principia Mathematica* is "pure logic" or "purified logic." For example, the philosopher Morton White, after noting that Russell insists that the philosopher should not be merely a passive spectator of science but should participate in the reconstruction of the foundation of science, cites as the most striking example of Russell's success "the way in which he has contributed to the derivation of mathematics from a *purified logic*. As a result of his work, . . . it is extremely difficult to say where logic ends and mathematics begins" (1955, p. 193, italics ours). Others question the "purity" of the logic employed by Russell and, in particular, whether the three controversial axioms are part of logic. Hence, they question whether mathematics, or any important branch of mathematics, has yet been reduced to logic. The logistic program "was to reduce mathematics to logic and not to logic plus nonlogical hypotheses" (Körner, 1962, p. 59). Some agree with the mathematician Hermann Weyl (1885–1955) that in *Principia Mathematica* mathematics is founded, not on logic, but on a sort of logician's paradise (1946). There are mathematicians who see little reason for preferring this logician's paradise to the paradise Cantor provided with his set theory. In brief, it is not universally agreed that the axioms we have been discussing belong to logic. Some are willing to extend the meaning of the term *logic* so that it includes these axioms. Others are not, either because of their conception of logic or because of their dissatisfaction with the controversial axioms.

It is therefore of interest to consider the following quotation from Russell:

> The proof of this identity [of mathematics and logic] is, of course, a matter of detail; starting with premises which would be *universally admitted to belong to logic* and arriving by deduction at results which obviously belong to mathematics, we find that there is no point at which a sharp line can be drawn with logic to the left and mathematics to the right. If there are still those who do not admit the identity of logic and mathematics, we may challenge them to indicate at what point, in the successive definitions and deductions of *Principia Mathematica*, they consider that logic ends and mathematics begins. (1919, p. 194, first italics ours)

As we have already attempted to show, the premises or axioms of *Principia Mathematica* are *not* "universally admitted to belong to logic." Does this then throw some doubt on the proof of the identity of mathematics and logic?

Excluded-middle axiom

Moreover, there are some other axioms of *Principia Mathematica* that are not universally accepted. For example, the axiom of the excluded middle (*P* or not-*P*) is used therein and is proved to be equivalent to the principle of contradiction (*P* and not-*P* together constitute a contradiction). We shall see in the chapters on intuitionism that this school of foundational mathematics accepts the principle of contradiction but is against the unrestricted use of the principle of excluded middle. The two are not equivalent in systems of logic acceptable to intuitionists (or even in logical systems acceptable to all formalists). The equivalence is a consequence of axioms in *Principia Mathematica* that relate various logical connectives (*implies, and, either-or, not*) (Wilder, 1952, p. 219). Such relations are not postulated and are not proved in systems of logic acceptable to intuitionists and some formalists. Here again we see that there is no universal agreement on what constitutes the domain of logic and whether the premises of *Principia Mathematica* fall within this domain.

Other Criticisms of Logicism

The *Principia* has been criticized on various grounds that we have not explicitly considered. Some criticisms refer to various technical defects some of which have since been remedied. The introduction of a hierarchy of orders (within a hierarchy of types) has been found to be "untenable and must be abandoned" (Black, 1934, p. 101). Various alternatives have been proposed in lieu of the introduction of orders. The hierarchy of types has been found to be "valid and useful" (p. 104), but it is not certain that it fully accomplishes its purpose. The hierarchy of types was introduced in order to guard against antinomies, and it has effectively barred the way to the known antinomies of set theory and logic. But there is no guarantee that new antinomies may not crop up against which even the hierarchy of types would be defenseless.

Moreover, it has been noted that the exposition of the material in the *Principia* would not have been possible if, throughout the exposition, there had been strict adherence to a hierarchy of types.

The objection has also been raised that the logistic approach does not clarify certain important concepts in mathematics, such as those of infinity and of the real number continuum, and that its definition of natural number involves circularity and other shortcomings (Waismann, 1959; Körner, 1962).

There have appeared criticisms of logicism from some of its former adherents. Notable among them are the attacks in *Tractatus Logico-Philosophicus* (1961, first appeared in 1922) by Ludwig Wittgenstein, once a pupil of Russell. There have also appeared defenses of logicism in the form of efforts to reconstruct certain aspects of *Principia Mathematica* (Chwistek, 1924–1925; Ramsey, 1931). Some of the attempts to remedy defects of *Principia Mathematica* have themselves been criticized as involving fallacious proofs. It has been said "that the logistic thesis is not proven and that elaborate reconstruction can save the technical achievements of the logistic method only at the expense of that method's ambitions" (Black, 1934, p. 144).

The period since *Principia* has been called the third period of logicism. According to Black: "Since *Principia Mathematica* little advance has been made by the logistic school and time has shown serious defects in that work, so that the third period has been one of successive attempts to consolidate a position which at one time Whitehead and Russell appeared to have reached triumphantly" (1934, pp. 18–19).

Recognition of shortcomings in *Principia Mathematica* should not blind one to its great merits. It represents a scholarly achievement of the first order, a magnificent tribute to the power and beauty of human thought. It has been characterized as the most representative work of modern logic and as having an "epoch-making" influence on the development of logical investigations (Tarski, 1946, p. 229). Even its shortcomings may have been blessings in disguise. For example, imperfections in the work have been traced to "insufficiently precise technique in manipulating systems of symbols" (Black, 1934, p. 139). But the present-day requirements of precision in manipulating complex systems of symbols are themselves, to a considerable extent, a product of the advances in precision and complexity represented by the *Principia*. There is no denying that the work rightfully deserves the place of esteem it holds in scholarly circles. This place is its due, regardless of whether or not it has succeeded in reducing mathematics to logic.

In the nature of a historical comment, it should be noted that soon after Whitehead's death, Russell (1948b) wrote that Whitehead had planned to write a fourth volume on geometry. This additional volume of the *Principia* never appeared. Perhaps a clue to Whitehead's failure to carry out this plan may be found in Russell's comment on the writing of the *Principia:* "Neither of us alone could have written the book; even together, and with the alleviation brought by mutual discussion, the effort was so severe that at the end we both turned aside from mathematical logic with a kind of nausea" (1948b, p. 138).

The Logistic Thesis Reconsidered

Let us now reconsider the logistic thesis that all *mathematical terms* are definable on the basis of *logical terms* and all *theorems of mathematics* can be proved by using only *principles of logic*. The meaning of this thesis depends on the meaning of the italicized phrases. In particular it depends on what is meant by *mathematics* and by *logic*. For example, is mathematics to include or exclude geometry? Is logic to include or exclude the axiom of infinity, the axiom of reducibility, the axiom of choice, the excluded middle principle, and so on? Paraphrasing a discussion of mathematics and set theory (Fraenkel and Bar-Hillel, 1958, p. 164), we point out that there does not exist a clear conception of either what is mathematics or what is logic which allows a dispassionate investigation into their relationship. Different conceptions of the disciplines color the conceptions of the relationship between them. Conversely, different conceptions of the relationships color the very conceptions of the disciplines themselves. In particular, the meaning of the logistic thesis varies with variations in the meanings of mathematics, of logic, and of the relationship between them. Thus, the thesis "runs the whole gamut between an uninteresting truism through a pious hope, whose basis is not quite clear, to an almost obvious falsity" (Fraenkel and Bar-Hillel, 1958, p. 163). A clue to the possible basis of the diversity of opinions concerning the logistic thesis and whether or not its aim has in fact been achieved can be traced to the diversities in conceptions of mathematics, of logic, and of the relationship between the two. Different people may well mean different things when they assert that mathematics is logic or that mathematics is reduced to logic.

"Mathematics is logic"

It may be instructive to consider the meaning of each word in the assertion "mathematics is logic." We have already noted how varied are the meanings of the word logic. Thus, the logic of Aristotle differs strikingly from modern logic; the logic of the intuitionists differs from the logic of the logicists; some logicians are willing to extend the meaning of logic so that it includes the controversial axioms of *Principia Mathematica*, and others are not, and so on. Let us discuss the meaning of the remaining two words.

Logicians have long recognized the ambiguity of the term *is* in everyday language. They have distinguished, for example, among the *is* of predication ("The apple is red"), the *is* of identity ("Lewis Carroll is Charles Dodgson"), and the *is* of existence ("There is a road leading into town"). They have been careful to distinguish between the *is* of class membership and the *is* of class inclusion or set inclusion ("The dog is an animal" in contrast to "The set of dogs is a subset of the set of animals"). Logicians, in fact, sometimes use different symbols for different senses of *is* to make clear what meaning is intended. For example, "X is in Y" may be denoted by $X \in Y$ where *is* refers to class membership—that is, X is a member of Y, but by $X \subset Y$ where *is* refers to set inclusion—that is, X is a subset of Y. Yet logicians seemingly fail to heed the need to distinguish among various meanings of *is* or to indicate precisely what meaning is intended, when they assert that "mathematics *is* logic." This phrase has been interpreted in various ways, sometimes by the same person. For example, it has been interpreted to mean that:

1. Mathematics is identical with logic.
2. Mathematics is a branch of logic.
3. Mathematics is an extension of logic.
4. Mathematics is reduced to logic.

The *is* of 1 refers to identity between mathematics and logic. But the *is* of 2 and 3 seems not to be—and need not be—the *is* of identity. To say that mathematics is a branch of logic suggests that there may be other branches of logic and hence that mathematics is a proper part of (not all of) logic. How "part" is to be understood is not entirely clear; 2 may indicate that "mathematics" is a subset of the set called "logic" or, on the other hand, that "mathematics" is a member of this set. Similarly, 3 may be interpreted to mean that "mathematics" is a subset of the set called "extension of logic" or, on the other hand, that "mathematics" is a member of this set. Moreover, 3 may be interpreted to mean that mathematics consists of logic plus an extension of logic so that logic itself is a proper part of mathematics—that is, the part that remains when the "extension of logic" is deleted from mathematics. Thus 2 suggests that mathematics is a proper part of logic, whereas 3 suggests that logic is a proper part of mathematics, and both differ from 1 which suggests identity.

Hence, evaluation of the thesis that mathematics *is* logic would seem first to require precise specification of the term *is*.

Reduction and the "nothing-but" attitude

Finally, let us consider interpretation 4, that mathematics is reduced to logic. Even if it is granted, for the sake of argument, that mathematics has been *reduced* to logic, it does not follow that mathematics *is* logic, unless one wishes to add to the burden of meanings customarily carried by this overworked two-letter word. The jump from the thesis that P has been reduced to Q, to the conclusion that P is Q, seems to us to be motivated by what may be called a "nothing-but" attitude, which in this case takes the form that P is nothing but Q. A glaring example of this is the statement that the value of a human being is nothing but the current market price of the chemicals of which his body is composed. (For discussions of the nothing-but attitude see Köhler, 1938c, pp. 12ff, and Conant, 1952.) Another example is furnished by the biology teacher who asked the class, "What is the only living matter?" When it turned out that no student furnished what she considered to be the "right" answer, the teacher required each student to write one hundred times: "Protoplasm is the only living matter." From the fact that the term *protoplasm* has been applied to the cell, the *unit* of living matter, the teacher apparently jumped to the conclusion that living matter is nothing but the unit of which it is composed or to which it may be reduced.

The reasoning involved in the living matter-protoplasm contention seems to strongly parallel that in the mathematics-logic contention.

1. All living matter can be reduced to something called a *cell* or *protoplasm*.
2. All living matter is nothing but protoplasm or, in other words, the only living matter is protoplasm.
1'. All mathematics can be reduced to something called *logic*.
2'. All mathematics is nothing but logic or, in other words, the only mathematics is logic.

The "nothing-but" attitude with regard to reductionism can also be illustrated by examples from psychology—for example, in the traditional associationistic contention that learning is nothing but S-R connections or bonds. Having "reduced" learning to S-R bonds, associationists then assumed that learning is nothing but these bonds. It is perhaps no more meaningful to say this than to say that a house is nothing but the bricks, cement, nails, and wood to which it can be "reduced." It is conceivable that the reduction process somehow alters or destroys characteristics of that which was reduced.

So it may be for mathematics and logic. Granted (for the sake of argument only) that mathematics has been reduced to logic, perhaps this means only that logic is an element (perhaps an essential element or an essence) of mathematics or that logic is involved in (or perhaps is essential to) the building up or in the composition of mathematics. Similarly, bricks may be involved in building a house, chemical elements in the make up of the human body, and cells in the composition of its tissues. But it may be no more justifiable to conclude that mathematics is logic than to conclude that a house is a pile of bricks, a body a compendium of chemical elements, or that the only living matter is a cell.

In any event, not all of mathematics has been reduced to logic. If it is assumed that *Principia Mathematica* reduced Peano's axioms to logic (an assumption which we have seen is not universally accepted) and if it is further assumed that Peano's axioms constitute a foundation for arithmetic, then it might be concluded that a *foundation* for arithmetic has been reduced to logic. To go further and to conclude that all of mathematics has thereby been reduced to logic is to overlook the difference between a discipline and a foundation of one branch of the discipline.

The meanings of mathematics

What is called mathematics at one time or in one culture differs from what is called mathematics at another time or in another culture (Schaaf, 1948; Smith and Ginsburg, 1934; White, 1949, 1950; Wilder, 1952). Moreover, within any one time and cultural setting there may be a diversity of answers. In our society, at present, people who differ with regard to philosophical views on the foundations of mathematics are likely to reflect these differences in their answers to the question of what mathematics is. Thus, today in the United States, an intuitionist, a formalist, and a logicist may give different answers.

But different answers are given even by those who share the same foundational views (or who have no explicitly formulated foundational views). For example, some mathematicians would exclude geometry from mathematics. This restriction is not as well formulated as it may seem, since its meaning in turn depends on the meaning of geometry. For example, is there to be included in geometry (and hence excluded from mathematics) the subject of topology, whose beginning, in the middle of the past century, has been characterized as a completely new development in geometry? If geometry is not intended to include all of topology (which in turn is richly imbued with concepts and methods of analysis and algebra), then where is the line to be drawn between geometry and topology? Is there to be included in geometry (and hence excluded from mathematics) the subject of geometric algebra (Artin, 1957) and the quite different discipline of algebraic geometry (Lang, 1958)?

In short, the question, "What is mathematics" may be answered differently depending on when the question is answered, where it is answered, who answers it, and what is regarded as being included in mathematics. As Wilder pointed out (1952, p. 270): "The question What is mathematics? has probably received as much attention as any question of fundamental character—and as many answers."

The attempt to answer this question with the statement that mathematics is logic does not actually result in a definite, concise answer but instead raises the very question it is intended to answer as well as other questions. As we saw, it raises the question of what is *mathematics*, what is *is*, and what is *logic*.

It has been said that logic is "considered the basis for all the other sciences" (Tarski, 1946, p. 18). But it has also been said that mathematics is the basis for all the other sciences and that "mathematics includes every subject in which you try to be logical" (Richardson, 1941, p. 34). Mathematics is said to comprise both pure and applied mathematics. Pure mathematics is the totality of all abstract mathematical sciences, where an abstract mathematical science is a hypothetico-deductive system, involving of course postulates and undefined concepts. Applied mathematics is the totality of the concrete interpretations or applications of the abstract mathematical sciences.

> The notion of mathematics as the totality of all abstract mathematical sciences and their concrete interpretations or applications is a tremendously broad conception, far transcending the old definition of mathematics as the science of space and quantity. In fact, it includes all subjects in which we reason logically, and amply justifies the assertion that mathematics is basic to all sciences. (Richardson, 1941, p. 32)

Thus, from this point of view, mathematics includes logic as well as the sciences.

Moreover, the contention that mathematics is logic seems to stress certain aspects of mathematics at the expense of others. More generally, adherents of a foundational school tend to characterize mathematics in terms of the features in their cognitive grasp (something like the blind men and the elephant). Intuitionists, for example, regard mathematics as a historical and cultural process and as a living activity involving processes in the mathematician's mind rather than as the communication of the results of these processes in verbal or written form. One does not have to be an intuitionist to recognize that logicism (and the contention that mathematics is logic) tends to neglect the aspect of mathematics as a historical and cultural process and as a living activity in mathematicians' minds.

Historically, mathematics was not identical with logic and did not evolve from logic per se. Even if logic is considered to be the foundation of mathematics, historically mathematics did not grow out of such a foundation. Indeed, mathematics did not grow out of its foundations, historically speaking, but rather the foundations grew out of mathematics. Moreover, as a living activity mathematics is neither exhausted by nor typified by logic. The contention that mathematics is logic tends to focus on the written expression of mathematics rather than on the activity whose end product is the written expression. It tends to stress, therefore, the postulational-deductive nature of mathematics and the formal verification or proof of theorems. Aspects which tend to be overlooked are the spirit of inquiry and the modes of discovery that lead to theorems. The theorems may subsequently be proved by methods in which, undoubtedly, logic plays an important role.

One can appreciate the significant contribution of logicism to mathematics without agreeing that mathematics is logic. For example, Richard Courant and Herbert Robbins, in a text entitled *What Is Mathematics?* (1941), noted that "the contemplative trend of logical analysis does not represent all of mathematics," although they recognized that it has made for more profound understanding of mathematical facts and their interrelations and for "clearer comprehension of the essence of mathematical concepts" (p. xvii).

Courant and Robbins would be difficult to pigeonhole into any foundational school (even though Courant was the student and colleague of Hilbert, the leader of the formalists). They maintained that logic is involved in mathematics but that so are other elements. They wrote of mathematics:

> Its basic elements are logic and intuition, analysis and construction, generality and individuality. Though different traditions may emphasize different aspects, it is only the interplay of these antithetical forces and the struggle for their synthesis that constitute the life, usefulness, and supreme value of mathematical science. (p. xv)

Moreover, they viewed with concern the current emphasis on the postulational-deductive nature of mathematics, a characteristic stressed by both logicism and formalism.

> There seems to be a great danger in the prevailing overemphasis on the deductive-postulational character of mathematics. True, the element of constructive invention, of directing and motivating intuition, is apt to elude a simple philosophical formulation; but it remains the core of any mathematical achievement, even in the most abstract fields. If the crystallized deductive form is the goal, intuition and construction are at least the driving forces. (p. xvii)

We add that the postulational-deductive nature of mathematics seems also to be stressed by many psychologists. They consider that psychology is made more mathematical or more scientific with increasing success in putting it into postulational-deductive form. Indeed, many psychologists insist that the postulational-deductive (also called hypothetico-deductive) method constitutes *the* scientific method or, at least, the scientific method at its best. As with mathematics, in psychology there may be dangers in the overemphasis on the postulational-deductive form. Such an emphasis may lead one to overlook the role of intuition and insight, not only in verification of hypotheses but, more important, in the processes of inquiry and discovery that are vital to both mathematics and psychology.

A Concluding Remark

At the present time we must conclude, as Wilder did in 1952, that whether the logistic thesis has been established or not "is a matter of opinion" (p. 229). We have suggested that linguistic or semantic factors contribute to the diversity of opinions. It would be foolhardy to consider that linguistic or semantic factors are the sole sources of the diversity. Given a group of people who agree on the meanings of such terms as *logic, mathematics, is,* or *reduced* or *founded* (and assuming that the group is not the null class or the unit class), then it might well happen that within the group there may be conflicting views concerning the attainment of the aim of logicism. For example, there may be honest differences of opinion as to the standards of rigor of proof in the *Principia*, the permissibility of the theory of types, and so on. More important may be emotional and psychological factors which have been recognized as influential in evaluations of the axiom of choice. There are fascinating problems involved in the study of the psychological factors that underlie diverse conceptions of mathematics, of logic, of the relationship between them, and of whether or not, and to what extent, the logistic aim has been attained. We recommend these problems to the psychologist.

CHAPTER 8

Logicism and Psychology

Logicism has probably had a more direct influence on psychology than formalism and intuitionism, perhaps because it is the best known of the foundational schools. Not only has logicism had a direct influence on psychology but also, as we shall see, it has had an indirect one through logical positivism, particularly via behaviorism.

Some psychologists believe that mathematics has been reduced to logic and, implicitly or explicitly, they incorporate this belief into their approach to psychology. Some, however, accept the logistic thesis only conditionally, noting, for example, that if logic actually is a foundation for mathematics, then it should be sufficient to use logical calculi rather than mathematical systems as models in psychology. Logical calculi have been used as models for various fields of psychology. Miniature logical systems or hypothetico-deductive systems also have been developed in psychology (for example, Hull et al., 1940). The hypothetico-deductive method, which the *Principia Mathematica* exemplifies, is regarded by some psychologists as the best scientific method or the only scientific method (Blake, Ramsey, and Moran, 1951; Stevens, 1939).

Analogous to—and influenced by—the goal of logicism to reduce mathematics to logic is the goal of some psychologists (the so-called reductionists) to reduce psychology to a "more fundamental" discipline such as biology, physics, mathematics, or logic. If the logistic thesis has not been demonstrated as correct (and perhaps cannot be achieved) what does it imply for the reductionistic goal? We shall return to this question and to a more detailed consideration of the reductionistic trend in psychology.

Language and Concepts

Logicism seeks to reduce mathematical concepts to logical concepts and to express mathematical theorems in the language of logic. Concern with language thus lies at the heart of logicism. This is not the case with formalism and intuitionism. Formalism focuses on form or structure and on abstract signs and symbols rather than on their content or meaning. Indeed, formalism has been criticized for neglecting to investigate mathematical concepts (Waismann, 1959, p. 107). Intuitionism is not particularly interested in the study of language since it regards mathematics as activities of the human mind and maintains that no language is adequate to convey them accurately.

Psychologists who look toward logicism for suggestions as to how to build their scientific foundations see a need to analyze and define carefully the nature and meaning of psychological concepts. They have pointed out that problems in psychology may exist primarily due to the uncritical acceptance of concepts from philosophy, folklore, and social and political ideologies (Spence, 1944; Bergman, 1951). Other problems may be due to semantic differences but not due to factual differences (see Luchins and Luchins, 1959, pp. 70, 102, 327 for examples in the fields of personality and learning).

Because of the belief that psychology becomes scientific to the extent that it develops precise and scientific terms, there has been increasing interest among psychologists in the logical analysis of psychological concepts and methodology (Pratt, 1939; Koch, 1959; Madden, 1962; Plutchik, 1963), in the search for a scientific language for psychology (Maatch and Behan, 1955; Mandler and Kessen, 1959), and in the interdisciplinary field of psycholinguistics (Osgood, 1963; Saporta, 1961). Some of these attempts to study and analyze the content and meaning of language are in the spirit of logicism. However, to the extent that the attempts are concerned with the form or structure of language, particularly of a formal language, as opposed to its content or meaning, they are more in the spirit of formalism and its allied discipline of metamathematics. After characterizing *metamathematics* as "that branch of mathematics which investigates the structure of formalized languages or theories and their relationship to other mathematical entities," Suppes (1957, p. 253n) notes that many philosophers call the study of formalized languages *semantics* and *logical syntax* rather than metamathematics.

There is considerable interest among psychologists in the utilization of logic and mathematics for the quantification or "mathematizing" of methods and concepts. There have been systematic attempts to subject particular words and their meanings to quantitative measurements—for example, Osgood's "semantic differential" technique with its ancillary "logic of semantic differentiation," which postulates a semantic space, assumed to be Euclidean in nature (Osgood, Suci, and Tannenbaum, 1957). Some of the Gestalt concepts and principles of organization (for instance, *good Gestalt*) that had been attacked as being vague and subjective have been quantified (Attneave, 1954, 1959; Hochberg and McAlister, 1953; Fitts, Weinstein, and Rappaport, 1956). Quantification of the concepts and principles makes them more meaningful and more acceptable to some psychologists. Some of these attempts at quantification of Gestalt terms have made use of information theory. The psychologists' interest in information theory and in mathematical theories of information and communication (for example, Shannon and Weaver, 1949) stems in part from the realization that these theories may be used to quantify concepts that involve organization or patterning (Hake, 1957; Summerfield and Legge, 1960). Moreover, Hochberg (1964) has reported on a program to develop new psychophysical methods to study in a quantifiable manner such concepts as attentivity, cuteness, and so on.

Some psychologists have taken seriously the task of developing a language that quantifies psychological phenomena or expresses them in mathematical or logical terms because these terms appear to be neutral to ideological and metaphysical issues. It is of interest to compare this attitude with those of the physicists during the Renaissance period as characterized by Heisenberg (1962). He notes that these physicists' aim to combine knowledge in the empirical sciences with mathematics may have been due in part to their beliefs that they would arrive, in this way, at knowledge which could be kept apart from philosophical disputes and that they would be able to formulate their findings without getting involved with personalities, the Diety, or fundamental causes. Possibly the interest in contemporary psychology to formulate empirical knowledge in logical and mathematical terms may also be due in part to a desire to be rid of concepts that involve psychology in problems and disputes of a metaphysical, theological, social, or political nature. Logical and mathematical symbols appear to be neutral and do not seem to lend themselves to such problems or disputes.

There are other suggestions for psychology which stem from *Principia Mathematica* and also from Russell's "theory of descriptions" (1918). Russell introduced the notion of a "singular description" by which he meant an expression that referred to one and only one thing (for example, the author of *Alice in Wonderland*) as compared to a kind (for example, a whale is a mammal). He also distinguished between use and meaning, pointing out, for example, that singular descriptions have no meaning but have use insofar as they contribute to meaning (Russell, 1938, p. x). Russell pointed out that the use of an expression can be exhibited by seeing the conditions under which it can be used and the kinds of reasoning in which it can be used. He referred to the need for contextual definitions—how the "expression is defined in use." Wittgenstein went even further than Russell in distinguishing between meaning and use, advocating a procedure which Wisdom (1953, p. 117) epitomized in the slogan, "Don't look for the meaning, look for the use."

This approach suggests the investigation of the actual use of the word in concrete situations. Rather than arguing in terms of philosophical or logical points of view about the meaning of such terms as *self, mind, role, thinking, creative, real, unreal, normal, abnormal, right, wrong, good,* and *bad,* psychologists should find out just how these words are used in particular sentences in daily speech. Research by Wertheimer (reported in Luchins, 1960) with the words *soul, mind,* and *self* revealed differences between the way these words were used in daily life and in theological and metaphysical discussions. These differences were used by Wertheimer to develop several new conceptualizations of the words as well as suggestions for concrete research of an empirical nature. We also have been engaged in similar research regarding the terms *creative* and *uncreative* (Luchins, 1960) and *real* and *unreal* (Luchins and Luchins, 1963d). Some behavioristically inclined psychologists in England have also been using this method. This approach does not solve all problems related to the meaning of a concept but it is a useful way of looking at the problem of meaning which leads to concrete research.

Focusing on the use of a word instead of speculating about its meaning is of value in facilitating veridical communications among psychologists (in their journals and at symposia). In a discussion or presentation of other people's work, we must describe just what they did rather than present only the explicit or implicit meaning of their work. It is important to distinguish between, on the one hand, possible theoretical meanings of a word and their metaphysical and epistemological implications and, on the other hand, just what the experimenter did and just how the term was used in a particular report. For example, Thorndike's concept of *belongingness* (1932) taken out of the context of his experiment has been called a Gestalt concept, whereas in his experiment it is actually an associationistic concept. Controversies in psychological literature often arise because readers' views center on the implicit theoretical meanings of a concept rather than on its specific use by the writer in his experiment or demonstration.

Symbolic Logic and Computers

Symbolic logic, to whose advance the *Principia Mathematica* contributed so much, has been applied to modern computers and to the study of the relationship between man and computer.

The relationship between man and machine has, through the ages, fascinated philosophers, psychologists, mathematicians, and engineers. Study of this relationship has developed into a discipline known as *cybernetics* (Wiener, 1948, 1950; Negley, 1942; Ashby, 1956; Guilbaud, 1960). Of particular interest has been the relationship between the human mind and electronic computers, popularly known as *electronic brains, giant brains, thinking machines,* or *mechanical minds* (Adler, 1960; Cohen, 1955; Gardner, 1958; Sluckin, 1954; Feigenbaum and Feldman, 1963).

Symbolic logic was applied to computers via circuit analysis. Shannon's 1938 paper (based on his 1937 Master of Science thesis at Massachusetts Institute of Technology) seems to have been the first published paper in the United States to establish a correspondence between the propositional calculus of symbolic logic and a calculus for manipulating equations that govern electrical relays and switching circuits. In this correspondence, the true and false values for a proposition correspond respectively to the open and closed states of a circuit; equivalence of two propositions (*P* if and only if *Q*) correspond to two circuits that open and close together, and so on. Shannon's paper helped to highlight the logical aspects of computer design and programming.

> Giving orders to a giant brain, telling it to perform certain steps under certain circumstances, is more a logical than an arithmetical matter, and new electronic computers are being constructed with more and more attention paid to special circuits which are designed specifically to handle the logical aspects of the computer's work. . . . [The] work of the symbolic logicians will assume increasing practical importance in the designing of efficient circuits for the more complicated automata. (Gardner, 1958, pp. 127–128)

This fate of symbolic logic is another illustration of how a "pure" academic subject has turned out to have great utilitarian value.

The analogy between electrical circuits and the working of the brain has also been utilized by neuropsychologists and neurophysiologists. By means of an assumed correspondence between electrical circuits and the propositional calculus, symbolic logic has been applied to the study of nets of nerve cells in the brain (Rashevsky, 1938; McCulloch and Pitts, 1943; McCulloch, 1949). This substitution of the hardware of the machine shop for the soft stuff of the brain has resulted in several new approaches to the study of human behavior. These models have led to the increasing use of such terms as *rational, decision making, choice, purpose,* and *goal seeking* because they have been removed from philosophical discussions to concrete and demonstrable behavior of the neurological and mechanical models (Miller, Galanter, and Pribram, 1960).

While a general-purpose computer has logical aspects and may be used to solve certain problems of the propositional calculus, other computers have been developed specifically to deal with problems of logic. These "logic machines" have been used to prove theorems in logic. For example, the *Logic Theorist* (Newell, Shaw, and Simon, 1958) involves a program in which Johnniac, a high speed digital computer, was given the axioms, definitions, and rules of inference in the *Principia Mathematica* and the task of finding proofs for some of the theorems. Logic machines as well as other computers have been used in investigations that seek to analyze and to simulate complex human behavior. Analogous to logicists' attempts to reduce mathematics or mathematical reasoning to logic, some psychologists are seeking to reduce other kinds of thinking and behavior to logic via the use of computers. Yet it might be countered that studies of machine-simulated thinking and problem solving have not actually reduced them to logic. Computers, including even the so-called logic machines, do not utilize only logical processes and logical concepts. In particular, various procedures which have not been reduced to logic have been used in machine studies of thinking. For example, a machine that dealt with geometric theorems was fed heuristic devices, such as the suggestion that when two parallel lines were encountered the machine might refer to the equality of alternate angles. A heuristic procedure may be contrasted with an algorithm in the sense that the latter, if used correctly, invariably leads to solution, whereas a heuristic is not guaranteed to lead to solution but may help; it is used for its suggestive value. (See Polya, 1954a, 1954b, for discussions of heuristics in mathematics; and see Roth, 1963 for a discussion of algorithms as used in computers.) In general, heuristic procedures have not been reduced to logic.

The following are examples of human behavior simulated by machines:

1. Learning: Cautela (1963); Feigenbaum (1961); Friedburg, 1960; Newell and Simon (1963); Vossler and Uhr (1962).
2. Problem solving and concept attainment: Bernstein and Roberts (1958); Feigenbaum and Feldman (1963); Gelernter and Rochester (1958); Hovland (1960); Minsky (1961); Newell, Shaw, and Simon (1958); D. W. Taylor (1958).
3. Perception: Dinneen (1955); Rosenblatt (1958); Uhr (1959, 1963).
4. Personality: the book of readings by Tomkins and Messick (1963).
5. Group behavior: Borko (1962); Hare (1961).

The use of machines and machine models to theorize about and simulate human behavior is increasing among psychologists as well as among other behavioral scientists. Not only is there a growing interest in and application of computers to human behavior, but also an expectation, among some, that this approach will lead to a breakthrough in the solution of the perennial problems of psychology. However, there have also been some negative reactions to the use of machine models, which we are about to consider.

Some see the danger that the increasing use of computer models may tend to dehumanize both the study of and the theories about human behavior and may tend to shunt psychology away from what is vitally human and therefore the central concern of psychology (compare Chein, 1963 and J. Cohen, 1955, 1961). Some are concerned about the tendency to endow the machines with characteristics of *Homo sapiens*. This is reflected in their popular names, "giant brains" and "thinking machines," and in the descriptions of their behavior as *thinking, reasoning,* or *intelligent.* There has been considerable discussion about whether or not such terms are justified, whether the computors actually think or reason, and whether their behavior is adequately described as "intelligent" (compare Turing, 1963 and Armer, 1963; see Roth, 1963). There is even some concern that the "thinking machines" may take over man's ability to think and may conquer and replace man. Some of the alarms resemble those raised in Samuel Butler's *Erewhon* (see Hook's *Dimension of Mind,* 1961).

Pertinent to the controversies over the use of computers is the issue of reductionism. Some argue that work with computers may be used to justify a view that seeks to reduce man to a machine—a view that man is nothing but a machine. We have more to say about reductionism elsewhere in this text. Suffice it to say here that it is one thing to use or to think in terms of a machine model or mechanical model of man and another thing to treat man as if he were nothing but a computer. Perhaps some of the fears that have been expressed are not as much over the use of a machine model as over the treatment of man as a machine. But, man has been treated as a mechanism by people who have advocated spiritual or *Homo sapiens* kind of models of man.

There may be some merits in the arguments that have been raised against the use of computers. It seems to us, however, that machines are not likely to take over man's ability to think nor are they likely to replace or conquer man. In the computers, man has developed new extensions of himself. Man has long been inventing extensions of himself in the production of various artifacts of his culture: He has invented extensions of his muscles in the tools and machines he has made to lift, carry, hoist and crush; he has developed instruments that extend the range of his sensorium (for example, his vision and hearing); he has invented computational devices and records to further his intellectual endeavors.

It seems to us that just as modern transportation devices have not immobilized man, and modern sensory and auditory apparatus have not stopped man from seeing or hearing, neither need the computers stop man from thinking. Indeed, some highly creative and sophisticated rational behavior is involved in the designing of "thinking machines" and in programming them to solve problems and to simulate other kinds of human behavior (Feigenbaum and Feldman, 1963; D. W. Taylor, 1958). Just as auditory and visual devices have extended the realm of man's senses and helped him to solve previously unsolved problems, so the thinking machines may open new vistas in man's intellectual world. Instead of conquering or replacing man, these new machines can help man to solve existing problems and replace them with new problems to be conquered.

Logical Positivism

Logical positivism, a term first used about 1930, is a movement in philosophical analysis that is sometimes described as synonymous with logical empiricism and at other times regarded as encompassing not only the latter, but also operationalism, as well as certain other philosophical trends. The dominant procedure of logical positivism is the logical analysis of language. Its primary goal is to provide a secure foundation for the empirical sciences through language analysis. Logical analysis of language leads to the "rejection of metaphysics" in the sense that "the points at dispute among the *traditional* forms of idealism, realism, and phenomenalism could not even be stated . . . in a properly clarified language" (Bergman, 1954, p. 2).

Logical positivism has operated from two main centers of intellectual thought: the Vienna Center in Austria (before the coming of the Nazis) and the Cambridge School of Analysis, or the Continental positivists, in England. Both centers have been strongly influenced by the *Principia Mathematica* and specifically by Russell's views. Discussing various sources from which members of the Vienna Circle drew their inspiration, Bergman (1954, p. 5) describes the *Principia Mathematica* as the most important source and describes Russell's influence on the Continental positivists as second only to Wittgenstein's. Carnap's attempts (1928) to formulate a language for logical analysis drew heavily on the language schema of the *Principia Mathematica* as well as on various ideas in Russell's writings. Russell himself, although not openly accepting logical positivism, wrote that with regard to method he is "more in sympathy with the logical positivists than with any other existing school" (1940).

A word of caution is needed with reference to Wittgenstein's stand on logicism. Although many writers claim that all logical positivists, including Wittgenstein, assume that mathematics was derived from logic or the *Principia Mathematica* (White, 1955, p. 208), other writers claim that "Wittgenstein holds that mathematics cannot be derived from logic" (Weinberg, 1960, p. 89). Moreover, while some writers state that all logical positivists agree on the tautological nature of logical and mathematical truths (Bergman, 1954, p. 2; White, 1955, p. 208), others claim that Wittgenstein considers logic to consist of tautologies, but mathematics to consist of equations (Weinberg, 1960, p. 98). (The concept of tautology, introduced by Wittgenstein in 1921, refers to a statement which is true by virtue of its logical form.) If one assumes that the *Principia Mathematica* has reduced all mathematics to logic (which some interpreters of Wittgenstein claim he does accept and others claim he does not), and if one also agrees with Wittgenstein's view that all logical truths are tautologies, then it follows that all mathematical truths are tautologies. Here is an area where some clarification of Wittgenstein's beliefs seems necessary.

Psychologists, eager to divorce themselves from metaphysics and to get some semblance of order and system out of the great diversity of phenomena and concepts, sought help in logical positivism. These psychologists may have the satisfaction of again being related to philosophy without becoming bogged down in metaphysical speculations and without giving up their endeavor to be scientific.

American psychologists, particularly the behaviorists, are attracted to logical positivism. This relationship is reciprocal. Logical positivism has been influenced by the development of behavioristic psychology in America. Bergmann (1954, p. 5) refers to the inspiration that members of the Vienna Circle drew from "the rising American school of behaviorism in psychology and the social sciences." Feigl (1949, p. 6) refers to twentieth-century logical empiricism (positivism) as having been conceived under the influence primarily of three developments one of which was "the reform of psychology by the behaviorists (Pavlov, Watson, et al.) . . . [who] by developing objective procedures for the study of mental life" showed that the content of psychology could be formulated in a "physical language," a language that referred to observable and measurable properties without a need for "mentalistic terminology." (The other two influential developments were the studies in the foundations of mathematics and the revision of basic concepts in physics due to the work of Einstein, Planck, and others.)

Logical positivism is influential in contemporary psychology. There are those who consider that it has helped to (1) clean up the language of psychology and make it more precise, (2) strengthen methodology and introduce more operational, quantifiable methods, (3) emphasize logical and mathematical models, and (4) remind psychologists of the rigorous standards of the *Principia Mathematica* and of the importance of doing for the empirical sciences what logicism did (or attempted to do) for mathematics. Logical positivism is able to have such influence because many American psychologists, particularly but not necessarily those who are behavioristically inclined, look to it for guidance in scientific procedures. However, some psychologists are disturbed by the role logical positivism plays in American psychology. The trend of seeing man's behavior through the eyes of logical positivists has brought a feeling of disquietude to psychologists who do not view man as a composite of part functions and who are interested in a psychology that will throw light on the peculiarly human qualities of man, rather than on those qualities he seems to share with animals, machines, and systems of symbolic logic. This has contributed to the development of the new association of humanistic psychology (with its own journal). Some who are not humanistic psychologists also wonder whether logical positivism may have led psychologists to neglect important concepts and topics on the grounds that they are meaningless or unscientific or unsuitable (Burt, 1960). They question the desirability of having logical positivism serve as the policeman of the empirical sciences.

Research Problems

The traffic between logicism and psychology need not be one way only, with logicism offering suggestions for psychology. There are areas of psychological research that may prove suggestive to logicism. This research may not solve the problems of logicism or help it attain its aim but, insofar as logicism involves mathematical and logical reasoning, research concerned with the so-called cognitive processes may be of value to logicists, philosophical analysts, and mathematicians interested in the foundations of mathematics. For example, one might hope to find suggestions in studies of productive thinking and problem solving among children and adults (Piaget, Inhelder, and Szeminska, 1960; Wertheimer, 1945) in the work on awareness and reconciliation of inconsistencies, contradiction, and in the research which has in recent years been called cognitive dissonance (Hovland, 1960; Heider, 1946; Newcomb, 1953; Festinger, 1957). Moreover, there are certain issues in logicism which are, actually, also problems for psychological research. Does logic portray actual thinking? What system of logic is most isomorphic to actual thinking? Is mathematical invention or discovery governed by logic? What kind of factors influence mathematical discovery? Is mathematics merely verbal knowledge as Russell claims was shown by *Principia Mathematica?* We shall consider these and related questions in later chapters after having surveyed the other schools of mathematical foundations whose views may enrich our understanding of some of these questions.

CHAPTER 9
Formalism

The Hilbert Program

Formalism was founded by the German mathematician David Hilbert (1862–1943). It was developed in attempts both to cope with intuitionistic criticisms of classical mathematics and to meet the crisis in mathematics fostered by the discovery of the antinomies in logic and set theory. To Hilbert, it seemed that the way to eliminate contradictions in mathematics was not to reduce mathematical concepts to logical concepts as the logicists proposed. As for the intuitionistic criticisms, it seemed to Hilbert that it was not proper to ignore them and yet not necessary to reject outright those parts of classical mathematics to which their objections applied. Rather, he proposed to formulate classical mathematics as axiomatic theories and then to prove that these theories were free from contradictions, using in such proofs only methods that would be acceptable to intuitionists. If such a proposal could be carried out it would, in one swoop, "salvage classical mathematics in the face of the intuitionistic criticism" (Kleene, 1952, p. 52), and eliminate worries over contradictions in it. Attempts to carry out this and related proposals, which constitute what came to be known as the Hilbert program, were not conceived as labors of love. Hilbert would rather have devoted himself to other mathematical pursuits; "this kind of research for him was a not too pleasant duty that he felt obliged to perform but which distracted him from other more attractive occupations" (Fraenkel and Bar-Hillel, 1958, p. 269). It was an obligation whose fulfillment would testify to the consistency and soundness of classical mathematics.

As developed by Hilbert and his collaborators (Hilbert and Ackermann, 1928; Hilbert and Bernays, 1944; Bernays, 1935), the original scope of the endeavor was broadened so that it included considerably more than the problem of contradictions. It included what have come to be known as the aims of the Hilbert program, aims that may be somewhat roughly

141

summarized in the following manner:

1. To establish each branch of classical mathematics (in particular, arithmetic, analysis, and set theory, and ultimately all mathematics) as an *axiomatic* theory in which, from a (finite) number of axioms, all other propositions of the theory can be deduced. The logic used for the deductions is also to be formulated and axiomatized. Together, the theory and the logic may be referred to as an axiomatic system.

2. To show that each such axiomatic system is *consistent* in the sense that it is *free from contradictions*. This means that a contradiction cannot be the consequence of deductions made from the axioms through use of the logic formulated in the system—for example, the axioms cannot yield both the propositions *P* and not-*P*.

3. To show that the axiomatic system is *complete* in the sense that any true proposition of the system is deducible from the axioms through use of the logic formulated in the system. This is sometimes expressed by saying that any true proposition of the system is provable within the system.

4. To show that a branch of classical mathematics is *categorical* in the sense that it constitutes essentially the only interpretation of the axiomatic system that corresponds to it or, more exactly, that it is *isomorphic* to any other interpretation of its axiomatic system. Thus, an axiomatic system is referred to as *categorical* if all interpretations (or models) of it are isomorphic, that is, if every two interpretations can be put in a one-to-one correspondence which preserves the relationships in the axioms.

5. To seek for *decision procedures*, that is, for general procedures which, within a finite number of steps, can yield a decision for every proposition of a given kind. In particular, the interest is in a decision procedure for an axiomatized system which, when applied to any proposition formulated in the symbols of the system, will indicate whether or not the proposition is provable—that is, is deducible from the axioms through use of the logic formulated in the system.

6. To carry through such objectives by using only concepts and methods acceptable to intuitionists. This means, for example, that only intuitively evident concepts and only *finitary methods* would be used—that is, methods that involve performable processes, processes that can be carried out, at least in principle, in a finite number of steps within a finite amount of time.

Research and writings that are directly or indirectly relevant to these objectives have not been limited to Hilbert and his collaborators but have been done by some of this century's most eminent mathematicians and logicians (for example, von Neumann, 1927, 1931–1932, 1947; Gödel, 1930, 1931, 1932; and Tarski, 1931, 1933, 1956). Such investigations have yielded far-reaching results with dramatic and quite unexpected consequences for the aims of the Hilbert program. We shall turn to a survey of some of these findings after first considering formalism in more detail.

A New Approach to Consistency

The approach to the problem of consistency, or freedom from contradiction, proposed by Hilbert differed radically from the previous approaches to this problem. Prior to Hilbert's proposal, the only method for proving the consistency of an axiomatized theory was to offer a model for it or an interpretation of it. A model or interpretation is a system of objects, which may be chosen from another theory, with the objects correlated to the objects or symbols of the axiomatized theory in such a way that the axioms are satisfied. The axiomatized theory is consistent if the theory from which the model was chosen is consistent. For suppose that the axiomatized theory is not consistent so that a contradiction is deducible from the axioms. Then a corresponding deduction made in the theory from which the model was chosen would yield a contradiction therein. Thus, consistency proofs via a model are relative, with the theory under investigation being consistent only if the theory from which the model was chosen is consistent. But how can the consistency of the latter theory be established? If the method of a model is again used, then the consistency problem has to be raised for the theory from which its model is chosen, and again for the latter theory, and so on. Hence, the method of a model leads either to circularity (where Theory A is established as consistent if Theory B is consistent, and vice versa) or to an indefinite regress.

It may seem that one way out of this difficulty is to find a model for a mathematical theory from physical reality, from the physical or the perceptual world. If such a model can be found, then the mathematical theory would be as consistent as physical reality. Quite aside from the problem of whether physical reality is free from contradictions, there are problems involved in trying to find such a model. If the number of objects or elements in the mathematical system is finite, then it may be possible to exhibit an interpretation of it which uses a finite number of objects that exist in physical reality (Richardson, 1941, p. 453). But if the number of elements is infinite, as it is in most systems of interest to mathematicians, then we cannot exhibit such an interpretation of it. Physical reality can then, at best, furnish an approximate model. Even what is called a mathematical representation of a given physical phenomenon or of a given realm of experience may not be an exact counterpart of it but may involve interpolation and exterpolation of facets of physical or experiential reality (Hilbert and Bernays, 1944, pp. 15–17). Hence, the given physical phenomenon or realm of experience may not be able to serve as an exact model of what purports to be its mathematical representation.

What Hilbert proposed was not a proof of consistency via a model from a mathematical theory or from any other theory or from the physical or perceptual world. What he proposed was to make that mathematical theory whose consistency was to be proved an object of mathematical study and to prove that no logical contradiction can arise in that theory. The mathematical discipline whose objects of study are mathematical theories is what we consider next.

Metamathematics

The Hilbert program, we saw, proposed to set up branches of classical mathematics, and ultimately all of mathematics, as axiomatic theories, and then to describe and study these theories. Thus, the mathematical theories themselves become the objects of study. The discipline concerned with the study of mathematical theories Hilbert called *metamathematics*. The prefix *meta*, meaning literally "beyond" or "above," has been used to identify a theory (or a language) in which the object of study is itself a theory (or a language). Metamathematics is thus mathematics in which mathematics is the object of study. The mathematical theory that is the object of metamathematical study may be called the *object theory*, whereas the resulting metamathematics or metamathematical theory (the theory about the mathematical theory that is studied) may be called the *metatheory*. Metamathematics describes the object theory and studies its properties.

In particular, Hilbert hoped to investigate the proofs involved in mathematical theories through metamathematics. Thus, in order to show that an axiomatized mathematical theory was consistent (that is, was free from contradictions and, in particular, from the antinomies of logic and set theory), Hilbert aimed to show that no contradictions can arise in proofs of all possible theorems that can be deduced from the axioms. Such proofs constitute the objects of investigation of metamathematics. Hence, as an alternative name for metamathematics Hilbert used the name *proof theory*.

Metamathematics, originally developed as the core of the formalists' program to establish the consistency of classical mathematics, is no longer confined just to this issue. Nor is it now exclusively a discipline or technique for formalists. "[Metamathematics provides] a rigorous mathematical technique for investigating a great variety of foundation problems for mathematics and logic, among which the consistency problem is only one. For example, metamathematical methods are applied now in studies of systematizations of mathematics arising from the logistic and intuitionistic schools, as well as from Hilbert's" (Kleene, 1952, p. 59).

If metamathematics was to meet intuitionists' criticisms of classical mathematics, then it must itself not be open to such criticisms. Formalists, therefore, restrict the kinds of concepts and methods that are permitted in metamathematics to those that are acceptable to intuitionists. In fact, Hilbert and Bernays (1944, p. 43) are even more restrictive than the intuitionists. Concepts and methods acceptable in metamathematics were described by Hilbert with the German word *finit*, which has been translated both as "finite" and as "finitary." The latter is the preference of Kleene (1952) (on the ground that the English word "finite" is also used to translate the German *endlich*); he describes finitary methods as those "which employ only intuitively conceivable objects and performable processes . . . . No infinite class may be regarded as a completed whole. Proofs of existence shall give, at least implicitly, a method for constructing the object which is being proved to exist" (p. 63). Proofs in metamathematics must be of a character that Hilbert called *anschaulich uberleckbar;* they must be clearly and immediately evident.

Just as intuitionists have not precisely specified what procedures they regard as admissible, so Hilbert did not offer a precise specification of what procedures were regarded by him as finitary. Fraenkel and Bar-Hillel (1958, p. 268) consider that perhaps the nearest to such a specification can be found in a report by the French mathematician Herbrand, who wrote:

> We understand by an intuitionistic [that is, finitary] argument an argument that fulfills the following conditions: one always deals with a finite and determined number of objects and functions only; these are well defined, their definition allowing the univocal calculation of their values; one never affirms the existence of an object without indicating how to construct it; one never deals with the set of all the objects X of an infinite totality; and when one says that an argument (or a theorem) holds for all these X, this means that for every particular X it is possible to repeat the general argument in question which should then be treated as only a prototype of these particular arguments. (1932, p. 3, n3)

Formalization of a Theory

Hilbert considered that ordinary mathematical theories are not ready for study via metamathematics but must first be formalized through a process known as *formalization*. A mathematical theory may be considered to involve a system of mathematical objects embodied in statements or propositions. A purpose of the formalization is to reveal the structure of the theory by making entirely explicit the conditions that determine what propositions hold in the theory. The method by which a theory is thus made explicit is sometimes referred to as the *logistic method;* this use of the term is quite distinct from, and should not be confused with, the use of the same word in connection with the *school* of logicism.

Formalization involves the utilization of the axiomatic-deductive method and the introduction of abstract symbolism in place of the terms in which the ordinary mathematical theory is expressed. Moreover, for strict formalization of a theory it is essential to omit the meanings of the terms involved but to be concerned only with the *structure* or *form* of the theory (hence *formalization*). In short, all meaning and content must be abstracted from the ordinary mathematical theory so that only its form (structure) remains in the formalization.

The first step in the formalization of a theory (which may not be necessary if the theory is axiomatized *ab initio*) involves a deductive arrangement of its propositions so that from some of them, specified as axioms, the others are logically deducible. The next step is to express by axioms the properties of the mathematical terms needed for the logical deduction of propositions. It should be possible to perform the deductions without taking into account the meanings of the mathematical terms. If this is not possible, then it indicates that not all the properties of the mathematical terms that are relevant to the deduction have been taken into account.

In addition, it is necessary to make explicit the structure of the logical system that is used in making deductions in the mathematical theory. There is therefore carried through, for the system of logic, steps similar to those previously outlined. Thus, axioms are introduced for the underlying system of logic along with rules of inference that indicate when one proposition (or a certain set of symbols) is an *immediate consequence* of one or more other propositions—for example, A is an immediate consequence of B and C if the application of a rule of inference to B and C can yield A as the next step in the deduction. Moreover, all properties of the logical terms that occurred in the original mathematical theory or in the logical system (for instance, *and, or, not, if–then*) are expressed by axioms. It should then be possible to deduce from the axioms of the logical system, without reference to the meaning of the terms, the logical principles that are used in the deductions made in the mathematical theory. Furthermore, it should be possible to deduce propositions from others in the mathematical theory without reference to the meaning of either the mathematical or the logical terms. When this stage is reached, so that all meaning or content has been abstracted from the original mathematical theory, leaving only its structure or form, it is said to constitute a *formal system*. At this stage, reference to the form alone should suffice to show which combinations of symbols constitute statements, which statements constitute axioms, which statements are immediate consequences of others, and whether or not a finite sequence of statements constitutes a deduction or proof. "By formalizing the theory, the development of the theory is reduced to form and rule. There is no longer ambiguity about what constitutes a statement of the theory, or what constitutes a proof in the theory" (Kleene, 1952, p. 63).

Formal and informal theories

In contrast to formal systems that are part of formal mathematics, ordinary mathematical theories are informal. An informal theory may be considered to provide the *intended interpretation* of the formal system to which it gives rise (through formalization)—that is, an informal theory provides the interpretations intended as the meanings of the symbols and formulas of its formal system. A formal system constitutes a formal image or model of the informal theory.

It is possible to start with a formal system from the onset by introducing axioms involving meaningless symbols and by ways of building up other objects from the symbols through preassigned rules of manipulations. A formal system, therefore, does not have to arise from an informal theory. The phrase *formal theory* (or *formalized theory*) may be used for those formal systems which arise from formalization of informal theories. Hence a formal theory is always a formal system, but not vice versa.

A particular formal system that is the object of study via metamathematics is called the object theory, and the metamathematics that describes and studies it is called its metatheory. Metamathematics uses ordinary mathematical language and is part of informal mathematics (unless and until it is itself formalized and becomes an object theory for metamathematics, which may then be called a metametatheory—a possibility which we shall not consider here, but which could be carried on quite indefinitely, at least in principle). Thus, there are various senses in which the term *theory* occurs: the informal theory, the object theory, the metatheory. To quote Kleene (1952):

> From the standpoint of the metatheory, the object theory is not properly a theory at all as we formerly understood the term, but a system of meaningless objects like the positions in a game of chess, subject to mechanical manipulations like the moves in chess. The object theory is described and studied as a system of symbols and of objects built up out of symbols. The symbols are regarded simply as various kinds of recognizable objects. To fix our ideas we may think of them concretely as marks on paper. . . . The other objects of the system are analyzed only with regard to the manner of their composition out of the symbols. By definition, this is all that a formal system shall be as an object of study for metamathematics. (p. 62)
>
> In the full picture, there will be three separate and distinct "theories": (a) the informal theory of which the formal system constitutes a formalization; (b) the formal system or object theory; and (c) the metatheory, in which the formal system is described and studied. (p. 65)

Let us compare (a), (b), and (c). As already noted (a) and (c) are part of informal mathematics, whereas (b) is part of formal mathematics. Whereas the form or the structure of (b) is explicitly and exactly determined, this is not the case for (a) and (c). We have said that (a) constitutes the intended interpretation of (b). Although the metamathematics may be guided by this interpretation, the final statement and proof of metamathematical results must not use or depend on this (or any other) interpretation of (b), but must treat (b) as a system of abstract symbols and of objects built from the symbols, subject to certain rules of manipulation. "Then (c) is a theory with (b) as its subject matter, which must apply to (b) without looking at (a) or more precisely without looking at the interpretation of (b) in terms of (a)" (p. 65). Finally, a distinction can be drawn among the three "theories" with reference to finitary concepts and methods, that is, intuitively meaningful concepts and intuitively evident and performable processes. As far as the formal system (b) is concerned, it is pointless to speak of it as involving or not involving concepts that have intuitive meaning, since it consists of abstract symbols and is devoid of content or meaning. The processes of (b) are performable in that they are carried out by mechanical rules of manipulation but they are not intuitively evident nor do the deductions involve intuitive inferences. In contrast, (c), the metatheory, since it belongs to metamathematics, must involve intuitively evident concepts and processes.

What about (a), the informal theory? Hilbert considers that it need *not* be restricted to finitary concepts and processes. This touches on an important distinction between formalism and intuitionism. Formalists consider that informal mathematics, in contrast to metamathematics, may involve both nonfinitary and finitary concepts and methods. Unlike intuitionists, they see no need to reject from classical mathematics the so-called nonintuitionistic parts. In this connection it is interesting to consider the distinction that Hilbert (1925, 1928) draws between real and ideal statements. *Real statements* are those used as having an intuitive meaning, and *ideal statements* are those which are not used in this way. An example of an ideal statement is one that treats an infinite set as a completed entity. Ideal statements may be regarded as adjoined to real statements, analogous to the manner in which, in projective geometry, an ideal point at infinity is added to each line, with parallel lines considered to have the same point at infinity and nonparallel lines distinct points at infinity. The adjoinment of the ideal point at infinity helps to complete the structure of projective geometry and to simplify its theory. Similarly, Hilbert considered that the ideal statements of classical mathematics help to complete its structure and to simplify its theory.

It was once thought that those statements of classical mathematics which we now recognize as ideal were true. Intuitionists object to characterizing such statements as true and would exclude them from mathematics. Hilbert grants that the ideal statements are not true, but he maintains that it is not necessary to reject them from informal mathematics. Rather, he proposes to investigate classical mathematics, including both real and ideal statements, and to show its consistency via the discipline of metamathematics.

Consistency and Completeness | Gödel's theorems

Among the foremost aims of the Hilbert program were those of establishing the consistency of a mathematical system (its freedom from contradiction) and also of establishing its completeness (the property that any true proposition of a formal mathematical system is provable by methods formalized in the system). Surprising consequences for both these aims followed from some remarkable theorems established in the 1930s by Kurt Gödel.

In order to discuss Gödel's theorems, it will be helpful to introduce a name for a formal system that includes a formalization of elementary number theory—a *formal number-theoretic system*. Almost all important parts of classical mathematics (including theories of arithmetic, algebra, and analysis), if formalized, constitute formal number-theoretic systems. All set theories "worth their name" (Fraenkel and Bar-Hillel, 1958, p. 304) constitute in their formalizations formal number-theoretic systems. In other words, almost all branches of mathematics are broad enough to include elementary number theory in their formalization and hence constitute formal number-theoretic systems.

In 1931 Gödel published a theorem, variously referred to as his *incompleteness* or *incompletability* or *undecidability* theorem. This theorem (or, more precisely, a modification of it by Rosser in 1936) demonstrates that any formal number-theoretic system, if consistent, contains an undecidable formula—that is, a formula that can neither be proved nor disproved, that can neither be affirmed nor refuted with the methods formalized in this system. That this is the case in particular for the system of *Principia Mathematica* was pointed out by Gödel, whose 1931 paper, translated from the German, is entitled "On formally undecidable propositions of *Principia Mathematica* and related systems."

It is important to recognize that this theorem and another of Gödel's theorems shortly to be referred to, which have become the most famous results in metamathematics and which "bear on the whole program and philosophy of metamathematics . . . [involve] strictly finitary metamathematical proof" (Kleene, 1952, pp. 204–206).

Gödel actually gave a method of constructing an undecidable sentence or proposition. Moreover, this proposition happens to be true when interpreted in the metamathematics or in what might be called the *metalanguage*. In the formal theory, in what might be called the *object-language*, the proposition consists of abstract symbols devoid of meaning, but which are interpretable in the metalanguage. This sentence states, in effect, in the metalanguage, that it, the sentence, is not provable in the system. Since the sentence is actually not provable, it is thereby a true statement. It is true, although undecidable (that is, not provable by the methods formalized in the system). Thus, Gödel's theorem shows that, under the interpretation, there is a consequence of the axioms which is not provable—that is, not deducible from the axioms by the logic formulated in the system—but the truth of this consequence can be recognized "by taking into view the structure of that system as a whole" (Kleene, 1952, p. 426). In other words, Gödel's incompletability theorem shows that in some deductive systems "certain statements are true in view of the structure of the system in its entirety but cannot be proved by means of the formal instruments available in the system" (Fraenkel and Bar-Hillel, 1958, p. 108). To express this in a less formal and more popular vein: The incompletability theorem indicates "that it is self-contradictory to suppose that mathematics can be *proved* free from self-contradiction— that, in fact, there must always be true but unprovable theorems" (Pledge, 1959, p. 190).

Thus we see that the formalization of a mathematical theory into a formal system is not the magic key that opens the door for the provability of all the true propositions of the system. If a formal number-theoretic system is consistent, then it must be incomplete; it must contain true propositions that are formally unprovable in the system. *In brief, the price of consistency is incompleteness.*

In short, Gödel's theorem and a modification of it indicate that two of the aims of the Hilbert program—to establish the consistency and completeness of mathematical systems—cannot both be attained for the same system, provided it is rich enough to be a number-theoretic system. If such a system is consistent it is perforce incomplete.

A statement which states that it, the statement, is unprovable in the system, is reminiscent of the famous liar antinomy—for example, "The statement I am now making is false"—which leads to a contradiction whether it is assumed to be true or false. Indeed, for heuristic purposes Gödel's theorem may be regarded as involving an attempt to arrive at an antinomy in a formal number-theoretic system. Paraphrasing the heuristic sketch of Gödel's reasoning given in Kleene (1952, p. 205), prior to the rigorous proof, let us denote by G the Gödel sentence which means (when interpreted in the metalanguage) that it, G, is unprovable. Then we have, (1) G means G is unprovable. Moreover, since we certainly would not want false propositions to be provable in the system, let us assume, then, (2) if G is false G is unprovable. The assumption that G is false leads to a contradiction. For, if G is false, then by (1) it would mean that G is *not* unprovable (or else G would not be false), but this contradicts (2) which states that if G is false, G is unprovable. Now if the assumption that G is true leads to a contradiction, then we would have an antinomy. But G can be true provided it is unprovable. Now assume that G is provable; then by (1) G is false (for if not false G would be unprovable), and since G is false, by (2) it is unprovable. The assumption that G is provable led to a contradiction so that G is unprovable (by intuitive *reductio ad absurdum*). But then by (1) G is true. Thus G constitutes a true but unprovable formula. And an antinomy was not arrived at since G can be true. As Fraenkel and Bar-Hillel so dramatically word it:

> This, then, is the revenge of the Liar's ghost: the attempt to arrive at an antinomy through the construction of a sentence within formalized arithmetic that (intuitively) states that it itself is non-provable [unprovable] does not

meet with success, but only because—contrary to expectation and hope—a sentence non-provable within such a formal system is not thereby necessarily refutable, there being sentences which are neither. (1958, p. 304)

A second theorem of Gödel's (actually a corollary of his incompletability theorem) strikes even more closely at the heart of the Hilbert program. It would, we think, be quite accurate to consider that the central aim of this program was to establish mathematical theorems as formal systems and then to prove the consistency of the system through use of methods formalized in the system. But Gödel's second theorem states that if a formal number-theoretic system is consistent, then its consistency *cannot* be proved by methods formalized in this system. This theorem may be considered as a corollary of the incompletability theorem, since it concerns the unprovability of a proposition that, interpreted in the metalanguage, states that the system is consistent (or words to this effect). The proposition can neither be proved nor disproved by the methods formalized in the system. In short, if the system is consistent, then its consistency cannot be proved metamathematically.

A proposition that is unprovable in a system (that is, incapable of being proved or disproved through the use of methods of the system) might become provable if methods other than those formalized in that system were utilized. This is the case, for example, for the true but unprovable proposition constructed by Gödel. In particular, the consistency of a system might be demonstrated through the use of methods outside of the system. This indicates that to tackle the problem of consistency (or the general problem of proving a proposition that is unprovable in a given formal system) we have to use methods other than those in the system.

Suppose an unprovable proposition in a formal number-theoretic system S can be proved if certain methods other than those in S are utilized. It may be possible to embed S in a larger formal system S' (which must itself then be a formal number-theoretic system) in such a way that S' contains a formalization of the methods that were used to prove this proposition. Hence the proposition, though formally unprovable in S, is formally provable in S'. In particular, the consistency of S may be formally provable in S'. This indicates that the concept of *provable* (or of *undecidable*) is not absolute but is relative to a particular system. A given proposition may be unprovable in one system but not in another.

An application of Gödel's results to S' shows that if it is consistent then it is incomplete and, moreover, it cannot have its consistency established solely by methods formalized in S'. Thus, it would be necessary to go outside of S' to get methods for establishing its consistency and for investigating and establishing the provability of certain of its propositions. Hence if classical mathematics was formalized and consistent, then to demonstrate its consistency and the provability of certain true propositions in the system we would have to go beyond classical mathematics. And if all of mathematics (classical and nonclassical, ancient and modern) could be set up as a formal system and was consistent, then to demonstrate its consistency and the provability of certain of its propositions, we would have to go outside of mathematics and put our trust in nonmathematical methods. It is not feasible to deal with mathematics, or virtually any branch of it, as a closed, isolated system.

To recapitulate: Gödel's theorems and their generalizations dealt a blow to the foremost aims of the Hilbert program. Classical mathematics, as well as virtually every branch of it, constitutes a formal number-theoretic system and hence is subject to the limitation that, if it is consistent, then it is incomplete, and, moreover, the problem of its consistency can neither be proved nor disproved by methods formalized in the system.

It should be mentioned that when Gödel's theorems first were published there were some doubts as to their validity, probably because of the novelty and difficulty of the nature of the theorems and of their proofs. Since then there have appeared proofs of the theorem which are easier to follow (see Kleene, 1952, for a highly rigorous but quite readable presentation; and Rosser, 1939, for a somewhat less formal presentation). There are some writers (see Goddard, 1958) who are "still unable to swallow the fact that there should be a sentence that is not provable in some object-language but can be shown to be true in its metalanguage" (Fraenkel and Bar-Hillel, 1958, p. 304n). Nonetheless, there is quite wide accord that Gödel's theorems seem beyond dispute and, indeed, that they were proved "according to standards of rigor which were the highest known, higher even than those customarily used in mathematical proofs" (p. 304).

In any event, Gödel's theorems have introduced a feeling of uncertainty of achievement regarding what once seemed attainable goals. Small wonder that Waismann concludes: "It is uncertain today whether the consistency of classical mathematics (arithmetic, algebra, analysis, function theory) can . . . be proved" (1959, p. 102).

Semantic completeness

A generalization of Gödel's theorem by Alfred Tarski (1931, 1956) is based on the latter's notion of *semantic definability*. Without becoming unduly involved in mathematical or semantic technicalities, we want here only to note that Tarski's *truth-theorem*, as it has been called, states that if a formal number-theoretic system is consistent, then the notion of truth (the set of all true propositions of the system) is not definable in the system. Tarski's theorem shows that there are concepts which are not definable within certain formal systems. Hence, a formal number-theoretic system not only is formally incomplete, in the sense that some of its true propositions are unprovable within the system, but it is also *semantically incomplete* in the sense that certain of its concepts are not definable within the system. These concepts may be definable in a larger or more comprehensive system, but then the latter must have concepts undefinable within itself. It has therefore been concluded that there is no formal system "in which *all* arithmetical propositions could be decided or in which *all* arithmetical concepts could be defined" (Waismann, 1959, p. 102).

From Tarski's theorem it follows that if classical mathematics were formalized then it would be semantically incomplete. There would be concepts in it that would not be definable within the system; in particular this would be the case for the concept of the set of its true propositions. To define such concepts one would have to go outside of classical mathematics. Likewise if all mathematics could be formalized, it would be semantically incomplete and one would have to go outside of mathematics to define some of its concepts.

Internal and external consistency

The phrases *simple consistency* and *internal consistency* are sometimes used to refer to the notion of consistency with which we have been dealing. This is to distinguish it from the notion of *external* consistency or external inconsistency. A formal system is called *externally inconsistent* if it contains a proposition, *P*, provable in the system, such that *P* contradicts another proposition that is intuitively true (Hilbert and Bernays, 1944, p. 282). Hence *P*, although provable, is intuitively false.

It should be remembered that Hilbert had hoped to defend classical mathematics against objections raised by the intuitionists. One of the problems that had to be faced was whether a formal system could be internally consistent and yet yield statements which, when interpreted in the metalanguage, would be intuitively false. It turned out that this can be the case. A formal system may be internally consistent and yet contain a provable proposition that contradicts a proposition in a finitary interpretation—for example, in the intuitive mathematics which is intended to be an interpretation of the formal system. Thus it is possible for a formal system to be externally inconsistent without being simply or internally inconsistent. Hence, simple consistency is not a guarantee against external inconsistency. "Thus a proof of simple consistency alone would not secure the formalized mathematics against the possibility of establishing something intuitively false" (Kleene, 1952, p. 212). In short, a proof of internal consistency does not obviate the possibility that provable propositions may be intuitively false or intuitively incorrect.

The finding that internal consistency does not assure intuitive truth or correctness supports views that have long been maintained by Brouwer, the leading intuitionist. In a controversy with Hilbert, which arose during the early years of the Hilbert program, Brouwer maintained that an incorrect theory that is not stopped by a contradiction is nonetheless incorrect, just as a criminal policy that is not checked by a reprimanding court is still criminal (1923). Brouwer does not accept the proposition that from the consistency of a statement there follows the correctness of that statement (1927), a proposition that he considers to be related to the law of the excluded middle.

Decision Problems

A decision method for a general question is a uniform method—a routine procedure that involves a finite number of steps, an algorithm—that actually can be utilized to obtain a "yes" or a "no" answer to every specific case of the general question. A decision problem for a given question is the problem of whether or not there exists a decision method for the question.

As a simple illustration of a decision problem, consider this question: Given two polynomials with coefficients from a field, is one a factor of the other? The so-called Euclidean algorithm (Birkhoff and MacLane, 1944, p. 18) serves as a decision method for this question. It is a uniform, routine procedure which allows us, given two polynomials $f(x)$ and $g(x)$ with coefficients (not all zero) from a field, to divide $g(x)$ by $f(x)$, or vice versa, and to determine whether the remainder of the division process is zero or different from zero. In the former case, the procedure yields a "yes" answer to the question whether $f(x)$ is a factor of $g(x)$, and in the latter case it yields a "no" answer.

In the case of a formal system, an example of a decision problem concerns the existence of a decision method for this question: Is a statement that is formulated in the symbols or vocabulary of the formal system provable through the methods formalized in the system? More succinctly, is there a decision method for the provability of propositions of this formal system? So important is this decision problem, that it has been called *the* decision problem for a formal system. In the case of a formal system that is also a formal theory (in other words, a formalization of an informal theory) another important decision problem concerns the existence of a decision method for this question: Is a statement that is formulated in the symbols of the formal system *true* when the symbols are given their intended interpretations, that is, when they are given the meanings that are intended to be attached to the symbols and to the objects built out of them in considering the system as a model for the informal theory? More briefly, is there a decision method for deciding the *truth* of statements of the formal system, under the intended interpretation? This may be referred to as the decision problem for truth (sometimes called *validity*) of a formal theory.

If a decision method exists for provability (or for truth, under the intended interpretation), then the formal system is said to be *decidable with regard to provability* (or with regard to truth). It is important not to confuse decidability of a formal system with decidability of propositions of the system. Thus, each proposition of the system may be decidable as to provability—that is, a decision can be made as to whether or not it is provable—and yet there may not be a *uniform* method for reaching the decision. It may be necessary to use different methods for different propositions of the system. Hence, the system would not be decidable as to provability. Similarly, each proposition of a formal theory may be decidable as to truth (under the intended interpretation) and yet the formal theory may not be decidable as to truth because there does not exist a uniform method of reaching the decision.

Clearly it is desirable for a formal system to be decidable as to provability.

> In a decidable theory, every problem that can at all be formulated in its vocabulary has an answer that can be obtained by mechanically following a fixed recipe, or, to use the terminology of computing machinery, a routine. It was hoped for a time—and it was the task of the Hilbert program to realize this hope—that the formal system into which classical arithmetic and analysis could be systematized and adequately axiomatized would be decidable as to provability as well as (formally and semantically) complete and categorical. (Fraenkel and Bar-Hillel, 1958, p. 297)

Yet this aim of the Hilbert school also turned out to be unattainable, although pursuit of it led to many interesting findings. Using decidability henceforth to refer to *decidability as to provability*, we may summarize results obtained by Church (1936) and Rosser (1936b) by saying that elementary arithmetic is undecidable. Moreover, it is *essentially undecidable*. A consistent formal system S is said to be essentially undecidable if every consistent extension of it (that is, every consistent formal system which includes S as a subsystem) is also undecidable. It has been proved that an essentially undecidable theory induces the property of essential undecidability in every consistent theory that is interpretable in it (Tarski, Mostowski, and Robinson, 1953). Since elementary arithmetic is interpretable in many axiomatic set theories, these in turn, if consistent, are essentially undecidable (because, as mentioned before, elementary arithmetic has this property).

The list of theories that have been proved to be undecidable is far larger than the list of those that have proved to be decidable. Among the theories that have been proved to be decidable are the classical propositional calculus, the theory of elementary Boolean algebra and the elementary theory of commutative groups. Among theories that have been proved to be undecidable are "the elementary theories of groups, of rings, of fields, and of lattices as well as that of the theories of more specific structures, such as commutative rings, ordered rings, non-densely ordered rings, modular lattices, complemented modular lattices, distributive lattices, Brouwerian algebras, closure algebras, abstract projective geometries, etc." (Fraenkel and Bar-Hillel, 1958, p. 312).

There are still many unanswered questions with regard to decidability. Even if a theory has been proved to be undecidable, there still remains the question of which subsets of the propositions of the theory are decidable in the sense that a decision method for provability exists for every proposition in the subset. In recent years attempts have been made to develop decision methods capable of being used in conjunction with fast electric computers. An example is the decision method for elementary algebra and geometry (Tarski and McKinsey, 1951). (See Davis, 1965, for a collection of papers on undecidability.)

Axiomatizability

We turn now to what may be considered the first step in the Hilbert program, namely, formalizing a theory, establishing it as an axiomatic system. The idea underlying this step was to find a *finite number* of axioms from which the other propositions of the theory could be deduced. It was once thought that all of mathematics could be so axiomatized. The failure to obtain axiomatizations for certain theories was thought to be due to insufficient mathematical ingenuity combined with insufficient luck; mathematicians had not been ingenious enough to discover, nor fortunate enough to stumble onto, the particular axioms that were needed for the theories. It turned out that the difficulty was far more basic and that some mathematical theories are inherently incapable of being axiomatized as formalized theories or formal systems, but that indeed they are nonaxiomatizable. "The proof of the existence of nonaxiomatizable formalized theories is doubtless one of the most important achievements of recent foundational research" (Fraenkel and Bar-Hillel, 1958, p. 321).

Actually, an example of an informal theory that cannot be axiomatized is obtainable virtually as a corollary of Gödel's incompletability theorem. The term *Skolem's arithmetic* (Skolem, 1934) has been applied to certain informal theories that are known to be consistent and complete. Skolem's arithmetic cannot be capable of axiomatization since, if it were, it would constitute a formal number-theoretic system, and, by Gödel's theorem, it could not be both consistent and complete.

In order to discuss the problem of axiomatizability, it is helpful to draw a distinction between a *specific axiom* (also called an *elementary axiom*) and an *axiom schema* (also called an *axiom form*). An axiom schema stands for an infinity of axioms, since it yields a specific axiom each time formulas (or propositions) are specified for the formula-variables it involves. An example of an axiom schema is that of mathematical induction. The axiom schema of mathematical induction states that if the natural number 0 has property P, and if whenever a natural number n has property P, then so does the next natural number $n + 1$, then every natural number has property P. A similar wording would hold with the phrase "satisfies proposition P" in place of "has property P." This axiom schema yields a specific axiom whenever P is specified. But there are infinitely many properties or propositions that can be substituted for P. Hence, the axiom schema stands for an infinity of axioms. It was not until 1953 that it was proved that the axiom schema of mathematical induction in elementary arithmetic cannot be replaced by a finite number of specific axioms (Ryll-Nardzewski, 1953).

In the axiomatization of the system of logic used in making deductions, axiom schemata are generally used. But, are they necessary for the axiomatization of the mathematical theory per se, for the so-called nonlogical axioms? If axiom schemata are not allowed (except for the axiomatization of the underlying system of logic) is each branch of mathematics finitely axiomatizable? In other words, can it be expressed as a formal system involving only a finite number of specific (nonlogical) axioms? An affirmative answer is what is implied in the statement that mathematics is finitely axiomatizable or, more briefly, that it is axiomatizable. An affirmative answer was taken for granted by many mathematicians. "As a matter of fact, Hilbert and many other mathematicians and logicians had assumed that all of mathematics is axiomatizable. . . . [However] many mathematical theories, including such 'simple' ones as the arithmetic of natural numbers, have turned out to be nonaxiomatizable, to the amazement of them all" (Fraenkel and Bar-Hillel, 1958, p. 280).

It was proved by Skolem that "the unique or complete characterization of the number series is impossible" (Skolem, 1934, p. 160). In other words, it is not possible to characterize uniquely the series of natural numbers by a finite number of specific axioms. No matter how many specific axioms are used in efforts to express properties of the natural numbers, as long as the set of axioms is finite, there will be structures or systems that satisfy the axioms but are not isomorphic to the number series. However, if an axiom schema is permitted (such as that of mathematical induction) then the system of natural numbers can be characterized uniquely in the sense that all interpretations of it are isomorphic. In short, Skolem's findings show that when a finite number of axioms is used to characterize the number series, more than one interpretation of the axioms is possible, where any two interpretations are not necessarily isomorphic. This means that the axiomatic system is *not categorical*. Yet the Hilbert program had hoped to establish that the branches of classical mathematics were not only axiomatizable but also categorical. Both objectives proved to be unattainable in general. Research has shown that many mathematical theories cannot be axiomatized in terms of a finite number of specific axioms. In fact, for some theories it is even uncertain if a finite number of axiom schemata suffice. Other mathematical theories, however, have been shown to be finitely axiomatizable. Moreover, it has been shown that finite axiomatizability can always be obtained through the device of adding rather artificial rules of inference to the logic underlying the system (Hermes, 1951) or through the device of suitably enlarging the original concepts or vocabulary of the mathematical theory (Kleene, 1952). But, barring such devices, theories remain that are not finitely axiomatizable. Thus, this fundamental objective of the Hilbert program is unattainable.

This question may be raised: What are the advantages of *finite* axiomatizability as opposed to, say, establishment of the system in terms of a finite number of axiom schemata? Whether or not there are *epistemological* advantages to finite axiomatizability is somewhat debatable (see Fraenkel and Bar-Hillel, 1958, p. 321). But certainly there are pragmatic considerations which indicate that finite axiomatizability is a desirable property. There would probably be high agreement with the statement that parsimony is one of the factors underlying a search for axiomatization, a desire to be able to deduce many statements (theorems) from a relatively few statements taken as axioms. From the point of view of parsimony, a case could certainly be made that the number of axioms ought to be finite in number.

Moreover, for metamathematical investigation of a theory, such as for investigation of its consistency, finite axiomatizability is desirable. Furthermore, it has been found that finite axiomatizability is related to other rather desirable properties of a formalized theory or formal system. For example, if a formal theory is complete, then finite axiomatizability is a sufficient condition for its decidability (Kleene, 1943, p. 56). Decidability, it may be recalled, refers to the existence of a uniform, routine method, involving a finite number of steps, which permits a decisive "yes" or "no" answer to the question of the decidability or provability of every proposition that can be formulated in the vocabulary of the theory. A corollary of this theorem refers to essential undecidability which, it may be recalled, indicates undecidability not only for a consistent theory but for every consistent extension of the theory. The corollary states that for a complete theory, the conditions of nonaxiomatizability, undecidability, and essential undecidability are all equivalent; in other words any one of these conditions implies the other two conditions. Hence, a complete theory is perforce decidable if it is finitely axiomatizable and perforce undecidable (even essentially undecidable) if it is not.

In short, there seem to be pragmatic as well as metamathematical considerations that suggest that finite axiomatizability is a property we would like theories to have. But, like it or not, it is a property that is not possessed by many mathematical theories, including even as relatively simple a theory as that of the natural number sequence.

Categoricalness

An objective of the Hilbert program was to establish the branches of classical mathematics (in particular, arithmetic, analysis, and set theory) as formal axiomatic systems with the property of *categoricalness*. It may be recalled that this means that all models of the system are isomorphic, that is, can be put in a one-to-one correspondence which preserves the relationships in the axioms. (See Church, 1956, pp. 329–330 for a more precise definition of categoricalness.) Note that the term *monomorphism* has also been used for categoricalness.

We have already seen that if the natural number sequence is a model for a formal system with a finite number of specific axioms, then there are necessarily other models for the system which are not isomorphic to the natural number sequence; hence, the formal system is not categorical.

It can be shown that categoricalness implies completeness (Wilder, 1952, p. 36). It can also be shown that noncategoricalness of certain formal systems follows from Gödel's incompletability theory. Other approaches have also been used to attest to the noncategorical nature of many (but not all) mathematical theories.

The findings concerning set theory are particularly interesting. An important theorem in this area is Cantor's set theorem, which states that the set of all subsets of a set S has a greater cardinal number than S. From this theorem it follows that there are nonenumerable infinite sets, whose members are sets. Recall that a set is called *enumerable* (*denumerable*, or *countable*) if its members can be placed in one-to-one correspondence with the natural numbers or a subset of the natural numbers; otherwise, it is nonenumerable. Thus, there are infinite sets of sets which have, so to speak, "too many" members to allow an enumeration.

Pertinent to our discussion is a theorem, proved as early as 1915 by Löwenheim, with a generalization and simpler proof given by Skolem in 1920. This Löwenheim-Skolem theorem tells us that if a certain kind of formula (a predicate-letter formula, or, as it is sometimes called, a well-formed formula of the first-order functional calculus) is satisfiable in some (nonempty) domain, then it is satisfiable in the domain of natural numbers. Such a formula is called *satisfiable* in a (nonempty) domain if there are objects in the domain which, when assigned as values to the variables in the formula, make the formula true (that is, satisfy the formula).

The Löwenheim-Skolem theorem also asserts that if a system consists of an enumerable number of such formulas (predicate-letter formulas) and if the system is satisfiable in an infinite domain, then it is satisfiable in an enumerable domain and, in particular, in the domain of all natural numbers. In short, the theorem states that if such a system has an infinite model, whether enumerable or nonenumerable, then it has an enumerable model. Thus if such a system has a nonenumerable model it also has an enumerable model; and since the two models certainly cannot be put in one-to-one correspondence, the system is not categorical.

Consider now an axiomatic set theory, that is, a system of axioms of which informal set theory is presumed to be an interpretation. Skolem (1922–1923) applied the Löwenheim-Skolem theorem to axiomatic set theories, some with a finite number of specific axioms and others with an enumerable infinity of specific axioms. Since the axiomatic set theory is satisfiable in some nonempty domain (informal set theory is the intended interpretation of it), it is satisfiable in an enumerable domain. But from Cantor's set theorem it follows that there are nonenumerable sets of sets. The so-called Skolem paradox then consists of this: There is an enumerable model for axiomatic set theory even though a theorem in the theory yields the existence of nonenumerable sets. In other words, informal set theory (by Cantor's set theorem) constitutes a nonenumerable model for the axiomatic set theory whereas the Löwenheim-Skolem theorem gives an enumerable model for it. The latter is called a *non-standard model* and informal set theory a *standard model*. Certainly these two models cannot be put in one-to-one correspondence, and hence axiomatic set theory is not categorical; it lacks the property of categoricalness or monomorphism.

Keep in mind that Skolem obtained this result not only for axiomatic set theories with a finite number of specific axioms but also for such theories with infinitely (enumerably) many specific axioms. Hence we have examples of noncategorical formal systems involving an infinite (enumerable) number of specific axioms.

It should be noted that Löwenheim's proof and Skolem's original proof of the Löwenheim-Skolem theorem made use of the axiom of choice. Subsequent proofs have dispensed with this axiom (Kleene, 1952, p. 394) but the proofs are still not sufficiently constructive to meet intuitionistic standards. In particular, the proof of the Skolem paradox is not intuitionistically satisfactory. Yet it is interesting that intuitionists have been willing to use the paradox as an argument against Cantor's set theorem and its implication. Cantor's set theorem involves an indirect, nonconstructive proof to assert the existence of certain sets; this is entirely unsatisfactory as far as intuitionists are concerned. In short, some intuitionists have been willing to use Skolem's paradox, although its proof is not constructive, as an argument against other propositions that are not constructively established.

The one-to-one correspondence which gives an enumeration may be considered as a set, namely, the set of all the corresponding pairs, where a pair consists of a member of the set which is enumerated together with the natural number to which it corresponds. One way of attempting to explain, or at least to understand, the Skolem paradox is to consider that an enumerating set is not among the sets definable within the axiomatic set theory (that is, within the formal system whose intended interpretation is informal set theory). However, we can define an enumerating set of corresponding pairs outside of the axiomatic set theory. Yet, even to know how to define an enumerating set we have to take into account the structure of the whole formal system, that is, the structure of the axiomatic set theory.

Thus it may be possible for the subsets of a given infinite set definable within the theory to be enumerable without the theory, and yet be non-enumerable within the theory, because no enumerating set of corresponding pairs is among the sets definable within the theory. The construction of the enumerating sets of pairs is accomplished by taking into account the structure of the axiom system as a whole, and this construction is not possible within the theory, i.e., using only the operations provided by the axioms. (Kleene, 1952, p. 426)

The situation here parallels that in Gödel's incompletability theorem. There, if a formal number-theoretic system was considered consistent, then the truth of some of its propositions could be recognized by taking into account the structure of the system as a whole, but their truth could not be recognized or demonstrated through methods formalized within the system.

Despite such an explanation of the Skolem paradox, it has been regarded as offering only two alternatives. Either we must accept that the concept of an arbitrary subset of a given set, as well as the concept of a nonenumerable set, cannot be axiomatized by any finite or enumerably infinite system of specific axioms; or else, if we wish to maintain their characterization by elementary axioms, then we must accept the conclusion that certain concepts, such as the two concepts just mentioned, are relative rather than absolute. For example, a set which is nonenumerable in a given axiomatization may become enumerable in another (say, by axiomatization of a larger system that includes an enumerating set of corresponding pairs for the original system). In short, enumerability and nonenumerability would be recognized as relative rather than absolute concepts. This relativism of set theory (or relativization of cardinal numbers) was first pointed out by Skolem (1922–1923).

This relativism, von Neumann (1925–1926) pointed out, applies not only to enumerably *infinite* sets but also to *finite* sets. Suppose, for example, that finiteness is defined in the sense of Dedekind: A finite set is one which cannot be put in a one-to-one correspondence with a proper subset of itself. This definition involves the concept of a subset and of a set of corresponding pairs. It is conceivable that a given set S may appear finite in one system and yet be infinite in another system. The same sort of relativism follows from considering various other definitions of finiteness. In short, the concept of a finite number or of a finite cardinal, along with the concepts of infinite numbers or infinite cardinals, may be relative rather than absolute.

It is tempting to use relativism to support one school of foundational thought at the expense of another. But one should beware of doing this.

If, on the one hand, it [relativism] seems to support the intuitionistic slogan that by formalistic (axiomatic) methods no reality can be reached and everything remains vague and relative, on the other hand the supposedly absolute original intuition of positive integer . . . forfeits as well its pretended evidence owing to indistinct passages from finiteness to transfinite denumerability [enumerably infinite]. Thus not only is categoricalness or monomorphism of set theory called in question but also the absolute authority and distinctness of the notion of integral number. (Fraenkel and Bar-Hillel, 1958, p. 109)

In short, the very notions of subset, of finiteness, of a finite number, of enumerability, of nonenumerability, and so on, may have to be made relative to a particular system and relative to the whole structure, or Gestalt, of the system. What is finite or enumerable in one system or in one Gestalt may be infinite or nonenumerable in another system or Gestalt.

It might be mentioned that Skolem's paradox and related results have shown that the notion of categoricalness is more complex than was originally suspected. In place of the concept of *absolute categoricalness*, various weaker notions of *relative categoricalness* have been introduced (Fraenkel and Bar-Hillel, 1958; Tarski, 1956; Wang, 1953; Vaught, 1954; Łoś, 1954). For example, one such notion is that of categoricalness relative to the natural numbers, where all models of the axiomatic system whose domains (or universes) contain only natural numbers are isomorphic. Although the theory of elementary arithmetic is not absolutely categorical, it is categorical relative to the natural numbers. In other words, models of axiomatic elementary arithmetic whose domains consist only of natural numbers are isomorphic to one another; but they are not necessarily isomorphic to models whose domains include other objects besides the natural numbers. Another notion of relative categoricalness says that a formal system is categorical relative to a particular subsystem of it if and only if any two models of the systems that are extensions of two isomorphic models of the subsystem are themselves isomorphic. Research on which formal systems satisfy these and other notions of relative categoricalness is currently an active field.

In summary: One of the goals of the Hilbert program was to show the categoricalness of various branches of classical mathematics. This goal has not been attained. Much, however, has been learned that reveals the difficulties in the way of achieving such an objective. It is now recognized that many (but not all) formal systems fail to be absolutely categorical. Relative notions of categoricalness are being investigated. Relativism has also been proposed for such notions of set theory as enumerability, infinite, and finite.

Comparisons
and Evaluations
of Formalism

We have seen that many aims of the Hilbert program have not yet been attained and in fact may be unattainable. Yet, this should not be construed as a weakness of the Hilbert program or of formalism. Unattainment and even ultimate unattainability of objectives do not make the objectives or the attempts to realize them trivial or valueless. Investigations in pursuit of the objectives of the Hilbert program have produced results of considerable significance as have investigations directly or indirectly stimulated by the program and by the formalistic outlook. The impetus that formalism has given to the establishment, description, and investigation of formal systems is a great contribution. Had it not been for this impetus, perhaps it might not yet be known today that complete formal number-theoretic systems are not consistent, or that consistent formal systems cannot have their consistency established by methods formalized in the system, or that many mathematical theories are undecidable with regard to provability, or that certain mathematical theories are not finitely axiomatizable and are not categorical, and so on. In brief, formalism has served directly or indirectly to stimulate research that has established properties of formal systems as well as limitations of formalization. Moreover, it has opened up a fount of questions for future research.

It has been claimed that the strength of formalism "lies in what it asserts, its weakness in what it leaves unsaid" (Black, 1934, p. 149). Specifically, formalism has been criticized for the lack of a clear exposition of the philosophy on which it is based. Yet, formalism "has always been the working attitude of a group of practicing mathematicians rather than a fully explicit philosophy . . . Formalism is a technique first, and only secondarily a philosophy" (pp. 148–149).

What has been regarded as a serious weakness of the formalist viewpoint is that in its focus on structure and abstract symbols, it has neglected the content of mathematics; in particular, it has neglected mathematical concepts. It has been said of formalism that "this way of thinking is one-sidedly preoccupied with the structure of the mathematical statements and, on the other hand, fails to investigate the mathematical concepts" (Waismann, 1959, p. 107). A related criticism is that by its neglect of the meanings of mathematical concepts, formalism has made of mathematics a meaningless game with meaningless symbols. Countering such a criticism, Black wrote that the formalist holds that if he has an adequate system of symbols or signs he need not worry about their meaning since he can see in the signs themselves "those structural properties which interest him. . . . This is not to say that mathematics is a meaningless game as the formalists have often been accused of asserting; they say that mathematics is concerned with the structural properties of symbols (and hence of all objects) independent of their meaning" (1934, p. 9).

Formalism has been criticized on several grounds by Körner. A weakness that he attributes to both logicism and formalism is a tendency to confuse empirical and nonempirical concepts. Formalists regard the concepts of metamathematics (and also the so-called real concepts of mathematics in contrast to the ideal concepts) as concrete and empirically evident. While these may be characteristics of strokes on paper, such strokes, and operations with them, do not form the subject matter of metamathematics any more than diagrams and constructions on paper form the subject matter of Euclidean geometry (1962, p. 104). The strokes may be regarded as symbols or concrete representations of the metamathematical concepts, which in turn may be regarded as abstractions or idealizations of the concrete representations. The strokes, although concrete and empirical, are not exact, whereas the metamathematical concepts, although exact, are neither concrete nor empirical. It is misleading to assume that the empirical and nonempirical concepts are isomorphic, just as it is misleading to assume that a diagram is isomorphic to a geometric object. "The inexactness of the empirical and the exactness of the non-empirical concepts precludes isomorphism" (pp. 104–105). Yet, formalists may implicitly assume such an isomorphism when they claim that metamathematical concepts are empirically evident.

The logic used by formalism is also criticized. Formalism sought to restrict itself to those parts of logic which are supported by mathematical constructions, constructions that could be perceived or thought of (thought experiments). But the mathematical construction has to be correct. "The proposition, however, that a construction is correct . . . is no longer perceptual but involves a logical implication or an inference the validity of which depends on logical principles" (p. 118). These logical

matics is suggested by his confession that this crisis was of distressing concern to him, "a constant drain on the enthusiasm and determination with which I pursued my research work" (Weyl, 1946). It might be said of Weyl that he was an intuitionist with regard to mathematics per se, but could accept formalism if mathematics were regarded as merged with physics to constitute a theoretical science about the world.

Ideal statements form a convenient reference point with which to discuss another difference between formalist and intuitionist views: traditional logic. "Classical mathematics adjoins the ideal statements to the real, in order to retain the simple rules of the Aristotelian logic in reasoning about infinite sets" (Kleene, 1952, p. 55). As might be expected, the law of the excluded middle as applied to infinite sets, is the center of the controversy. Hilbert grants that this law must not be unqualifiedly applied in metamathematics, and also that in general one must beware in proof theory of applying methods suitable for finite sets to infinite sets. Thus he writes:

> The infinite comes into proof theory as soon as we introduce the notions "all" and "there exists." The former is equivalent to an infinite "and" and the latter to an infinite "or." From the Law of the Excluded Middle for finite sets we conclude that either all elements of a given finite set have a particular significant property P or else there exists an element of the set that does not have property P. . . .
>
> But if we thoughtlessly apply to infinite totalities a procedure that is permissible in the finite case, then we open gate and door to error . . . Similarly we cannot treat the infinite logical sums and products in the same way as the finite, unless proof theory offers justification for such treatment. (1923, pp. 154–155)

Although excluding from proof theory or metamathematics the use of the law of the excluded middle for infinite sets, Hilbert concedes that it is used and may be used in ordinary, informal mathematics. To Brouwer's contention that the unqualified law of the excluded middle has no place in mathematics, Hilbert (1928) retorted that taking away the law of the excluded middle from the mathematician would be akin to denying the astronomer the telescope or the boxer the use of his fists.

In short, the intuitionistic influence on formalism is pronounced in metamathematics (pointed out by Brouwer, 1927) but not in ordinary mathematics. This would perforce be regarded as a deficiency of formalism by a confirmed intuitionist.

There is a fundamental difference between the two schools which we have not made explicit. Intuitionists maintain that mathematics cannot be formalized, that formalization is antithetical to the nature of mathematics, that there is no language, no symbolism, adequate to convey mathematics; a contrary view lies at the very heart of formalism. As Wilder so well summarizes it: "In contrast to the intuitionistic tenet that language and symbolism are not basic to mathematics, stands the formalist conviction that symbols and operations with them constitute the very heart of mathematics" (1952, p. 250). Heyting, an intuitionist, assures us that "no formal system can be proved to represent adequately an intuitionistic theory" (1956, p. 102) and insists that his own attempts at formalizing intuitionistic propositional and functional logic should not be treated as adequate representations. This is in keeping with "one of the basic tenets of the intuitionistic approach [which] is that no formalized theory can do full justice to intuitive (which is for them intuitionistic) mathematics or any of its subtheories" (Fraenkel and Bar-Hillel, 1958, p. 317). It is therefore of interest that Beth (1959) has shown that Heyting's attempts at formalizations do constitute very adequate representations of the intuitionistic propositional and functional logic, being formally and semantically complete under a notion of intuitionistic truth. In short, a basic difference between intuitionism and formalism centers on formalization of theories; yet there are intuitionists who are using formalizations to represent certain intuitionistic theories—and successfully so, despite avowals to the contrary.

Formalism and Logicism

Let us now briefly compare formalism with logicism. From the latter point of view the chief defect of formalism probably is its lack of an attempt to reduce mathematics to logic. Although Hilbert at one time seemed to be very much impressed by the logistic thesis, he and other formalists do not believe that mathematics has been reduced to logic. It has been said that formalists "deny that mathematical concepts can be reduced to logical concepts and assert that the many difficulties of logic which beset the path of the logistic philosophers have nothing to do with mathematics" (Black, 1934, p. 8). Hilbert recognized that, even if mathematics could be reduced to or derived from logic, there would still remain the problem of the consistency of logic. Rather than seek to reduce mathematics to logic, formalism treats mathematics and logic concurrently, attempting to axiomatize, symbolize, and formalize each, and to study the property of the total formal system, including the logical axioms and the other axioms. Moreover, logicism has been concerned with analysis of mathematical concepts (if for no other reason than to express them in terms of logical concepts), whereas formalism has been criticized for its neglect of mathematical concepts.

Undoubtedly formalism has been influenced by logicism and its forerunners, particularly by the work of Peano and by the *Principia Mathematica*. Logicism's doctrine "of the necessity for symbolizing mathematical proof has been completely adopted and improved in important technical aspects by the formalists, who use the logical notation evolved in essence by the logistic school" (Black, 1934, p. 11). Methods used by Hilbert have been described as "a *union* of the axiomatic and logistic methods" (Wilder, 1952, p. 250). Moreover, formalists admired logicists' efforts to work with mathematics as a formal system. "Formalists held that, as a result of the work of Whitehead and Russell, one had at last a clear formalization of what it was that had to be proved consistent" (Benacerraf and Putnam, 1964, p. 10).

Certainly, logicism and formalism have much in common: their mutual emphasis on abstract symbolism, their joint concern with rigorous proofs, and their common reliance on the axiomatic-deductive method. Perhaps the strongest link is the significant role that symbolic or mathematical logic plays in both foundational schools, although not necessarily the same system of logic. If symbolic logic is the scaffold on which the logicist builds, it is also the spectacles through which the metamathematician views mathematical theories. A glance at Kleene's book (1952), a text on metamathematics, reveals that two out of its four parts bear the title of *mathematical logic;* indeed, the book has been used as a text for courses in symbolic logic. Moreover, their common ancestry links the two schools, both of which are indebted to those who developed symbolic logic, including Leibniz, De Morgan, Boole, Peirce, and Schröder, and to those who worked to axiomatize and in a sense to formalize portions of mathematics, including Weierstrass, Frege, and Peano.

Finally, linking all three schools is metamathematics—perhaps formalism's greatest contribution. Metamathematics was, in part, an outgrowth of investigations originating from diverse foundational viewpoints, and is itself now applied to the systematization of the results of investigations which arise from intuitionism, logicism, and formalism.

In short, formalism has been influenced (seemingly quite willingly so) by both intuitionism and logicism, while yet retaining its place as a distinctive and important school of foundational thought. In turn, it has provided metamathematics as a discipline which transcends division lines in the foundations of mathematics.

CHAPTER 11
Formalism
and Psychology

It may be recalled that among the objectives of the Hilbert program was that of establishing branches of mathematics and, ultimately, all of mathematics, as formal systems. This involves the axiomatization of the mathematical discipline (unless it happens to be given, at the onset, as a deductive postulational system). Also involved is the formalization of the system, which requires abstraction of the content or meaning of the terms so that the form or structure of the system is made explicit. Complete formalization involves also the axiomatization of the underlying system of logic and abstraction of the meaning of the logical terms involved in the mathematical system.

This objective of the Hilbert program may be considered to have its parallel in the social sciences, where interest runs high in axiomatization and formalization. Alluring to many psychologists is the goal of establishing at least portions of their discipline as postulational deductive systems. The work of Hull (1943, 1951) and Lewin (1936, 1951) provide examples of attempts to formalize or axiomatize psychological theories. More recent examples may be found in Koch (1959), Mandler and Kessen (1959), and Miller, Galanter, and Pribram (1960). Concern with axiomatization and formalization is also evident from reports in psychological journals. Indirectly we know it exists because psychological research is geared to the testing of hypotheses that are "logically" deduced from theories. (For discussions of this trend in psychological research see Luchins, 1957b, and Luchins and Luchins, 1959.) This trend may also partly underlie the relatively greater concern with experimental design and form rather than content, which is found among some psychologists and in some psychology departments.

It is questionable to what extent the formalization of mathematical theories can be carried through (Kleene, 1952). Even more questionable is the extent to which psychological theories can be formalized. There is also the question of the extent to which it is *advisable* to attempt to for-

171

malize a mathematical theory or a psychological theory. We have pointed out that there are diverse opinions as to the value of formalizing mathematics. "There are very many mathematicians, and even more so other scientists, who doubt it very much whether mathematical (and other) theories should be formalized, even if they can be so in principle, suspecting that the fruits of formalization are not worth the effort" (Fraenkel and Bar-Hillel, 1958, p. 318). Fraenkel and Bar-Hillel themselves believe that only through formalization can many important problems be formulated so as to make attempts at their solution worthwhile. Likewise, there are diverse views as to the value of formalization in psychology in particular and in the behavioral and social sciences in general. Important methodological issues are related to the problems of whether or not it is of value to psychology or to the foundations of psychology to have the language of psychology formalized and to have psychological theories axiomatized and formalized. Is the postulational-deductive method the best method to use in the development and in the presentation of a theory? There is the question of whether psychologists should present their findings and their theories in terms of abstract symbols, which are devoid of meaning or from which all content and meaning have been abstracted, so that only the form or the structure remains. These are questions which have received varied answers.

As representative of the viewpoint that psychology has been insufficiently concerned with formalization and formal structure, we mention a paper by Rozeboom (1961), which has been described as constituting "a powerful argument for the importance of analysis of the formal structure of the language of psychology" (Buchwald, 1961). Rozeboom, concerned with a "kind of methodological problem which as yet has received little or no recognition in psychology—namely, that of formal structure," writes:

> By the "theory of formal structure," I mean the systematic study of the logical forms of scientific assertions and, derivatively, the formal properties of the symbolic elements employed. . . . The primary objective of formalizing a set of propositions is not, as might be supposed, to make possible rigorous deductions, though this is always a useful consequence, but to bring out the logical structure of the set.
>
> It is my intense conviction that it is just as important for the scientist to be explicit about the formal structure of his assertions as it is for him to be tough minded about his concepts and his evidence. . . . The whole point of formal analysis is that assertions made in informal English, even when fortified with technical terms and special notations, simply are not *clear*. . . . Nor is mathematization of the science likely to increase its logical clarity to any appreciable degree—quite the contrary, a chief virtue of mathematical formulae is their extraordinarily compact condensation of ideas which would be of horrendous complexity if written out in logical fullness. In any case, the philosophically untrained scientist is seldom aware of the full content of the statements he subscribes to, whether these be finely spun theories or sup-

posedly simple generalizations from known data. The research scientist, in particular, is jeopardized by the hidden commitments of his language; for what he believes to be little more than a summary of his observations may in fact sneak in further assumptions which not only are unwarranted by the data at hand, but may be in conflict with other known data or established belief. . . . One of the great disputes of modern learning theory—namely, What does the organism learn during conditioning?—has been a controversy of precisely this kind. When an apparent clash of data arises in this way, the solution is not to rush back to the laboratory, but to look for methodological therapy. When impacted ideas become infected, extraction is necessary, and the instrument for this is formal analysis. (1961, pp. 475–476)

As representative of the viewpoint that perhaps behavioral scientists have been overly concerned with formalization, we mention a paper by Hochberg (1959). Hochberg is skeptical about the value of "uncritical" attempts to introduce axiomatization. He mentions "some hopelessly misguided attempts to interpret abstract axiomatic systems" in attempts to get empirical laws "wholesale" (p. 430) and then continues:

> Gestalt psychologists have sometimes talked of using topology for axiomatizing a psychological theory. This would mean that they hope to interpret an axiom set from a certain branch of mathematics so as to arrive at psychological laws. When one realizes what topology is, the absurdity of the program manifests itself. This case also pointedly illustrates the futility of introducing axiomatization uncritically and prematurely. Taking advantage of what I called the "wholesale" acquisition of laws depends on a certain level of development of a theory and a science. (1959, p. 430)

Hochberg doubts that the behavioral sciences have reached this level of development. He is wary of social scientists who call for "complete formalization" of scientific theories, since this would involve formalization of the underlying system of logic. Once logical systems are formalized by logicians, "the empirical scientist, and even the mathematician, may and does take such logical systems for granted in making deductions," so that to ask for complete formalization is to ask "for a needless repetition of what the logician has already accomplished" (p. 428). Hochberg considers possible motives that may account for the status that the goal of formalization has attained in the social sciences. He mentions the rapid growth of modern logic, aided by formalization; the awe with which systems of logic are regarded; the similarity which some see between mathematical and logistic systems, coupled with the false assumption that to formalize statements is to introduce quantification into a science; the erroneous belief that scientific discoveries are achieved through formalization; and the confusion between formalization of theories in the social sciences and the models used in physics, a factor enhanced by the prestige enjoyed by contemporary physics.

In short, whereas Rozeboom suggests that psychology has been insufficiently concerned with formal structure and formalization, Hochberg suggests that the behavioral sciences, including psychology, have been overly concerned on this score, and that some of their attempts at formalization are premature and are out of keeping with their level of development. Regardless of which view the reader may espouse, he may be interested to explore with us some suggestions for psychology that may be found in the attempts to formalize mathematics, especially in the attempts to fulfill the aims of the Hilbert program.

Formalization and Axiomatizability

Recall the finding that some mathematical theories are inherently incapable of finite axiomatization, that they cannot be presented as formal systems involving a finite number of specific axioms. For some mathematical theories it is even questionable whether a finite number of axiom schemata would suffice. The findings should give pause for thought to those who consider that a scientific theory must be an axiomatic system. Yet, a theory is sometimes defined as an axiomatic system. For example: "A theory is a set of laws and definitions deductively interrelated—in short, a theory is an axiomatic system" (Hochberg, 1959, p. 427). Is this perhaps too restrictive a characterization of a theory? Can there be theories (in mathematics and in the empirical sciences) which are not axiomatic systems?

The finding that some mathematical theories are inherently incapable of finite axiomatization should also give pause for thought to those who consider the axiomatic formulation of a theory as an ideal at which to aim. It is sometimes implicitly assumed that a theory in psychology or another discipline would be capable of axiomatization if we but knew what axioms to select. However, that most psychological theories have not yet been axiomatized may not be due to a lack of luck or ingenuity in finding suitable sets of axioms, but may perhaps be due to their inability to be axiomatized.

This is not to say that we ought to give up attempts at axiomatizing psychological theories. Rather, one facet of foundational work in psychology might be concerned with ascertaining whether certain theories are axiomatizable or, more generally, with seeking to ascertain conditions that are necessary or sufficient for axiomatizability (or for nonaxiomatizability).

Thus, there is nothing intrinsically wrong with pursuing the aim of axiomatizing psychological systems or theories. But, the findings of foundational research in mathematics suggest that it may be advisable to exercise certain cautions in the pursuit, and perhaps even a certain degree of humbleness in the presentation of purported axiomatics. One should be wary, for example, of asserting that his particular list represents axioms on which to base learning theory, personality theory, or clinical theory or practice. One should be even more wary of asserting that a given list represents necessary and sufficient conditions for learning or for psychotherapeutic effects or that it involves *the* axioms or the most adequate axioms on which to base a theory of learning or clinical practice. Such claims are difficult (perhaps inherently impossible) to justify.

Recall that in mathematics, axiomatization did not obviate the need to be concerned with truth.

> After axiomatization, there must still be some level at which we have truth and falsity. If the axiomatics is informal, the axioms must be true. If the axiomatics is formal, at least we must believe that the theorems do follow from the axioms; and also there must be some relationship between these results and some actuality outside the axiomatic theory, if the mathematicians' activity is not to reduce to nonsense. (Kleene, 1952, p. 41)

In psychology also, if the psychologists' activity is not to reduce to nonsense, there must be some level at which we have truth and falsity. Either the axioms must be true or, if they involve undefined terms, there must be some relationship between the axiomatic theory and some actuality outside of it. This calls for "correlating" the undefined concepts in the axioms with aspects of "actuality" or "reality" so that a "model" is established therein for the theory. To determine the adequacy of the relationship, and the truth or falsity of the axioms when interpreted in terms of this relationship, we cannot stay within the realm of formal axiomatics. Observation and experimentation are still essential tools for supplementing and, in a sense, "validating" axiomatics and giving it meaning, if the psychologists' activity is to be more than a game with words or symbols at best, and nonsense at worst.

Categoricalness in Psychology

One of the objectives of the Hilbert program was to show that each branch of classical mathematics is categorical in the sense that it constitutes essentially the only interpretation of the axiomatic system to which it corresponds—more precisely, that it is isomorphic to any other interpretation of this system. But as relatively simple a system as that of the natural numbers proved to be noncategorical; any finite axiomatization of it has nonisomorphic models. In other words, the natural numbers cannot be *uniquely* characterized by a finite number of specific axioms. Rather, if such a set of axioms is satisfied by the natural numbers, it is also satisfied by structures that are not isomorphic to the natural number system. Moreover, no matter how many more specific axioms are added in attempts to characterize the natural numbers, as long as the total number of axioms is finite, there will be nonisomorphic interpretations

of the axiom system. There are also other mathematical systems that
are not categorical. In short, the Hilbert program's objective to establish
classical mathematical disciplines as categorical systems is not generally
attainable.

It is possible that systems dealt with in psychology are also noncategorical. A psychological system may be incapable of an axiomatic
characterization with only isomorphic models. Given a set of axioms for
which the "intended interpretation" is a certain informal psychological
theory (or a certain psychological phenomenon), there is the possibility
that the set of axioms is satisfied by nonisomorphic interpretations. Hence
it may be advisable to be alert for nonisomorphic models. In short, just
as it is impossible to characterize uniquely the theory of the arithmetic
of natural numbers, it is perhaps impossible to so characterize some or
all of our psychological theories. Until there is proof to the contrary, the
possibility should be entertained that a set of axioms satisfied by a certain psychological theory may also be satisfied by other, quite different,
theories. (See Luchins and Luchins, 1959, for some examples in the fields
of personality and learning.)

Relative versus absolute notions

It is also of interest to consider whether the mathematical notion of
relative categoricalness has a psychological counterpart. Relative categoricalness of a system denotes that it is categorical relative to a given
domain (for example, the domain of natural numbers). In other words,
an axiom system is said to be categorical relative to a given domain if
there exists an isomorphism among all of its models (interpretations)
whose elements belong to this domain. Given a psychological axiom system, the question may be raised whether or not it is categorical relative
to a particular domain or realm (for instance, the human realm or the
subhuman realm, perceptual activity or motor activity).

Returning to mathematics, we remind the reader that the so-called
Skolem paradox states that axiomatic set theory (whether it involves a
finite number, or an enumerably infinite number, of specific axioms) is
noncategorical; the paradox is that there is an enumerable model for
axiomatic set theory even though one of the theorems in set theory
asserts the existence of a nonenumerable set whose members are sets.
In attempts to account for the Skolem paradox, it has been noted that
the subsets of a given infinite set may be nonenumerable within the axiomatic set system and yet enumerable from outside the system, where
the enumeration from outside takes into account the structure of the
system as a whole. In other words, "the enumeration from outside utilizes the structure of the system as a whole which cannot be reached by
operations within the system" (Fraenkel and Bar-Hillel, 1958, p. 108).

Here we see reflected the influence of the frame of reference; within the system, the reference-frame with regard to enumeration of the subsets of a given set is quite different than the reference-frame from outside of the system. The recognition by mathematicians of the importance of the frame of reference should be of interest to psychologists who, of course, have studied intensively the influence of various frames of references on attitudes, social norms, values, perception, judgment, and so on. It is also of interest to note the close parallel here with the stress Gestalt psychologists place on taking into account the structure of a system as a whole in attempts to study and comprehend the system and its parts.

The Skolem paradox has been interpreted as leading to two alternatives. One alternative is to conclude that such concepts as that of an arbitrary subset of a given set or the concept of a nonenumerable set cannot be characterized by means of any finite or enumerably infinite system of specific axioms. However, if we wish to maintain that such characterizations are possible, then the second alternative is to conclude that certain concepts, including the two concepts just mentioned, are relative rather than absolute notions. In other words, the second alternative is to accept the relativism of certain concepts which have long been regarded as absolute. Among them are the concepts of enumerable, nonenumerable, infinite, finite, finite number, integral or whole number, and so on. The suggestion is that these concepts be regarded not as absolute but as relative to a particular system, relative to the whole structure of the system. For example, what is considered enumerable or finite or a whole number relative to one system's structure may be nonenumerable or infinite or not a whole number relative to another system's structure.

That such an alternative should be suggested by mathematicians ought to be of interest to psychologists familiar with the role of relativism in psychology. An apt illustration is the attempt by Gestalt psychology to explain Stumpf's paradox in discrimination. This paradox refers, for example, to the following phenomenon. A subject, given two adjacent paper squares, one square of a certain shade of gray and another of a different shade of gray, does not discriminate between shades A and B or between shades B and C but does discriminate between shades A and C. Thus, to the subject shades A and B are "equal" and shades B and C are "equal" and yet shades A and C are "not equal." A Gestalt psychological explanation of this apparent paradox is that a percept is not correlated to an absolute stimulus but is relative to a certain structure; in particular, the B of the structure AB plays a different role than the B of the structure BC and is not the "same" stimulus for perception in each structure. Note the parallel between this attempt to account for Stumpf's paradox in psychology and attempts to account for Skolem's paradox in mathematics. More generally, Gestalt psychological accounts of perceptual discrimination and learning (compare Köhler, 1925, 1941; Koffka, 1925,

1935; Wertheimer, 1959) introduce relativism in relation to structure for certain concepts that are regarded as absolutes in other attempts to account for the psychological phenomena involved (see Spence, 1936, 1940). The above should not be construed to mean that Gestalt psychology uses no absolute concepts or that it accepts all the conclusions that have been derived from a radical cultural relativistic orientation (for example, that all values are relative). For quite a different approach to the study of values see Wertheimer, (1934, 1935) and Köhler (1938c).

Finally, it may not be out of place to mention that in order to be able to take into account the structure of the system as a whole, one may find it advisable to utilize a method of analysis that Wertheimer (1938d) characterized as the method "from above" to distinguish it from a method "from below," the latter a piecemeal analysis of the parts of the system (see also Luchins, 1951; Luchins and Luchins, 1963a, 1963b).

In summary, there seem to be interesting suggestions for psychology in mathematical writings on categoricalness, relative categoricalness, and relativism of certain concepts in relation to the whole structure of a given system.

Completeness and Consistency

Among the foremost aims of the Hilbert program were those of establishing the *consistency* and *completeness* of branches of classical mathematics. Consistency refers to freedom from contradiction. A proof of consistency of the axiomatic system would ensure that a contradiction cannot be deduced from the axioms through use of the underlying logic (that is, the logic formalized in the system). Completeness indicates that *all* true propositions of the system are deducible from the axioms through use of the underlying logic.

These aims may be regarded as having analogies in psychology. Certainly, completeness is a desirable feature of any formalized theory, since it ensures that all true propositions of the system can be logically deduced from the axioms. Consistency not only is desirable but would seem to be essential for a useful theory in or out of psychology. It is apparent that one part of a theory ought not to contradict another. If the theory is not consistent, then a contradiction can arise in it. The contradiction constitutes a false hypothesis which, in many systems of logic, can logically imply any conclusion, including a false conclusion.

It is usually assumed, explicitly or implicitly, that a theory in psychology, whether formalized or not, is consistent. It might not be far-fetched to say that the persistence with which some psychologists adhere to a given theory reflects the (perhaps implicit) belief that the theory is consistent and therefore can provide consistency for their research or practice. Perhaps the current predilection for what we have elsewhere called *theoretical monotheism* in psychology (Luchins and Luchins, 1959) is fostered by the psychologist's desire or need for a consistent theoretical orientation. The theory can provide consistency and order and give one a structured frame of reference without which things may seem disjointed, confused, and foggy (see Kendler's defense of his theoretical stand, 1951). Striving for consistency may be related to the search for structure in cognition and may be fostered by some of the structural factors dealt with by Wertheimer in his description of thinking (1945). Striving for consistency may itself help to account for the tendency to abstract consistencies from empirical observations and research findings and, in some cases, to assume or read consistencies into them.

Gödel's theorems and psychology

Gödel's famous theorems (1931) are pertinent to the consistency and completeness of formal systems that contain a formalization of elementary number theory (formal number-theoretic systems). The incompletability theorem, as modified by Rosser (1936b), demonstrates that if such a system is consistent, then it is necessarily incomplete. It contains true propositions that can neither be proved (that is, deduced from the axioms by means of the underlying logic) nor yet disproved by the methods formalized in the system. In short, for such systems the price of consistency is incompleteness.

The possibility should be kept in mind that for some formalized psychological theories also the price of consistency may be incompleteness. At least, we should be wary of taking for granted that a psychological theory is necessarily both consistent and complete. Of course, in psychology there may be less reason than in mathematics for restricting methods of proving propositions to methods formalized in the system. Nonetheless, until it is proved to the contrary, we should at least be alert to the possibility that psychological theory may not be both consistent and complete. Indeed, the whole problem of how to establish the consistency or the completeness of a psychological theory (or of any theory in an empirical science) is open and challenging.

Gödel gave a method of constructing a proposition that is not deducible from the axioms by the logic formalized in the system and yet is true in the metamathematics or metalanguage. What Gödel showed was that in some deductive systems certain statements are not provable but their truth can be recognized by considering the structure of the system as a whole. Here again we have a case where the whole structure or Gestalt is taken into account.

Another of Gödel's results is that if a formal number-theoretic system S is consistent, then its consistency cannot be established by methods formalized in S. It may be possible to establish the consistency of S by using methods not formalized in the system. In other words, if S is consistent, then its consistency cannot be proved as long as S is treated as a closed, isolated system; the proof of consistency requires that we go outside of S.

Analogously, in psychology it may not be feasible to establish the consistency (or certain other properties) of a formal theory as long as it is dealt with in isolation. To study the properties of a psychological system S, we may have to turn to methods and sources outside of S. As in mathematics, it may be possible to answer some of the problems about S by embedding it in S', but then to deal with S' we may have to utilize sources other than those formalized in S'. We may find that formalization is not enough and that in order to study a formal system or a psychological theory, it is advisable to turn to "informal" and "nontheoretical" sources, such as empirical observation and experimental research. It may even be necessary to go outside of psychology in order to discover or establish certain properties of a psychological system.

A generalization of Gödel's theorem by Tarski (1931, 1956) states that if a formal number-theoretic system is consistent, then the notion of truth (the set of all true propositions of the system) is not definable in the system. Thus, a formal number-theoretic system that is consistent is not only formally incomplete, in the sense that some of its true propositions are unprovable within the system, but it is also semantically incomplete, in the sense that certain of its concepts are not definable within the system. Although these concepts may be definable in a more comprehensive system, the latter, if consistent, also has undefined concepts. Hence, if all of classical mathematics (or all of mathematics) was established as a formal system and if it was consistent, then the task of defining certain of its concepts would require that we go outside of classical mathematics (or outside of mathematics altogether).

Analogously, perhaps certain psychological systems are semantically incomplete. In particular, the notion of truth (the set of true statements) or the notion of validity in the system may not be definable within the system but may be definable in another system. If all of clinical psychology or all of learning theory was established as a formal theory or system, then it might be impossible to define or characterize certain concepts that pertain to such a system within the system, and instead we might have to go outside of clinical psychology or outside of learning theory or even outside of psychology. In short, it may be necessary to go outside of a discipline in order to characterize some of its concepts and in order to formulate and solve some of its problems.

Internal and external
consistency

In mathematics, the term *consistency* (also called *simple consistency* or *internal consistency*) is distinguished from external consistency. A system is called *inconsistent* if a contradiction is deducible from the axioms through use of the underlying logic. In contrast, a system is called *externally inconsistent* if it contains a proposition P which is provable in the system but which contradicts another proposition that is intuitively true. In short, although P is provable, it is intuitively false. Moreover, a formal system may be internally consistent and yet externally inconsistent. Although the system is internally consistent, it may contain a provable proposition that contradicts a proposition in the intuitive mathematics which is intended to be an interpretation of the formal system. Hence, a proof of internal consistency does not rule out the possibility that something proved in the system is intuitively false.

Analogously, it is conceivable that also in psychology internal consistency does not guarantee external consistency. A psychological formal system may possibly be internally consistent and yet contain a provable proposition P that is "intuitively false." The last phrase may indicate, for example, that the proposition P contradicts another proposition that is known to be true in the empirical realm of psychology. In other words, the proposition P, which is provable within an internally consistent theory, may be empirically false or incorrect because it is contradicted by empirical facts or experimental evidence.

It is not unusual in psychology for a theory to be adhered to despite signs of external inconsistency. For example, it has been candidly admitted by proponents of a theory of learning and of a theory of psychotherapy, respectively, that their respective theories are inconsistent with or are contradicted by certain experimental findings or facts (compare Kendler, 1951 and Rogers, 1959). That the proponents do not discard the theories may stem from the assumption, sometimes regarded as tantamount to a scientific dictum, that a theory is never overthrown by facts, but only by a better theory. Or it may rest on the assumption that the virtues of the theory, including its formal properties, override the external inconsistencies that were found. This leads to the problem of how many and what kind of external inconsistencies must be found before a theory is discarded. More generally, it leads to the issue of relative consistency, including degrees of internal consistency and degrees of external inconsistency. Concepts of relative consistency have been formulated in mathematics (see Fraenkel and Bar-Hillel, 1958, p. 288). It should be of interest to introduce their counterparts in psychology and to discuss the problem of what degree or amount (or kind) of external inconsistency vitiates a certain degree or amount (or kind) of internal consistency, or vitiates other properties considered desirable in a formal theory. In particular, it should be of interest to determine the intended interpretations of the theory and to consider which of these are to be taken into account in studying the external consistency of the theory.

External inconsistency of certain theories may be a partial source of the conflicts between theoreticians and practitioners. The theoretician or academician may say or do something which seems to be perfectly consistent with his theory, but which may not be consistent with the facts or with the actual situation or particular phenomenon in the clinic, school, or factory to which the theory is intended to apply. Theories of psychotherapy and learning, for example, may be internally consistent and yet may miss the mark with regard to the actual problems and practices of psychotherapy and teaching. Is the clinical psychologist or teacher justified in rejecting a theory if it is inconsistent with the living phenomenon with which he has to deal? The clinical psychologist, for example, is not paid for the formal elegance or beauty of the theory or hypothetico-deductive system he is using; his task is to cure, or at least help, patients. It is not that practitioners appreciate less than theoreticians the importance of internal consistency of a theory. Possibly it is that they appreciate more the importance of external consistency. Perhaps one way of lessening the conflicts between theoreticians and practitioners, between theory and practice, would be to place more emphasis on external consistency in the presentation of the theory.

Decision Problems in Psychology

It may be recalled that a decision method for a general question is a uniform method—a general, mechanical, routine method involving a finite number of steps—that actually can be utilized to obtain a "yes" or a "no" answer to every specific case of the general question. A decision problem for a given question is the problem of whether or not there exists a decision method for the question. In mathematics and logic, there is much interest in decision problems and decision methods. It seems that there is a corresponding interest among natural and behavioral scientists who also are searching for uniform, objective procedures to deal with certain decision problems. In psychology, for example, there is a desire for preassigned rules or routines or algorithms that offer a means of obtaining answers to all particular instances of general questions. It is, of course, desired that the rules be theoretically well founded and that they constitute valid guides. Such decision methods have the advantages of not having to be varied from one instance to another of a general question or a general case and of eliminating subjective factors or keeping them at low ebb.

The search for decision methods is clearly seen in statistics, some of whose procedures amount to routines for answering such questions as: "Is this finding statistically significant at the .05 level of confidence?" or "Is there justification for dismissing the null hypothesis?"

Psychological testing and diagnosis also involve a search for decision methods. For example, certain factor analytic procedures that have been proposed in the area of personality and motivation measurement and assessment are in the nature of decision methods. Some tests or batteries of tests purport to offer, or are sometimes utilized as if they offer, decision procedures for such questions as whether a given individual is feeble-minded or not. Considerable effort has been expanded in attempts to evolve routine schemes for the assessment of personality and decision methods for such problems as whether a given individual is neurotic, psychotic, or schizophrenic. Particularly welcome to clinical psychologists would be decision methods for such problems as whether a given individual is treatable in the sense that he is profiting from, or that he can profit from, psychotherapy. This problem might be posed for individual psychotherapy, group psychotherapy, a certain type of therapy, or a specific therapy program. The "therapy machines" that have been used experimentally with psychotic patients (essentially intermittent reinforcement devices that offer rewards such as candy) may be regarded as offering a built-in decision procedure for determining whether or not a patient should receive a reward at a given time. There is some interest in the development of machines that can do diagnosis and even therapy, not only in the psychotherapeutic area but also in general medicine and in other healing arts.

Some of the diagnostic procedures in medicine amount to decision methods. These are uniform procedures which yield a "yes" or "no" answer to the question of whether an individual has a certain disease. Although the answer may not have the certainty characteristic of decision methods, certain medical diagnostic procedures approach close to this certainty. A good deal of diagnostic research in medicine amounts to a search for decision procedures. As already noted, it has even been speculated that machines may eventually be able to do at least some medical diagnosis.

Education is also concerned with certain decision problems. Some of the testing done in schools represents a search for a routine which will yield a decision as to whether a given individual has learned certain subject matter or is ready for other learning experiences. "Learning machines" that have become increasingly popular in the past decade include machines to teach school subjects and even psychology (E. J. Green, 1962; Skinner, 1958). Some learning machines may be regarded as affording built-in decision methods for determining whether or not a person should go on to the next step in the learning program. In effect, certain learning machines "decide" that the individual may not go on to the next question until he offers certain predetermined answers to preceding questions. While neither learning machines nor other educational devices can decide with complete certainty that an individual is ready for a given learning experience, research goes on in the hope of developing more certain methods. The hope is to develop, for education and for vocational guidance, decision procedures with the efficiency and certainty with which the litmus paper test can be used to decide whether a given substance is acid or alkali.

The concept of the Turing machine (Turing, 1936–1937; Kleene, 1952; Adler, 1961) has been appealed to in connection with certain decision problems in mathematics and logic. It has also been appealed to in connection with a decision method for a linguistic problem (Post, 1947; Markov, 1947) and, more recently, for problems in the psychology of thinking and other problems in psychology (Bruner, 1960).

Many decision problems in mathematics have proved to be unsolvable. It is not entirely unlikely that many decision problems in psychology are also unsolvable so that there exists no general uniform method which will give a "yes" or "no" answer, in a finite number of steps, to every particular instance of the problem. Research is needed to determine how we can discover means that may lead to the establishment of the solvability or unsolvability of certain decision problems in psychology. Such a research program also requires criteria on the basis of which to determine just what constitute decision methods in psychology. It is very likely that we shall have to be content with less than strict analogies of mathematical methods and settle for approximations to such decision methods. But, before decision methods are sought, we have to know just what constitutes a decision problem in psychology. After this we can turn to the task of formulating psychological problems and issues so that they are in the nature of decision problems. Here there is the danger that the process of formulation may so change the original problem that it is not equivalent to the decision problem. In other words, the process of reformulating a problem so that it has the format of a decision problem may yield a decision problem that is not equivalent to the original problem but perhaps is only peripherally related to it. It is advisable to consider the relationship between the original problem and the decision problem, to notice which aspects of the original problem are retained or absent in the decision problem, which aspects of the decision problem are absent in the original problem, and whether aspects that play a certain role in one problem play a different or less central role in the other problem. Moreover, it is important to be alert to the influence of a method on the problem, both in its original formulation and in its formulation as a decision problem. As Köhler pointed out (1929), it is important to consider the effects on a problem or a phenomenon of the methods used in attempts to solve or understand it. The methods may influence not only what is learned about the problem or phenomenon but may themselves influence and change the problem or phenomenon to which they are applied.

Metatheory for Psychology

The prefix *meta* has been used to identify a theory (or a language) in which the object of study is itself a theory (or a language). Thus the term *metamathematics* refers to a discipline in which mathematics is the object of study. The latter is called the object theory while the metamathematics is called the metatheory. A similar distinction is sometimes made in terms of object language and syntax language, where the latter is the language with which one describes the former or, more exactly, its syntactical form (Carnap, 1937).

Some such distinction is useful for the behavioral sciences. It is of value, for certain purposes, to distinguish between a metatheory and its object theory, between a metalanguage, or syntax language, and its object language. To do so may lessen semantic confusion. At present, it is not always possible to distinguish psychological theories from theories *about* psychological theories. The same discussion may jump abruptly from one to another and from statements about objects of psychological investigations to statements about the statements. It is of interest, for example, to consider a critical evaluation of Freudian psychoanalysis and try to separate statements in Freudian theory (here considered as the object theory) from statements about these statements (here considered as part of the metatheory). More generally, it may be worthwhile to attempt to separate statements (or questions) about objects studied in psychology from statements (or questions) about the foregoing. Carnap makes such a distinction in terms of *object-questions* and *logical-questions*.

> The questions dealt with in any theoretical field—and similarly the corresponding sentences and assertions—can be roughly divided into *object-questione* and *logical-questions*. . . . By object-questions are to be understood thoss that have to do with the objects of the domain under consideration, such as inquiries regarding their properties and relations. The logical questions, on the other hand, do not refer directly to the objects, but to sentences, terms, theories, and so on, which themselves refer to the objects. . . . For instance, in the domain of zoology, the object-questions are concerned with the properties of animals, the relations of animals to one another and to other objects, etc.; the logical questions, on the other hand, are concerned with the sentences of zoology and the logical connections between them, the logical character of the definitions occurring in that science, the logical character of the theories and hypotheses which may be, or have actually been, advanced, and so on. (Carnap, 1937, p. 277)

In psychology, also, it may be of value to distinguish object-questions from logical-questions, object-statements from logical-statements, and object-language from syntax-language. More generally, it may be worthwhile to distinguish between psychology and metapsychology.

Certain textbooks and courses tend to confound problems and issues of psychology with those of metapsychology. This is illustrated by (but not confined exclusively to) some textbooks on history and systems of psychology. The student who is not alerted to the distinction between psychological and metapsychological issues may get the idea that psychology is dependent on the solutions of certain problems that are metapsychological in nature. This raises the question of whether or not the functioning and development of psychology as a science is dependent on the solution of these (or any other) metapsychological problems. Is the functioning and development of mathematics dependent on metamathematics and that of physics dependent on metaphysics? There are other problems involved also. What are the advantages and disadvantages of interrelating metapsychology and psychology? Should psychological issues be separated from metapsychological ones? What are the advantages and disadvantages of separating or not separating them, of interrelating them, and of confounding them? Should courses which deal with metapsychology be named accordingly? Courses in metamathematics are sometimes distinguished, by title and content, from courses in mathematics per se. The separation is perhaps even sharper in the natural sciences where a student who takes a course in physics does not expect to get involved with the formal problems of metaphysics, and, as far as we know, seldom does. If he is interested in metaphysics, he turns to a philosophy course. Should metapsychology be dealt with in courses and textbooks on the philosophy of psychology? Whether or not this is done, should metapsychological issues be raised, where they seem relevant, in texts and courses on psychology? If so, how can this be done without unduly confounding psychology and metapsychology? These are, we believe, questions worthy of consideration by those who plan psychology curricula.

A mathematical theory is formalized before it becomes the object of metamathematical investigation. Must a theory in the behavioral sciences also be formalized before it is subjected to metatheoretical study? In particular, must a psychological theory be formalized before it can become the object of metapsychological investigation? Can an informal psychological theory be studied via metatheory without any intervening attempts at formalization? It would be of interest to consider arguments for affirmative as well as negative answers to these questions. Different answers may reflect diverse conceptions of the nature of metapsychology.

Involved, also, are the problems of the direction that formalization should take and the extent to which a theory should be formalized before it can be (or should be) the object of metapsychological study. Complete formalization of a mathematical theory involves formalization of the system of logic utilized. This may be neither necessary nor desirable for psychological theory, so that only partial formalization may suffice. How far should the partial formalization go? For example, assume that there is a theory B with abstract symbols which, when certain interpretations are given to the symbols, yields part of an informal theory A as an "interpretation." How much of the informal theory A must be obtainable from B in this way in order for B to be regarded as a formalization or partial formalization of A? And how far must the formalization proceed before metatheoretical investigation is undertaken?

For metamathematical investigations, formalists limit the permissible methods and concepts more severely than they do for (informal) mathematics per se. For metamathematics they insist on methods and concepts that are intuitively convincing. We raise the question whether some restriction should also be placed on concepts and methods used in metapsychology as compared to those in informal psychology. Should the ultimate test of whether a concept or method is admissible in metapsychology be whether it is "intuitively convincing"? What are the criteria for determining that something is intuitively convincing, and how do these criteria compare in mathematics and in psychology?

Perhaps for metapsychology the concern should not be with whether methods and concepts are intuitively convincing but with whether they are scientific. Perhaps more severe standards of scientific rigor should be imposed on methods and concepts used in metapsychology than on those used in informal psychology. After all, mathematical rigor may be regarded as the motivation behind the insistence on intuitive methods and concepts for metamathematics. Correspondingly, a desire for maximum scientific rigor might suggest certain criteria that might have to be met by methods and concepts in order for them to be admissible for metapsychology.

But what criteria should be established for selection or rejection of methods and concepts? To insist that they must be scientific in turn raises the problem of what is meant by *scientific*. There are differences of opinion on this matter. Moreover, conceptions of what is scientific change in time, even over relatively short periods of time. A case in point is that of the concepts of purpose and reasoning. These and related concepts were for a long time regarded as unscientific by psychologists who favored mechanistic explanations and models of behavior. In recent years, due to advances in the technology of calculator engineering, machine models have been developed which have characteristics that represent, or seem to correspond to, purpose and reasoning (or rationality) in man. Therefore, such concepts are now more acceptable to psychologists with predilections for mechanistic models. Psychologists are beginning to admit that such terms as *purpose* and *rational* may be permissible in scientific psychology. In short, it seems that some psychologists consider that an aspect of human behavior is acceptable for scientific study, or at least is more acceptable, when a correspondent of the behavior is demonstrated in a mechanical model. Other psychologists consider that this is neither essential nor desirable because such a restriction may ignore essential features of human behavior. They consider intuitively evident aspects of human behavior, such as purpose, reasoning, value, and so on, as important aspects of human behavior that ought to be studied scientifically, regardless of whether or not a mechanical model exists for them. Moreover, there are psychologists who maintain that the modern calculators that are regarded as demonstrating purpose and reasoning actually are not demonstrating these properties and that it may be misleading to consider their processes as the analogues of purposeful or reasoning processes in human beings. Calculators are models and as such may be representations of aspects of human behavior but are not isomorphic with them (Chapanis, 1961; Roth, 1962, 1963).

The above is intended to illustrate the difficulties of determining criteria to be applied to concepts or methods in order to determine whether or not they are scientific. A similar discussion could be carried through if experimental verifiability were proposed as a criterion for selection of methods and concepts. Such a criterion would raise problems concerning what is meant by experimental verifiability and what criteria have to be met before experimental verifiability can be regarded as attained (Nagel, 1961).

In summary, one might want "higher standards" of scientific rigor for metapsychology than for the psychology that is the object of metatheoretical study. Complex problems, which are worthy of serious consideration, center on what is meant by *higher standards* and on what the standards should be in psychology and in metapsychology, respectively.

Discussions in the experimental literature and even the experimentation itself suggest that in some cases standards for admissible concepts and methods are actually standards of metapsychology. Perhaps they should not be used to evaluate experimental and empirical issues in psychology. It may be that the use of metapsychological standards, along with the accompanying discussions, tend to cloud the particular phenomenon under investigation. This is suggested, for example, in discussions of as well as in experimentation on the so-called continuity versus discontinuity controversy, the nativism versus empiricism controversy in perception, trial and error versus insight learning, the hereditary versus the environment controversy, and the so-called instinct controversy.

CHAPTER 12

Intuitionism:
History and Tenets

Intuitionism is a label applied to the views of a relatively small number of mathematicians. Because intuitionists differ somewhat in their beliefs with reference to mathematical foundations, it is perhaps more appropriate to speak of the various trends or schools of intuitionism. The major and best-known of these is the so-called Dutch school, whose nucleus consists of L. E. J. Brouwer and his students and colleagues in Amsterdam. Brouwer's 1907 doctoral thesis was the first step in the establishment of this school. Brouwer, also known for his contributions to topology, cognizant that his foundational views represent a distinct trend in intuitionism, refers to them as *neointuitionism*. But some members of the Dutch school refer to it simply as intuitionism (for example, Heyting, 1956). Modern intuitionism is popularly identified with Brouwer's views and Brouwer himself is considered the leading intuitionist. Brouwer and his colleagues have been, and still are, attempting to rebuild classical mathematics to meet neointuitionistic requirements. They have partially succeeded and their success may increase in the future, but certain parts of classical mathematics seem incapable of meeting neointuitionistic conceptions of what constitutes legitimate mathematics.

The origin of the name *intuitionism* is not entirely clear. It does *not* seem to refer to the role of intuition in mathematical discoveries. It may have arisen from the notion of the intuition of a natural number. It may have arisen from a more basic or "primordial intuition," with which Brouwer has been concerned and which we shall later discuss. It may have arisen from the conception that the only source for the study of mathematics is "an intuition which places its concepts and inferences before our eyes as immediately evident" (Heyting, 1934). Intuitionists insist that concepts and methods be intuitively clear. Some areas of mathematics (including classical analysis and Cantor's set theory and even elementary number theory) abound with concepts and methods that are not acceptable to intuitionists.

Early Intuitionists

Some of the attitudes of intuitionism can be traced back at least as far as the ancient Greeks (see Fraenkel and Bar-Hillel, 1958, p. 201). In more modern times, we find some of the doctrines of modern intuitionism expressed by Kronecker, one of the most distinguished mathematicians of the latter part of the nineteenth century. Kronecker's views included the following (see Wilder, 1952, pp. 192–194):

1. The natural numbers and operations with them are intuitively founded and constitute a suitable foundation for mathematics.

2. (In modern terminology, Kronecker might be called a constructionist and finitist.) Definitions and proofs should be *constructive*, in the sense that a given rule should permit the construction of a mathematical entity in a *finite* number of steps starting from the natural numbers (or from mathematical entities, which are themselves constructed on the basis of the natural numbers). Such construction is essential for mathematical existence. Thus, in order for a proof of the existence of a mathematical entity to be acceptable, it has to give a rule or method for constructing the entity. In particular, indirect proofs, based on *reductio ad absurdum*, were generally not acceptable (to Kronecker) since they did not give a method of construction, but instead surmised the existence of an entity because a contradiction was logically deduced from the assumption that the entity did not exist. Illustrations are furnished by proofs of the fundamental theorem of algebra that logically deduce the existence of a root (because the assumption that there is no root leads to a contradiction) but that do not give any method of constructing the root.

3. Logical arguments do not necessarily yield theorems of mathematics. For example, a *reductio ad absurdum* proof may be logically correct, but it is not necessarily mathematically valid.

4. It is not permissible to consider an infinite set as a completed entity, or an already existing totality. Intuitively, we can conceive of a constructible collection, which is growing, which is increasing step by step, but we cannot conceive of infinitely many objects as if they were in an array before us, constituting a completed collection. (Apparently Kronecker was distinguishing between what is now called the *potential infinite* and the *actual* or *completed infinite*.) A natural number (to Kronecker) is not a member of the set of all natural numbers, an already completed infinite totality. Rather it is a natural number because it can be obtained by beginning with the natural numbers 1, 2, 3, and successively adding 1 to construct the next number. "If one objects that each and every natural number is so attainable, and hence the existence of the 'set of all natural numbers' again follows, it can be pointed out that this assumes an *infinity* of operations in order to construct each and *every* natural number. For the 'finitist,' only the 'constructible' concept of the natural numbers is acceptable" (Wilder, 1952, p. 193).

Kronecker argued against certain methods and concepts, popular in his day and still popular today. Such well-known mathematicians of his time as Dedekind, Weierstrass, and Cantor made use of the notion of the infinite as a completed totality (for example, in Dedekind's concept of a real number as a set of infinitely many rational numbers and in Cantor's theory of infinite sets). Kronecker contended that many of the definitions these mathematicians used were meaningless, since they did not indicate how the object supposedly defined was to be constructed.

Poincaré, "the greatest genius which our science has known during the last half century" (Hadamard, 1945, p. 12), also held some (but not all) of the views today enunciated by intuitionists. He considered that every mathematical concept should be capable of explicit definition. He thought that some of the concepts, methods, and results of Cantor's set theory did not constitute a part of legitimate mathematics. Foreshadowing modern intuitionism, he stressed mathematical induction as a primary tool of mathematical reasoning. He believed that mathematical induction was so intuitively clear that it was, so to speak, forced on our intuition, and that it could not be reduced to more elementary or intuitively clearer methods (Poincaré, 1902, 1913, 1963). Unlike modern intuitionists, Poincaré believed that a proof of freedom from contradiction can serve as the basis for an assertion of mathematical existence.

Moreover, he was not opposed to the axiom of choice. Yet, he did not completely accept some principles equivalent to the axiom of choice (they imply and are implied by this axiom). Among these is the well-ordering theorem (or principle) which states that every infinite set can be well ordered in the sense that any nonempty subset of it has a smallest member. The set of natural numbers is well ordered but it is not apparent that other infinite sets (for example, the sets of rational numbers, real numbers, or complex numbers) can be well ordered. Yet, the surprising result that every set can be well ordered is equivalent to the axiom of choice. The first proof of the well-ordering theorem (Zermelo, 1904) provoked intuitionistic-type arguments from Poincaré and some of his French colleagues, among them Baire, Borel, Hadamard, and Lebesgue. These men formed the kernel of what has come to be known as the Paris school of intuitionism (or semi-intuitionism or half-intuitionism). It is of interest that some of these Paris intuitionists had applied Cantor's set theory to analysis and that neointuitionism considers some of their contributions (for example, Lebesgue's concept of an integral) to be outside the realm of legitimate mathematics. As the name perhaps suggests, semi-intuitionism accepts some but not all of the tenets of certain other schools of intuitionism. For example, a shibboleth of neointuitionism is the mathematical invalidity of the law of the excluded middle, in its general sense, whereas the "Paris school and other intuitionistic trends have not accepted the attitude of the Dutch school to the excluded middle" (Fraenkel and Bar-Hillel, 1958, p. 215).

It has become customary to preface discussions of neointuitionism with a remark that the obscurity of Brouwer's writings makes it difficult to know whether a correct interpretation of his views has been attained. At present there is, perhaps, somewhat less justification for such a remark,

since in the last few years there have appeared several very readable
accounts of intuitionism, written in English, by members of the Dutch
school (see, for example, Heyting, 1956). Heyting, who was a student of
Brouwer, is now one of the most lucid expositors of neointuitionism. True,
these expositors do not claim that their writings constitute a codification
of neointuitionism and Brouwer himself has not given official sanction to
all the interpretations of his views made by various members of the
Dutch school. Nonetheless, the recent writings in English in conjunction
with earlier writings by Brouwer and other members of his school and
commentaries on these writings proved to be very helpful to us and were
the basis for the following discussion of what seem to be the important
tenets of neointuitionism.

Neointuitionistic Conception
of Mathematics

Central to neointuitionism is the conception that mathematics consists
of activities in the human mind. Mathematics, "from the intuitionistic
point of view, is a study of certain functions of the human mind, and as
such is akin to [the social sciences]," it is "a phenomenon of life, a natural
activity of man" (Heyting, 1956, pp. 9–10). Some (but not all) non-
intuitionists would grant that mental activities constitute part of mathematics, but they consider that the more *exact* parts of mathematics are
the formal expressions written or spoken by mathematicians. However,
to Brouwer, mathematics and mathematical exactness lie in the nature
of thought activities, not in attempts to communicate these activities.
"The question where mathematical exactness does exist is answered differently by the two sides; the intuitionist says: in the human intellect, the
formalist says: on paper" (Brouwer, 1913, p. 83). Heyting (1934) words
it: "According to Brouwer, mathematics is identical with the exact part
of our thinking."

A different interpretation (with the stress on nonexactness rather than
exactness) is offered by Black, who writes that Brouwer regards mathematics "above all as a product of the activity of human minds and, as
such, liable to be affected by all the defects to which our thought is essentially subject" (1934, p. 171). Black sees neointuitionism's concern with
mental activities as a concomitant of a dynamic attitude toward mathematics in contrast to a static attitude attributed to adherents of formalism
and logicism. *Static* refers here, to paraphrase Black (p. 169), to a conception of mathematics as a system of theorems that may be extended
but not controverted, analogous to a library that acquires new volumes
but does not destroy the old volumes. A static attitude calls for a science
that does not make mistakes. It stresses the permanency and invulner-

ability of mathematics. In contrast, the dynamic attitude stresses the growth, development, and changeability of mathematics.

Thus just as the supporters of static attitudes will tend to emphasize the external forms of mathematics, its formulae *qua* physical objects, just because these are the most permanent and tangible features of mathematical activity, so also the supporters of dynamic evolutionary attitudes emphasize mathematical *thought* just because it is that element in mathematics which is most intangible, changing, and capable of development. The dynamic attitude is consistent with an evolutionary conception of history and naturally arises from it. (Black, 1934, p. 171)

That neointuitionists emphasize mental activities rather than the mathematical symbolism and formalism emphasized by other foundational philosophies is viewed as a concomitant of the difference between the dynamic and static attitudes. Black writes that for neointuitionists "the body of mathematical truth is not the timeless, objective structure that it appears in the formalist and logistic philosophies" but rather, it "grows, it is a becoming, a process, which can never be completely symbolized" (1934, pp. 9–10).

Formalists and logicists also believe mathematics capable of growth and development. Yet how does their view differ from the so-called dynamic view? It seems to us that a difference is suggested in these words from a rabbinical commentary on the fourth line of Psalm 144: "Would that life were like a shadow cast by a wall or a tree; but it is like the shadow of a bird in flight." Although a shadow of a wall or tree changes, the changes differ in rapidity and regularity from those undergone by the shadow of a bird in flight. So changes in mathematics concomitant with a static attitude, differ from changes concomitant with a dynamic attitude.

Mathematics and Language

That neointuitionists view mathematics as consisting of mental activities rather than as the communication or expression of these activities can readily be seen to influence their conception of the relationship between mathematics and language. For communication of mathematics, language may be essential; but mathematics per se is considered by Brouwer (1929) as not intrinsically related to language or necessarily dependent on it. This view is pertinent to the issue, of considerable interest to psychologists and to some mathematicians (for example, Hadamard, 1945), of whether thinking, and in particular creative mathematical thinking, is dependent on language and verbalization.

It seems to us that the distinction which Brouwer makes between mathematics and language may be related to the distinction between impression and expression of mathematics. (Compare this with the distinction between the impression and expression of personality, Luchins, 1957a.) The mathematician has an impression of his mental activities that constitute mathematical thought. For this impression, language is not essential. But to express this impression so that it can be conveyed to others, language is essential. Unfortunately, there is no language adequate to express mathematical thoughts exactly; divergency between impression and expression is inevitable.

As Fraenkel and Bar-Hillel word it, neointuitionism stresses the weakness of mathematical language in comparison to mathematical thought:

> . . . for any language is maintained to be vague and exposed to misunderstanding, even symbolic language. . . . Hence mathematical language is ambiguous and defective; mathematical thought, while strict and uniform in itself, is subject to obscurity and error when transferred from one person to another by means of speaking or writing. It would therefore be a fundamental mistake to analyze mathematical language instead of mathematical thought. . . . Hence *for mathematics there exists no safe language* which excludes misunderstanding in talk and prevents mistakes of memory. (1958, p. 213)

Some neointuitionists believe that they can attempt to convey their thoughts to others by means of a nonformalized language. But they do not deceive themselves that their thoughts are precisely conveyed and understood. However, the formalization of a language is considered to offer no guarantee that mathematical thoughts will be conveyed exactly from one person to another. With a nonformalized language, there is less likelihood that such a guarantee will be erroneously presupposed and that verbal expressions will be regarded as precisely expressing certain mathematical thoughts.

Referring to the establishment of parts of intuitionistic mathematics as formal systems, Heyting warns that "we clash against the obstacle of the fundamental ambiguousness of language. As the meaning of a word can never be fixed precisely enough to exclude every possibility of misunderstanding, we can never be mathematically sure that the formal system expresses correctly our mathematical thoughts" (1956, p. 4). Nonetheless Heyting, who has expressed aspects of intuitionistic logic as formal systems, concedes that it may be helpful and clarifying to formalize intuitionistic mathematics. But he adds that it is never necessary to do so. On the other hand, Beth (1959) suggests that formalization may be necessary.

> If intuitionistic mathematics is at all a legitimate form of mathematical thought, then it must admit of a presentation which, in lucidity and rigor, attains a level equal to that which is characteristic of classical mathematics in its most outstanding contemporary manifestations. In order to achieve this end we must, in particular, try to eliminate such subjective, and sometimes even mystical, elements as can be found in most intuitionistic writings. On the other hand, no satisfactory insight can be obtained by simply studying those

formal systems which result if, from extant formalisations of classical mathematics, we drop such principles as are open to intuitionistic criticism.

We must rather start from the truly mathematical, that is objective, content of intuitionistic mathematics and try to construct a language (a terminology, or a conceptual apparatus) in which this content can be adequately expressed. If such a construction turns out to be impossible, it seems to follow that intuitionistic mathematics is condemned forever to remain a purely subjective experience. (p. 15)

Mathematical Construction and Existence

What are the mental activities to which neointuitionists give the name *mathematics*? They have been characterized as certain mental mathematical constructions. "Intuitionistic mathematics consists . . . in mental constructions" (Heyting, 1956, p. 8). A fundamental thesis, which seems to underlie all varieties of intuitionism, is that mathematical existence coincides with mathematical construction. "In the study of mental mathematical constructions 'to exist' must be synonymous with 'to be constructed'" (Heyting, 1956, p. 2). Heyting says that he is attracted by mathematics in which an object is believed to exist only after it has been constructed because he is "unable to give an intelligible sense to the assertion that a mathematical object which has not been constructed, exists" (1959, p. 69). In short, intuitionists consider that an object has been proved to have mathematical existence only if a constructive proof can be given, in the sense that the "proof actually exhibits an example [of such an object], or at least indicates a method by which one could in principle find such an example" (Kleene, 1952, p. 49). Many so-called existence proofs of classical mathematics are unacceptable to intuitionists because they are not constructive. Some of these proofs derive the existence of an entity from the axiom of choice or from principles of traditional logic (for example, because the assumption that the entity does not exist leads to a contradiction). But intuitionists, we have seen, consider that "to squeeze *existence* out of such logical manipulation is not valid *mathematically*" (Wilder, 1952, p. 194).

Intuitionists have had moderate success in obtaining constructive proofs for some classical nonconstructive existence proofs. Moreover, mathematicians who do not identify themselves with intuitionism have been spurred to offer constructive existence proofs, or what some call *effective* proofs. Such proofs have been given not only for older parts of mathematics but also for more recent mathematical research. For example, a report entitled "A Note on Constructive Methods in Banach Algebras," points out that a previous proof has the disadvantage "of not yielding a constructive method for obtaining the object whose existence is asserted by the theorem" and then offers a constructive version of a Banach algebra proof (P. J. Cohen, 1961, p. 159). Another example is a constructive algebra proof by Lemke and Howson (1964) of the existence of equilibrium points for bimatrix (two-person matrix) games; the proof, which is valid for any ordered field, leads to an efficient scheme for computing an equilibrium point. Constructive proofs for solutions to a wider class of problems in mathematical programming are given by Lemke (1964).

Not only theorems and proofs but also definitions must allow for the construction of the object defined in order to meet intuitionistic requirements. For example, an integer is considered to be well defined only if a method for calculating it is given. In this connection, consider the following definitions (Heyting, 1956, p. 2).

1. Let k be the largest prime number such that $k - 1$ is also a prime or let $k = 1$ if such a number does not exist.
2. Let l be the largest prime number such that $l - 2$ is also a prime or let $l = 1$ if such a number does not exist.

Classical mathematics has paid insufficient attention to the difference between these definitions. The number k can actually be calculated as 3, since 2 is the only even prime. But there is no method for calculating l and, in fact, it is not even known whether the set of pairs of twin primes p, $p + 2$ is finite or not. Therefore intuitionists reject the second definition.

Heyting's charming text (1956) is in the form of a dialogue between spokesmen for various foundational views. Mr. Class (presumably a spokesman for the classical point of view) argues that it does not matter whether or not l can actually be calculated or constructed. Mr. Int (presumably an adherent of neointuitionism) claims that this argument is metaphysical in nature, since if "to exist" does not mean "to be constructed," it must have some metaphysical meaning. "It cannot be the task of mathematics to investigate this meaning or to decide whether it is tenable or not. We have no objection against a mathematician privately admitting any metaphysical theory he likes, but Brouwer's program entails that we study mathematics as something simpler, more immediate than metaphysics" (Heyting, 1956, p. 2).

Mr. Class notes that definition 2 would suddenly become a real definition of an integer if the problem of twin primes were solved. Let us say that on January 1, 1970 it is proved that an infinity of twin primes existed; then from that date on definition 2 defines l as being equal to 1. Mr. Class wants to know whether $l = 1$ before that date. Mr. Int's reply is so neat a characterization of neointuitionistic views that we reproduce it:

A mathematical assertion affirms the fact that a certain mathematical construction has been effected. It is clear that before the construction was made, it had not been made. Applying that remark to your example, we see that before January 1, 1970 it had not been proved that $l = 1$. But this is not what you mean. It seems to me that in order to clarify the sense of your question you must again refer to metaphysical concepts: to some world of mathematical things existing independently of our knowledge, where "$l = 1$" is true in some absolute sense. But I repeat that mathematics ought not to depend upon such notions as these. In fact all mathematicians and even intuitionists are convinced that in some sense mathematics bear upon eternal truths, but when trying to define precisely this sense, one gets entangled in a maze of metaphysical difficulties. The only way to avoid them is to banish them from mathematics. (Heyting, 1956, pp. 2–3)

To banish them, Brouwer proposes to investigate mental mathematical construction as such, without reference to whether or not the objects constructed exist independently of our knowledge of them.

What is mathematical construction?

Since intuitionists consider that mathematical construction is requisite for mathematical existence, it is understandable that they have been asked just what they mean by mathematical construction. No decisive answer has been given. Construction seems to have somewhat different meanings for different intuitionists.

To Kronecker, mathematical construction seemed to mean starting with the natural numbers and building up entities in a finite number of steps, and only those entities that could be so constructed had mathematical meaning. Since, for example, irrational numbers and real numbers were not so constructed, Kronecker would not grant them mathematical existence. In fact, one of his reasons for introducing modular arithmetic (now of interest in its own right, see Andree, 1959) was that it enabled negative integers, irrational numbers, and, in fact, all real and all complex numbers, to be expressed in terms of natural numbers. Through the medium of modular arithmetic, mathematicians would be able to get by with the intuitively founded natural numbers and have no need to introduce "illegitimate" entities.

Unlike Kronecker and some other intuitionists, Brouwer has found ways of introducing irrational numbers and, in fact, all real numbers in ways that he considers constructible and intuitionistically satisfactory. Hence these entities are granted mathematical existence in neointuitionism.

Mathematical induction, on which Poincaré placed so much stress, seems to be regarded by some of the Paris intuitionists as the only acceptable method of constructing nonfinite mathematical entities. Mathematical induction remains the prototype of transfinite constructions that are acceptable to intuitionists. Yet it would be misleading to describe it as the only method they find acceptable. For example, some of Brouwer's concepts (such as that of set or species and free-choice sequence) actually amount to modes of construction.

In short, we see that the nature of mathematical construction, and, concomitantly, the realm of entities regarded as having mathematical existence vary somewhat within intuitionism.

Intuitive evidence

Neointuitionism is concerned with what has been called *intuitive evidence* or *cognitive evidence*. It seeks for evidence in mental mathematical construction and not in the so-called external or physical world. This is clearly revealed by Heyting when he writes: "The characteristic of mathematical thought is that it does not convey truth about the external world, but is only concerned with mental constructions" (1956, pp. 8–9). He notes that "intuitionistic assertions must seem dogmatic to those who read them as assertions about facts, but they are not meant in this sense . . . a mathematical theorem expresses a purely empirical fact, namely the success of a certain construction." Here "empirical" refers to mental octivities and not to the external world. This distinction seems sometimes to be overlooked, particularly by those who label intuitionism "empiricism."

Cognitive evidence is considered to determine uniquely the premises of neointuitionism. As Mr. Int puts it to Mr. Class, "While you think in terms of axioms and deductions, we think in terms of evidence; that makes all the difference. I do not accept any axioms which I might reject if I chose to do so" (Heyting, 1956, p. 13). In other words, neointuitionism does not start from "more or less arbitrary assumptions. Its subject, constructive mathematical thought, determines uniquely its premises and places it beside, not interior to classical mathematics, which studies another subject, whatever subject that may be" (p. 4).

In short, for intuitionists, the evidence and empirical facts on which mathematical existence, meaning, and truth are founded is to be found in mental activities. Using the distinction between the external and the phenomenal world or between the geographical and the behavioral world (Koffka, 1935, pp. 27–67), we may say that intuitionists seek for evidence in the phenomenal or behavioral world rather than in the external or geographical world.

Infinite Sets and Antinomies

Equating mathematical existence and mathematical constructivity can account for the intuitionistic view of the infinite. Like Kronecker, modern intuitionists do not regard an infinite set, such as the totality of natural numbers, as having mathematical existence.

> Brouwer made it clear, as I think beyond any doubt, that there is no evidence supporting the belief in the existential character of the totality of all natural numbers. . . . The sequence of numbers which grows beyond any

stage already reached by passing on to the next number, is a manifold of possibilities open toward infinity; it remains forever in the status of creation, but is not a closed realm of things existing in themselves. That we blindly converted one into the other is the true source of our difficulties, including the antinomies. . . . Brouwer opened our eyes and made us see how far classical mathematics, nourished by a belief in the "absolute" that transcends all human possibilities of realization, goes beyond such statements as can claim real meaning and truth founded on evidence. (Weyl, 1946, p. 9)

Neointuitionism considers an infinite set to be defined when a law of construction of its terms is given. Only if we have such a law may we speak of it as a set. This conception of an infinite set has profound consequences for set theory, with much of Cantor's set theory becoming meaningless from this point of view. For example, the set of all subsets of the set of natural numbers is not considered a well-defined set and, concomitantly, there is no need for the transfinite cardinal $2^{\aleph_0}$, which is assigned to this set in Cantor's theory. (*Transfinite* indicates that the cardinal or "number" of a set is greater than $\aleph_0$, the cardinal assigned to the set of natural numbers, so that an infinite set is said to have a transfinite cardinal number if its members cannot be put in one-to-one correspondence with the natural numbers.) In Cantor's set theory, $2^{\aleph_0}$ turns out to be the cardinal of the real numbers; since the real numbers are considered to be in one-to-one correspondence with the points of the line (the so-called Euclidean real line), which is often referred to as the linear continuum, $2^{\aleph_0}$ is called the *cardinal* (or the *power*) of the continuum. Neointuitionists do not deal with cardinals greater than $\aleph_0$ so that the famous "continuum problem," the problem of whether any cardinal lies between $\aleph_0$ and $2^{\aleph_0}$, is to them a meaningless question. Cantor's proof that there exists an unending sequence of increasing transfinite cardinals is not an acceptable proof from Brouwer's point of view. It is not a constructive proof, and, moreover, the sets it deals with are not well defined from the intuitionistic standpoint. Indeed, from this standpoint, Cantor's set theory is a "pathological" case in the development of mathematics.

The intuitionistic conception of an infinite set influences also the school's attitude toward the axiom of choice. Only where there is a law of construction of the terms of the set, may the axiom be used. For example (to use Bertram Russell's illustration), if there are infinitely many pairs of shoes, then a set may be constructed consisting of a left shoe from each pair. But one does not need the axiom of choice to do this, since a law of construction of its terms defines a set. If there are infinitely many pairs of socks, then a set consisting of a member from each pair is not well defined, and the axiom of choice does not make it so.

Furthermore, the intuitionistic conception of an infinite set has consequences, we shall see, for traditional logic and for the antinomies that were such prominent symptoms of the current foundational crisis in mathematics.

The known mathematical antinomies do not pose problems to neointuitionists. For example, neither the set of all sets nor the set of all sets that are members of themselves constitute sets in neointuitionistic mathematics, since a rule is not given for the construction of the sets. All known mathematical antinomies involve impredicative definitions in which an entity is defined in terms of the totality to which it belongs. But, in general, impredicative definitions are outlawed in neointuitionism, which requires that a definition provides a means of constructing the entity defined. Hence, from the neointuitionistic viewpoint, the antinomies are mere words; they do not refer to constructive mathematical thought and do not belong to mathematics. There is no problem in resolving the antinomies, since antinomies do not exist as part of mathematics for neointuitionists.

The Principle
of the Excluded Middle

Brouwer (1908) challenged the belief that the principles of traditional logic, as formulated by Aristotle (384–322 B.C.), are valid in all contexts and for all subject matter. Although others have also discussed the possibilities that for certain objects another logic may be more adequate than the classical one, "it was Brouwer who first discovered an object which actually requires a different form of logic, namely the mental mathematical construction" (Heyting, 1956, p. 1). The reason for this inadequacy is that mathematics deals with the infinite, whereas Brouwer considers that classical logic was made for reasoning about finite collections and was abstracted from such reasoning. "Forgetful of this limited origin, one afterwards mistook that logic for something above and prior to all mathematics, and finally applied it, without justification, to the mathematics of infinite sets" (Weyl, 1946). One principle of traditional logic that Brouwer rejects in its general sense is the principle of the excluded middle (*tertium non datur*, more literally, *excluded third*). This principle states, in brief, that for a proposition P, either P or not-P (the negation of P) holds.

The principle of the excluded middle should not be confused with the principle of contradiction. The former is essentially an existence statement which asserts that either P or not-P must exist. The principle of contradiction, which states that P and not-P cannot both hold simultaneously without implying a contradiction, is acceptable to neointuitionists provided that P and not-P are intuitionistically meaningful. How strongly neointuitionism differs from logicism may be gleaned from the fact that in the *Principia Mathematica*, because of certain relations assumed to hold between the logical connectives (*implication, negation, and, or*), the principle of the excluded middle is equivalent to the principle of contradiction, that is, one principle implies the other. This is decidedly not the case in the formal system corresponding to intuitionistic logic (Heyting, 1930, 1956).

Brouwer does not deny that the excluded-middle principle is valid in certain cases, but he places restrictions on its realm of applicability. Only where an investigation involving a finite number of steps actually suffices to establish that P or not-P holds is the principle acceptable. "Thus, according to the Dutch school, *the principle of the excluded middle*, far from being a logical axiom or an *a priori* statement, *only constitutes the anticipation of a result* that may actually be reached by an investigation of a finite character" (Fraenkel and Bar-Hillel, 1958, p. 217). In particular, the principle is not acceptable when an infinite collection is involved or when it is not known whether the collection is finite or not (for instance, as in the case of the sequence of twin primes, p and $p + 2$).

That neointuitionism does not accept the excluded-middle principle in its general sense has become a battle cry of the school. Small wonder that this is often regarded as the most characteristic feature of intuitionism. Yet some trends in intuitionism, such as the Paris school, do not reject the excluded-middle principle. The rejection of this principle can be considered to be a consequence of the conception of mathematics as mental mathematical constructions. The point of view underlying Brouwer's program, which is to investigate mental mathematical construction without reference to questions concerning the nature of the constructed object, "leads immediately to the rejection of the principle of the excluded middle" (Heyting, 1956, p. 1). Heyting demonstrates this by the example that refers to the definition of the natural number l as the largest prime such that $l - 2$ is also a prime or, if such a number does not exist, then $l = 1$. The excluded-middle principle, which in effect states that either a proposition P or the proposition not-P holds, indicates that either the sequence of twin primes is finite (P) or it is not finite (not-P). If the excluded-middle principle were accepted, then the criteria for l would actually define an integer. But intuitionists consider that an integer is well defined only if a method of constructing or calculating it is given. This conception of what constitutes a definition—which in turn is related to the conception of mathematics as mental constructions and the conception of mathematical existence—therefore leads to the rejection of the excluded-middle principle. In short, we see that rejection of the excluded-middle principle, often regarded as the primary characteristic of intuitionism and of Brouwer's views, can actually be regarded as secondary, as a concomitant of other features of neointuitionism.

What is particularly important about the excluded-middle principle is its utilization in the indirect method of proof. To prove P, one assumes not-P, establishes a contradiction (by *reductio ad absurdum*), and, through an appeal to the excluded-middle principle, concludes that P holds. Indirect proofs are widely used in many branches of mathematics and they often rely on the excluded-middle principle. For some indirect proofs, direct proofs are also known. But, for many indirect proofs, including some basic existence proofs in classical analysis, direct proofs have not been found.

The reader may recall examples of indirect proofs. For example, in high school geometry, to prove that two lines are parallel (given the equality of a pair of alternate interior angles formed by a line that cuts the two given lines), one assumes that the two lines are not parallel, deduces a contradiction, and hence concludes that the lines are parallel. The reasoning involved in an indirect proof may be summarized as follows:

Premises:

1. Either P or not-P (principle of excluded middle)
2. Not-P (temporary supposition)

Conclusion: A contradiction C, that is, a false conclusion.

Through valid inference there has been deduced a false conclusion. In other words, the premises logically imply C, and C is false. But in traditional valid reasoning, a false conclusion can be implied only by false hypotheses or premises, since if the premises were true, the conclusion would have to be true. Now, if the first premise, the excluded-middle principle, is accepted as true, then it must be the second premise that is false. Since not-P does not hold, by the law of the excluded middle, P holds.

If not-P is intuitionistically meaningful and if its assumption leads to a contradiction, then neointuitionists might conclude that it is not the case that not-P or, in other words, not-(not-P). But not-(not-P), in neointuitionistic logic, is not necessarily equivalent to P, although such equivalence prevails in classical logic.

To illustrate this point, let P be a statement that a certain mathematical object (for example, a number with a certain property) exists. Then not-P is a statement that it is not the case that such an object exists. Suppose the assumption of not-P leads to a contradiction. Then by an appeal to the excluded-middle principle, P is invoked, and the object it refers to is considered to exist. But neointuitionists would not draw this conclusion. Granted that not-(not-P), P does not necessarily follow. Recall that for the proof of the existence of a mathematical object it is necessary to give a constructive proof, one which at least in principle allows the construction of the object in a finite number of steps. Through a constructive proof for the existence of the object considered in P, P is considered to be established. But it is not considered to be established by an appeal to the excluded-middle principle. In short, neointuitionism considers that a "proof of the impossibility of the impossibility of a property is not in every case a proof of the property itself" (Heyting, 1956, p. 17).

To illustrate the point further, let us consider the following statements:

1. Every A is a B, that is, every A is a member of the set B.
2. There is an A that is not a B, that is, there is an A which is not a member of the set B.
3. It is not the case that every A is a B.

Let statement 1 be denoted by P. Then statement 3, which is the negation of the general statement made in 1, is not an existence statement, as is 2. Yet traditionally 2 and 3 have been regarded as equivalent. From the neointuitionistic viewpoint they are not necessarily equivalent and a proof of 3 is not necessarily a proof of 2. To prove 2 we have to indicate how to construct an A that is not a B. In other words, we have to establish constructively the existence of such an A; we have to construct a counter-example to P, rather than to assume it from the negation of P. This illustrates that what is meant by the negation of a statement differs in classical and intuitionistic logic. In order to highlight this difference, Brouwer prefers to refer to statement 2 as the absurdity (rather than the negation) of statement 1.

The excluded-middle principle says that P or not-P must hold, which in our case would mean that statements 1 or 3 (classically, also 1 or 2) must hold. But it may happen that we cannot constructively demonstrate 1 or 2 or 3. Yet, if the principle of the excluded middle is considered to hold, then 1 or 3 (classically, also 2) must hold. Hence, as a consequence of the neointuitionistic criterion that to exist means to be constructed, it follows that the excluded-middle principle must be rejected. In short, we see again that the renouncing of this principle, in its general sense, is a consequence of the neointuitionistic conception of the relationship between mathematical existence and construction.

Suppose we can demonstrate one of the above statements. For example, suppose we can demonstrate in a manner satisfactory to neointuitionists that not-P is impossible. Then we may claim that we proved the impossibility of the impossibility of P, but we may not claim that we proved P. To prove P we have to demonstrate constructively that every A is a B. In particular, if there is an infinite class of As, we need a law for construction of its terms and then we have to demonstrate that A satisfies the law for construction of the terms of B. To affirm that not-P is false is not necessarily to prove P. Here we see again that in neointuitionistic logic, negation and falsity may be interpreted differently than in classical logic and, moreover, not-(not-P) does not necessarily imply P. Yet, if the excluded-middle principle were recognized, then a proof that not-P does not hold would immediately imply that P must hold, since the principle asserts that P or not-P holds. This would mean that a nonconstructive argument would have to be recognized as establishing existence, and this would be counter to the neointuitionistic dictum that "to exist" is synonymous with "to be constructed."

More on Intuitionistic Logic

Logic is not the ground upon which I stand. How could it be? It would in turn need a foundation which would involve principles much more intricate and less direct than those of mathematics itself. A mathematical construction ought to be so immediate to the mind and its results so clear that it needs no foundation whatsoever. One may very well know whether a reasoning is sound without using any logic; a clear scientific conscience suffices. (Heyting, 1956, p. 6)

In this manner does a spokesman for neointuitionism reject the logistic thesis that logic is the foundation for mathematics. Although one may know that reasoning is sound without using logic, neointuitionism does use a brand of logic which has come to be known as intuitionistic logic. That the principle of the excluded middle is not acceptable to this logic is well known. But just how this logic compares in other respects with classical logic was not made very clear in intuitionistic writings until Heyting (1930) offered a symbolization and formalization of what might be called the propositional calculus of neointuitionism. This has greatly facilitated the comparison of classical and intuitionistic logic and has been called the most decisive step since Brouwer's thesis in 1907 in clarifying the school's views for outsiders (Fraenkel and Bar-Hillel, 1958, p. 228). Yet such a formalization is not regarded by the Dutch school as an "orthodox codification" since "an exposition in the language of symbolic logic with its static character is, in principle, inadequate to describe the dynamic and never closed domain of mathematical activity" (p. 229). Indeed, Heyting suggests that his attempts should not be regarded as completely describing neointuitionistic mathematics. "It must be remembered that no formal system can be proved to represent adequately an intuitionistic theory. There always remains a residue of ambiguity in the interpretation of the signs, and it can never be proved with mathematical rigour that the system of axioms really embraces every valid method of proof" (Heyting, 1956, p. 102). Nonetheless, the formal systems that have been developed by Heyting and others for the propositional, predicate, and number-theoretic calculus have the property that every formula which is provable in one of these systems, when suitably interpreted, expresses a theorem of intuitionistic mathematics.

The intuitionistic propositional calculus has been developed as a formal system (Heyting, 1930, 1956) on the basis of eleven axioms, with conjunction, disjunction, implication, and negation taken as undefined concepts. The rules of inference are the same as in the classical propositional calculus. This system may be interpreted in terms of mathematical constructions (Heyting, 1956). A proposition P may be taken to be a mathematical assertion, that is, a statement which can be expressed in the form, "I have effected in my mind a (mathematical) construction with certain properties." Such a construction is considered to prove P and is called a proof of P. For the sake of brevity, the construction of P is itself called P. A conjunction, $P \& Q$, may be asserted if and only if I have effected in my mind the construction of both P and Q; a disjunction, $P \vee Q$, if and only if I have effected in my mind the construction of at least one of P and Q. The implication $P \rightarrow Q$ may be asserted if and only if I possess a construction R, which when joined to any construction that proves P (supposing that the latter construction be effected), would automatically effect a construction that proves Q. The negation of P, $\daleth P$, may be asserted if and only if I have effected a mental mathematical construction which deduces a contradiction from the supposition that a construction that proves P has been carried out. It is important to distinguish this mathematical negation from factual negation. For example, a factual negation of the assertion that I have effected a construction of a mathematical proposition P is, "I have not effected a construction of P." This statement is not in the form of a mathematical assertion and should not be confused with $\daleth P$.

The interpretations of negation and implication differ most strikingly from the usual classical interpretations in terms of truth variables. And it is mainly with regard to formulas involving negation that the chief differences occur between classical and intuitionistic logic. For example, the excluded-middle principle is such a formula. But some of the formulas that do not involve negation also differ. For example, that P implies Q or Q implies P, expressed as $P \rightarrow Q \vee Q \rightarrow P$, may not in general be asserted in intuitionistic logic; however, it is valid in classical logic (where P and Q are either true or false, and, moreover, a false proposition implies every proposition and a true proposition is implied by every proposition).

Various alternative formalizations of intuitionistic logic have also been proposed. For example, one of the axioms in Heyting's propositional calculus is $\daleth P \rightarrow (P \rightarrow Q)$. This axiom is not as intuitively evident as the other axioms and it suggests an interpretation of implication which some intuitionists question. Dropping this axiom, but retaining the others, Johansson (1936) has developed another formal system of intuitionistic logic, known as the *minimal calculus*, which may be regarded as interpreting implication in a narrower sense than Heyting's propositional calculus.

An interpretation of Heyting's propositional calculus as a calculus of problems has been offered by Kolmogoroff (1932), where the terms *problem* and *solution* are not defined but may be understood in their usual sense. With propositions P and Q each considered to correspond to a problem, a conjunction (*and*) may be asserted if and only if we possess a method of solving both problems involved; disjunction (*or*) if and only if we possess a method of solving at least one of the problems. $P \rightarrow Q$ (implication) means that the solution of Q can be reduced to the solution of P, that is, that the solution of P yields the solution of Q. From this point of view, the excluded-middle principle asserts that we possess methods of solving any given problem or its negation. Thus, from this point of view, the excluded-middle principle asserts that any mathematical problem P can be solved, either by being proved (P holds) or disproved (not-P holds). Long before Kolmogoroff's interpretation, Brouwer was aware of the bearing that the excluded-middle principle had on the thesis that any problem can, in principle, be solved. The psychological impact that the rejection of the excluded-middle principle had on the once widely accepted belief that any mathematical problem can be solved is well described by Fraenkel and Bar-Hillel (1958, pp. 226–227).

Is intuitionistic logic a part of classical logic or vice versa? Offhand, it would seem that intuitionistic logic can be considered as part of classical logic, the part that results when the axiom of the excluded middle is omitted. Or, starting with the intuitionistic system, we might consider obtaining classical logic by adding the excluded-middle principle. Essentially the latter procedure can be carried through for the formal system given in Kleene (1952) that corresponds to the intuitionistic propositional calculus. By adding another axiom, $\daleth\daleth P \rightarrow P$ which is shown to be equivalent to the excluded-middle principle, one obtains the classical propositional calculus. To start with a formal system corresponding to classical logic and to omit the excluded-middle principle, does not suffice to yield the intuitionistic system. Instead, Kleene proceeds by replacing an axiom of the classical system, $\daleth\daleth P \rightarrow P$ (which, it was mentioned, is equivalent to the excluded-middle principle) by a weaker axiom, $\daleth P \rightarrow (P \rightarrow Q)$, where P and Q are any propositions. The latter (an axiom of Heyting's system but not of Johansson's) may be considered a weaker axiom, since it is deducible from $\daleth\daleth P \rightarrow P$ but not vice versa. Thus the weaker axiom perforce belongs to the classical system. The system that results from the classical system by the replacement referred to (with the other axioms of the classical propositional calculus retained) is known as the corresponding intuitionistic system. In short, the intuitionistic propositional calculus can be interpreted as part of classical logic. In this interpretation, it is essential that the intuitionistic connectives be regarded as corresponding to their usual counterparts within the classical system.

On the other hand, it was shown by Gödel (1933) that classical logical systems can be interpreted as parts of the intuitionistic systems under an interpretation in which the connectives in the classical system are *not* correlated with their usual counterparts in the intuitionistic system but another correspondence prevails. Of several such interpretations, we mention Kleene's treatment (1952), wherein the classical disjunctive connective (*or*) is considered to correspond to $\neg(\neg P \,\&\, \neg Q)$ in the intuitionistic propositional calculus, while the connectives of conjunction, negation, and implication are correlated with their respective counterparts. In the predicate calculus and in the number-theoretic calculus (elementary arithmetic), the classical existential operator $\exists x P(x)$ (there exists an x such that $P(x)$ holds) is considered to correspond in the intuitionistic system to $\neg \forall x \neg P(x)$, where $\forall x$ (for all x) is the generalizing operator. (In the intuitionistic system, if x is a variable ranging over a mathematical set S, then $\forall x Q(x)$ may be asserted if and only if we possess a general method of construction which by specialization yields for any element s of S the construction $Q(s)$.) Under such a correspondence the classical systems can be developed as part of the intuitionistic systems. Findings of this sort led Gödel (1933) to conclude that intuitionistic logic and arithmetic are not narrower than classical logic and classical arithmetic, respectively, but under a suitable interpretation each includes the corresponding classical system.

Of interest in this connection is the notion of a *stable interpretation*. Define a statement (proposition, formula) to be stable if it is implied by its double negation, that is, P is stable if and only if $\neg\neg P \to P$. In intuitionistic logic, $P \to \neg\neg P$ but the converse does not always hold. However, for stable statements the converse is also true so that P is equivalent to $\neg\neg P$. Hence, the excluded-middle principle (which is equivalent to $\neg\neg P \to P$) holds even in intuitionistic mathematics as long as we are restricted to the stable portion of it. In short, beginning with an intuitionistic system and restricting the realm of propositions to stable statements, we obtain the corresponding classical system. van Dantzig (1947) who has contributed to work with the "stable interpretation," believes that not only classical logic and elementary arithmetic but virtually all of classical mathematics can be interpreted within the stable portion of intuitionistic mathematics.

This belief should not make us lose sight of what may be essential differences between intuitionistic and classical logic. These differences seem to be even more striking for the predicate and number-theoretic calculus than for the propositional calculus. To discuss some of these differences, we introduce the notion of *realizability* (Kleene, 1945, 1952). A formula is said to be realizable if it is true under a certain intuitionistic interpretation. The formula $\forall x[P(x) \lor \neg P(x)]$, which we denote by K, is provable in the classical system where it indicates that $P(x)$ or its negation holds as x ranges over all members of a certain set. It is proved by an appeal to the excluded-middle principle. But K is not realizable and, in this sense, is untrue intuitionistically and also unprovable by intuitionistic methods. On the other hand, the formula $\neg K$, that is,

$\daleth\forall x[P(x) \vee \daleth P(x)]$ (which is the negation of the above formula and hence is unprovable and untrue in the classical system) is realizable and therefore in a certain sense intuitionistically true. Moreover, when the latter formula is added to the intuitionistic formal systems corresponding to the predicate calculus and the number-theoretic calculus, then the formulas that are provable in the enlarged systems are all realizable. But the enlarged systems have a formula that is unprovable and untrue in classical predicate calculus or in classical number theory and thus they diverge from the classical systems. We may think of K as playing a role analogous to that of the parallel postulate in plane geometry.

> Thus we should obtain an extension of the intuitionistic number theory, which has previously been treated as a subsystem of the classical, so that intuitionistic and classical number theories diverge, with $[\daleth K]$ holding in the intuitionistic and $[K]$ in the classical.
>
> Such divergences are familiar to mathematicians from the example of Euclidean and non-Euclidean geometries, and other examples, but are a new phenomenon in arithmetic. (Kleene, 1952, p. 514)

Finally, we touch on a few other differences between the intuitionistic and classical systems. It is well known that the classical propositional calculus can be dealt with on the basis of truth tables with two truth values (*true* and *false*). On the other hand, the intuitionistic propositional calculus cannot be treated on the basis of truth tables for any finite number of truth values but can be for $\aleph_0$ truth values, that is, an infinite set of enumerably many truth values (Jaśkowski, 1936; Rose, 1952). Moreover, the logical connectives in the classical propositional calculus are dependent, in the sense that some of them can be expressed in terms of the others. For example, in the *Principia Mathematica* the two undefined connectives are *negation* and *disjunction*, and it is in terms of these two that conjunction and implication are expressed. In contrast, it has been shown that in the intuitionistic propositional calculus the four connectives are independent, in that none of them can be expressed in terms of the other connectives (McKinsey, 1939). In short, there seem to be some fundamental differences between the two systems of logic.

Natural Numbers
and the Basal Intuition

To Kronecker, natural numbers were the foundations of mathematics. Natural numbers are also fundamental in neointuitionism. Heyting (1956, p. 15) offers the following as the chief reasons that the notion of natural number is able to serve as one of the basic concepts of mathematics: it is readily understood by young children and indeed by any person who has even a minimal amount of education; it is universally applicable in the counting process; and it underlies the construction of mathematical analysis.

Intuitionists do not seek to define the concept of natural number. Mathematics is considered to begin after the concepts of natural number and of equality between natural numbers have been formed. Natural number is not considered to be an irreducible concept.

We start with the notion of the natural numbers 1, 2, 3 etc. They are so familiar to us that it is difficult to reduce this notion to simpler ones. Yet I shall try to describe their sense in plain words. In the perception of an object we conceive the notion of an entity by a process of abstracting from the particular qualities of the object. We also recognize the possibility of an indefinite repetition of the conception of entities. In these notions lies the source of the concept of natural numbers. . . . The concepts of an abstract entity and of a sequence of such entities are clear to every normal human being, even to young children. (p. 13)

In short, the notions of the natural numbers and of their indefinite continuation are regarded as simple, clear notions on which to found mathematics; and yet intuitionism recognizes that these notions themselves stem from more fundamental notions. It is of interest that the only reference which Heyting's text makes to these fundamental sources of the natural numbers is in the paragraph just cited. Nor does his text refer by name to the primordial or basal intuition (*Urintuition*) which plays an important role in Brouwer's views and from which the name *intuitionism* may have been derived. This primordial intuition, on which Brouwer bases mathematics, has been described by him as a basal intuition of "the bare two-oneness," or, as it is sometimes translated, "the abstract bi-unity." This concept is influenced by Plato's and Kant's views, particularly by Kant's conception of time. Kant regarded both time and space as pure intuitions. Brouwer, who has been called a neo-Kantian, accepts Kant's notion of time as a pure intuition but rejects Kant's conception of an a priori space. Kant, who regarded Euclidean geometry as the science of a priori space, held that its axioms are inherent in the human mind and are valid for "real" space. "This belief in the axioms of Euclidean geometry as unalterable truths, existing in the realm of pure intuition, was one of the basic tenets of Kant's philosophy" (Courant and Robbins, 1941, p. 219). This belief, whose untenability was demonstrated by the discovery of non-Euclidean geometries, is rejected by Brouwer. Referring to the development of non-Euclidean geometries and their impact on intuitionism, Brouwer writes:

However weak the position of intuitionism seemed to be after this period of mathematical development, it has recovered by abandoning Kant's apriority of space but adhering the more resolutely to the apriority of time. This neo-intuitionism considers the falling apart of moments of life into qualitatively different parts, to be reunited only while remaining separated by time, as the fundamental phenomenon of the human intellect, passing by abstracting from its emotional content into the fundamental phenomenon of mathematical thinking, the intuition of the bare two-oneness. This intuition of two-oneness, the basal intuition of mathematics, creates not only the numbers one and two, but also all finite ordinal numbers, inasmuch as one of the elements of the two-oneness may be thought of as a new two-oneness, which process may be repeated indefinitely. (1913, p. 86)

It is of interest to consider the notion of bi-unity in relation to Brouwer's views on the historical and sociological background of mathematics (1913). He conceives of mathematics as a branch of science and holds that a scientific attitude involves two stages, first a causal outlook and then a temporal outlook. It is the latter which gives rise to mathematics, and accounts for its exactness, and which is related to the primordial intuition. As Black words it:

The origin of [mathematical] exactness is the fact that mathematics arises out of the *temporal* outlook in which visual perceptions are regarded as separating into two parts (in the relation of before and after). From this is obtained the intuition of the primitive "two-oneness," the whole as capable of division into two parts, in turn capable of division into two parts, and so on. (1934, p. 193)

Intuition of natural number has been characterized in neointuitionism in terms of observation and perception. Underlying the concept of a natural number is that of an abstract entity, which is considered to derive from the perception of an object by a process of stripping the object of its particular qualities. The concepts of an abstract entity and of a sequence of such entities are regarded as the sources of natural numbers. Brouwer associates the totality of perceptions with the notion of time, and he associates the focusing of attention on a single perception with the notions of abstract entity and natural number. Time, and concomitantly the totality of perceptions, is regarded as continuous and the abstract entity associated with the single perception is regarded as a discrete unit. Brouwer's views have been interpreted as attributing a primitive or basal character to continuity and hence conceiving of a fundamental unity of continuity and discreteness.

Mathematics is, according to Brouwer, not a *theory* . . . but a certain fundamental part of *human activity*, a method of dealing with human experience, consisting primarily in concentrating attention to a single one among our perceptions and distinguishing this one from all others. While acts of distinguishing a single perception lead to the primordial intuition of integer . . . Brouwer associates the totality of perceptions (from which a single one is picked out) with the notions of continuity and of time; for this reason a primordial character is attributed to these two notions as well. Thus somehow the abyss between discreteness and continuity is denied from the first and it is maintained that "the primordial intuition of mathematics and of every intellectual activity is the substratum of all observations of change when stripped of all qualitative properties; a unity of continuity and discreteness." (Fraenkel and Bar-Hillel, 1958, pp. 207–208)

The reference is to Brouwer (1907, p. 8) who describes the unity of continuity and discreteness as constituting "the possibility of mentally joining several units, connected by a 'between' that is never exhausted by the intercalation of new units."

Intuitionistic Extension of the Number Concept

The divergence between the classical and the intuitionistic approach becomes more pronounced with the introduction of irrational numbers. There are various classical methods of introducing the irrational numbers, none of which is acceptable to the intuitionists. Elsewhere in this text we refer to the representation of real numbers by means of Dedekind cuts (1872). Let R denote the set of rational numbers, A a subset of R, and $R - A$ the complement of A in R; that is, $R - A$ is the set of rational numbers which belong to R but not to A. Then a real number may be defined as a Dedekind cut A which is a set of rationals A such that A is not empty, $R - A$ is not empty, A has no greatest member, and every member of A is less than every member of $R - A$. If $R - A$ has a least member r, then A is defined to be rational and is considered to correspond to r. If $R - A$ does not have a least member, then A is defined to be irrational. Dedekind goes on to define operations with the cuts, both rational and irrational, such as what is meant by addition of two of them or what is meant by one of them being less or greater than another (Landau, 1960). Under these definitions, an isomorphism which preserves the defined operations can be established between the rational cuts and the rational numbers, for example, if r and s are rational numbers that correspond to the rational cuts A and B, then r is less than s if and only if A is less than B.

Intuitionists object to the Dedekind cut representation of real numbers on the grounds that infinite sets of rationals are treated as completed entities. Moreover, they point out that the law of the excluded middle is used in the definitions of operations with these sets and in the proofs of theorems about them.

The description that follows of the neointuitionistic approach to the real numbers is based largely on Heyting (1956). Suppose that a theory of rational numbers has been developed which includes the order relations between these numbers (less, greater). This may be done as in classical developments. For example, fractions may be introduced as ordered pairs of natural numbers and a rational number $[m, n]$ as the set of all fractions that are similar to the fraction (m, n) where (a, b) is similar to (m, n) if $an = mb$. For example, the rational number $[1, 2]$ is the set of all fractions $(1, 2)$, $(2, 4)$, $(3, 6)$, $(4, 8)$, and so on.

Let $(a_n) = a_1, a_2, a_3, \cdots$ be a sequence of rational numbers. In neo-intuitionistic mathematics this is a *Cauchy sequence* (a convergent sequence, one that converges to a limit) if for every natural number k we can find a natural number m, which may be denoted as $m(k)$ to show that m depends on k, such that $|a_{m+p} - a_m| < 1/k$ for every natural number p. In other words, given k we can find m, such that for every natural number p, the absolute value (the unsigned value) of $a_{m+p} - a_m$ is less than $1/k$. This is much like the classical definition of a Cauchy sequence, but with one important exception. Given k we must be able actually to construct or effectively to determine $m(k)$ rather than merely to indicate that such a number exists. Hence of the classical Cauchy sequences, some are and others are not Cauchy sequences in neointuitionism.

For example, the sequence $(1/2^n)$ is a Cauchy sequence both classically and intuitionistically, since, given any natural number k, for any natural numbers m and p, we have

$$\left| \frac{1}{2^{m+p}} - \frac{1}{2^m} \right| = \left| \frac{1 - 2^p}{2^{m+p}} \right| \leq \frac{2^p - 1}{2^{m+p}} < \frac{2^p}{2^{m+p}} = \frac{1}{2^m}$$

(dividing numerator and denominator by 2^p) $= 1/2^k$ (taking m to be k) $< 1/k$.

To illustrate a sequence which is a Cauchy sequence classically but not intuitionistically, we first refer to a certain unsolved problem which is repeatedly alluded to in the neointuitionistic literature. This is the problem of whether or not the decimal expansion of π (where π is the ratio of the circumference of a circle to its diameter), contains the sequence 0123456789 (as consecutive members in just this order).

Consider the sequence (a_n) defined as follows. Let $a_n = 2^{-n} = 1/2^n$ unless the sequence 0123456789 occurs in the decimal expansion of π. In that case, if the 9 of the sequence 0123456789 is the jth digit after the decimal point in the decimal expansion of π, let $a_j = 1$. For example, if j were 14, then the sequence (a_n) would be $(2^{-1}, 2^{-2}, \cdots, 2^{-12}, 2^{-13}, 1, 2^{-15}, 2^{-16}, \cdots)$. In any event, the sequence (a_n) differs from (2^{-n}) in at most one term so that classically it is a Cauchy sequence. But as long as we do not know whether or not a sequence 0123456789 occurs in the decimal expansion of π, then given a natural number k we are not able to produce an m such that $|a_{m+p} - a_m| < 1/k$ for every p. Hence, in the intuitionistic sense the sequence (a_n) is not a Cauchy sequence. In short, a sequence of rational numbers which classically is a Cauchy sequence may not be a Cauchy sequence intuitionistically.

Classically a Cauchy sequence of rational numbers has a real number as a limit, that is, it converges to a real number. Intuitionistically a Cauchy sequence of rational numbers is called a *real number-generator*, or, more briefly, a *number-generator*. Definitions are offered of the negative and inverse of a number-generator as well as of the sum and product of two number-generators. Thus, if A and B denote the real number-generators defined by the sequences (a_n) and (b_n) respectively, then $-A$ is defined as the sequence $(-a_n)$, $A + B$ as the sequence $(a_n + b_n)$ and AB as the sequence $(a_n b_n)$; the inverse will be defined below. It can be shown that there is closure under these definitions, that is, the negative, inverse, sum, and product of number-generators are again number-generators.

The Cauchy sequence every one of whose members is r is identified with the rational number r. Under this correspondence the system of real number-generators is an extension of the system of rational numbers.

Equality and inequality relationships between real number-generators are more varied than the corresponding classical relationships between real numbers. For number-generators A and B, defined by the Cauchy sequences (a_n) and (b_n), respectively, the following relationships are defined:

1. *Identical:* A and B are said to be identical, expressed as $A \equiv B$, if $a_n = b_n$ for every n.
2. *Coincide:* A and B are said to coincide, expressed as $A = B$, if for every natural number k, we can find a natural number $m = m(k)$, such that $|a_{m+p} - b_{m+p}| < 1/k$ for every natural number p. For example, $1.0000 \cdots$ and $0.9999 \cdots$ coincide.

Parenthetically we note that it might be advisable to distinguish between *identical* and *coincide* even in classical mathematics. A case in point is the following example which puzzled college students.

Let
$$x = 0.999 \cdots$$
Then
$$10x = 9.999 \cdots$$
And
$$9x = 9.000 \cdots$$
Hence
$$x = 1.000 \cdots$$

We started with $x = 0.999 \cdots$ and yet concluded that $x = 1.000 \cdots$. How do you account for this? Many students could not and considered it as due to an error in computation with infinite series or as revealing a paradox or a fundamental weakness in mathematics. Apparently they did not realize (or would not accept) that classical mathematics equates numbers which coincide, so that $0.999 \cdots = 1.000 \cdots$. In intuitionistic mathematics they are regarded as coinciding but not as being identical.

In place of classical inequality, various relationships are introduced in intuitionistic mathematics.

1. *Absurdity of equality:* If $a = b$ leads to a contradiction (that is, if the supposition that the number-generators a and b coincide leads to a contradiction) then we write $a \neq b$.

2. *Apartness:* For two number-generators a and b, a is said to be apart from b (expressed by $a \mathbin{\#} b$) if natural numbers m and k can be found such that $|a_{m+p} - b_{m+p}| > 1/k$ for every p.

If $a \mathbin{\#} b$ then $a \neq b$ but the converse is not a justified assertion. Brouwer (1920) gives an example of two number-generators A and B such that $A \neq B$ but $A \mathbin{\#} B$ is still unproved. A and B are not rational, since for rationals no distinction is necessary between $\neq$ and $\#$; for, if a and b are rationals and if $a \neq b$, then $a - b$ is a rational other than 0 so that $|a - b| = m/n > 1/2n$ and hence $a \mathbin{\#} b$.

The relationship $a \mathbin{\#} b$ is a stronger condition (for number-generators that are not rational) than $a \neq b$, since for the latter it suffices to show that the supposition that $a = b$ leads to a contradiction, whereas to establish $a \mathbin{\#} b$ it is necessary to produce the numbers m and k. It may be said that $\neq$ is a negative relationship since it requires only a contradiction, whereas $\#$ is a positive relationship since it requires the constructive indication of the numbers m and k.

With the apartness relationship introduced, we can define the inverse, as promised earlier. If $A \mathbin{\#} 0$, where A is determined by the sequence (a_n), then the inverse of A, denoted by A^{-1}, is defined as the sequence (b_n), where $b_n = a_n^{-1}$ provided that $a_n \neq 0$ and $b_n = 0$ if $a_n = 0$.

Properties that are proved for the apartness relationship include the following. If $A \mathbin{\#} B$, then $B \mathbin{\#} A$ (symmetry); if $A \mathbin{\#} B$ and $A = C$, then $C \mathbin{\#} B$; if $A \mathbin{\#} B$ is impossible in the sense that its supposition leads to a contradiction, then $A = B$; if $A \mathbin{\#} B$, then for any real number-generator D, either $A \mathbin{\#} D$ or $B \mathbin{\#} D$. The apartness relationship with respect to 0 is of particular interest. It is proved that if $A \mathbin{\#} 0$ and $B \mathbin{\#} 0$, then $AB \mathbin{\#} 0$ and, conversely, $AB \mathbin{\#} 0$ implies $A \mathbin{\#} 0$ and $B \mathbin{\#} 0$. Moreover, if $A + B \mathbin{\#} 0$ then either $A \mathbin{\#} 0$ or $B \mathbin{\#} 0$.

Theorems about $\#$ as well as their proofs tend to be simpler and easier to handle than those involving $\neq$. As in classical mathematics, it can be shown that if $A \neq 0$ and $B \neq 0$ then $AB \neq 0$. However, the proposition that if $AB = 0$, then $A = 0$ or $B = 0$ is not provable intuitionistically even though it holds in classical mathematics. An unsolved problem can be appealed to in order to illustrate that this familiar proposition is not provable in intuitionistic mathematics. Consider once more the unsolved problem of whether or not the sequence 0123456789 occurs in the decimal expansion of π. Define the real number-generators A and B by the sequences (a_n) and (b_n), respectively, where $a_n = b_n = 1/2^n$ if 0123456789 does not occur in the first n digits of the decimal expansion of π. If it does occur there, and the 9 is the jth digit after the decimal point in π, then if j is odd let $a_n = 1/2^j$, $b_n = 1/2^n$, whereas if j is even let $a_n = 1/2^n$, $b_n = 1/2^j$. If 0123456789 does not occur in the first n digits, then $a_n b_n = 1/2^{2n}$; otherwise, whether j is even or odd, $a_n b_n = 1/2^{j+n}$. In either case AB can be shown to coincide with the Cauchy sequence corresponding to

0. Given any natural number k, we can find a natural number m which may be dependent on k, such that for every natural number p,

$$|a_{m+p}b_{m+p} - 0| = |a_{m+p}b_{m+p}| \leq \frac{1}{2^{m+p}} < \frac{1}{2^m} < \frac{1}{m} < \frac{1}{k}$$

for $m > k$. Hence $AB = 0$ by the definition of what it means for two number-generators to coincide. But, we are unable to decide whether or not $A = 0$ or $B = 0$ as long as the problem remains unsolvable as to whether 0123456789 occurs in the first n digits of the decimal expansion of π (or as long as there are other such unsolvable problems). In short, whether or not A coincides with 0 or B coincides with 0 can be made to hinge on the fate of an unsolved problem, whereas AB coincides with 0 independently of the unsolved problem.

In summary, if $A \neq 0$ and $B \neq 0$ then $AB \neq 0$ in both classical and intuitionistic mathematics, whereas in classical mathematics (but not intuitionistically) it is provable that if $AB = 0$ then $A = 0$ or $B = 0$. Note that the latter proposition is the negative converse of the former. In classical logic if a proposition holds its negative converse (contrapositive) holds, that is, whenever "if P, then Q" holds so does "if not-Q, then not-P," where the roles of hypothesis and conclusion are reversed in addition to each being prefaced with a *not*. Here P is "$A \neq 0$ and $B \neq 0$," Q is "$AB \neq 0$." Then the negative converse is: if not ($AB \neq 0$), then not ($A \neq 0$ and $B \neq 0$). Classically this becomes if $AB = 0$, then $A = 0$ or $B = 0$. The theorem in classical logic that if a proposition holds so does its negative converse rests squarely on the law of the excluded middle. The excluded-middle law says that either P or not-P must hold. Now if not-Q is the hypothesis, then by the excluded-middle principle either P or not-P. But the supposition that P holds together with the original proposition, if P, then Q, leads to the chain of reasoning: if not-Q, then P, then Q which is a contradiction since both not-Q and Q are considered to hold. Hence the only alternative left by the excluded-middle principle is: if not-Q, then not-P. In short, given that a proposition holds, we can conclude in classical logic by utilizing the excluded-middle principle that the negative converse also holds. This is by no means always the case in neointuitionistic logic with its rejection of the general excluded-middle principle.

Thus the neointuitionistic development of the number system, and especially the introduction of real numbers (including irrationals), seeks to avoid the use of the excluded-middle principle and of the *completed infinite*. We have seen that the treatment introduces a variety of relationships that are classically equivalent but intuitionistically distinct (such as identical and coincide as well as absurdity of equality and apartness). In short, the intuitionistic approach introduces richness of nuances in number relationships which are overlooked in the classical treatment.

The order relations between number-generators are defined as follows, where A and B are number-generators determined by the sequences (a_n) and (b_n), respectively. It is said that $A < B$ if natural numbers n and k can be found so that for every natural number p

$$|b_{n+p} - a_{n+p}| > 1/k$$

$A > B$ if and only if $B < A$. The expression $A \nless B$ denotes that the supposition that $A < B$ leads to a contradiction. Likewise, $A \ngtr B$ denotes that the supposition that $A > B$ leads to a contradiction.

It can be proved that if $A < B$, then $A \# B$ and, conversely, if $A \# B$, then either $A < B$ or $B < A$. Certain counterparts of the classical order relations can be established. For example, the transitive property holds: if $A < B$, and $B < C$, then $A < C$. Moreover, it is shown that if $A < B$ and $B < A$ both lead to contradictions, then $A = B$. However, there is not a counterpart of the classical trichotomy principle which states that one and only one of the following relations prevails for any real numbers A and B: $A < B$ or $B < A$ or $A = B$. In particular, in the intuitionistic system $A \ngtr B$ is not equivalent to $A < B$ or $A = B$ (Brouwer, 1925, p. 252). Brouwer has also constructed an example of a number for which we are unable to decide whether it is equal to 0, greater than 0, or less than 0. Both these examples are based on an unsolved problem, such as the occurrence of the sequence 0123456789 in π.

To go from real number-generators to real numbers, Brouwer utilizes the notion of a certain kind of set. He prefers to avoid the use of such terms as *set* and *class* because of their classical connotations. He deals with various kinds of sets, including a set defined by a common mode by which its elements are generated. Such sets are referred to as *spreads*. He also deals with a set which is defined by a characteristic property of its elements; such sets are referred to as *species*. Although spreads and species are classically lumped together as sets, intuitionistically they can be distinct. Here again is an illustration of finer nuances in the intuitionistic concepts than in the corresponding classical concept.

We shall not deal with spreads (Brouwer, 1918–1919, p. 3; 1924, p. 244; 1954, p. 8), but shall briefly comment on species. An example of a species is given by the real number-generators which coincide (expressed by $=$) with a given number-generator—that is, the property of coinciding with a given number-generator is a species. This species is called a *real number*.

Two species are called equivalent if a one-to-one correspondence has been established between them. A species is called *finite* if it is equivalent to the species that consists of the natural numbers from 1 through n, for some natural number n. A species that is equivalent to the species of all natural numbers is called *denumerably infinite*. A species that contains a denumerably infinite subspecies is called *infinite*.

There are examples of species that cannot be finite (the assumption that such a species is finite leads to a contradiction) and yet which are not necessarily infinite. In fact, an example can be given of a species for which we are unable to decide whether it is the null species (has no elements) or a finite or infinite species. Such an example is furnished by the species of numbers n such that the nth to the $(n + 9)$th digits in π form a sequence 0123456789. It is unknown whether there are no elements in this species or a finite number or infinitely many members.

Two species S and Q are called *equal* if every member of S is a member of Q and every member of Q is a member of S. If T is a subspecies of a species S, then $S - T$ is the species of those elements of S that cannot belong to T. It is of interest that the union of T and $S - T$ (elements in T or in $S - T$) is not always equal to S, since the union contains only those elements of S for which it is known whether they belong to T or not. For example, it is at present unknown whether a certain real number, Euler's constant C, is rational or not. Hence, if S is the species of real numbers and T is the subspecies of rational numbers, then C belongs to S, but it is not known whether it belongs to T or not, and hence C cannot be said to belong to the union of T and $S - T$. A subspecies of S is called *detachable* if the union of it and its complement is equal to S. A species that is equivalent to (has been placed in one-to-one correspondence with) a detachable subspecies of the species of all natural numbers is called *numerable*. Heyting (1956, p. 40) notes that the species of twin primes $(p, p + 2)$ is numerable, although we do not know whether it is finite or infinite.

A neointuitionistic theory of cardinal numbers (Brouwer, 1924), which differs strikingly from Cantor's theory, permits two species to be incomparable with regard to their cardinal numbers (whether one is equal, greater, or less than the other) and introduces a variety of intuitionistically distinct concepts in place of the classical concept of denumerability.

Intuitionistic theories have been developed not only of arithmetic and cardinal numbers but also of derivatives, integrals, point-set topology, Hilbert spaces, and so on (Heyting, 1956). In some cases, the concepts used differ radically from the classical concepts; for example, Brouwer's treatment of cardinal numbers. In other cases, one of several classically equivalent concepts or approaches is selected, whereas others are discarded because they are not intuitionistically equivalent and do not meet intuitionistic requirements, for example, Brouwer's use of a constructive definition of integral from the classical literature where it is one of several classically (but not intuitionistically) equivalent definitions. For some theories a classical approach has been modified and adapted to intuitionistic requirements, for example, van Rootselaar's treatment of a theory of derivatives (1954).

Intuitionism:
Evaluations
and Comparisons

Neointuitionism and Constructionism

There are mathematicians (who may be called *constructivists* or *constructionists*) who accept the thesis that mathematical construction is requisite (or at least highly desirable) for mathematical existence and yet who do not necessarily accept other tenets of neointuitionism. It might be said that intuitionists are constructivists, but constructivists are not necessarily intuitionists. This is well illustrated in a text which contains the proceedings of the international colloquium on "Constructivity in Mathematics" held at Amsterdam in 1957 (Heyting, 1959). For example, a participant in the colloquium, after noting that there are different directions in the foundations of constructive analysis, writes that according to the ideas elaborated in Poland, constructive analysis "is not a part of intuitionistic mathematics. All methods of proof are allowed" (Grzegorczyk, 1959, p. 43). Another participant distinguishes between constructive results and constructive proofs, noting that the latter are considered in intuitionistic mathematics whereas the former are possible "within the framework of classical mathematics . . . [even] where a notion of constructive proof has no application" (Kreisel, 1959, p. 101). Still another participant, in a report entitled "On Various Degrees of Constructivism," speaks of "a multitude of constructivistic programmes" (Mostowski, 1959, p. 192). In a somewhat similar vein, Dienes (1952) distinguishes between different degrees of rigor in construction. To speak of degrees of constructivity suggests that it is a relative rather than an absolute concept. Brouwer has been criticized for treating it as an absolute.

Thus the question loses its dogmatic character and . . . assumes the form: what parts of mathematics or of a certain mathematical branch can be obtained from a given starting-point by means of such-and-such "constructive" methods? . . . Brouwer impetuously opposes this opinion and maintains that there is an *absolute* concept of constructiveness and that this concept settles what is comprehended in mathematics and what parts should be excluded as belonging to pseudoscience. (Fraenkel and Bar-Hillel, 1958, p. 212)

Some attempts have been made to describe constructibility (for example, Rosser, 1936a; Nelson, 1949). But Brouwer has not offered any clear characterization of mathematical construction, constructivity, or constructibility. Nor does Heyting (1956) offer any characterization. In part, this may be because of the neointuitionistic view that language is weak and inadequate to convey mental construction. It may also be that constructibility is a premathematical concept that cannot be precisely defined. For example, in the symposium on constructivity, Kalmár (who is not a neointuitionist) claimed: "There are pre-mathematical concepts which must remain pre-mathematical ones, for they cannot permit any restriction imposed by an exact mathematical definition" (1959, p. 79). Among such concepts, he believes, are those of effective calculability, solvability, or provability by arbitrary correct means "the extension of which cannot cease to change during the development of Mathematics" (p. 79). Also of interest in this context are Fraenkel and Bar-Hillel's remarks that "any list of mathematical principles of construction is not only incomplete but would *necessarily remain incomplete;* for . . . one must not limit the liberty of creative mind to further extend its constructive faculties" (1958, p. 212).

In the conference on constructivism, Heyting noted that a constructive theory—a theory in which an object is considered to exist only after it has been constructed—must be self-contained, and that, in particular, the notion of a constructible must be a primitive object. Another participant (Péter, 1959) indicated that an attempt to define the notion of a constructive theory must necessarily be circular. However, some participants did attempt to characterize or at least describe constructivism. Consider the following description:

> Constructivism in the widest sense is the tendency to read mathematics in terms of cognitive evidence. Unlike the naive platonism motivating classical mathematics, it considers abstract mathematical objects to be objects of thought. As such constructive concepts are explications of particular cognitive structures. . . . To that extent a general characterization of constructive concepts is an epistemological task. . . . While classical mathematics owes its development to a naive metaphysical conception of the physical world, from the constructivist point of view mathematics may rather be regarded to be an abstract reconstruction of a private phenomenological world. (Löb, 1959, pp. 159, 164)

There are those who see such characterizations of constructivism as raising epistemological issues. We see them as raising certain issues and research problems for psychology since "cognitive structures" and "private phenomenological world" are of concern to psychologists.

The emphasis in constructivism on the explication and demonstration of cognitive structures has been interpreted as an operational point of view (Walker, 1936, p. 116). In this respect constructivism has some similarities to operationalism in the behavioral sciences (Stevens, 1939). The emphasis in constructivism on a private phenomenological world may be interpreted as a phenomenological point of view. In this respect constructivism has some similarities to contemporary phenomenology in the behavioral sciences (Rogers, 1959). Contemporary phenomenology has been criticized as bordering on solipsism and leading to the egocentric predicament. Such criticisms may be made of constructivism also.

Criticisms of Intuitionism

Often regarded as a major defect of intuitionism is its rejection of large portions of classical mathematics (Hilbert, 1922). This alone has been considered as sufficient ground on which to adjudge intuitionism as a wrong attitude (Kreisel, 1951). In turn, intuitionists retort that not all of classical mathematics is really mathematics, that what is in mathematical texts is not sacred and does not have to be preserved at all costs, and that the manner in which intuitionism has enriched mathematics helps to compensate for the loss of certain parts of classical mathematics, if indeed this can properly be called a loss. For example, in Heyting's text (1956), when the spokesman for formalism contends that for most mathematicians the value of intuitionism "is affected fatally by the fact that you destroy the most precious mathematical results; a valuable method for the foundation of mathematics ought to save as much as possible of its results," the spokesman for neointuitionism replies:

> As to the mutilation of mathematics of which you accuse me, it must be taken as an inevitable consequence of our standpoint. It can also be seen as the excision of noxious ornaments, beautiful in form, but hollow in substance, and it is at least partly compensated for by the charm of subtle distinctions and witty methods by which intuitionists have enriched mathematical thought. (pp. 10–11)

Distinctions that neointuitionism introduces (for example, between equality and apartness and among various kinds of denumerability) have been used as arguments both in its favor and disfavor. The just-cited remark illustrates a favorable view toward the distinctions. Similarly, Nelson (1959, p. 215) remarks that an argument in favor of intuitionistic logic over classical logic is that intuitionistic logic allows the classical distinctions in meaning in addition to other distinctions; in contrast, classical logic is seen as open to possible objection in its identification of certain entities that are constructively distinct. On the other hand, it has been suggested that intuitionistic distinctions are shortcomings which complicate mathematics. For example, referring to distinctions which Brouwer introduces in place of the classical notion of equivalence between sets, Fraenkel and Bar-Hillel point out that "the ensuing complication may be measured by the fact that the classical concept of denumerability is split up into eight different properties which are largely independent" (1958, p. 262).

Also regarded as a shortcoming of intuitionism is the complicated nature of its proofs. The complications result, for example, from distinctions among concepts that are classically equivalent and from the avoidance of indirect proofs. Nor can the intuitionistic proofs entirely replace the classical proofs in the training of mathematicians. In order to build up a branch of intuitionistic mathematics, "it is necessary in the first place to have a thorough knowledge of the corresponding branch of classical mathematics, and in the second place to know by experience where the intuitionistic pitfalls lie" (Heyting, 1956, p. viii). But even if a student will not contribute to intuitionistic mathematics, in order even to learn it, it is necessary or at least advisable that he also learn classical mathematics. For pedagogical reasons, particularly in view of the difficulty of intuitionistic proofs, "even intuitionists would be compelled first to teach the 'illusive' classical proofs before criticizing and replacing them with their own demonstrations" (Fraenkel and Bar-Hillel, 1958, p. 259). It has been estimated that it would take as much as four years more to cover the same ground now covered by a mathematics major. Intuitionism, it has been said, is akin to binding one leg to hop through a field; it does not make the journey easier or more practical. In fact, if intuitionistic methods were the only ones available, we would search for better, or at least easier and more practical, ways.

Why then do mathematicians pay heed to intuitionism and why has Brouwer been as successful as he has in winning respect for his views? One answer may be that mathematicians have respect for those who impose restrictions that do not conflict with mathematical rigor. Mathematicians are interested in solving problems under restrictions that may increase their difficulty. Consider that the Greeks imposed a restriction to compass and straight edge on the famous construction problems, problems that fascinated mathematicians (and nonmathematicians) for centuries. They could have (but did not) shrug off the restrictions and insist, for example, on using a ruler rather than a straight edge. There are mathematicians who are willing to regard intuitionistic mathematics as starting from assumptions which impose certain restrictions on the nature of the proof. From this point of view, classical mathematics starts from another set of assumptions, and there is room for both sets of assumptions in mathematics. But neointuitionists are not quite willing to be accepted on these terms. Constructive mathematical thought is regarded as determining uniquely the premises from which neointuitionism starts. Some neointuitionists consider that when other premises are used, when neointuitionists' requirements are not met, then what results is not legitimate mathematics. It is this attitude, which has been interpreted as an intolerance of other views, that some mathematicians find distasteful about neointuitionism; and yet such an attitude, it seems to us, is not inherent in neointuitionism any more than in logicism or formalism.

That some of Brouwer's writings are quite unreadable is not in itself a charge against neointuitionism, but it does help to explain difficulties that outsiders have had in understanding this school of thought and in following Brouwer's demonstrations. However, as was noted earlier, more recent writings constitute highly readable accounts of neointuitionism. Nonetheless, there are still aspects of the school's views which some mathematicians consider to be mystifying or metaphysical.

Metaphysics

Speaking of metaphysics, we point out that charges of using it as a basis for mathematics have been made against both classical mathematics and intuitionism. For example, intuitionists contend that "to exist" has a metaphysical meaning in classical mathematics, since it does not mean "to be constructed" and hence must refer to some world of mathematical entities existing independently of our knowledge about them. Neointuitionism equates mathematical existence and construction and thereby does not get "entangled in a maze of metaphysical difficulties" (Heyting, 1956, p. 3).

However, metaphysical entanglements are forthcoming from other sources, particularly from Brouwer's acceptance of Kant's notion of time as an a priori intuition, as knowledge in the mind before experience. By basing neointuitionism on this Kantian notion and the concomitant and mystical concept of primordial intuition, is Brouwer proposing to found mathematics on metaphysics? Should a metaphysical concept be a main support of mathematics? Should mathematics or any science have to depend on metaphysical beliefs? Discovery of non-Euclidean geometries destroyed Kant's conception of space as an a priori intuition. Suppose further discoveries make untenable the conception of time as an a priori intuition. This could have the effect of toppling a mathematical foundation supported by such a conception. There are those who believe that mathematics ought to be independent of metaphysical fashions. Metaphysics may be used to evaluate science and to help to explain the role it plays in our lives, but it should not become the grounds for a science nor should a science become a special case of metaphysics. Moreover, there is less likelihood that agreement will be reached on a ground for science in general or for mathematics in particular if agreement must first be reached on metaphysical assumptions.

Mathematics, Language, and Logic

Contributing to difficulties in understanding neointuitionism, and perhaps enhancing its apparent relation to metaphysics, are the facts that its adherents do not speak a formalized language, that many of the terms they use are not precisely defined, and that they have not described exactly their conception of a proof. "The intuitionists do not attempt to give an exact description of their notion of a proof in general, and they say that in principle no such description is possible" (Kleene, 1952, p. 498). Neointuitionists maintain that the mental construction of a proposition itself constitutes its proof, but there still remains the question of just *which* mental constructions constitute proofs. One need not be a formalist to sympathize with the words of a spokesman for this viewpoint when he complains to Mr. Int, "Only I wonder how there can be beauty in so indefinite a thing as intuitionism. None of your terms are well-defined, nor do you give exact rules of derivation. Thus one for ever remains in doubt as to which reasonings are correct and which are not" (Heyting, 1956, p. 3). The intuitionistic argument for a nonformalized language on the grounds that any language, including formalized mathematical symbolism, is ambiguous seems to overlook the possibility that there are different degrees of ambiguity, and that a formalized language may cut down on ambiguity and make it easier to detect misinterpretations.

Distinctions that neointuitionism draws among mathematics, logic, and language are not acceptable and not even credible to some critics. One point of view is that mathematical thinking, language, and logic are so interrelated that it is artificial to seek to divide them or to regard them as proceeding on different levels. That thinking should be regarded as mathematical reality and as providing empirical evidence whereas language and logic are somehow less real, is difficult to grasp. It is particularly difficult for those who consider that a written proof, which can be communicated to others, is at least as real and empirical—if not more so—than mental constructions, which are subjective phenomena until they are communicated to others.

Even some constructionists, who agree with the neointuitionists on the importance of an empirical or experiential characterization of mathematics, doubt the wisdom of a division among language, logic, and mathematics. For example, Nelson notes that the intuitionistic contention that mathematics may be carried on independently of logic or language may not adequately describe the relationship of mathematics to experience and may constitute an "oversimplification of the actual process of construction and observation in mathematics" (1959, p. 208). He goes on to point out that members of the school of thought known as *significists*, "while in basic agreement on the importance of the experiential foundations of mathematics have offered criticisms of what these experiential foundations amount to" (p. 209).

The long-standing belief among some psychologists that verbalization is a necessary concomitant of abstract thought has been used as an argument against Brouwer's views. But there is some evidence which suggests that verbalization plays less of a role in abstract thinking, including scientific thinking, than is usually believed. Scientific thinking, including mathematical thinking, apparently can occur without words and without the formalized, logical form in which it is subsequently presented (Hadamard, 1945; Wertheimer, 1945; Luchins and Luchins, 1959).

Wertheimer (in a seminar at The New School for Social Research) said that he admired Brouwer for wanting to face the content of mathematical thought openly and concretely without becoming entangled in language and formalization. These latter are artifacts of the communication, or expression, of thought activities, but are not necessarily involved in the original thought processes themselves. Moreover, Wertheimer considered—as do some psychologists today—that cognitive processes can be studied, that they are not purely subjective in the sense that they are incapable of scientific study or incapable of being described by certain principles or laws. From this point of view, cognitive evidence is as real and empirical as any other facet of experience.

Rejection of the Excluded-Middle Principle

Neointuitionism has often been criticized for its rejection of the excluded-middle principle. Hilbert (1928) has said that to deny the mathematician the use of this principle is akin to denying the astronomer his telescope or the boxer the use of his fists. Brouwer retorts that the belief in this principle is comparable to the long-standing belief in the rationality of π, the ratio of the circumference of a circle to its diameter. Neointuitionists are aware that the use of the excluded-middle principle allows for indirect arguments which apparently constitute simpler proofs, but they maintain that while these are simpler they do not necessarily constitute proofs. Nonetheless, the rejection of the principle does make for complications. "He who is familiar with the lucidity and simplicity of the classical logical calculus which is due to the excluded middle formula . . . will not readily submit to the complications involved by the [neointuitionist] restrictions" (Fraenkel and Bar-Hillel, 1958, p. 237).

A customary interpretation of the excluded-middle principle is that either P is true or not-P is true in which case P is false; that is, either P is true or false. Yet there are instances where this principle, particularly in this interpretation of it, does not hold. Consider, for example, the statement, "All Xs are Ys." Is this statement true or false? The question is pointless until the variables X and Y are assigned definite values or meanings. Such statements as "All Xs are Ys" have been called propositional (or sentential) forms since they yield different propositions (or sentences) when different meanings are assigned to the variables. What we see is that the excluded-middle principle does not apply to propositional or sentential forms.

Now let us consider whether the excluded-middle principle holds for all propositions or sentences. Let P denote a "liar" sentence such as, "This statement I am now making is a lie." But we saw that if the liar statement is true then it is false and vice versa, so that a contradiction results in either case. In this case the assumption of the excluded-middle principle leads to a contradiction. Does the excluded-middle principle hold for this P? Here again it does not seem applicable.

Or let P be the statement, "The king of the United States wears bow-ties" (Wilder, 1952, p. 27). Does the excluded-middle principle apply? Must P or not-P hold? The statement P may be called *meaningless* since there does not exist a king of the United States. But this shows that further restrictions must be placed on the kinds of statements to which the excluded-middle principle is applicable, restrictions in terms of the meanings of the expressions it involves or the existence of the objects in the expressions. Again we see some justification for Brouwer's thesis that the excluded-middle principle is not universally applicable. Indeed, traditionally the excluded-middle principle has been restricted to *meaningful* propositions but just what *meaningful* designates has not always been clear. In fact, it has been suggested that Aristotle thought it necessary to restrict the principle, particularly for propositions having to do with future events or with events subject to free will or indeterminism (Fraenkel and Bar-Hillel, 1958, p. 222). For further discussion of the excluded-middle principle see: Bocheński, 1951; Brouwer, 1918–1919; Church, 1928; Dewey, 1929; Hilbert, 1931; Mesthene, 1950; Nagel, 1929.

On Contradiction and Negation

Whereas some mathematicians criticize neointuitionism for rejecting the excluded-middle principle, others criticize it for not having rejected enough. Under attack are the concept of negation and certain principles that involve the negation connective, such as the principle of contradiction (that P and not-P imply a contradiction). Some constructionists maintain that the negation of a statement or property cannot be constructively established and that it is not possible to realize intuitively (or have intuitive evidence for) a statement that subsequently turns out to be false. Why then should negation, falsity, and contradiction figure in constructive or intuitionistic mathematics? Griss (1948), who has criticized neointuitionism for its use of negation and contradiction, has attempted to build up intuitionistic mathematics without these concepts. And van Dantzig (1947), who omits also the disjunctive connective (*or*), has built up parts of mathematics without using negation or contradiction as primitive notions. The mathematics that results when such notions are omitted has been referred to as *negationless*, or *affirmative*, mathematics.

It should be noted that in neointuitionism the concept of contradiction is not defined but "must be taken as a primitive notion. It seems very difficult to reduce it to simpler notions, and it is always easy to recognize a contradiction as such" (Heyting, 1956, p. 98). Some constructionists have criticized intuitionists not only for accepting the principle of contradiction but also for not distinguishing among notions of contradiction that are classically equivalent but "experientially distinct." For example:

> In both the intuitionistic and classical logic all contradictions are equivalent. . . . I feel that it may be possible to conceive a logic which does more justice to the uncertainty of the empirical situation insofar as negation is concerned. The intuitionistic logic takes cognizance of the inadequacy of classical logic as a logic of what is experientially known insofar as the principle of excluded middle is concerned; however, I believe regarding other negation principles [including that of contradiction] it maintains what might be called an idealistic position. (Nelson, 1959, p. 209)

In support of his views Nelson describes a system in which a formula *P* and not-*P* is provable and yet not every formula is provable. If *P* and not-*P* lead to a contradiction, as the principle of contradiction states, then the contradiction, constituting a false hypothesis, should imply every proposition or formula (since a false hypothesis implies any conclusion). For this system, consider a set of statements {*P*} and a set of interpretations {*I* } where each interpretation gives a value, true or false, to some of the statements and furnishes evidence, according to some standards, for their truth or falsity. Only those statements will be called *true* which are true under all interpretations; statements will be called *false* which are false under any interpretation. "A situation of this sort might arise in establishing a natural law, where the statement corresponds to a universal statement, the interpretations, to observations of individual events, the evidence to a description of certain standard methods of observation" (Nelson, 1959, p. 220). Allow the possibility that for a statement *P*, some interpretations may offer evidence for both the truth and the falsity of *P*. Then if all other interpretations offer evidence for the truth of *P*, the criterion establishes both the truth and the falsity of *P*. This may be regarded as establishing *P* and not-*P*. Yet not every formula is true or provable in this system.

Classical and Intuitionistic
Mathematics

We saw that, under a suitable interpretation, classical logic and arithmetic may be regarded as parts of the corresponding intuitionistic systems. Such an interpretation seems to be acceptable to some neointuitionists. For example, Heyting (1956, p. 112) states that Gödel (1932) proved that the classical propositional calculus and classical arithmetic can be developed as parts of the corresponding intuitionistic systems. Now, it seems to us that there are interesting points for discussion here. If a branch of classical mathematics constitutes a part of a corresponding intuitionistic system, then a property that is supposed to hold throughout the intuitionistic system must perforce hold for the classical system that is part of it. Concomitantly, some of the properties of the classical system might be imputed to the intuitionistic system of which it is a part. For example, if intuitionistic mathematics is entirely constructive, then it follows that classical logic and arithmetic (if they are part of the corresponding intuitionistic systems) must also be entirely constructive. Yet intuitionists have criticized these and other branches of mathematics as not being constructive.

In short, it seems in order for intuitionists to consider which of the virtues that have been attributed to intuitionistic systems are inherited by the classical systems interpreted as parts of them and which of the faults they have attributed to classical systems are perforce faults of the intuitionistic systems. On the other hand, a similar evaluation (with a reversal of the roles of virtues and faults) might be made by those who have been critical of intuitionistic systems.

On the antinomies

In favor of neointuitionism is its avoidance of the known antinomies and hence its avoidance of the corresponding threat to the consistency of mathematics. But neointuitionism goes considerably further than is necessary to avoid the antinomies. There are less extreme ways to do so, which (to use some of the figures of speech that have been applied in this context) do not "throw out the baby with the bathwater" or "cut off the toe to save the foot." Interestingly enough, some adherents of neointuitionism do not even argue about the fate of the antinomies or consistency. Characteristically, the spokesman for Brouwer's views in Heyting's (1956) dialogue does not mention the antinomies and, as one of the other participants notes, undoubtedly regards consistency as but a welcome by-product of intuitionism rather than a major *raison d'être* (p. 11).

Intuitive evidence

Intuitionists seem to be more concerned with intuitive, or cognitive, evidence than with consistency. But we have seen that there are constructionists, who although they recognize the importance of cognitive evidence, do not necessarily agree with the neointuitionists on just what constitutes cognitive evidence. Other mathematicians do not understand just what these terms denote and desire a more explicit characterization than neointuitionists offer. Some hold that mathematics could well dispense with intuitive evidence (see Curry, 1951).

Granted that neointuitionism appeals to intuitive or cognitive evidence, where is the intuitive or cognitive evidence for some of the doctrines on which neointuitionism supposedly is founded? Where, for example, is the evidence for neointuitionistic doctrines concerning natural numbers and their sources? Where shall we turn to find intuitive evidence for them? We shall discuss this problem in the next chapter.

CHAPTER 14

Intuitionism
and Psychology

It might be said of neointuitionism (and to some extent of construc-tionism in general) that in its concern with intuitive evidence, cognitive evidence, mental activities, perception, and so on, it is stepping into the realm of psychology and even attempting to found mathematics on psy-chology. Is psychology a suitable foundation for mathematics? Neointu-itionists say that absolutely no other discipline can serve as a foundation for mathematics and that a "mathematical construction ought to be so immediate to the mind and its results so clear that it needs no foundation whatsoever" (Heyting, 1956, p. 6). But since a mathematical construc-tion is a mental act and since such concepts as *immediacy* and *clarity to the mind* are invoked in neointuitionism, it would seem that an appeal is being made to the study of mental activities. Some consider this area of study to be part of psychology. That psychology should even be con-sidered as a foundation for mathematics is disturbing to some mathe-maticians. It might also be disturbing to some psychologists who seek a foundation for their own discipline in mathematics. For if A is founded on B, can B be founded on A, if A and B are distinct?

This problem aside, there are specific assumptions and issues involved in neointuitionism that are related to research problems in psychology. Before turning to these, we want to point out that we are not seeking to use psychology to explain neointuitionistic mathematics or any other mathematics. It may not be out of place to mention that there have been attempts to use psychology to explain mathematics and logic. Notable among these is the doctrine of psychologicism, which was gaining ground at the turn of the century, but which has been severely criticized by many philosophers, including the phenomenologist, Edmund Husserl (1913). We do not wish to get involved in the merits or demerits of psychologicism or of any other attempt to explain mathematics through psychology, but we wish to indicate some research problems for psy-chology that are suggested by intuitionistic views.

The Excluded Middle
and Psychology

Returning to the excluded-middle principle, let us consider some statements that pertain to psychological issues, some of which are the center of quite lively discussions. Let P be the statement, "Learning is due to insight." Then, not-P is sometimes formulated as "Learning is not due to insight." Is the excluded-middle principle applicable here? Is it the case that either P or not-P must hold, that one or the other must be true? There are those who see this as a genuine issue. Some debates and controversies that have been waged over the issue implicitly accept the excluded-middle principle. (But as we shall soon try to show, the principle does not seem to apply here.) Experiments have been conducted in efforts to refute P or not-P, which thereby purportedly would establish not-P or P, respectively, through the (perhaps implicit) assumption of the excluded-middle principle. Yet, experimental evidence may be cited against each of P and not-P; so, by the same token, the conclusion may be drawn that both hold, which would be a contradiction, and, hence, that neither holds, which would mean that the excluded-middle principle is not applicable.

The view expressed by P—that learning is due to insight—has been attributed to Gestalt psychologists. Actually, as far as we know, Gestalt psychologists did not, and do not, claim that *all* learning is due to insight or, on the other hand, that all learning is *not* due to insight. (See Köhler's report on associative learning, 1941.) What they claim, and what they have demonstrated, is that some learning, or that learning under some conditions, is due to insight. It is this conditional aspect which is absent in P and in not-P, both of which are general statements. Moreover, the excluded-middle principle cannot take conditions into account unless they are incorporated in P and not-P. In short, the principle asserts that either P or not-P holds but does not delineate the conditions under which P holds or under which not-P holds. See Wilder (1952, p. 27) for a discussion of a similar point outside of the context of psychology: for example, the proposition, "Today is Wednesday" and its negation may both hold or neither hold, provided that different geographical locations are permitted.

What has been said above is equally applicable to such issues as whether or not past experiences influence perception, whether discrimination and judgment are made on a relational or an absolute (nonrelational) basis, and whether learning is continuous or discontinuous (that is, not continuous). It can be said that Gestalt psychologists do not see the issue as "Past experiences influence perception" (proposition P) versus "Past experiences do not influence perception" (proposition not-P). They do not claim to have established either that past experiences *always* or *never* influence perception. What they have done is to give counterexamples to the unqualified thesis that past experience has universal applicability as an explanatory concept. They have demonstrated that there are certain cases where the influence of past experience seems to be negligible. For example, Gottschaldt (1938, p. 113) refers to his experiments on perception as showing that there are "*some* cases where 'past experience' (in the sense of bare repetition) is practically without effect," and he suggests that the theory of past experience "renounce all claim to universal validity and indicate instead its own range of application." Such criticism of the theory of past experience has been regarded as a rejection by Gestalt psychology of empiricism, which stresses past experience and, moreover, as an implicit acceptance of nativism which rejects past experience as an explanatory concept (Hochberg, 1962). Yet, Wertheimer (1939) and Koffka (1935) have disclaimed both empiricism and nativism. Perhaps there would be less controversy concerning the Gestalt position (see Postman, 1963) if Gestalt psychologists made it clear that they do not accept an unqualified excluded-middle principle, and that their rejection of the empiricistic position does not mean that they subscribe to the nativistic position.

Köhler's transposition experiments (1938a) demonstrated that under certain conditions choices are made on a relational rather than on an absolute basis. If P (not-P) refers to the proposition that choices are made (not made) on a relational basis, then experimental evidence can be marshalled against both P and not-P. In this case neither P nor not-P always holds, so that the excluded-middle principle does not apply. The conditions under which P holds or under which not-P holds have to be taken into account.

In the same vein, learning conceivably may be *continuous* under some circumstances and *discontinuous* under others (assuming that the italicized terms have been defined so that they are applicable to learning). The excluded-middle principle may not apply for the unqualified propositions, "Learning is continuous" and "Learning is not continuous."

In short, it seems to us that some of the discussions and related experimentation in psychology pertain to falsely (in terms of matter of fact) formulated issues which can in turn be traced to the (perhaps implicit) assumption of an excluded-middle principle. Such issues, sharply and dichotomously formulated, may be fine for college debates. But experimentation that revolves around these false issues in psychology may dissipate time and energy that might be better spent on more genuine issues.

It might be noted that in all these illustrations from psychology, P refers to general statements. It may be recalled that Brouwer has denied the admissibility of general statements in the excluded-middle principle.

The excluded-middle principle may also underlie the testing of the null hypothesis. Basically, the null hypothesis is an alternative to the research hypothesis. If the null hypothesis is rejected (at a certain level of statistical significance), then the research hypothesis may be accepted. Chapter 15 on logic and thinking discusses the role played by the testing of the null hypothesis in psychology. Research in the behavioral sciences, in general, is geared to testing of the null hypothesis whose formulation has been described as the first step in making a decision concerning the acceptability of hypotheses.

> The first step in the decision-making procedure is to state the null hypothesis (H_0). . . . . It is usually formulated for the express purpose of being rejected. If it is rejected, the alternative hypothesis (H_1) may be accepted. The *alternative hypothesis* is the operational statement of the experimenter's research hypothesis. (Siegel, 1956, p. 7)

According to the excluded-middle principle, either a hypothesis or its negation must hold. One wonders whether this principle has influenced research involving the testing of the null hypothesis. One effect may be to limit the alternative hypotheses so that (at least in some research) only a hypothesis and its negation are considered and other alternative hypotheses are overlooked. Another influence is the assumption that if the null hypothesis (not-H) can be rejected, then the research hypothesis (H) can be accepted which rules out the possibility that neither H nor not-H prevails or is acceptable.

Sociological Views

Brouwer (1913) appeals to sociology and history for support of neo-intuitionism and for support of its criticisms of other foundational views. He believes that to understand the development of opposing foundational views, one ought first to understand the concept of science, since mathematics is considered to have originally taken its place in historical thought as part of science. Referring to Brouwer's views on science and sociology, Black writes:

> Science he conceives to be the systematic cataloguing as laws of nature of causal sequences of phenomena, especially such as are important in social relations. Mathematics, in particular, is a branch of scientific thought concerned with the structure of phenomena. A mathematical attitude towards phenomena arises as an act of will of the individual produced by an urge towards self-preservation, and the choice of structures for consideration is therefore determined by the exigencies of the individual in his relation to society. . . . By his own ordered activity, [man] supplements the natural phenomena and widens the applicability of his laws. This is notably the case with counting and measuring, which are the activities *par excellence* by which man introduces order into nature. (1934, p. 192)

One may, as Black concludes, agree that mathematical activity is rooted in sociological activity and yet still disagree with the intuitionists.

We do not agree with Brouwer's conception of science as the systematic cataloguing as laws of nature of causal sequences of phenomena. And we wonder what evidence there is for the thesis that a mathematical attitude toward phenomena is produced by an urge toward self-preservation. Granted that mathematics is concerned with the structure of phenomena, in what sense is neointuitionism concerned with such structures and with what kind of structures is mathematics concerned? Gestalt psychology, for example, is also concerned with the structure of certain phenomena. Phenomenologists, whether Gestalt psychologists or not, are often concerned with the structure of phenomena. Are these psychologists mathematicians to the extent that they are concerned with structure? Or does structure have a different meaning in psychology than in mathematics? Indeed, what is meant by structure in each discipline? And, specifically, what is meant when it is stated that mathematics (or intuitionism) is concerned with the structure of phenomena? Such questions still await adequate answers. The difficulty is not attributable solely to intuitionists. Many mathematics texts, with no inclination toward intuitionism, use the term *structure;* but few define it or yet specify that it is to be taken as an undefined concept.

Returning to consideration of the quotation from Black, let us note that it indicates that the choices of structures for consideration are determined by the exigencies of the individual in his relation to society. If this be so, then certainly numbers, as we know them, are not the only structures that can be so determined nor counting and measuring the only activities by which man introduces order into nature. Why, then, do natural numbers and counting play fundamental roles in intuitionism? Is intuitionistic mathematics suitable for certain cultures only and another type of mathematical foundation suitable for other cultures? Let us consider some conceptions of number in cultures other than our own.

Conceptions of Number

Heyting (1956, p. 7) writes: "This elementary notion of natural numbers, *familiar to every thinking creature*, is fundamental in intuitionistic mathematics . . . we contend that it is sufficiently clear to build mathematics upon" (italics ours). That the notion of natural number is familiar to every thinking creature is a questionable thesis. It is on the same order as Kronecker's thesis that the whole numbers are "natural" or divinely created. Of interest in this connection is Wertheimer's 1912 paper on numbers and numerical concepts in primitive peoples (see Wertheimer, 1938a). "There are structures [*Gebilde*] which, less abstract than our numbers, nevertheless serve analogous ends or can be used in place of numbers" (p. 265). These structures, which serve some primitive peoples in place of numbers, do not abstract from the natural context and natural relationships in which they are involved, at least not to the same extent as do our numbers. Our numbers may be regarded as abstractions from reality, for example, abstractions of properties of groups of objects. These abstractions enhance the applicability of our numbers, giving them the quality of being transferable (applying to aggregates of different kinds of objects). But this abstraction of number from concrete actuality makes it difficult for many primitive peoples to grasp the notion of number as we know it, since they seem not to be facile at abstracting from concrete actuality. "Generally speaking, the execution of a numerical or other intellectual operation whose meaning is not rooted in actuality is almost if not entirely impossible for primitive peoples" (Wertheimer, 1938a, p. 267).

In contrast to the views of a spokesman for neointuitionism, who states that children in elementary school understand what natural numbers are and accept that the sequence of such numbers can be indefinitely extended (Heyting, 1956, p. 7), Wertheimer discusses the difficulty that children, even in our society, have in grasping the notion of number as an abstract sum, a summative manifold of units.

Wertheimer's paper also casts some doubt on the thesis that "natural number is universally applicable in the process of counting" (Heyting, 1956, p. 15), given as one reason for using natural number as a fundamental concept in neointuitionistic mathematics. Although we count by adding 1, Wertheimer writes that "It is not true that all (meaningful) counting consists in the addition of 1 more, as Locke claimed" (1938a, p. 272). "Counting, for example, in the sense of repeated additions of unity does not constitute the only factor in the genesis of numbers" (p. 265). Instead,

> [it is] probable that not counting, but natural group- and quantity-structures relative to real biological relationships constitute the genetically important origin of numerical concepts. The primary structures are probably not such concepts as 1 and continued additions of 1 but conceptually analogous individualized structures. Plurality is not genetically a quantity of identical terms but an articulated whole. (p. 272)

Our numerical system arises from "the multiple application of one unique quantity," but there are other numerical systems (for instance, in New Guinea) that operate on different principles. Yet, the other systems may involve operations upon and with structures that take the place of our numbers so that, for example, there are "progressions toward larger structures analogous to those attained by our own abstract methods of addition and multiplication" (p. 270).

In short, primitive people think, and they have numerical systems, and yet the notion of natural numbers and of counting based on the addition of a unit may not be familiar to them. Perhaps neointuitionism is ignoring the evidence of ethnology and taking an ethnocentric view of mathematics.

The conception of the nature of number and the nature of counting may influence methods of teaching. In the Middle Ages, arithmetical operations were taught by methods that involved concrete objects—for example, an abacus with beads taught counting and addition. Methods in use today tend to be based more on abstractions. Some teaching methods are not concerned with structural properties of an arithmetical operation. For example, the task of adding three squares when they form a

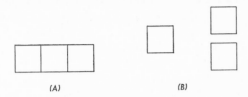

(A)   (B)

whole unit (as in Figure A) is not considered different from adding three squares when they are separate and apart (as in Figure B). Yet, to some children in our society and to many primitive peoples, there is a difference. Moreover, there are conceptions of teaching arithmetic that are not based on the successive addition of a unit to form numbers. An example is Catherine Stern's approach to the teaching of arithmetic (1949), which makes use of Gestalt psychological principles. Stern's methods recognize that early in the child's intellectual development, even before he can grasp the notion of a number as a manifold of units, he may be aware of gaps in structures, of where something "fits in" to complete a figure to form a "good Gestalt." Numbers may be understood in terms of their relation to other numbers and not necessarily as a sum of units. For example, in our number system, with the central role it accords to 10, it may be more meaningful for a child to begin with a structure corresponding to 10 (say, a rectangle composed of 10 squares) and to consider 5 as half of 10 (rather than as the sum of 5 units) and to consider 9 as 1 less than 10 (rather than as the sum of 9 units). In short, children can be taught to deal with numbers in what Wertheimer would call "sensible" ways, ways that are not based solely on summation of units but are concerned with the notions of a "good Gestalt," the requirements of a figure or structure, the realization of gaps, and the "fitting in" to complete gaps.

Gestalt psychology also seems to cast some doubts on Brouwer's conception of the primordial intuition of abstract bi-unity as the "basal intuition of mathematics." Recall that this is considered the source not only of the numbers one and two, but also of all finite ordinal numbers, since one of the elements of the two-oneness may be thought of as a new two-oneness, a process that may be repeated indefinitely (Brouwer, 1913). Brouwer seems to be suggesting that the source of all numbers is a kind of division or bisection process in which a unit is split into two parts or units, each of which is divided into two identical parts, and so on. But it should be clear from the previous quotations from Wertheimer's paper that he does not regard such a division or bisection process as the source of all numbers. "Identity of parts is not the universally decisive factor in division" (1938a, p. 271), states Wertheimer. For example, if a stick is broken, then there are two sticks; but if a spear is broken in two, there are not two spears. "In the first case 'two' is abstract; I began with one unity, later I had two. In the other, more concrete instance we have a structure in which the parts still depend for their character upon the whole from which they were derived (e.g., one is the head-piece; the other, part of the shaft)" (p. 271).

A pair-structure, to take one example of a natural grouping, may involve not just any two objects but two that belong together. The pair may consist of identical items (as a pair of socks) or it may consist of items that differ (a pair of shoes, a pair of gloves, a married couple). The latter pairs are not obtained by adding one unit to an identical unit. Thus there are natural groupings that are unlike aggregates arising out of the bi-unity process in which units are divided into two.

Perceptual and Cognitive Acts

Neointuitionism considers that underlying the notion of natural number is that of an abstract entity, which in turn is derived in the perception of an object by a process of abstracting from the particular qualities of the object or stripping the object of all qualitative features. "In the perception of an object we conceive the notion of an entity by a process of abstracting from the particular qualities of the object" (Heyting, 1956, p. 13). But Gestalt psychology does not hold that the notion of an entity always arises in perception through such a stripping process. It does not consider that the notion of an entity results from what might be called "subtractive abstraction" (Wertheimer, 1945; Luchins and Luchins, 1959, pp. 168–193), a process that arbitrarily subtracts properties or qualities and is concerned with what remains. The notion of a Gestalt, for example, is not considered to arise from a process of subtractive abstraction, from abstracting qualities or stripping properties, and yet a Gestalt is an entity, even an abstract entity (Grelling and Oppenheim, 1938a, 1938b). Here we see that some ideas on perception that are accepted by neointuitionists are questionable from a Gestalt psychological orientation.

Brouwer considers the process of bi-unity to be an abstraction of a process that is the fundamental phenomenon of the human intellect.

Neointuitionism considers the breaking-up of moments of life into qualitatively different parts, which, separated by time, can be reunited, as the fundamental phenomenon of the human intellect (Brouwer, 1913). Gestalt psychology does not consider this the fundamental process underlying human intellectual activities. The process Brouwer describes sounds somewhat like breaking a jigsaw puzzle into parts and reassembling or reuniting them. Gestalt psychology holds to a very different conception of intellectual activities (in which roles are played by such operations as structuring, restructuring, recentering) rather than only by the reuniting of parts separated by time. Moreover, Gestalt psychology considers that the part itself need not remain identical but may change in time, depending on its place and function in the whole in which it occurs (see Ternus, 1938). In short, reuniting of parts seem inappropriate, from the Gestalt psychological viewpoint, as the fundamental intellectual phenomenon.

Continuity and Discontinuity

Brouwer has attempted to bridge the gap between continuity and discreteness by assuming that time is an a priori intuition, that time constitutes a continuum, and that a bi-unity process is involved. We do not wish to reject or endorse these assumptions. What is interesting is that psychologists have been concerned with the problem of bridging the gap between continuity and discreteness as well as with problems involved in the perception of continuity and discreteness.

It is of interest to compare Brouwer's attempts to bridge the gap between continuity and discreteness with the recognition, by some psychologists, that continuity and discreteness are, so to speak, two sides of the same coin, two aspects of the same phenomenon. Similarly, homogeneity and heterogeneity have been considered as aspects of the same phenomenon, as have part and whole, as well as togetherness and apartness, or whatever terms happen to be used to refer to the two sides of the coin. For example, Gestalt psychologists recognize that to speak of a part presupposes a whole of which it is a part and that one may speak of a whole while recognizing that it has component parts. The relationship between togetherness and apartness is well described by a transactional psychologist.

> The necessity for differentiating the part from the whole before the perception of a "thing" can occur is commonly experienced. Animals have protective coloration which serves the function of preventing other animals and man from having a perception of their "thingness" as differentiated from the background behind them. Only when we become aware of the "togetherness" of the animal apart from the "togetherness" of the background do we see the animal. "Togetherness" and "apartness" are therefore aspects of the same phenomenon. (Kilpatrick, 1961, p. 40)

Rather than accept or reject Brouwer's assumptions about time and the perception of temporal events, we raise such questions as these: What is meant by a continuum and by continuity? How do we perceive time? Under what conditions do we perceive it as continuous? More generally, when do we perceive continuity and when discontinuity, when do we perceive homogeneity and when heterogeneity, when do we perceive togetherness and when discreteness or apartness? Such questions have been investigated by some psychologists (for example, Fitts, 1951) and need still further investigation. Such investigations may help us to learn more about conditions under which continuity or discreteness prevails. Whether the findings of such investigations are compatible with Brouwer's notions would then have to be determined. In any event, we are dealing here with problems in which acceptance or rejection of philosophical assumptions on a priori grounds is not the only approach; a research-oriented approach is also feasible.

Pertinent to the discussion of continuity-discontinuity, homogeneity-heterogeneity, togetherness-discreteness, and so on, are problems that have been studied in psychology under the rubric of *differential threshold* or *discrimination threshold*. Such terms have been used to refer to the point at which a subject first differentiates or discriminates between two stimuli. It has been found that a subject may not be able to discriminate between stimulus A and stimulus B (that is, the difference between them presumably is below his discrimination threshold), and not be able to discriminate between stimulus B and stimulus C, and yet be able to discriminate between stimulus A and stimulus C. Positively expressed, the subject perceives A as equivalent to B (in the sense that he does not discriminate between them) and B as equivalent to C, and yet he perceives A as not equivalent to C. If the perceptual equivalence may be denoted as equality, we have: A equals B and B equals C, and yet A does not equal C. Surprisingly, this (perceptual) equality lacks the transitive property of logical or mathematical equality or of other mathematical equivalence relationships (for example, similarity for triangles). This perceptual phenomenon, with its apparently paradoxical nature, has come to be known as Stumpf's paradox (see Koffka, 1935, pp. 465–528).

We illustrate one experiment wherein Stumpf's paradox has been observed. A series of paper squares are used, all the same size, each square of uniform brightness, but the whole series representing gradations of gray (for example, from a square that is uniformly almost white to a square that is uniformly almost black). Two squares are projected adjacent to one another. If the subject reports two distinct squares, then he presumably can differentiate between the two. On the other hand, if he reports seeing a rectangle, without any discernible break in it, then he presumably cannot differentiate between the two squares. It has been found that when certain squares, A and B, are projected together, the subject reports a rectangle of uniform brightness and likewise when B and C are projected together, whereas when A and C are projected together he reports seeing two distinct squares or a rectangle composed of two shades of gray. Here, again, if equality is used to denote this perceptual equivalence, A equals B and B equals C, but A does not equal C.

How can Stumpf's paradox be accounted for? The Gestalt answer is that this apparent paradox arises because the situation is viewed in a piecemeal manner where each stimulus is considered to be correlated with a particular sensation and the resulting perception is considered as the and-summation of the individual sensations. Wertheimer conducted experimental variations to demonstrate that the differential threshold does not depend only on the specific stimuli that are to be differentiated but on the whole constellation in which they appear. To return to the example of the paper squares, we note that Wertheimer pointed out that the A in rectangle AB is not identical with the A in rectangle AC and that the B in rectangle AB is not identical with the B in rectangle BC. The perception of the A or of the B is affected by the particular constellation in which it appears and may change when the constellation changes. The difficulties connected with Stumpf's paradox arise because the perception of A is treated as an element that should remain invariant regardless of the constellation in which A appears. What is overlooked is that perception of the part depends on the whole in which it appears and on its role and function in this whole. A given stimulus may play a different role in various situations.

Wertheimer pointed out that if conditions are such that there is a tendency to perceive unit structure, or *unum*, then the perception of homogeneity is enhanced more than if there is a tendency to get a two-part structure, or *duum*. Wertheimer concluded that certain conditions favor the development of homogeneity and others of heterogeneity in the perceptual field. Whether a homogeneous or heterogeneous manifold arises depends upon structural features of the situation. There are laws governing the appearance of homogeneity or heterogeneity and they have to be investigated. Personality factors, attitudinal factors, cultural factors, momentary sets of the individual, as well as spatial arrangements of the stimuli, all seem to play a role in determining the extent of homogeneity or heterogeneity in what is perceived. In short, certain conditions foster continuity of the visual field; other conditions foster discreteness, division into parts rather than a continuous whole.

The same may be the case for perception of temporal events. Rather than assume an a priori relationship between continuity and discreteness of temporal events, we may be interested in investigating the relationships that prevail under various conditions. For example, are there conditions under which time does not seem to be divided into a *before* and an *after* (as in the bi-unity process) but instead seems to be divided in some other manner, or seems to remain undivided, such as an apparently unlimited present?

One more example of the issues involved can be obtained from Wertheimer's classical experiments on the so-called phi phenomenon. A vertical line is projected on a screen and then a horizontal line. If the time interval between the presentation of the two lines is about 1.2 seconds, subjects see distinct lines, a succession of items. If the time interval is considerably smaller, about 0.03 seconds, subjects see a capital L, that is, they report simultaneous exposure of the two lines. Somewhere in between the above two rates of exposure, at about 0.09 seconds, a phenomenon of optical movement is observed in which the vertical line is seen to sweep over and fall down into the horizontal position. It is to such apparent movement that the name phi phenomenon has been given (see the tabular description).

Description of Phi Phenomenon

Case	Time Interval (in seconds)	Figure Perceived	Nature of Structure
1	1.2	$\lfloor$ __	two units, succession of items
2	0.03	L	one unit, apparently simultaneous exposure
3	0.09	L↘	one unit, apparently moving

What is "before" and "after" in temporal events, as far as the experimenter is concerned, may not be "before" and "after" as far as the perceiver is concerned. From the experimenter's point of view, the vertical line was always before the horizontal line; yet in case 2, the two lines are seen as temporally simultaneous and not as a before and after. The concept of primordial intuition was introduced in relation to the notion of before and after in temporal events. Yet in this experiment, two units, separated by time, may be seen as not separated. Moreover, how they get reunited in time depends on the interval between the before and after and on the kind of structure the units produce. How units separated by time get reunited may not be as simple or uniform as Brouwer's writing suggests. The kind of structure that results is not determined just by the before or the after but by what happens during the interval. Important problems regarding the role of structural features of the perceptual process seem to be involved. Here is a field where the psychologist can make a contribution in helping to determine the laws governing the structuring of temporal events in perception.

Moreover, the phi phenomenon illustrates the influence of conditions on perception of continuity or discreteness. In case 1, with the largest time interval, two distinct units are perceived, whereas in case 3, with the intermittent time interval, continuous movement is perceived instead of discreteness. We see that perception of continuity-discreteness lends itself to experimental investigation and not only to philosophical speculation.

Cultural and language factors are among those that may influence our perception of the continuity-discreteness relationship. For example, when shown a rainbow or a spectrum from a prism, an American may describe some six or more different hues, such as purple, blue, green, yellow, orange, red. "The continuous gradation of color which exists in nature is represented in language by a series of discrete categories. This is an instance of structuring of content. There is nothing inherent either in the spectrum or the human perception of it which would compel its division in this way" (Gleason, 1961, p. 4). The specific method of division used by the American is part of the structure of English. Speakers of other languages might classify colors quite differently. Gleason cites the cases of speakers of Shona (a language of Rhodesia) who divide spectral colors into three categories, and speakers of Bassa (a language of Liberia) who classify them into two categories (see Whorf, 1950, 1956; and Carroll, 1956 for other examples).

As with the rainbow, so the conceptions of time and its divisions may differ in different cultures (see Sherif, 1934). Moreover, in the same society, young children may have different conceptions than adults. Perhaps those conceptions of time and its division which Brouwer accepts are not universal but are culture-bound.

Intuitive Clarity
as a Research Problem

The intuitionistic demand for intuitive clarity and for cognitive evidence raises problems for psychological research. What is meant by intuitive clarity and by cognitive evidence? Who determines that intuitive clarity is involved? That the answers are by no means self-evident is suggested by a demonstration that has received considerable attention in transactional psychology (see Kilpatrick, 1961). An apparatus has three peepholes, A, B, and C, and through any one you can look with one eye at the contents of a compartment. Through each peephole you see the same thing: a chair. Yet when you look over the top of the screen that hides the compartments from direct view, or if you walk around behind the screen, you find that the three objects you were looking at are quite different. The object in the compartment behind peephole A is a set of strings and a piece of cardboard arranged as the parts of the chair, with the cardboard the seat. Behind peephole B is a set of strings and a white diamond painted on the back wall of the compartment. The strings are of different lengths and at different angles so that they now "present no aspect of 'chairness,' and appear to be nothing but a bit of jumbled three-dimensional nonsense" (p. 38). The object behind C is a set of strings and a piece of cardboard, all arranged in a plane, like a perspective projection or projective drawing of a chair.

Yet each of these three different configurations is seen as a chair through the peepholes. In fact, when a tube containing a lens and a piece of ground glass is slid over each peephole, the images on the ground glasses are all alike. These images have essentially the characteristics of the image cast on the retina of a perceiver with one eye at the peephole. "This means that the *same* physiological stimulus pattern is being produced by three entirely *different* sets of configurations in space" (p. 39).

In short, from the peepholes an image of a chair is cast upon the retina and presumably there are concomitant cortical processes corresponding to the perception of a chair. Hence, things that are actually different are seen as similar. In each case you have a cognitive grasp of the image of a chair and it seems intuitively clear that you are looking at a chair. But when looking above or behind the screen, it is just as intuitively clear, and there is cognitive evidence, that you are not looking at chairs but at three very different objects.

Thus the chair demonstration indicates that under certain conditions of exposure, or from a certain point of regard, it is possible to demonstrate that various objects have the same structure (in terms of retinal image), and yet, under other conditions of exposure or from another point of regard, it is possible to demonstrate that these objects have different structures.

Heyting (1934) points out that for neointuitionism there is no source other than an intuition which places its concepts and inferences before our eyes as immediately clear. But, as the three-chair demonstration indicates, what is placed before our eyes as immediately and intuitively clear may differ depending on the point of regard. What shall be meant by intuitively clear and what shall be taken as intuitively clear? Neointuitionism insists on cognitive evidence. The physiological stimuli are alike when you look through the peepholes and presumably, also, the cortical correspondents are alike, so that there is cognitive evidence that the objects are alike. But the physiological stimuli and presumably the cortical correspondents differ when you look behind the screen so that there is cognitive evidence that the objects are different. Which cognitive evidence should we trust or accept?

In neointuitionism each inference is immediately tested on its evidence (Heyting, 1934). Here the reference presumably is to cognitive evidence. But there is cognitive evidence for the inference that the objects in the compartments are alike and also cognitive evidence for the inference that these objects differ extremely. If each inference is *immediately* tested on its evidence, then one would first conclude that the objects are alike (that all are chairs) and then one would conclude that these objects differ.

Neointuitionism wants to limit mathematics to what is intuitively clear and intuitively convincing. Even assuming that we know the meanings of these terms, we can say only that some mathematical demonstrations are intuitively clearer and more convincing than others. But this, in turn, is related to research problems that Wertheimer and his colleagues have stressed, which are important for understanding thinking and learning processes. What are the properties of the various kinds of demonstrations? Why are certain demonstrations or certain ideas easier to grasp than others? Moreover, what can be done to present an idea so that it will be intuitively clear and convincing?

It may be arbitrary to seek to restrict mathematics to what is intuitively clear *en vacuo*. It may be more fruitful to determine how demonstrations can be made intuitively clearer and more convincing. A mathematical "object" may be demonstrated in diverse ways, some of which are intuitively clearer than others. For example, it is possible to describe a geometric figure in such a way that it is readily visualized or to describe it in another way that makes it difficult to visualize (Luchins and Luchins, 1963b). In the teaching of plane and solid geometry, students' difficulties can sometimes be traced to their inability to visualize the structure of a figure involved or the structure of the proof. Good teaching may involve the discovery of a demonstration that permits students to visualize the figure involved or to get a clear cognitive grasp of the structure of a proof. Sometimes all that is needed is a certain rearrangement of the items in the description of a figure or of the order of presentation of the hypotheses, or "givens," in a problem. Restructuring or recentering a demonstration to bring it into agreement with the structural properties of a figure or of a proof may help to make it intuitively clearer. For example, the demonstration that vertical angles are equal can be given in a manner which is intuitively clearer than the standard proof (Wertheimer, 1945). In so-called intuitive geometry, the concept of *area* can be taught in ways so intuitively clear that even very young children can grasp the concept (Luchins and Luchins, 1947).

Whether or not one agrees that the mathematics of the future is the study of structures (Kovach, 1960), perhaps the psychology of the future may render a service in studying conditions that affect the realizing, grasping, and demonstrating of structural properties. This does not mean that psychology is going to give us mathematical proofs, but it does mean that psychology can help both in teaching mathematics and in furthering the understanding of the processes involved in mathematical creation. The dynamic properties of mathematical thought may be quite different than the formal, logical properties of a mathematical proof. This is not to say that psychology is to replace or supplant logic in mathematics. Psychology can render quite a different service than logic, one with which logic by its very nature is not concerned. Dynamics of mathematical thought and conditions that can enhance the intuitive clarity of mathematical demonstrations are related problems whose study can help us to understand the processes as well as the end-products of mathematical activities.

Intuitionistic Logic and Psychology

The experimental work on logic done by psychologists focuses on classical logic. The rejection of some of the principles and concepts of classical logic by intuitionists and constructionists suggests new areas for research. For example, experiments can be devised in which restrictions are placed on the logical principles or concepts that subjects may use. They may be told that they are not permitted, according to the "rules of the game" to use the principle of the excluded middle or the principle of contradiction. Similarly, restrictions may be placed on the subjects' use of the concept *not* or other negation concepts (in accordance with negationless or affirmative logic). What effects would such rules and restrictions have on the subjects' patterns of thinking? What effects would these changes have on their communication of their thoughts to other subjects who are not given the same restrictions, to other subjects who are told to operate in accordance with the rules of classical logic, and to other subjects who are given no rules or restrictions? What verbal or nonverbal responses would the various kinds of subjects use to communicate their thoughts? What would be the effects on their interpersonal relations?

Some dissatisfaction has been expressed by psychologists (for example, by Chein, 1963; J. Cohen, 1961; Wertheimer, 1938c) with psychological concepts which do not reflect what is the vital and essential nature of the phenomenon, particularly the individual or person. Perhaps the nuances and fine distinctions which the intuitionists have drawn with respect to various concepts (for instance, the concept of inequality) may suggest to these psychologists ways to develop psychological concepts that do reflect what the present concepts neglect.

Also of interest is the investigation of life situations to discover those situations where traditional logic is appropriate and those situations where intuitionistic logic (or another system of logic) is more appropriate. Such research might also be concerned with the relative appropriateness of various systems of logic that have more than the two truth values of traditional logic. We shall have more to say about such logical systems in the chapter on truth. They may be regarded as introducing more nuances with reference to the concept of truth. It has been shown that the intuitionistic propositional logic cannot be treated by the traditional two truth values or by any finite number of truth values (Gödel, 1932) but can be interpreted in terms of an enumerable infinity of truth values (Jáskowski, 1936).

CHAPTER 15

Logic and Thinking

Relationship between Logic and Thinking

Traditional logic was long regarded as both a *description* of thinking and a *prescription* for thinking. This accounts for the frequent application of the phrase "laws of thinking" to Aristotle's rules of logic. In the present century (and even earlier) many criticisms have been raised about this supposedly intimate relationship between logic and thinking. We shall shortly turn to some of these criticisms.

What about the relationship between modern logic and thinking? A book on logic for the general reader states that modern logic is the "model for clear, modern thinking" and that it puts Aristotelian logic on a "firm, modern basis" (Lieber and Lieber, 1947, p. 198). An elementary text on logic states that a certain branch of modern logic, the sentential calculus, is basic to virtually all scientific reasoning: "Almost all reasonings in any scientific domain are based explicitly or implicitly upon laws of sentential calculus" (Tarski, 1946, p. 44). Another logician, Quine, considers that although traditional logic "figured in natural sciences only tacitly and at a pretty rudimentary level of inference," modern symbolic or mathematical logic is a more effective tool. "To the scientist longing for nonquantitative techniques, then, mathematical logic brings hope. It provides explicit techniques for manipulating the most basic ingredients of discourse" (1951a, pp. 7–8).

However, Rosser, in a book on logic for mathematics, states that the symbolic logic he describes is "fairly inadequate for the logical needs of even the most mathematical sciences. For one thing no symbolic treatment of the relationship involving cause and effect has yet been devised" (1953, p. 6). Hence, unlike the logicians whose views were previously quoted, Rosser suggests that neither the sentential calculus nor symbolic logic as a whole is adequate to meet the logical needs of mathematical scientists. He is presumably referring here to physicists, biologists, psychologists, and others who apply mathematics to the sciences.

Rosser goes on to note that if attention is restricted to "purely mathematical reasoning," in contrast to applications of mathematics to the sciences, then some "quite satisfactory symbolic logics are available" (p. 6). He concludes that the symbolic logic which his text describes "is not intended as a model for how mathematicians should think but only as a model of how at the present time they do think" (p. 522).

Does symbolic logic serve as a model for how mathematicians and how mathematical scientists think? And how is symbolic logic related to everyday thinking? Can symbolic logic serve as a model for how discoveries or creative findings are obtained in mathematics, in psychology, in still other sciences, and outside of the sciences? As a prelude to discussions of these questions we turn to some critical evaluations that have been made of the relationship between thinking and logic by two philosopher-logicians.

A philosopher-logician's views—Russell

Bertrand Russell has some caustic comments on the treatment in traditional logic of deductive inference and especially of syllogistic inference, regarded as the prototype of inference in Aristotelian logic.

> [Deductive] inference is supposed to be a mark of intelligence and to show the superiority of men to machines. At the same time, the treatment of inference in traditional logic is so stupid as to throw doubt on this claim, and syllogistic inference, which was taken as the type from Aristotle to Bacon (exclusive), is just the sort of thing that a calculating machine could do better than a professor. . . . I have never come across any . . . case of new knowledge obtained by means of a syllogism. It must be admitted that for a method which dominated logic for two thousand years, this contribution to the world's stock of information cannot be considered very weighty.
>
> The inferences that we actually make (inductively) in daily life differ from those of syllogistic logic in two respects, namely, that they are important and precarious, instead of being trivial and safe. The syllogism may be regarded as a monument to academic timidity: if an inference might be wrong, it was dangerous to draw it. So the medieval monks, in their thinking as in their lives, sought safety at the expense of fertility. (1927, pp. 79–80)

A philosopher-logician's views—Peirce

The kind of reasoning which interests the mathematician may differ considerably from that which interests the logician. This has been pointed out by the philosopher Charles S. Peirce, the son of the eminent mathematician Benjamin Peirce. Father and son, the younger Peirce notes (1933), were struck by the "contrary nature" of their interests in the same propositions. For example, the algebra of logic assumed different aspects for them.

The mathematician asks what value this algebra has as a calculus. Can it be applied to unravelling a complicated question? Will it, at one stroke, produce a remote consequence? The logician does not wish the algebra to have that character. On the contrary, the greater number of distinct logical steps, into which the algebra breaks up an inference, will for him constitute a superiority of it over another which moves more swiftly to its conclusions. He demands that the algebra shall analyze a reasoning into its last elementary steps. Thus, that which is a merit in a logical algebra for one of these students is a demerit in the eyes of the other. (p. 200)

Propositions that can be immediately deduced from others by reasoning of the kind that logicians or philosophers extol are generally relegated by mathematics to the category of *corollaries*. They are so obvious as not to be quite worthy of being called theorems. Reasoning of this "corollarial" kind, Peirce contends, is generally not enough to establish the theorems of mathematics. The assertion of the theorem is not evidently true nor is it evident how the assertion follows from the hypotheses or premises. Besides thinking in general terms, it is usually necessary to set down or imagine a schema or diagram, such as a figure in geometry or an array of letters in algebra. Moreover, even after the schema is constructed or imagined, corollarial reasoning may not suffice. Peirce writes: "Thinking in general terms is not enough. It is necessary that something should be DONE" (p. 194). For example, in geometry subsidiary lines are drawn and in algebra certain permissible transformations are made of the letters. Peirce points out that, in a sense, schemata are also used in corollarial reasoning, but in this case the very words themselves serve as schemata. In mathematical theorems such verbal schemata may not suffice. Accordingly, Peirce characterizes thinking of the corollarial kind, where the conclusion evidently follows from the premises, as "reasoning with words," whereas "mathematical reasoning proper is reasoning with specially constructed schemata."

It is clear, then, that Peirce does not regard mathematics as involving only reasoning with words. He would probably not agree with the view that mathematics is merely verbal knowledge. Yet, this is precisely the view expressed by Russell when he wrote that one result of logicism has been "to dethrone mathematics from the lofty place that it has occupied since Pythagoras and Plato" and to show that it "is, in fact, *merely verbal knowledge*" (1945, p. 831, italics ours).

Logic, Psychology, and Thinking

Some psychologists consider logic to be the science that deals with the principles and conditions of correct thinking. They believe that psychology advances in its study of the thought processes by accepting the view that logic teaches the laws of thought. Assuming that ordinarily one thinks in accordance with the laws of logic, some psychologists and philosophers consider deviations from logical thinking as aberrations due to personality factors or to situational factors. Thus, there is a division of labor between the disciplines: logic is considered to deal with "correct thinking" and psychology with "errors of thinking."

Other psychologists and philosophers seem to reject this dichotomy. Some of them even tend to reduce logic to psychology. Such a point of view is related to the doctrine of psychologism, the doctrine that logical relations can be accounted for by psychological relations (see Mill, 1950, originally published in 1843). Psychologism has been subjected to various attacks. The philosopher Husserl (1913), for example, insisted that logic deals with propositions whose truth or falsity, like that of mathematical propositions, is independent of the time and place of their formulation and also independent of psychological factors (for instance, association of ideas). Psychological factors may be involved in whether one accepts or rejects a proposition but not in its truth or falsity. Thus a distinction is made between the processes of logical analyses of propositions and the psychological or mental processes of judgment involved in their acceptance or rejection.

More generally, a distinction is drawn by critics of psychologism between the logical and psychological realm. It has been said that "Husserl's main endeavor was to free logic from the shackles of psychology. Equally he has succeeded in freeing psychology from the shackles of logic" (Humphrey, 1951, p. 8). Humphrey believes that this has helped to keep psychological research from being encumbered by many of the epistemological difficulties that had confounded early psychological research (for example, the work of the Würzburg school of psychology).

At present, one can find traces in psychology of both the doctrine that logic deals with correct thinking and the doctrine that logic can be reduced to psychology. For example, the former doctrine is implicit in some theories that accept the conception of man as a rational being, the so-called rational man model. "The 'rational man' concept, long out of fashion in the behavioral sciences, is now undergoing a remarkable revival in the study of cognition. More and more, theory and research are being based on the postulate that a person's need to maintain harmony between his feelings, thoughts, and actions is a powerful determinant of his belief systems and his gross behavior" (McGuire, 1960, p. 65). Personality theories of the psychoanalyst and of the nondirective therapist as well as theories and concepts in social psychology regarding attitudes and attitude changes (for instance, the concept of cognitive dissonance, Festinger, 1957; Heider, 1946; Newcomb, 1953) assume that in a person there are, on the one hand, rational factors or a tendency toward rationality—often equated with, or considered to be operating in terms of, the laws of logic—and, on the other hand, irrational factors which are due to emotioconative or other personality and social variables. It is assumed that a person's thinking tends to be in line with logic unless disturbed by these irrational factors. Indeed, analytic and nondirective therapy are often devoted to freeing the person from bondage to these irrational factors so that he can act rationally. Moreover, in studies of attitudes and effects of communications, some psychologists have developed as their experimental design a "formal logic" model involving syllogistic reasoning (McGuire, 1960).

In the neurological theories of psychology, both Gestalt-oriented and others, there is an implicit tendency toward psychologism. In fact, as early as 1935 Koffka raised the question of whether Gestalt theory leads to psychologism.

> Such a theory seems to imply an extreme *Psychologismus* . . . (which) was violently attacked by some of our best philosophers, notably Edmund Husserl, who claimed to have refuted it once and for all. But his argument rested on the assumption, implicit or explicit, in all "psychologistic" theories, that psychological relations were merely factual or external. A "psychologism" based on this assumption was indeed refuted by Husserl and other philosophers. But this refutation does not affect our psychologism—if our theory can rightly be given this name—since in our theory psychological and physiological, or rather psychophysical, processes are organized according to intrinsic or internal relations. . . . It means that in our theory psychology and logic, existence and substance, even, to some extent, reality and truth, no longer belong to entirely different realms or universes of discourse between which no intelligible relationship exists. (1935, pp. 570–571)

In other words, Koffka claimed that the psychologism criticized by Husserl was based on factual or external relations (for example, J. S. Mill's position), whereas the "psychologism" of Gestalt theory was based on "dynamic intrinsic relations" between psychological events and physiological events and between psychology and logic.

Ryle (1957) traces some of the developments in the relationship between logic and psychology. He notes that the term *philosophy* once had a broader meaning than at present. During the seventeenth, eighteenth, and most of the nineteenth centuries, the term *philosopher* was applied to almost any learned man, including astronomers, chemists, and botanists. In English, there was no specific term for what are now *scientists*, a term that seems to have been coined about 1840. When distinctions were drawn, they were between *natural* philosophy on the one hand and *moral*, or *mental*, or *metaphysical*, philosophy on the other. Natural philosophy, which included the biological and physical sciences, dealt with physical, external phenomena. Metaphysical philosophy, under which often fell what we now call philosophy and logic, was concerned with mental, internal phenomena. Philosophy was sometimes equated with what we now call psychology. Indeed, it is only in recent years that university departments of psychology have separated from philosophy departments.

As already noted, logic was often placed under mental philosophy. Mathematics, too, was regarded by some as belonging here since it did not belong to natural philosophy. But there were those (for example, Frege and Russell) who protested that mathematics was neither an empirical science nor a mental or introspective science, and similarly for logic. But if logic and mathematics belonged neither to natural nor to mental philosophy where did they belong? One answer was that, in addition to the natural and the mental or the psychological realms, there was a third realm of nonmaterial, nonmental, and nonpsychological "logical objects," such as numbers, truths, falsehoods, classes, and implications. This viewpoint of a third realm, still found on the contemporary scene, is regarded by Ryle as an unfortunate development creating all sorts of philosophical problems. (See Freytag-Löringhoff, 1951 for a discussion of some of these philosophical problems of mathematics.)

In summary, we have touched on a number of views concerning the relationships among logic, psychology, and thinking. One viewpoint regards logic as the science of thinking and in effect seeks to reduce the psychology of thinking to logic. Another viewpoint seeks to reduce logic to psychology. Still another viewpoint sees the psychological (or mental) realm as separate from the logical realm. Whether psychology can be or should be reduced to logic, or vice versa, raises the broad issue of reductionism which is dealt with in a later chapter. The issue of reductionism can be considered independently of the scientific study of thinking by psychologists. As far as psychological research is concerned, each viewpoint seems to have stimulated research of both practical and theoretical value. For example, Gestalt psychologists—in spite of their tinge of psychologism—have pointed to new directions in research on thinking. Those who regard psychology as concerned with errors in thinking or those who separate psychology from logic have contributed to the discovery of personality and social factors that are related to illogical thinking as well as to the discovery of the kinds of organization and communication of propositions which lead to invalid conclusions. Moreover, logical reasoning has been studied by psychologists who do not commit themselves to one or another view concerning the relationship between logic and psychology. The study of syllogistic reasoning has received the attention of psychologists for about half a century and seems to be going strong.

A cursory survey of the literature on psychological research on thinking reveals that it has been an active and fruitful area of research for the past fifty years:

1. Syllogistic reasoning, induction, and deduction have been studied, particularly with regard to understanding the factors that maximize or minimize valid conclusions. (See Johnson, 1955; Vinacke, 1952; Woodworth, 1938, Woodworth and Schlosberg, 1954 for surveys of the literature.)
2. Psychologists interested in developmental and social behavior (for example,

Koffka, 1925; Lévy-Bruhl, 1926; Piaget, 1949; Werner, 1940) have studied the range of applications of the laws of formal logic (identity, excluded middle, and contradiction) across cultures and the developmental range.

3. Concept formation, intension and extension of concepts, processes of abstraction, the nature of definitions, and the analysis of propositions have been studied in our culture and other cultures by experimental as well as developmental psychologists (for example, Johnson, 1955; Vinacke, 1952; Werner, 1940; and Woodworth and Schlosberg, 1954). Such studies have also been done with mental patients as well as with brain-damaged individuals (for example, Goldstein and Scheerer, 1941).

4. More recently, studies on simulated thinking by computers, including so-called logic machines, have brought psychologists into the field of mathematical logic.

Even after a cursory survey we can agree with the conclusion drawn by Woodworth and Schlosberg (1954, p. 847) at the end of their chapter on thinking that this is one area of research for which psychologists need not be apologetic and that "it is a field that promises well for the future."

That logic is an aspect, an important and productive aspect, of thinking cannot be denied. It also cannot be denied that traditional Aristotelian logic had long been dictating the conception of what is the nature of correct thinking and influencing the nature of the psychological study of thinking. But this should not be construed as an inherent weakness of traditional logic any more than Kant's assumption that our conception of space is necessarily Euclidean is a weakness of Euclidean geometry. Psychologists and other behavioral scientists need not accept the description of thought implicit in one system of logic any more than physicists must accept the description of the universe implicit in Euclidean geometry. Moreover, even if it is shown that much of ordinary thinking in our society or in other societies is not in line with existing systems of logic, logic will still have a place in the study of thinking. Such findings may be taken as a challenge to logicians and psychologists to analyze thinking and to devise "logics" that include the aspects of thinking that are not covered by the existing systems of logic. Here is an area where logicians and psychologists can join in the development of new logical concepts, methods, and systems for use in theory and practice.

Logical Reasoning and Validity

Logical reasoning is also referred to as valid reasoning, valid argument, deductive reasoning, logical deduction, logical inference, and so on. The conclusion of a valid argument is said to be logically derived from the premises (or to be a logical inference from the premises). It is frequently said that an argument is valid if *any* of the following conditions hold:

1. If one accepts the premises of the argument, then one must accept the conclusion of the argument.

2. If the premises of the argument are true, then the conclusion must be true.
3. It is not possible for the premises of the argument to be true and the conclusions to be false.

Logical validity is also referred to as logical correctness. Rosser (1953), after noting that symbolic logic offers a precise definition of logical correctness, states that different systems of symbolic logic differ somewhat in the underlying conceptions of logical correctness. But it is not usually made so explicit that what is called logical correctness, logical validity, valid reasoning, logical inference, and so on depends on a particular system of logic. When the system is changed, the conception of valid reasoning may change. Systems of logic that differ from the classical system in their interpretation of "if-then" or logical implication (Lewis, 1912; von Wright, 1951a) may differ in their conception of logical validity. Similarly, systems that differ in what they accept as logical truths (or tautologies) may differ in what they regard as logically valid. For example, the intuitionistic sentential calculus, which does not accept an unqualified principle of the excluded middle, would not consider an argument as valid if it made use of such a principle.

The principle of the excluded middle is tacitly involved in some of the characterizations of a valid argument. For example, consider the characterization that an argument is valid if, when the premises are true, then the conclusion is necessarily true. Let us write the argument whose validity we are discussing in the form: "If P, then Q." By the law of the excluded middle, either Q or not-Q must hold. But if the argument: "If P, then Q" is valid, then the supposition that not-Q holds implies not-P. Again, the principle of the excluded middle is appealed to in order to assert that either P or not-P holds. But if not-Q and if P, then by the argument, "If P, then Q" we get Q which together with not-Q constitutes a contradiction. Hence, not-Q implies not-P, or otherwise expressed, "If not-Q, then not-P." Here we have used the law of the excluded middle to show that the negative converse of a valid argument is valid. As we said, not-Q implies not-P. But if P is true, then not-P together with P yields a contradiction. Hence, if the premises P of a valid argument are true, then the conclusion Q must be true—provided we accept the excluded-middle principle. In short, the cited characterization of a valid argument is implicitly dependent on acceptance of the excluded-middle principle.

More generally, what constitutes a valid argument is dependent on a particular system of logic. In an attempt to make this dependence explicit, we might modify a common characterization of a valid argument to read as follows: An argument is valid if when one accepts the specific premises of the argument as well as the underlying system of logic, then one must accept the conclusion. It is not enough to accept only the specific premises of the argument. If one accepts the P of the argument "If P, then Q," but does not accept the underlying system of logic in which this argument is valid, then he need not accept the conclusion.

In short, what constitutes a valid argument or a logical inference in one system of logic may not be so regarded in another system of logic. Hence, although valid argument (logical inference, valid reasoning, logical deduction, and so on) is often spoken of as an absolute, it is more properly regarded as relative—relative to a particular system of logic.

Conclusion Implicit in Premises

Logical reasoning is often characterized as a technique that makes explicit in the conclusion what is already in the premises. This is variously described by the phrases that the conclusion of a logical inference is implicit, contained, stated, stipulated, or concealed in the premises. These different phrases are sometimes used by the same writer, as shown in the following citations (wherein italics are ours).

> Mathematical as well as logical reasoning is a conceptual technique of making explicit what is *implicitly contained* in a set of premises. (Hempel, 1953, p. 160)
> It is typical of any purely logical deduction that the conclusion to which it leads simply re-asserts (a proper or improper) part of what has already been *stated* in the premises. . . . The same situation prevails in all other cases of logical deduction; and we may, therefore, say that logical deduction—which is the one and only method of mathematical proof—is a technique of conceptual analysis; it discloses what assertions are *concealed* in a given set of premises, and it makes us realize to what we committed ourselves in accepting these premises; but none of the results obtained by this technique ever goes by one iota beyond the information already *contained* in the initial assumptions. (Hempel, 1949, pp. 240–241)
> The nature of the peculiar certainty of mathematics is now clear: . . . the theorem, if rigorously proved, simply re-asserts part of what has been *stipulated* in the postulates. (Hempel, 1949, p. 24)
> Due to the tautological nature of logical inference we often say that the conclusion of a valid argument contains nothing that is not already *stated* in the premises. It simply serves to make explicit what is already *implicitly* there. As some have picturesquely put it, if our minds were such that we could see all that is *contained* in our premises we would not need to make deductions. Not having such mental powers we find deduction, tautological though it be, indispensable in our pursuit of knowledge. (Hochberg, 1959, p. 419)

We shall later question the advisability of using such terms as *contained* and *stated* as synonymous with *concealed*. First, we want to comment on another aspect of the terminology. To say that a conclusion is implicit in the premises (or is contained, stated, or stipulated in the premises) suggests that the conclusion is a function of only the premises. The terminology suggests that the premises alone suffice to yield the conclusion. But this is not the case. The terminology conceals the role played by a particular system of logic. As we saw, the logical system stipulates criteria for logical validity and hence influences what is regarded as a logical consequence of other statements.

Perhaps our point can be made clearer in the following manner. It is commonly said that if the premises of a logical argument are accepted, then the conclusion also must be accepted. But, as we have seen, this is not quite the whole story. Not only the premises must be accepted but also the underlying system of logic, or, at least, the rules of logic used in the particular argument. The system of logic essentially stipulates, as we saw, what constitutes logical validity and hence affects the conclusions that can be logically deduced. For example, given a set of premises, we may derive a conclusion, utilizing a classical sentential calculus, which is not a conclusion if, say, intuitionistic logic is used, perhaps because the unrestricted principle of the excluded middle was utilized in the deduction of the conclusion. A conclusion that is "implicit" or "contained" in the premises when one system of logic is used may therefore not be "implicit" or "contained" in the premises when another system of logic is used.

It may be of value to draw an analogy with money put out at interest. To say that the total amount is implicit in the principal put out for investment is to overlook the fact that the amount depends also on the particular system of interest and the number of interest periods involved. Analogously, a conclusion depends not only on the premises but also on the particular system of logic and its rule of inference or its criteria of logical validity. As the total amount of money is realized when a number of steps are carried out in accordance with the system of interest, so the conclusion of logical reasoning is realized when a number of steps are carried out in accordance with the system of logic. If other systems of interest are used, the total amount may differ. Analogously, if other systems of logic are used, the conclusions may differ. In short, the logical frame of reference in which the inference is made influences the nature of logical validity, the role and function of the premises, and the kinds of conclusions to which the premises lead via logical reasoning.

That a conclusion is to a certain extent dependent upon particular logical tools and not inherent in the premises is also suggested in studies of thinking of certain primitive peoples (Wertheimer, 1938a). They may accept the premises and accept certain conclusions and yet not other conclusions, all of which could be described, from the frame of reference of a particular logical system, as "implicit" in the premises. They refuse to play the rules of the game, refuse to accept the rules of our logic, sometimes because to do so leads to a conclusion that is meaningless or senseless in their cultural context or violates certain particular "empirical facts" they possess.

To describe the thinking of such people as *primitive* or *illogical* is beside the point. It depends on the definitions of these terms. As Wertheimer tells us:

> To us it seems a great advantage to be able to abstract from the natural relationships of things. . . . But there are others whose thinking may be described thus: Wherever there is no natural relationship, no vividly concrete and relevant connection amongst things themselves, there is also no logical connection, nor is any logical manipulation of these things possible. (1938a, p. 267)

Stated versus concealed conclusions

We saw that in characterizations of valid reasoning such terms as *contained* and *stated* have been used as if they were synonymous with the word *concealed*. Now, in their ordinary connotations the words *contained* and *stated* have quite different meanings than the word *concealed*. There are cases of valid reasoning where the conclusion simply restates what is in the premise, the most trivial case being where the conclusion is one of the premises. But such cases are not of much interest. Where the conclusion is already stated or contained (in their everyday sense) in the premises, mathematicians would probably not single out the reasoning involved as a theorem but would designate it as a lemma or a corollary if they mentioned it at all. (We saw that such a point was made by Peirce in cases where the conclusion is an immediate consequence of the premises.) Except in trivial cases, the conclusion is not one of the premises and is not apparently stated in the premises but may be well concealed in the premises. Moreover, a conclusion that is concealed to one person may be revealed to another. There are some interesting examples of this in the history of mathematical logic itself. For example, Whitehead and Russell based the propositional calculus of *Principia Mathematica* (1910–1913) on five axioms. Yet it was later shown by Bernays (1926) that the fourth axiom could be logically inferred from the four remaining axioms. Is it not surprising that Whitehead and Russell, outstanding logicians and masters of deductive reasoning, should not have recognized that the fourth axiom was "contained" or "stated" in the remaining axioms? Apparently it was very well concealed.

To consider one more example: The eminent logician Quine, in the 1931 edition of a book on foundations of mathematical logic, included axioms on class theory. These axioms were subsequently shown by Rosser (1939a) to be contradictory. This difficulty was corrected in a revision of Quine's work (Quine, 1951a). The contradictory consequences of the axioms may have been contained, asserted, or stipulated in the axioms, but they may be more appropriately described as cleverly concealed.

A shortcoming of logical
reasoning

It seems to us that a weakness of the thesis that thinking is based on
(or is adequately portrayed by) logic, whether traditional or modern, is
the following: Logical reasoning has no provision for distinguishing between conclusions which are obviously or literally contained or stated in
the premises and those conclusions which may be arrived at only after
months or even years of pondering or which have not yet been deduced.
Logical inference does not differentiate valid reasoning, which is empty
and sterile as far as advances in knowledge are concerned, from valid
reasoning that genuinely advances knowledge. It does not distinguish between a trivial argument that is logically correct and productive thinking.
One might protest that it is not the task of logic to be concerned with
such a distinction. This is not the issue here. The problem is: A characterization of reasoning in terms of logical inference does not distinguish
between valid reasoning that genuinely advances knowledge, and valid
reasoning that is trivial, sterile, that, for example, deduces a conclusion
that is literally contained in the premises. The characterization in terms
of logical inference *excludes* criteria that distinguish highly productive
reasoning from trivial cases, and it *includes* cases which would not be
likely to be considered either as productive or as scientific reasoning.
Relevant here are criticisms Wertheimer has made of the traditional
treatment of syllogistic inference.

> Does it follow that every syllogism is a *petitio*, a mere recapitulation of
> things already known? . . . But if [the major premise already contains]
> everything that could possibly pertain to it, then no "new" knowledge about
> it is possible. It is into this *impasse* that the traditional logic is predestined to
> fall. Such a logic is suitable only for one who already knows everything and
> needs only a system of classification; for a genuine advance in knowledge it is
> useless. (1938b, pp. 276–277)

Such a criticism seems applicable in considerable measure to modern
logic if modern logical inference is, as is often asserted, only a technique
of making explicit what is already contained in the premises. How could
modern logic then help to make for actual advances in knowledge?
A distinction is sometimes made between what is "objectively" or
"theoretically" new, on the one hand, and what is "subjectively" or
"psychologically" new, on the other. For example:

> Since all mathematical proofs rest exclusively on logical deductions from
> certain postulates, it follows that a mathematical theorem . . . asserts
> nothing that is *objectively* or *theoretically* new as compared with the postulates
> from which it is derived, although its content may well be *psychologically new*
> in the sense that we were not aware of its being implicitly contained in the
> postulates. (Hempel, 1949, p. 241)

The terminology seems unfortunate. It suggests that a theory presented in postulational form cannot lead to anything theoretically or objectively new. Why call it a theory then? Can a postulational approach really add nothing new to theoretical or objective or scientific knowledge? Where then is its scientific value? Moreover, the terminology suggests that "psychological newness" is distinct from "objective newness." Is what is psychologically new not objective?

In any event, using some of this terminology, we may say that a short-coming of the thesis that logic adequately accounts for reasoning is that logical inference or logical validity does not distinguish between what is psychologically new and what is psychologically explicit in the premises.

It may not be out of place to add that there are psychologists who go to great pains to show that thinking is nothing but the repetition of habits learned in the past. What appears to be psychologically new is regarded as reduced to past experience, that is, the supposedly new response was already in the response repetoire of the organism. From this point of view, what appears to be psychologically new is itself not new. What shall be meant then by saying something is psychologically new in contrast to its being not new psychologically?

Varied uses of "implication"

Misunderstanding is fostered by the varied uses of the word *implication*. It may refer to what is explicitly stated as logically derived from various premises, or it may refer to what is "concealed" in the premises or to what has been "revealed." Moreover, the term is also used without the connotation of logical implication. Thus, it is sometimes said that P implies Q when P suggests or hints at Q. Concepts are sometimes said to "imply" certain theoretical positions or philosophical orientations. Such varied meanings make it desirable to stipulate what kind of implication is referred to, what operator drew the implication, and the basis of the operations on which it was drawn.

Perhaps a distinction also should be made between what a writer explicitly states and accepts and the implications others find in his report. Even though these implications may be logically derived from the report, they may not be what the writer "bargained for" or what he intended to imply. For example, axioms for logical systems have been proposed and were later shown to be contradictory; the proposers of the axioms did not knowingly introduce contradictions. It may lessen misunderstanding if such implications are cited in the names of the persons who discovered them and their logical systems, rather than be reported in the literature as if the original writer meant to make the implications and agrees with them. An implication may be described as found in A's report by B, on the basis of a certain system of logic, rather than as A's implication. The latter is confusing if we do not know whether A explicitly drew the implication or was unaware of it, and whether he subscribed to it and the system of logic on which it was derived.

In the psychological literature there are discussions which attempt "implication and explication" of a particular report or of theoretical and systematic approaches. This may take the form of attempting to make explicit or to clarify the meanings of concepts and the nature of assumptions and implications. The result may be that the discussants talk about something that was not the intent of the report or of the theorist. It sometimes happens that a viewpoint is attributed to a certain school of thought in psychology as an "implication" of or as a concomitant of its theoretical position even though representatives of the school have not (and perhaps would not) subscribe to the viewpoint. It is for such reasons that we suggest that a separation be made between what a report states and what is obtained through analysis of the report, whether logical analysis or otherwise. There may be several implications and suggestions discovered, only some of which fit the intended meaning, content, and structure of the report. Hence, the implications and suggestions should not be treated as representing the original writer's view or as "implied" by him. At least he should have an opportunity to state his views concerning the implications and suggestions.

We recognize that analysis of a report for the purpose of making implications and explications can be very valuable to the original writer and others. It may help the writer to revise his formulations, to be clearer in the use of language, and perhaps to change certain statements in order to rule out undesired implications. One difficulty here is that a discussant may have a list of "words" which to him stand for a certain theoretical position (for example, Neurath's index of prohibited words; see Frank, 1961a, p. 45) and one who uses such words may automatically be regarded as subscribing to the concept. A more general difficulty is that a gifted research worker may not be facile at communicating his ideas to others so as to avoid "implications and explications" which he does not intend. He may find that he is spending more time worrying about the details and nuances of language than on his research. He may come to regard words and logic as tricks to trap him into implying what he does not intend to imply. There is no pat solution to such difficulties. We can only suggest that the research worker communicate his ideas as clearly as he can and leave "logical analysis" of his report to those who are qualified and are concerned with such matters. They, in turn, should be prepared to state the bases on which they derived their implications and explications.

Discovery and Proof

The thesis that mathematical reasoning is adequately accounted for by logic seems to rest on the assumption that mathematical reasoning is largely confined to the formal verification of the logical validity or logical correctness of mathematical proofs. This assumption seems also to underlie the thesis that mathematics reduces to logic or that mathematics is logic. Yet some of the writers who consider that mathematics reduces to logic also admit that logic plays a relatively small part in the mathematical activities that lead to the *discovery* of theorems and of their proofs. For example, Quine (1951a) who writes that "mathematics reduces to logic" (p. 5) describes discovery in mathematics as largely a matter of luck rather than logic. Thus he writes that "a [mathematical] proof once discovered can be mechanically checked, but the actual discovery of the proof is a hit and miss matter" (p. 6). Characteristically, "the mathematician hits upon his proof by unregimented insight and good fortune, but afterwards other mathematicians can check his proof" (p. 87). Or again: "appropriate to each formula which is a theorem there is a device (a so-called proof) discoverable in general only by luck, which once discovered enables us to see by a finite amount of inspection that the formula is a theorem" (p. 291). Thus, logic may be extremely useful for the verification of proofs but not for the discovery of proofs. Quine's view that mathematics reduces to logic, taken in conjunction with the minor role of logic in mathematical discovery, suggests that this aspect (mathematical discovery) is absent from what is reduced to logic. Excluded from mathematics are activities that lead to mathematical discoveries of theorems and proofs and perhaps even the products of these activities. But there are writers who consider that such activities belong to mathematics. Intuitionists might add that mathematics is just the mathematical reasoning that leads to discoveries and not the formal exposition of results or formal verification of the logical correctness of results. In any event, if mathematics is considered to include mathematical discovery, then it is difficult to defend the thesis that mathematics is logic or that it reduces to logic. Similarly, if mathematical reasoning is considered to include the processes of inquiry that lead to the discoveries of mathematical theorems and proofs, then it is difficult to defend the thesis that logical reasoning is adequate to account for mathematical reasoning.

In short, there is involved here also the problem of what constitutes mathematics. It would seem that mathematics was not and is not discovered through logical reasoning per se, although the fruits of mathematical inquiry may be put into logical form and its correctness checked through criteria established within logic. But the activities of mathematicians and of mathematics involve inquiries which lead to discovery or invention, in addition to verification of logical correctness.

The role of chance
in discovery

The view that mathematical discovery or invention, along with invention in general, is based on chance rather than logic, has been expounded by a number of psychologists and biologists. Hadamard (1945, p. 6) writes that the psychologist Souriau in 1881 seems to have been the first to maintain that invention occurs by pure chance rather than the more traditional theory that invention occurs through the use of logic and systematic reasoning. An extreme formulation of the theory that chance is an explanation of invention is offered by the biologist Nicolle who considers that the act of invention is like a creation and "such an act owes nothing to logic or to reason. The act of discovery is an accident" (cited in Hadamard, 1945, p. 19). Chance is a popular explanation of invention and thinking even in contemporary psychology. Examples are provided by theories that use trial and error as explanatory concepts. But Gestalt psychologists maintain that the part played by chance in creativity and productive thinking has been overrated. What is attributed to chance may actually be in accordance with certain laws or principles that have not been adequately recognized (Wertheimer 1938b, 1945). Some creative acts once attributed to chance, or dissected in rather fruitless attempts to force them into the mold of traditional logic, have since been dealt with by principles of Gestalt psychology (Duncker, 1945; Koffka, 1925, 1935; Köhler, 1925, 1929, 1941; Wertheimer, 1945).

The laws of traditional logic are not concerned with the part played by recentering and restructuring. Yet, sometimes the conclusion to a syllogistic argument is obtained only when the relationship of the premises to each other is "re-formed, re-grasped, re-centered in a specific way" (Wertheimer, 1938b, pp. 280–281). To effect this process may require examination and "penetration into the nature and structure" of the premises, processes that are not portrayed by chance or by the laws of logic.

The history of science provides many instances of scientific discoveries based on reasoning which involved restructuring, recentering, and seeing a premise in a different light.

> The history of science has provided many examples: comprehension of the nature of stellar movements ("falling" toward one another); the theory of the screw (i.e., seeing the screw as a wedge); the history of the conception of inertia. Until recently such accomplishments were thought of as essentially the results of "imagination," or "chance," or "the intuition of genius." But it is not these alone. *Formal* determinations, expressible in definite laws, are also involved. (p. 281)

Wertheimer seems to suggest that such laws are also laws of reasoning, so that it would be inadequate to say that all or most scientific reasoning is based exclusively on laws formulated in systems of logic or chance.

The role of logic
in discovery

Wertheimer was discontent with those discussions of creative thinking which tried to bring it into the format of traditional logic.

In comparison with actual, sensible, and productive processes [of thinking], the topics as well as the customary examples of traditional logic often look dull, insipid, lifeless. To be sure, the treatment is rigorous enough, yet often it seems barren, boring, empty, unproductive. If one tries to describe processes of genuine thinking in terms of formal traditional logic, the result is often unsatisfactory; one has, then, a series of correct operations, but the sense of the process and what was vital, forceful, creative in it seems somehow to have evaporated in the formulations. On the other hand it is possible to have a chain of logical operations, each perfectly correct in itself, which does not form a sensible train of thought. . . . In short, there is the danger of being empty and senseless, though exact; and there is always the difficulty with regard to real productiveness. (Wertheimer, 1945, p. 10)

What about modern systems of logic? Are they adequate for dealing with productive thinking? Wertheimer hints that they are not. He is reminded of what has frequently occurred in the history of logic. "In the introduction or in some early chapter a book may seem to start a new approach, altogether different from the customary treatment of logic; in fact, certain formulations may almost appear akin to those of Gestalt theory. And yet, when it comes to dealing concretely with a problem, the old operations, old rules, old attitudes appear again" (p. 12). In short, contemporary systems of logic, even if not Aristotelian in nature, tend to assume traditional garb and deficiencies when dealing with productive thinking.

The role of intuition
in discovery

Wertheimer does not suggest, nor do we not intend to imply, that logic plays no role in productive thinking and, particularly, in mathematical discovery. But while formal logic may enter into the mathematical discoveries, it does not play the same central role there that it does in the verification of the logical correctness of proofs. In fact, for discovery it may be better not to adhere to formal rigorous methods, but to rely largely on intuitive methods. This is suggested by Hadamard's report (1945) of several eminent mathematicians' observations and introspections into their own processes of mathematical discovery or invention. It is also suggested in Courant and Robbins' text (1941) on the nature of mathematics. They note that, for mathematical discovery, formal logic and rigorous adherence to the axiomatic, postulational-deductive form do not suffice. They state that "a significant discovery or an illuminating insight is rarely obtained by an exclusively axiomatic procedure" (p. 216). Noting that the ideal of rigor is neither necessary nor desirable as one explores an unfamiliar field, they point out that pioneers in the field of topology did not present their results in traditional axiomatic form but instead relied largely upon geometric intuition. "Even today a student of topology will find that by too much insistence on a rigorous form of presentation he may easily lose sight of the essential geometric content in a mass of formal detail. Still, it is a great merit of recent work to have brought topology within the framework of rigorous mathematics, where intuition remains the source but not the final validation of truth" (pp. 235–236). In many other branches of mathematics, intuition also is a source of truth, or, at least, of fruitful hypotheses.

We found of interest the distinctions drawn between intuition and symbolic (mathematical) logic in Rosser's text (1953). He notes that for discovering answers intuition may be better than formal arguments, which are needed for proving answers. "For getting answers, it is better to use intuitive arguments, even rather vague ones. For proving answers, only rigid, formal arguments can be trusted" (p. 2). Even for *decisions*, intuitive notions can suffice. For example, an intuitive notion of continuity (say, in terms of a smooth, unbroken curve) may be adequate for deciding about the continuity of most curves; for proving the continuity, a precise definition of *continuity* is needed. Similarly, "the vague intuitive notion of logical correctness is adequate for deciding about the correctness of a logical step" (p. 2). But, if one wishes to *prove* the correctness of a logical step, then a precise definition of logical correctness will be needed. Symbolic logic furnishes such a definition. Since mathematicians differ somewhat, as Rosser points out, in their intuitive conceptions of logical correctness, it is not likely that any one definition will completely satisfy all of them, but one can at least aim at making precise what seems to be the "common denominator" of various intuitive conceptions. That a vague, intuitive notion of logical correctness is adequate for deciding about the logical correctness of a step may help to explain why mathematicians seldom have to stop and explicitly concentrate on the logical correctness of their reasoning and may help to explain why they seldom make logical errors even if they have not taken courses in logic.

We do not intend to suggest that it does not require reasoning or intelligence to check the logical correctness of a proof, once the proof is discovered. But it may be of a different level or perhaps even different kind than that needed to discover proofs. Rosser expresses this point well.

. . . one could build a machine which would check the logical correctness of any given proof of a mathematical theorem. That the check is mechanical does not mean that it requires no intelligence at all. There are many machines

of a sufficient complexity that at least a low order of intelligence is required
to match their performance. (1953, p. 7)
   This does not mean that it is now any easier to discover a proof for a difficult
theorem. This still requires the same high order of mathematical talent as
before. However, once the proof is discovered, and stated in symbolic logic,
it can be checked by a moron. (p. 7)

It might be noted that no adequate symbolic treatment has yet been
developed for the concept of *mathematical talent*. Mathematical talent
does not correspond to, and is not adequately portrayed by, any of the
concepts or principles of logic or any combination of the logical concepts
and principles. There is the advantage that a moron or a machine can
check the logical correctness of a proof, if it is reduced to symbolic logic,
but there is the disadvantage that symbolic logic as well as traditional
logic has no place for talent, intuition, creativity, or even luck, and does
not adequately distinguish between the "mechanical reasoning" used by
a moron or a machine in checking a proof and the productive or creative
reasoning of a mathematical genius discovering a proof. In short, we
might say that the genius of logic is that it ingeniously *reduces* the reasoning of a genius to a sequence of ingenuous steps; but, fortunately or unfortunately, it can likewise reduce moronic or mechanical reasoning to a
similar sequence. (See Luchins and Luchins, 1959, for further discussion
of logic and productive thinking.)
   Although Rosser considers that the average mathematician will find a
study of symbolic logic helpful in carrying out "mechanical reasoning,"
he recommends that formal methods of reasoning should be regarded as
supplements to, and not as substitutes for, intuitive methods of reasoning. We endorse Rosser's admonition to the mathematician:

   He should not forget that his intuition is the final authority, so that, in case
   of an irreconcilable conflict between his intuition and some system of symbolic
   logic, he should abandon the symbolic logic. He can try other systems of
   symbolic logic, and perhaps find one more to his liking, but it would be difficult
   to change his intuition. (p. 11)

Noting that symbolic logic is a formal system, Rosser continues:

   However, a formal system is merely a model devised by human minds to
   represent some facts perceived intuitively. As such, it is bound to be artificial.
   . . . Probably the only time that the artificiality of a formal system does any
   harm is when the users of the system ignore or overlook the fact that it is
   artificial. Thus, for two thousand years it was supposed that the physical
   universe was actually a Euclidean three-dimensional space. This inhibited
   men's thinking tremendously and was a great misfortune. Though [astronomi-
   cal measurement] demonstrates the artificiality of Euclidean geometry,
   nonetheless Euclidean geometry is still extremely useful, as useful in fact as
   it ever was. (pp. 10–11)

Paraphrasing Rosser, we may say that any system of logic is a formal
system and as such an artificial one. There has been some tendency to

ignore or overlook the artificiality. It has been assumed, implicitly or explicitly, that all reasoning, or all scientific reasoning, or all mathematical reasoning, is actually in accordance with logic or with a particular system of logic. This can have ill effects insofar as it blinds us to other possibilities. Factors not encompassed in a particular sentential calculus or in logic in general may be needed to characterize reasoning. This in no way detracts from the usefulness of a sentential calculus or of any system of logic, provided that its artificiality is not lost sight of and provided reasoning is not regarded as necessarily falling into a particular logical mold. The classical sentential calculus, part of traditional logic, is related to certain experiences and observations in our society's culture and may be regarded as abstractions from them. When these abstractions are applied to facts and experiences that they do not encompass and that they do not fit, difficulties arise and the artificiality of the system becomes a shortcoming.

Logic of Discovery

From ancient times to the present, philosophers have sought to formulate a logic of discovery or to devise a method or methods for finding new knowledge. So keen was interest in this problem in the sixteenth century that the "search for a method that would give certain knowledge" has been characterized as that century's "paramount scientific problem" (Randall, 1940, p. 220). Prominent among those concerned with the problem were Francis Bacon (1564–1641), Galileo Galilei (1564–1642), and René Descartes (1596–1650).

Bacon's views

Bacon maintained that the inventions and discoveries of the past had occurred by chance. In order for mankind to advance it needed a method, or art, of invention. In his *Novum Organum* of 1620, the *new logic*, or the *new tool*, he described a procedure for making discoveries. It was not the syllogism of Aristotelian logic; Bacon regarded this as inadequate for making discoveries. Nor did discovery result from cursory, unsystematic, and biased survey of phenomenon on which the ancients (Bacon claimed) tended to base their generalizations. Our everyday perceptions do not lead to true knowledge, Bacon pointed out, because of our uncritical habits of thinking and irrational prejudgments. The prejudgments he called *idols* because they stand between truth and men and are phantoms of our mind that mistakenly are accepted as reality. (Incidentally, it is of interest to note the similarity of Bacon's use of the word *idols* with its use in the writing of some medieval philosophers, for example, Maimonides

(1135–1204); see Minkin, 1957.) Bacon presented a fourfold classification of them.

1. The *idols of the tribe* have their foundations in human nature and in the tribe or race of man. Bacon said that human understanding "like a false mirror . . . distorts and discolors the nature of things by mingling its own nature with it" (cited in Burtt, 1939, p. 34). Human understanding supposes more order, regularity, and homogeneity than it finds. In line with the natural tendency to persist in a view or opinion, man's attention is drawn to things that support his views. He overlooks negative instances since he is moved more by affirmations than by negations of his views. Moreover, the will and affections color and infect understanding in numerous and sometimes imperceptible ways. "For what a man had rather were true, he more readily believes" (p. 37). This influences even the sciences, resulting in "sciences as one would have them." The greatest aberration of human understanding stems from the incompetency, dullness, and deception of the senses. Things that strike the senses tend to be given more weight than those that do not immediately strike them, even though the latter may be more important. Human understanding tends to give substance and reality to fleeting things and is prone to create abstractions and overgeneralizations.

2. The *idols of the cave* are those idols of the individual which he possesses in addition to the errors that he has in common with all mankind. Everyone has a den or cave of his own which tends to refract and discolor nature's light. These idols stem from the person's idiosyncratic mental and bodily constitution, his habits, education, judgment, and predilections, and so on. Bacon describes what today would be called *individual differences* in psychological functioning and the effects of personal frames of reference. (It is instructive to compare Bacon's idol of the cave with the cave in Plato's Republic.)

3. Other errors result from the association of men with each other and are called *idols of the market place* because of the commerce and relations of men there. These most troublesome of all idols result from the association of words and ideas. Although men believe that reason governs their words, it also happens that words influence their reason. Words may attribute an improper division to nature and may themselves stand in the way of the acute understanding and diligent observation needed to get at the true division. Often discussions of learned men end in empty controversies over words and names. Errors due to words result from names of things that actually do not exist as well as names of things that do exist but are ill-defined, hastily defined, and, in a confused way, abstracted from reality. In short, understanding is obstructed by imprecise use of words.

4. The *idols of the theater* are not innate but are openly impressed on, or accepted by, the mind. These errors refer to dogmas of various philosophical systems and to many scientific principles and axioms that are accepted on the basis of tradition, faith, or sheer negligence. These idols may have an empirical basis or arise from either sophistry or superstition. Bacon refers to the "play-books" of philosophical systems, implying that the systems are like the script of a play (more compact and elegant than the true story of history or nature) in which the actions are carried out without critical thinking or innovations. Willingness to accept dogmas uncritically is enhanced "by the craft and artifices of those who have handled and transmitted sciences" (cited in Burtt, 1939, p. 60) and by the schools, academies, and colleges which discourage speculation or "boldness to use any liberty of judgment" (p. 64).

In order to make a discovery, Bacon maintained, one must purge himself of these idols. If one wants to discover the truth about a phenomenon, he must have as little as possible of himself or of others between him and the phenomenon. The proper remedy for divesting oneself of the idols, Bacon suggested, is the formation of ideas through true induction. He outlined an inductive process in the *Novum Organum* (1620, later 1878). The first step consists of an intensive and exhaustive collection of particular instances (of a phenomenon). This is followed by analysis and comparison of these instances. Looking out for negative instances and differences in degree, and avoiding hasty generalizations, one proceeds gradually from the particular to the general. These steps are described by Bacon in terms of *tables of discovery*. The first step is preparation of a natural and experimental history. To get a suitable view of the phenomenon one then sorts the data into "tables and arrangements of instances." But even here human understanding is incompetent unless directed and guarded. Therefore the third step is to use "true and legitimate induction" to help yield the true, underlying forms of the phenomenon. Induction is helped by the formation of a "table of essence and presence" (instances where the phenomenon is present), a "table of deviation or absence" (instances where the phenomenon is absent), and a "table of degrees or of comparisons" (instances where the phenomenon is found in different degrees). Bacon stressed that one should seek the "simple form" of the phenomenon, such as the factor that is always present when the phenomenon appears, always absent when it disappears, and varies directly with an increase or decrease of the phenomenon. The question has been raised (Cushman, 1946) whether seeking the "simple form" is akin to the Aristotelian idea of determining the essence of a phenomenon or akin to the Platonic idea of the causes of the phenomenon.

Bacon's method of collecting instances and classifying them has not been the method followed in physics. But methods similar to Bacon's have been used in biology, geology, natural history, zoology, and various classificatory disciplines—even to some extent in psychology. It has been said, with some justification, that no important law or discovery has resulted from Baconian induction (Jones, 1952, Vol. II, p. 608) and that Bacon did not give us a logic or method of discovery. Yet, his proposed methods have influenced some of the sciences, and, as we shall see, his writings have stimulated others to seek for a logic or method of discovery.

Galileo's views

Galileo (1564–1642), who was Bacon's great contemporary, also proposed a method of discovering knowledge other than the traditional syllogism. Like Bacon, he believed in starting with observation of the phenomena. But, unlike Bacon, he did not advocate an exhaustive collection of instances, but, rather, intensive study of a particular instance or of a characteristic case (for example, the study of motion on an inclined plane).

It might be said that, in modern terminology, Galileo advocated a *pure case approach*. Moreover, Galileo called for observations that focused on the measurable aspects of the phenomenon, their quantitative aspects. The next step was to formulate a quantitative or mathematical principle or theorem based on analysis of the quantitative data derived from the observations. From this mathematical principle or theorem deductions were drawn. Demonstrations and experiments were conducted to test the deductions. The mathematical principle was considered to be corroborated to the extent that deductions from it were verified by experiment and to the extent that the principles accounted for the observed cases of the phenomena as well as for those which could not be directly observed. Thus Galileo's method featured observation and demonstration or experimentation, linked by quantitative or mathematical relationships. His method was a combination of the inductive and deductive, of the synthetic and analytic, methods. Induction was used to infer a mathematical principle from the observations and from experimentation with particular instances; deduction was used to draw deductions from the mathematical principle. The deductions were then put to the test of observation and experimentation. Galileo did not regard deductions of the syllogistic kind as unnecessary, but believed that deduction and induction were both needed for scientific discoveries.

Galileo contributed to the study of the pure case and to the development of the *ideal law* which need not exactly portray even one actual case of an observed phenomenon but which hypothesized what happened under certain ideal conditions. That his method stressed mathematical relationships and principles helped to put mathematics in the fore in the new science. It has been said that Galileo's method and logic were essentially geometric and that "while the empirical spirit was reforming the notion of relevance, the mathematical spirit was expanding the notion of validity" (Jones, 1952, Vol. II, p. 626). Galileo's methods are generally regarded as having influenced even those sciences to which he did not actually contribute. "Galileo saw so clearly the problem in his own special science and the means for the solution of the problem that he *gave to modern thought the correctly formulated method of dealing with all the new materials of the nature-world*" (Cushman, 1946, p. 43).

Descartes' views

Descartes (1596–1650) went even further than Galileo in advocating mathematics as a basis for obtaining knowledge. He believed that the method of mathematics was universally applicable to all sciences and all reasoning. During his formal schooling mathematics delighted him because of the certainty of its reasoning. As for the rest of his formal instruction, completed when he was seventeen, he reports: "I found myself embarrassed with so many doubts and errors [and] the increasing discovery of my own ignorance," a feeling which was not dispelled by his attempts to study "the book of the world" through travel and soldiering. Here too he found so much diversity of opinion that "I learned to believe nothing too certainly of which I had only been convinced by example and custom" (Descartes, 1637, later 1931, pp. 83–87). Doubts and awareness of errors were important concepts in his intellectual journey. Descartes maintained that men's opinions change so often and they are so often deceived by their senses that it is necessary to doubt them. We cannot even be sure if we are asleep or awake. More generally, we must doubt everything that can be doubted. But this does not mean that all is doubtful. That I doubt is itself of utmost certainty. That I reason is also certain, since doubting is itself an act of reasoning, more generally, of cognition. But that I doubt proves that I exist as a thinking being because to doubt or otherwise cogitate I must exist or be conscious of existence. Hence, the famous aphorism: *Cogito, ergo sum.* Doubting does not replace or displace reasoning. "The power of forming a good judgment and of distinguishing the true from the false, which is properly speaking what is called Good sense or Reason, is by nature equal in all men . . . to be possessed of good mental powers is not sufficient; the principal matter is to apply them well" (pp. 81–82). How to apply reasoning, the method that should be used, had long interested Descartes: "I always had an excessive desire to distinguish the true from the false" (p. 87). He searched for a method that would be certain to yield truth, an infallible method that would be universally applicable. Descarte's *Discourse on Method* has been aptly described as an "autobiographical account of this intellectual journey of discovery (and) his quest for certainty" (Jones, 1952, Vol. II, p. 661). In his *Rules for the Direction of the Mind*, Descartes declares: "There is a need of a method for finding out the truth" where by a *method* he means "certain and simple rules, such that, if a man observe them accurately, he shall never assume what is false as true" (p. 646). Specifically, he focused on the deductive method used in geometry, believing that all things that fall within the scope of man's knowledge succeed each other in the same way as do the long chains of reasons that geometers employ. If we abstain from accepting as true any opinions that are not true, and if we observe the necessary order in deducing one step from another, then there is no knowledge so remote that it cannot be reached or so hidden that it cannot be discovered. Thus Descartes is advocating the deductive method of geometry, which is used in logic. In short, Descartes' answer to the question of how to initiate inquiry is "purely rationalistic. One intellectually doubts everything which can possibly be doubted and then, from the indubitable minimum which remains, one deduces the remainder of one's knowledge. . . . Its method is the deductive one of formal logic rather than the empirical procedure of the natural sciences" (Northrop, 1947, p. 9). Such concepts are attained by being as certain of them as we are of the aphorism *Cogito, ergo sum* (I doubt therefore I am). An idea so conceived must be true. Thus intuitions are self-evident truths and are sometimes referred to as *innate ideas*.

In his *Rules*, Descartes admits only two mental operations for arriving at knowledge of things. One of these he calls *induction*, but he uses the name interchangeably with deduction (which he describes as necessary inference or deductions from other facts that are known with certainty). The other mental operation he refers to as *intuition*. Intuition "springs from the light of reason alone" and is a conception about which we have no doubt. Intuitive concepts are ideas that we conceive very clearly and distinctly and of which we are intuitively certain. It may, therefore, not be out of place to recall the criticisms that have been leveled against the notion of self-evident truths, for example, against Kant's belief that Euclidean geometry corresponds to an innate, self-evident conception of space.

Descartes' method includes the following rules:

1. Avoid prejudice, prejudgment, and others' opinions and accept only those ideas which so clearly and distinctly present themselves to the mind that you have no doubt about them (intuitions).
2. Reduce propositions and difficulties step by step to simpler ones until you reach those which you intuitively apprehend. Then attempt to reach the more complex knowledge again by "deduction" from the simpler ones.
3. A related rule, which contains the "chief secret of method," is that all facts can be arranged in a series from the simplest ones to the most complex ones.

Descartes' method may be regarded as primarily deductive, or analytic. Yet it has some aspects of an inductive, or synthetic, approach. He has been regarded as having used an inductive or synthetic approach to arrive at his principle that to doubt establishes consciousness of existence or self-consciousness. Descartes "demanded that the method of induction or resolution should lead to *a single principle of highest and absolute certainty. . . . The certainty of the Being or existence of consciousness* is the one fundamental truth which Descartes finds by the analytic method" (Windelband, 1958, Vol. II, pp. 390–391). The analytic method may also be considered to be involved in the reduction of a proposition to simpler steps.

Some similarities can be noted among Bacon, Galileo, and Descartes. Like Bacon, Descartes suggested that one should get prejudgments out of his mind, which in the latter's case is to be done through doubting. But instead of the inductive, empirical procedure of Bacon, Descartes focused mainly on a deductive, formal procedure. He did not apply his procedure to the problems of physics as systematically as did Galileo. Descartes has been judged to have had less influence on physics and the natural sciences than did Galileo but to have had a more powerful influence on systems of philosophy. Even more than Galileo, Descartes saw in the deductive method of mathematics a universal tool for all reasoning. He believed that he had "a way of generalizing the method of mathematics to serve as a universal instrument" (Jones, 1952, Vol. II, p. 665). Yet some believe that Descartes did not succeed, that his method is not suitable for every investigator. "His extension of the method of mathematics into a general method of reasoning and discovery is not adequate to the varied needs of the investigator" (Carmichael, 1930, p. 7). It is of interest to note that although his method of inquiry is considered not to have had a great influence on science, he did devise analytic geometry, which has made important contributions to science and mathematics. Moreover, stripping Descartes' formulation of its outmoded words, we may say that what he advocated was the use of the axiomatic-deductive approach as illustrated by Euclidean geometry. Today, one of the goals in virtually every science and every branch of mathematics is to put it in axiomatic-deductive form, starting, however, with axioms which are not necessarily self-evident truths or intuitively clear. Many psychologists, in particular, consider this an important goal and some even regard the axiomatic-deductive or hypothetico-deductive method as the best scientific method, possibly the only scientific method.

Mill's views

One of the most systematic attempts in the nineteenth century to formulate a logic of discovery was by John Stuart Mill (1806–1873). In the Baconian tradition, he was motivated by a desire to better the lot of mankind. In order to accomplish this, he considered sound methods and theory necessary. This led him to a study of the logical structure of the empirical sciences and to the presentation of connected views of the principles of evidence and the method of scientific investigation. Mill's logic is based on views that some present-day psychologists and logicians have rejected (for example, that the raw data out of which the mind is created are sensations and the mind's consciousness of itself, and that the organization of the mind's complex ideas are due to the laws of association). His logic, like Bacon's, describes how one proceeds in observation, goes from observation to hypotheses and develops hypotheses so that they can be applied to the phenomena being studied. Moreover, like Bacon, Mill believed that his methods would focus the investigator on the data, make him aware of the evidence, and help him to avoid errors of judgments and prejudgments. Some logicians consider that Mill completed what Bacon began in the Novum Organum. It has also been said (see Sellars, 1925, p. 227) that Mill further developed the methods for isolating and verifying causal laws described by the astronomer Sir William Herschel (1738–1822) in his Discourse on the Study of Natural Philosophy.

Mill's methods are described in terms of regulating principles or canons.

1. *Method of agreement:* If two or more instances of the phenomenon under investigation have only one circumstance in common, the circumstance in which alone all the instances agree is the cause (or effect) of the given phenomenon (Mill, 1950, p. 214).

2. *Method of difference:* If an instance in which the phenomenon under investigation occurs and an instance in which it does not occur have every circumstance in common save one, that one occurring only in the former, the circumstance in which alone the two instances differ is the effect, or the cause, or an indispensable part of the cause, of the phenomenon (p. 215).

3. *Indirect method of difference* (or joint method of agreement and difference): If two or more instances in which the phenomenon occurs have only one circumstance in common, while two or more instances in which it does not occur have nothing in common save the absence of that circumstance, the circumstance in which alone the two sets of instances differ is the effect, or the cause, or an indispensable part of the cause, of the phenomenon (p. 221).

4. *Method of residues:* Subduct from any phenomenon such part as is known by previous inductions to be the effect of certain antecedents, and the residue of the phenomenon is the effect of the remaining antecedents.

5. *Method of concomitant variations:* Whatever phenomenon varies in any manner whenever another phenomenon varies in some particular manner is either a cause or an effect of that phenomenon, or is connected with it through some fact of causation.

Examples of Mill's canons are found in the history of science, particularly biology, where, for example, Koch's postulates in bacteriology reflect these canons.

It may be said that Mill was aware that the canons cannot be used in a routine way to grind out new discoveries, or else he would not have written the sections that precede and follow the descriptions of the canons in his treatise on logic. But it may be claimed (see Sellars, 1925, p. 227; Churchman, 1948, p. 95) that Mill was a little too inclined to regard the canons as guides to secure results, whereas they have to be used in conjunction with other methods of induction. Mill's methods do not reflect the mathematical orientation and mathematical procedures of Galileo, Newton, and modern physical scientists. It may be said of Mill's methods, as was pointed out in our discussion of Bacon's ideas concerning the logic of discovery, that they may be of considerable value in classificatory sciences but have only very limited application in the other sciences. Since Mill's logic was intimately bound with his social philosophy which went into eclipse in the twentieth century, his logic went along with the social doctrines. Also contributing to the decline of Mill's logic were advances in science and in philosophical criticism as well as in psychological criticism. However, Mill's work has influenced discussions of induction in logic and science. His methods are said to furnish the point of departure for nearly all treatments of causal induction (Sellars, 1925, p. 227). Even in contemporary times, "influences of his contributions to the philosophy of logic and scientific method have not vanished entirely. His love of clarity and his passionate devotion to carefully reasoned analysis have won him admirers and emulators" (see Nagel in the introduction to Mill, 1950, p. xlvii).

Logicians' and mathematicians' views

Since Mill's day, philosophers and logicians, including Dewey (1909), Peirce (1933), and Schiller (1917), have attempted to deal with the problems of the logic of discovery. But recent decades have witnessed an increasing belief that a logic of discovery is impossible to formulate because there is none (Popper, 1959; Reichenbach, 1938). Yet, there are still pleas made that the door should not be shut on discussion of this problem. In this connection, it is instructive to consider Hanson's discussion of the problem in a symposium of scientists and philosophers (Feigl and Maxwell, 1961). He asks: "Is there *anything* in the idea of a 'logic of discovery' which merits the attention of a tough-minded, analytic logician?" (p. 21). In the tradition of Aristotle, Schiller, and Peirce, he notes that the original suggestion of a scientific hypothesis may be a reasonable affair and that a logic may underlie the promulgation of the hypothesis just as a logic underlies the establishment or proof of the hypothesis. The original suggestion of a hypothesis H is "not as dependent on intuitions, hunches, and other imponderables as historians and philosophers suppose when they make it the province of genius but not of logic. If the establishment of H through its predictions has a logic, so has the initial suggestion that H is likely to be of one kind rather than another" (p. 30). It is the possibility of a "logic of discovery" (in contrast to a logic of proof) which Hanson believes needs discussion and inquiry, rather than the assumptions at the onset that the logic of discovery is identical with the logic of proof, or that there is no logic of discovery, or that inquiry can yield only the psychology, sociology, or history of a discovery but not its logic.

Not only logicians and philosophers but also mathematicians have been interested in the logic of discovery. It may be asked whether the mathematician Hadamard (1945) is studying only the psychology of invention or also its logic. Similarly, it may be asked whether the mathematician Polya is throwing light on the logic of discovery in his books (1954a, 1954b) which are concerned with heuristics of discovery. The answers may depend in part on the relationships assumed to hold between psychology and logic and between heuristics and logic. For example, is the logic of discovery a heuristic logic? Certainly there have been mathematicians who have explicitly expressed interest in the logic of discovery. For example, Veblen directed an experiment on reasoning at Princeton University, using graduate students in a projective geometry course. Of the experiment he wrote that it "brought out vividly the problem of the significance of the logical processes as a method of discovery" (cited in Carmichael, 1930, p. 110). The mathematician Carmichael's book, *The Logic of Discovery*, deserves the attention of psychologists for its suggestions for concrete research. Carmichael distinguishes between a logic of proof or demonstration and a logic of discovery "in the sense of a logic by which one infers from the known to that unknown which hitherto has not been apprehended or suspected" (p. 43). While the logic of demonstration may itself be used for discovery, such use "does not afford a typical instance of the logic of discovery" (p. 21), "so that we need some logic of discovery different from that which is suitable in demonstration" (p. 26). He touches on various so-called heuristic logics, raises the question of whether they vary from one science to another, and answers that "it seems not improbable that a certain heuristic logic in one science may have no conceivable place at all in another" (p. 22). Carmichael also raises the question of whether either the logic of demonstration or the logic of discovery varies. He conjectures that the logic of demonstration is a unit but that the logic of discovery is not, that it does not have a unitary character. "We can have not so much a logic of discovery as logics of discovery each relative to some field or subject matter of investigation" (p. 44). The assumption that the logic of discovery has a unitary character has been a primary hindrance to its development, Carmichael concludes. It should be of interest to see whether more progress will be made if it is assumed that there is a multiplicity of logics of discovery.

In recent years we have witnessed reformulations of the teaching of science and mathematics which seem to be motivated in part by the objective of encouraging and developing original and creative work. Of the various proposals for reformulations, some emphasize the deductive approach, some the inductive approach, others a combination of the two approaches, and still others the "case method." Analysis of the various proposals and their success in enhancing discovery may be useful in developing a logic, or logics, of discovery—or in deciding that there are none. Moreover, teachers and other educators who study the effects of different ways of organizing and presenting material may collect the kind of information needed to understand what kind of logical structure (of the material or of the mode of presentation) lends itself best to insightful discovery and what kind lends itself to reproductive, mechanical behavior. Perhaps such information will yield clues about the nature of the logic or logics of discovery.

Psychology of Discovery

One of the arguments against inquiries directed toward a logic of discovery is that such inquiries can at best contribute to a *psychology* of discovery. It has been suggested that it is not even the business of logic or logicians to be concerned with the nature of discovery but that this problem should be left to the psychologists. It is therefore fitting that we should turn to see what psychologists have had to say about discovery and creative thinking or problem solving.

Since the early days of experimental psychology, there have been research attempts to characterize the thought process. Although many psychologists have described it as a process of "trial and error," some have objected that trial and error may describe some aspects of the process but not the whole process, and that it is a descriptive term and not an explanation. Some psychologists believe that the problem still remains open: Why is one solution (or hypothesis) proposed and rejected, whereas another is proposed and accepted (see Humphrey, 1951).

Several descriptions of the "whole" problem solving process have been proposed. Dewey's five steps, written in the context of functionalistic psychology (1909, p. 70), are still found in psychology textbooks. They are, in his words, as follows:

1. A felt difficulty
2. Its location and definition
3. Suggestion of possible solutions
4. Development by reasoning of the bearings of the suggestion
5. Further observations and experimentations leading to its acceptance or rejection

Other psychologists' descriptions of the problem solving process involve different numbers of steps; four-step descriptions have been suggested (for example, preparation, incubation, illumination, and verification) and also three-step descriptions (for instance, preparation, production, and judgment). Most of the descriptions of stages of creative thinking have come from the observations of or introspections of creative individuals. However, some of the descriptions have resulted from or have been utilized in research, for example, the just-mentioned three steps have been used by Johnson (1962) in the design of his experiments. Moreover, psychologists have studied in laboratory settings the solution of certain problems involving invention of a method or discovery of a novel procedure— for example, Duncker (1945), Székely (1950), Maier (1933). Koffka (1935), Humphrey (1951), Vinacke (1952), and Johnson (1955) survey research along these lines. Duncker made one of the most detailed analyses of processes that involved the invention or discovery of a method to solve a "natural" problem. For example, the subjects were told that an inoperable tumor would be destroyed if certain rays were applied to it with sufficient intensity; the problem is as follows: How can the rays, at the required intensity, be applied to the tumor without destroying the healthy surrounding tissue? Analysis of attempts at solution of such problems led Duncker to the following description of the process of discovery. First there is a survey or a cognitive grasp of the problem situation which indicates the "general range" of directions that possible solutions may take. The subject then tries out some of these directions or some of the methods suggested by them. While doing this, he may reformulate or reorganize his cognitive grasp of the situation, thus narrowing the range of possible solutions and resulting in a proposal of a "functional solution." This functional solution is further reformulated so that there results a proposal of a "specific solution." If this fails to solve the problem, the subject reverts back to the initial "general range." Duncker and others working in the Gestalt tradition have used this formulation and similar formulations in their research regarding the factors that maximize or minimize the organization and reorganization of the cognitive grasp of the problem situation. Illustrations are found in the following: Duncker (1945); Koffka (1935); Köhler (1925); Luchins (1942); Luchins and Luchins (1959); Maier (1933); Wertheimer (1945). Their results may not have led to a logic of discovery but they have had important implications for teaching and learning (see Osgood, 1953).

Wertheimer, his colleagues, and his students have stressed the need to study actual productive acts. In general, they have been interested in studying creative thinking in laboratory and in natural situations and in reconstructing or analyzing the processes that lead to scientific discoveries and inventions. Wertheimer found the operation of what he called *organizing, reorganizing, centering, recentering, direction, good and bad errors,* and so on. He hoped to formulate these findings in a publication to follow his 1945 book, *Productive Thinking,* in which he intended to propose a "Gestalt logic"—a logic which he hoped might be capable of capturing the qualities of creativity and discovery that seem to elude the concepts and systems of modern logic just as they have eluded the rules of traditional logic. In short, he had faith that psychologists and logicians would eventually be able to create a logic of discovery.

It seems to us that one form of research necessary for the development of a logic of discovery is clarification, conceptually, of what is meant by *discovery* and *creativity.* Just what do these terms point to in daily life? Is just any variation, no matter how "senseless," a creative act or a discovery? Moreover, what is meant by *logic* and by *logical structure?* The meanings of such terms can influence the definition of a logic of discovery and the directions in which we seek for such a logic.

Discovery and creative acts do not take place in a Platonic realm of pure ideas but in people who are part of social situations. The personality structure and the social situation may influence the structure of the logic of the act. There is much evidence that personality factors, such as anxiety, motives, needs, different attitudes, and so on, may at times help (and at other times interfere) with the person in a problem situation. Similarly, his past experience, his habits of thinking, the "rules" of problem solving that he learned, may have good or bad effects. The roles of such variables have been the center of much research. (See Luchins, 1960, for a discussion of such factors in relation to creativity in thinking.) Even though the creative act may be a private affair, its fate may depend on social field conditions that may offer varied opportunities for creativity and for recognition, acceptance, or rejection of the creative act and opposition to it (see Luchins, 1960; Veblen, 1952; Wilder, 1950, 1952). It is not merely a question of the value of the discovery but also of the existing thought and language forms of a society at a certain time and place. These forms may make the discovery seem understandable and required, or absurd and incomprehensible. Because the form of the expression of the discovery and the acceptance of the expression of creativity depend on social field conditions, there is an increasing concern with the determination of conditions that will not only allow but will encourage creativity and discovery. C. W. Taylor (1964) has a survey of the recent literature in this area.

In the history of the study of thought, there have been psychologists who have not been content to capture the flavor of what happens in discovery but who have sought the relationship between such problem solving behavior and fundamental psychological mechanisms. Here one can witness the influence of Mill's assumptions as to the genesis of thinking. For various reasons, many psychologists who wish to get at the roots of problem solving behavior use an S-R learning model (Cofer, 1957; Galanter and Gestenhaber, 1956; Kendler and Kendler, 1962; Underwood, 1952). Fewer psychologists are working in the tradition of the Gestalt psychologists (see Maier, 1964) who believe that productive thinking is not adequately dealt with by the S-R and associationistic learning models. Until recently, much research on thinking was concerned with showing the adequacy or inadequacy of one or the other of these learning theories. In recent years, another approach has developed among workers in the area of man–machine relations and organization or system analysis. Here we find the application of psychological principles (and the formulation of principles) to the development, invention, and use of complex machine–man systems in industry. Related to this psychotechnology is the growing use and study of autoinstructional devices which have focused "attention on what may be called 'productive learning' . . . programs are designed to insure the acquisition of capabilities of performing classes of tasks . . . rather than tasks requiring the reproduction of particular responses" (Gagné, 1962, p. 356). Such research does not involve testing the generality of a particular learning theory but the preparation of situations that will enhance the operator's efficiency in solving problems, in finding and repairing the "trouble" in a malfunctioning machine, and so on. In line with this general interest in human engineering is the study of thinking by simulating it in computers. In a description of a theory of problem solving that has come out of such work, Newell, Shaw, and Simon point out that their theory resembles "associationistic theories largely in acceptance of the premise of mechanism. . . . It resembles much closer some of the Gestalt theories . . . most closely the theories of directed thinking of Selz and de Groot" (1958, p. 64). It is of interest that, by means of programming computers to simulate human problem solving, psychologists, working with logicians, mathematicians, and engineers in the field of computer operation, are developing what may be called *descriptions* of the process of discovery. They seem to have escaped from the theoretical controversies that have bogged down psychologists in their pursuit of the understanding of the process of discovery. This is an exciting area of research and deserves watching to see whether a logic or logics of discovery will be forthcoming. (See Minsky in Feigenbaum and Feldman, 1963, for a bibliography of this area of research.)

Although this is only a cursory survey of the ways in which psychologists have been attempting to find the laws involved in creative acts and discovery, we cannot conclude the survey without mentioning some other approaches. One is the psychometric approach in which the factors involved in creativity are sought via tests and the use of factor analysis and other statistical procedures (for example, Merrifield, Guilford, Christensen, and Frich, 1962). Another is the study of the development of cognition and thought (including concept formation) from infancy to maturity (see Piaget, 1949, 1953). There is also the experimental analysis of problem solving situations which we discussed earlier; this has been applied to both natural and laboratory situations, using animals as well as human beings of different chronological ages and different cultures. One conclusion seems apparent: Psychologists have not found a generally accepted answer to the problem of the nature of creativity or to the question of the existence and nature of a logic of discovery, but they continue to seek answers via various approaches. This may be a more productive attitude than to assert that what appears as genuine creative or productive thinking can be reduced to cases of reproduction of habits learned in the past (see Thorndike, 1932) and/or to assert that it is not possible to formulate a logic or logics of discovery. Working in conjunction with logicians and mathematicians, psychologists may be able to contribute to a formulation of a logic of discovery or at least to add to the knowledge of the factors that maximize or minimize discovery. It also seems timely to reconsider the relationship between logic and psychology, especially (but not exclusively) as it bears on discovery. Perhaps there is a need for a psychology that makes more use of logical concepts and logical structures. Perhaps there is a need for a logic that incorporates some of those concepts which have been applied to productive thinking, such as direction, insight, organization, centering, reorganization, recentering, and so on. Whether these can be directly incorporated as logical concepts or whether certain concepts can serve as the logical counterparts of these "psychological" concepts is a problem for discussion and investigation. Whether a sharp distinction can be or should be drawn between the psychology and the logic of discovery is another question to be settled by interdisciplinary research. One new direction for cooperative research among logicians, mathematicians, and psychologists is the search for answers to such questions as these: What is a problem? What is a solution to a problem? Are there assumptions as to the nature and as to the admissibility conditions for a solution that affect the answer to the question of what is a solution? Must there be a unique answer (solution) to each of the questions of what is a solution and what is a problem? How do we know that a problem is solved or is solvable? What determines the decision that a problem is unsolvable? See Luchins and Luchins (1953) for a discussion of some of these points.

Machine Models of Thinking

What was said about systems of logic as models of thought is also applicable to machine models, which are rather popular in contemporary discussions of learning and thinking (see Bruner, 1960; D. W. Taylor, 1958). Machine models of thinking, some of which are based on a sentential calculus, are themselves abstractions of certain facts perceived intuitively and, like other formal systems, are bound to be artificial. The artificiality is a shortcoming only if it is overlooked. The danger is that the model, through interpolations and extrapolations, may be applied where it is inappropriate; moreover, it may become the gauge for human thought. Just as the universe was considered to be Euclidean in nature, and just as thinking was considered to follow the laws of traditional logic and now is considered by some to follow the laws of a modern logical system, so it is possible to conceive of thinking as following this or that machine model. We must beware of regarding thinking that is not in accordance with a machine model as not constituting proper thinking, or as not worthwhile investigating, or as not capable of being investigated scientifically, or as necessarily being capable of reduction to a form that fits the machine model. Just such assumptions were made with regard to thinking that did not seem immediately to fit the model of traditional logic. In short, the attractiveness of machine models of thinking should not blind us to their artificiality.

It has been pointed out that the use of machine models to simulate human thinking is most successful where thinking can be reduced to a succession of single steps (Turing, 1963; Newell and Simon, 1963). Hovland noted this, adding that it is much more difficult to simulate "those processes where a number of stages are going on simultaneously, in parallel fashion. It certainly appears that much of our perceptual and thought processes operate in this way" (1960, p. 692).

It is not denied that machines may be used to simulate certain aspects of human reasoning and that machine models may be useful for studying and theorizing about certain aspects of thinking. But these aspects are not all there is to thinking. If investigators overlook this and regard the machine model as the paradigm of reasoning, or of reasoning which should be studied, then the disadvantage of the artificiality of machine models may outweigh their advantages.

There are also some philosophical issues involved with regard to the nature of man. The history of human thought is replete with conjecture that man is "nothing but" a machine and that thinking involves no creativity or newness but can adequately be explained as the inertia of past experience (Hume, 1896), the recombination of associations formed by past experience (Welch, 1960), and so on. These conjectures were mainly philosophical speculations until recent years when they seemingly received support from the development of computers that could simulate what had seemed to be uniquely human thinking. The machines can *perceive, learn, solve problems*, and even *create problems and solutions*. In some cases such activities are better executed by machines than by man. Does this vindicate the machine conception of man? Does it demonstrate that man should not be regarded as having unique characteristics that set him apart from the machines? For some answers to these questions see Armer, 1963; Cohen, 1955; Deutsch, 1951; Hook, 1961; MacKay, 1954; Roth, 1963; and R. Taylor, 1950.

Affirmative answers to these questions seem to overlook that machines are made by man and not man by machines. Although this observation is often made, it is by no means trite in its implications. A machine is essentially only an algorithm created by man to routinize certain processes (Roth, 1963). Even if machines could replicate all of man's past and present intellectual accomplishments (at present this is certainly not the case), it would not mean that man could be replaced by machines or that machines could match man's capability for future accomplishments. Man is able to create new ideas and new world forms that are beyond the capability of existing machines. The machines may even help him by freeing his mind for these creative activities. As man creates new ideas, he may program machines to duplicate them. Man is a step ahead of the machine each time. The machines do not necessarily set limits to man's intellectual horizons but may free him for explorations beyond present limits. Of course this does not preclude the possibility that man might use machines to mechanize other men. Man, not the machine, will enslave man.

It may be helpful to draw an analogy with the development of algorithms for arithmetical computations that make it possible for primary grade children, at present, to do the kind of mathematics that required university training in the Middle Ages. This did not make the child replace the university scholar nor did it make obsolete university training in arithmetic and other branches of mathematics. Freed from having to toil with cumbersome notations for arithmetical computations, the university student of mathematics is now able to concentrate on other aspects of mathematics. That machines, from manually operated adding machines to complex computators, can do arithmetical tasks faster and more effectively than man, has not replaced man's work in arithmetic. It freed him for more intensive and extensive investigations of the properties of numbers. There is no prospect that machines can solve all the open problems in the foundations of arithmetic and in the theory of numbers which continue to challenge some of our best mathematical minds. And even if machines could solve some, one certainty is that man would find new problems to solve, new intellectual worlds to conquer.

In short, the belief that machines can replace man's need to think seems to be baseless. It rests on the untenable assumption that machines set the limits to man's intellectual capabilities and it neglects one of man's unique characteristics: reasoning.

In any event, all this is speculation. As far as mathematical reasoning is concerned, there cannot be a machine that will solve all mathematical problems. For example, discussing Church's thesis (Church, 1936) that there is no decision procedure for the sentential calculus, Rosser concludes: "There can never be a system or mechanical process for solving all mathematical problems. In other words, the mathematician will never be replaced by a machine" (1953, p. 102).

But if mathematics were identical with logic or mathematical reasoning with logical reasoning, then it should be a relatively simple matter to develop a "logic machine" to discover and then to solve mathematical problems. Theoretically, such a machine would have to be fed only the basic concepts and axioms of logic and it should then be able to discover and verify all the theorems of mathematics. Needless to say, such a machine does not exist. But let us consider a simpler task. Suppose in addition to basic concepts and axioms of logic, the machine were also fed basic concepts and axioms of Euclidean geometry. If logic sufficed, then the machine should be able to discover and solve all theorems of Euclidean geometry. Such a machine also does not exist. Let us simplify the task still further and set the machine, not to *discover* any theorems of Euclidean geometry, but to verify or solve such theorems. A program whereby a high-speed computer solves many theorems of Euclidean geometry has been developed by Gelernter and Rochester (1958) of the International Business Machines Corporation. Describing this geometry machine, Hovland noted that when it is given a proposition to be proved, the chief problem "is to find a possible method of proceeding, out of the almost infinite number of alternatives" (1960, p. 689). Thus, the chief problem seems to be one of inquiry, of discovering which steps to take. As aids in this process of inquiry, short-cuts and heuristic rules of thumb (Polya, 1954a, 1954b) are programmed into the machine. For example, the machine is instructed that in case the proposition to be proved involves equality of angles and parallel lines it is worthwhile to try the following theorem: The alternate interior angles of two parallel lines (intersected by a third line) are equal. Through use of these heuristics, which often but not necessarily help in the situations for which they are suggested, the machine simulates a human solver in having "a flash of insight as to a possible means of solution . . . [trying] likely and plausible methods of solution . . . making leaps in the solution and trying out schemes which have been successful in the past" (Hovland, 1960, pp. 688–689). Typically, a successful solution involves setting up a sequence of subgoals which are worked on in succession. Once the machine has found a sequence of subgoals that seems to lead from the axioms to the proposition to be proved, it is a routine matter for it to test or verify the adequacy of the proposed solution, "since once one has a possible proof, checking it is largely clerical" (p. 688). In this routine, clerical process of verification of a proposed solution, logic undoubtedly plays the major role. But this seems not to be the case in the preceding process of inquiry. Formal logic does not concern itself with flashes of insight, leaps in solution, likely and plausible methods, or with heuristics or the trying out of schemes that were successful in the past. For the geometry machine, as for the human solver, in the process of inquiry and discovery, logic is necessary but by no means sufficient. Hence, if mathematics is considered to include not only formal proof but also the activities of inquiry and discovery that help to give rise to mathematical theorems and their solutions (and indeed, to the discovery of whole branches of mathematics), then mathematical reasoning is not adequately portrayed by logical reasoning, and mathematics is not a branch of logic.

Psychology and Validation

If all mathematical theorems were known, or all systems of axioms leading to these theorems were known and the only task was to test the logical correctness or validity of purported proofs, then perhaps logic and the hypothetico-deductive method would be the chief tools. But all mathematical theorems and proofs are not known and logical validation is not the only task. Likewise, there is no field of science in which validation is the sole task. Inquiry and discovery are important in every science, although one might gain the impression from psychologists' research reports that validation is their sole or chief task. The importance of inquiry and discovery is a point well made by Bitterman in his observations on research in animal learning.

> For many years, the field of animal learning has been dominated by a controversial, deductive spirit. Most of us have acted as though we knew all about the learning processes, and as though the only purpose of our experiments was to demonstrate the validity of our convictions. . . . I have come again to a kind of research that is at once more satisfying and more productive. Its function is inquiry, not proof. (1960, p. 711)

What has been said about the field of animal learning is applicable, in varying degrees, to other fields of psychology. They tend to be characterized by a focus on validation (logical, experimental, and statistical validation) and by a deductive spirit rather than by a spirit of inquiry and discovery. It would seem that research is undertaken to verify or to prove or disprove certain hypotheses, "derived" from theories, rather than to inquire and discover. There seems to be relatively little research in which, as Bitterman puts it, the researcher has "not the slightest notion what the answer will be [but] can only wait eagerly for the outcome" (p. 711).

The prevailing intellectual climate in psychology seems to be strongly influenced by the focus on validation and the postulational-deductive approach. Ofttimes research is considered trivial unless it is conducted to validate or invalidate hypotheses deduced from a theory or from a set of postulates. Application forms for research grants sometimes emphasize validation rather than inquiry. They may, for example, require the researcher to formulate the hypotheses which his research will validate or invalidate. Prevalent research models that make use of statistical tests of the null hypotheses also stress validation and may even assume that before he does his research the experimenter already has the answer. Of course, protocol prohibits him from voicing his convictions openly. He formulates, in the null hypothesis, the opposite of what he hopes to prove. He does his best to disprove the null hypothesis (for example, by the precautions he takes in his experimental design). Thus it is a sort of game he plays, where he conjures up a devil that he knows or suspects or hopes does not exist and then defeats the devil by lowering on it the boom of an "acceptable" level of statistical confidence. To cite Gulliksen:

> The usual application of statistics in psychology consists of testing a "null hypothesis" that the investigator hopes is false. For example, he tests the hypothesis that the experimental group is the *same* as the control group even though he has done his best to make them perform differently. Then a "significant" difference is obtained which shows that the data do *not* agree with the hypothesis tested. The experimenter is then pleased because he has shown that a hypothesis he didn't believe, isn't true. (1958, pp. 3–4)

In reading the psychological literature, we sometimes wonder whether hypotheses, advanced at the beginning of the report and perhaps described as deductions from a theory, were really discovered only after the described experimentation or related preliminary experimentation was well underway. Reports sometimes read like exercises in logic and lack the spirit of inquiry that may have played much more of a part in the studies than the reports indicate (Luchins, 1957b). Perhaps the forms approved for scientific reports leave too little room for the portrayal of the roles played by inquiry, discovery, and intuition in scientific research. Or perhaps writers of scientific reports have become skilled at concealing these roles.

The concern with validation and the hypothetico-deductive approach may also be fostered by (and in turn may foster) the emphasis on formal planning in scientific work. Experiments must be carefully planned in accordance with certain stipulated methodological rules and must meet stipulated criteria of experimental design. Students should know that to be successful in research they must take courses in research planning, logic of research, and experimental design. In such courses more weight may be given to formal planning and design of experiments than to actual productivity in research. Even undergraduate psychology courses stress experimental design. Similarly, research reported in the literature has been reviewed and evaluated in terms of how it conforms with such formal criteria. Research that is not completely planned in advance or research that does not meet certain criteria of experimental design may be dismissed as not scientific. In this conception of scientific work, there seems to be little or no room for the flash of intuition, for the appreciation of the unexpected, and for the unplanned but illuminating experience commonly called *insight*. Yet, such factors have been considered to play roles in some outstanding advances in scientific thinking (see Hadamard, 1945; Wertheimer, 1945). Perhaps it is timely, therefore, to pay more attention to such factors in teaching, training, research, report writing, and in the evaluation of these activities. Concomitantly, it may be timely to consider the disadvantages of lulling students and psychologists into believing that by developing facility in experimental design and by learning the logic of research, they will be able to make genuine contributions to the science of psychology. Such facility does not guarantee scientific fertility.

Logical Operators and Thinking

It seems to us that contributing to the inadequacy of logic to serve as a model for thinking are the roles played by logical operators, including the logical connectives (for example, *and*, *or*). As we shall see, the roles of the connectives do not differ essentially in many systems of modern logic from what they were in traditional logic.

In what follows we shall have occasions to contrast the views of Alfred

Tarski with the views of Max Wertheimer, using, as sources of citation, texts that appeared only about a year apart (Tarski, 1946; Wertheimer, 1945). Tarski is not only an eminent logician but also an outstanding mathematician, and Wertheimer, founder of Gestalt psychology, was a professor both of psychology and of logic.

Conjunction

The term *and* (which may be designated by the ampersand sign & or some other symbol) is used to join two statements to make a single statement which is called the *conjunction* of the two. A conjunction is considered to be true in logic if and only if the statements that are combined are both true individually. In modern logic as in traditional logic it is not necessary that the two sentences that are combined have common form, content, or subject matter. "Any combinations, however absurd, are permitted" (Suppes, 1957, p. 4). Thus, such a sentence as "Two plus two equal four *and* Paris is the capitol of France" is a permissible and true conjunction. In short, the logical *and* is not concerned with the relationship between the two components that it combines; it may be used to combine statements that are structurally related or to make absurd and nonsensical combinations. Moreover, the conjunction in no way affects the individual components and each is just what it was before the conjunction: the *A* in "*A* and *B*" is taken to be unaffected by the connection and to be precisely what it would mean if *A* were alone or if *B* were replaced in the conjunction by another statement, say, *C*.

This conception of *and* has the advantage that logic and logicians do not have to be concerned with the admittedly difficult problems of what constitutes common subject matter or common form. Nor do they have to deal with the notion of structural relationship or the notion of the effect of the context (conjunction) on a part (a component of the conjunction). As far as these notions are concerned, the logical *and* is neutral or empty. But there is the disadvantage that in mathematical and other scientific discourses we are not particularly interested in absurd conjunctions. Moreover, *and* is often used in a manner that is not neutral to structural or dynamic relationships between components of a conjunction. In the words of Wertheimer:

> [The logical "and"] may combine any two things, or propositions, whatever they may mean to each other, whether or not they belong to each other structurally. . . . The content of both, taken together, is nothing but their and-sum; the actual content of each means nothing to the actual content of the other; the subject matter of the two has no structural relation. In the and-sum each is just what it would be without the other, or with the other changed. . . . In living thought "and" is for the most part not of this character. There is the "and" that combines two things which belong to each other, which require each other structurally. There is the "and" that states two

things are together which should not be together, which violate each other. Both these are different functionally from the neutral, structure-blind "and." The real "and" is often of a very serious character in that it involves dynamic consequences to which the use of the empty "and" is blind. (1945, pp. 211–212)

Wertheimer goes on to point out that the method used in logic to determine the truth value of a conjunction is adequate when the two components deal with subject matters that are not structurally related, so that *and* means nothing except that each component is true independently. But there are cases in "living thought" in which the combination of two subject matters is not and-summative in nature. The *and* may change the meaning of a statement that it combines from what the statement meant when considered alone and separately. Hence, Wertheimer contends that the method of truth tables, which is used in logic to determine the truth or falsity of a conjunction (and of other logical connectives), is essentially "structure-blind," blind to the structural relationships between the components and to the consequences of the *and*. Wertheimer believes: "Even in formal logic we should differentiate basically between the various kinds of 'and,' because the general use of the empty 'and' may blind the thinker to what he really does in putting things together" (1945, p. 212). Whether or not one agrees that this is a task of formal logic, it seems to us that it is advisable to recognize:

1. In logic, the *and* may be used to join any two statements, regardless of their relationship, whereas in mathematics and in productive thinking in general there is little interest in absurd, arbitrary combinations of unrelated statements.
2. In logic, the conjunction is treated as an *and-summation* in which the A of "A and B" is precisely what it is alone or if the B were changed to C, whereas there are cases of reasoning in which a component of a conjunction affects and is affected by the conjunction.

The distinction between and-summations and other kinds of structures is by no means a trivial point for psychology. A fundamental criticism that Gestalt psychology has made of traditional associationistic theories is that they take and-summations to be the prototypes of processes involved in learning, thinking, perception, human values, and so on. Granting that and-summations can exist in all these processes, Gestalt psychologists claim that there are also other kinds of structures involved which are not cases of and-summations and which cannot be reduced to and-summations without a loss of essential characteristics. Moreover, Gestalt psychologists contend that methods and theories based on and-summations may not be adequate to deal with, and to account for, other kinds of structures. In particular, logical conjunctions may not be adequate to account for the function of *and* in cases of reasoning which involve conjunctions that are not and-summations and wherein the *and* is not neutral with regard to the relationship between the components it connects. In short, logical conjunction need not correspond to psychological conjunction.

Disjunction

In common language the term *or* is used in both an exclusive sense and an inclusive (nonexclusive) sense. The exclusive sense is illustrated by the statement made to a child who is offered only one of two alternatives: "You may have an ice cream cone or an ice cream soda." The nonexclusive sense is illustrated by the statement made to a wife: "If I get a raise or a bonus, I'll buy you a fur coat." It is also illustrated by the sign that proclaims: "Beggers or dogs not allowed on these premises" or "Begging or soliciting prohibited." In short, the exclusive *or* means "either *A* or *B* but not both," whereas the nonexclusive *or* (which is sometimes denoted by and/or, particularly in legal documents) leaves open the possibility of both *A* and *B*, so that it means "either *A* or *B* or both." There are instances in ordinary language wherein it is not clear which sense of *or* is intended.

As Rosser points out (1953, p. 13), in English the exclusive sense of *or* is the grammatically correct one, with leading dictionaries offering it as the only correct use. Some languages use two words for the two senses. For example, in Latin the word *aut* is reserved for the exclusive sense and the word *vel* for *and/or*. In logic the word *or* is generally used in the nonexclusive sense, with **v** (from the Latin *vel*) often serving as a symbol for it.

In ordinary language, two statements are usually joined by the word *or* only if they are intrinsically related in some way. But in logic, any two statements may be joined by the word *or*, regardless of whether or not they have common form or content. The single statement that results is called the *disjunction of the two components*. In logic a disjunction is considered to be true if at least one of the components is true. For example, "Paris is the capital of France or 2 is greater than 3" is a permissible, meaningful, and true sentence in logic since the first component is true. In the words of Tarski:

> The creators of contemporary logic, when introducing the word *"or"* into their considerations, desired, perhaps unconsciously, to simplify its meaning and to render the latter clearer and *independent of all psychological factors.* . . . Consequently, they extended the usage of the word *"or,"* and decided to consider the disjunction of any two sentences as a meaningful whole, even should no connection between their contents or forms exist; and they also decided to make the truth of a disjunction . . . dependent only and exclusively upon the truth of its members. (1946, p. 23, italics ours)

As with the logical *and*, the logical *or* also may be described as neutral and structure-blind with regard to what it connects as well as with regard to how a component affects and is affected by the disjunction. Arguments that may be raised against the logical *or* so far as its adequacy to account for reasoning that involves *or* parallel those that were mentioned for the logical *and*. We need not repeat them.

Negation

In logic, the negation of A means "not-A" or, in other words, "It is not the case that A holds." The negation of a true statement is considered to be false, the negation of a false sentence to be true. Noting that the logical concept of negation is neutral, empty, and structure-blind, Wertheimer writes:

> . . . the concept of negation may be taken in an empty, structure-blind sense. But, again, this is a limiting case of negation, applicable only in special instances. On the other hand, negating something may mean that this something is appropriately not the case, the negation being just what is required by the structural nature of the situation. But there is still another "not" which states the lack of something that would in fact be structurally required by the situation. Both are in contrast to the use of an empty negation, which has no structural meaning whatsoever. (1945, p. 213)

Implication

In traditional logic, as well as in many contemporary systems of logic, implication is denoted by the phrase "If A, then C." The "if-then" may be used to join any two statements whatsoever regardless of whether or not they are in any way intrinsically related. The statement that follows the *if* and precedes the *then* is often called the *antecedent* or *hypothesis* or *premise;* the statement that follows the *then* is often called the *consequent* or *conclusion*. In traditional logic a logical implication is considered to be true if the antecedent is false or if the consequent is true. In other words, a logical implication is considered to be false when the antecedent is true and the consequent false. Hence such a statement as "If London is the capital of France, then 3 is greater than 2" is considered permissible and true, as is the statement, "If London is the capital of France, then 2 is greater than 3."

Logical implication differs strikingly from the way in which implication and the phrase if-then are used in reasoning outside of formal logic. In mathematics, and in all sciences other than logic, there is some intrinsic relationship between the subject matter or form of the statements joined by if-then; the consequent (as the very name suggests) has to be in some sense a consequence of or deducible from the antecedent. Moreover, this is usually (but not always) characteristic of implication and if-then as used in everyday talk. But in logical implication, the consequent need in no way be related to, be a consequence of, or be deducible from the antecedent. The phrase *material implication* is sometimes applied to the usage of implication in traditional logic to distinguish it from other usages of the term.

Divergencies between material implication and implication as used in mathematics and in other sciences, as well as in ordinary language, have been the sources of heated discussions extending over centuries. The very beginnings of material implication are believed to be shrouded in controversy (see Tarski, 1946, p. 27n). The Greek philosopher Philo of Megara, in the fourth century B.C., is believed to have been the first to advocate the use of material implication, doing so in opposition to the views of Diodorus Cronus, whose disciple he was, and who preferred to use implication in the sense of a certain relationship between antecedent and consequent. The puzzlement engendered by logicians' use of the term is summarized by the philosopher G. E. Moore who exclaims, "Why logicians should have thus chosen to use the word 'implies' as a name for a relation for which it never is used by anyone else, I do not know" (1922, p. 296). A possible explanation of why logicians did choose to use the word implies and the phrase if-then as they did, is offered by Tarski.

> The logicians, with due regard for the needs of scientific languages, adopted the same procedure with respect to the phrase "*if . . . , then . . .*" as they had done in the case of the word "*or.*" They decided to simplify and clarify the meaning of this phrase and to free it from psychological factors. For this purpose they extended the usage of this phrase, considering an implication as a meaningful sentence even if no connection whatsoever exists between its two members, and they made the truth or falsity of an implication dependent exclusively upon the truth or falsity of the antecedent and consequent. (1946, p. 25)

As might be expected, Wertheimer characterizes the "if-then" or "if-so" of material implication as neutral, empty, and structure-blind. He writes:

> . . . it is important to study this most empty, structure-blind type also. We sometimes have to deal with constant connections of this kind in actual life, sometimes even in the initial phases of productive processes. But in sensible thinking, "if-so" is rarely, or at least almost never *remains*, of this empty kind. . . . "If-so" for the most part involves some structural justification. It does not simply mean an "if-so" with regard to structurally unrelated subject matter. The sensible "if-so" calls for some kind of inner coherence, some kind of intrinsic structural relatedness. Thus the empty type appears merely as an extreme in which all structural relatedness disappears and only an external form remains, which is indifferent to the issues under "if" and under "so." (1945, p. 214)

It is noteworthy that some logicians regard material implication as leading to the paradoxes (Lewis, 1912, 1917). Attempts have been made to introduce in logic, in addition to material implication, a concept of implication which makes a certain connection between the consequent and antecedent (for example, that the former be deducible from the latter)—a necessary condition for the implication to be true (1912). Some logicians "even desire, so it seems, to place the new concept in the foreground" (Tarski, 1946, p. 28). Nonetheless, many systems of contemporary logic utilize material implication as the only sense of implication.

Logical operators as generalizations or limitations

Attempts to account for the manner in which connectives are used in logic and, in particular, for divergencies between this usage and everyday usage have indicated that each of the connectives lacks a standard, precise meaning in ordinary language. The meanings of the terms fluctuate somewhat from person to person and from one context to another. What logicians have done, it has been pointed out, is in accordance with the scientist's aim, when introducing a concept from ordinary language into science, to make the content of the concept "clearer, more precise and simpler, and free it from inessential attributes" (Tarski, 1946, p. 28). The scientist may abstract from, extend, or generalize the ordinary concept to obtain the scientific concept.

There are opposing views on the thesis that the logical connectives represent extensions or generalizations of the corresponding concepts in ordinary language. For example, Tarski notes that the creators of contemporary logic "extended the usage of the word 'or'" and of if-then and that a concept of implication which makes the meaningfulness and truth of the implication dependent on a certain connection between antecedent and consequent "is narrower than that of material implication" (p. 26). On the other hand, Wertheimer maintains that the "and" and "if-then" of material implication "appear merely as an extreme, in which all structural relatedness disappears" (1945, p. 214), and that logical negation is a "limiting case of negation applicable only in special instances" (p. 213). It would seem that what one calls an extension or generalization the other calls a limitation.

Wertheimer makes the point that the most basic items of logic have traditionally been "considered and used in blindness to the structural problems . . . [and] seem to be merely limiting cases of the broader issue" (p. 211). He refers here not only to the logical connectives but also to the logical concepts of relation, truth, identity, and so on, as well as to the traditional logical principles of identity, contradiction, and sufficient reason. In a paper entitled "On Truth" (1934), Wertheimer discussed a four-valuate logic where the terms *true* and *false* were each to be taken in an atomistic sense or in a structural sense. A special case of this four-valuate logic is traditional logic with its atomistic conception of truth and falsity. Referring to the and-summative nature of a logical conjunction and to the method of determining the truth of the conjunction through truth tables, Wertheimer states that the "form of the table of the truth-values in the mere and-summative case appears merely as a limiting case of the very much richer and deeper set which we get by considering structural features" (1945, p. 212).

Logical identity

Logical identity (Tarski, 1946, pp. 54–86) is characterized by Wertheimer as piecemeal identity where "piecemeal identity is merely a special case [of structural identity], appropriate only when structural conditions allow" (1945, p. 214). Piecemeal or atomistic identity is distinguished by Wertheimer from structural identity in the following example. From an atomistic viewpoint, the first two notes of a musical composition A, may be identical with the first two notes of another musical composition B, but from the viewpoint of structural identity, they may really be very different (pp. 208–209). Anyone who grasps melodies A and B would not regard these notes as identical since the second note in A is the tonic, whereas the "identical" second note in B is the leading tone which drives toward the tonic, the third note in B; the first note in A is a major third in the harmony, whereas in B it is a minor third; similarly, the relationship between the two notes, although similar when viewed piecemeal, differs when viewed in the context of the melodies as wholes.

> Traditional logic regards it as a very basic rule that the items of discourse—concepts, propositions, and so on—have to remain rigidly identical if repeated. Important as this rule is for certain questions of validity, it does not generally fit real thinking. In real thinking processes, items often do not remain rigidly identical; and as a matter of fact, precisely their change, their improvement is required. If an item, concept, or proposition recurs in the process and appears from an atomistic point of view as identical, it very often is not really so. Its functional and structural meaning has actually, and fortunately, changed. Blindness to such a change in meaning often impedes productive processes. In real thinking the *functional* meaning of an item, of a proposition, that meaning which changes as thinking advances, is of the utmost importance—without it thinking gets sterile; without realization of that change one does not grasp the line of progress. For statements, etc., have a direction in their context. It is here that a basic feature of traditional logic comes to the fore: its disregard of the intense directness of live thought processes as they improve a given situation. (p. 215)

Wertheimer suggests that the treatment of logical identity illustrates how traditional logic focuses on the static features of thinking but does not come to grips with the direction or dynamics of thinking. The same charge could be leveled against many systems of modern logic and one does not have to be an intuitionist to do so.

Logical concepts
and psychological factors

In discussing logical concepts, Tarski (1946) writes that everyday concepts tend to be dependent on subjective or psychological factors, whereas the logician seeks to free the concepts from their dependence on psychological factors. If logicians were motivated by the desire to free the everyday concepts from psychological factors, then it is ironic that the resulting logical concepts, presumably stripped free of dependence on psychological factors, should in turn be used (by some psychologists as well as by some logicians) to account for psychological phenomena, such as the psychological form of mathematical reasoning. For example, Tarski writes: "It should be observed what an extremely elementary form—from the psychological point of view—*all mathematical reasonings* assume, due to the knowledge and applications of the laws of logic and the rules of [logical] inference" (p. 49). He notes that through applications of the laws of logic and rules of inference "complicated mental processes are entirely reducible to such simple activities" as alternative observation of statements previously accepted as true, the perception of sheerly external connections among these statements, and the execution of the mechanical transformations prescribed by the rules of inference.

From the Gestalt psychological point of view, it is only illusionary that all mathematical reasoning assumes such an elementary form and that the mental processes involved are entirely reducible to the simple activities with which logic is concerned. Such an elementary form and such "reduction" are achieved at the price of losing essentials of the reasoning process which the logical operations fail to capture.

In conclusion, it is not denied that mathematical thinking and other kinds of thinking can be shown to involve a chain of logical operations. It may be helpful to think of this chain as constituting the skeleton of the reasoning and the individual logical operations as its bones and skeletal connections. But in this "reduction" of thinking, it should not be overlooked that the flesh and blood that were stripped from the reasoning process to reveal this skeleton may be as vital to it as the skeletal form which remains.

In other words, formulation of reasoning in terms of logic, whether traditional or modern, may reveal that reasoning seems to involve a chain of logical operations. But this is not all that is involved in the reasoning. Moreover, it is possible to have a chain of logical operations, each correct in itself, which does not constitute a sensible train of thought. Logical concepts and logical operators are indifferent to and do not distinguish between sense and nonsense, between creative thinking and noncreative activities. This frees logic from having to be concerned with problems of creativity and discovery and of portraying the vital forceful nature of productive thinking. But perhaps this very freedom denies logic the possibility of being used to characterize completely mathematical reasoning, scientific reasoning, or other kinds of genuinely productive thinking.

It may not be out of place to conclude with suggestions for research by psychologists. First, we need to discover ordinary life situations in which logical operators, including the connectives, are used as stipulated in logic (call them situations A) and other situations in which they are not used in this way (call them situations B). What are the characteristics of situations A and B? Experiments may be devised in which all or some individuals in situation A are instructed to use the kind of operators which are used in situation B, and vice versa. What dynamic and structural changes would occur in the situations? What effect would it have on the group's reaching their objectives, on the group member's interpersonal relationships, and so on? A more laboratory type of experiment could be devised using group or individual problem solving situations where (1) the solution is possible by an and-summation of steps, and (2) where the solution is not possible by an and-summation of steps. What would happen in 1 if the individual or group members treated the problem as if it were of the 2 kind and what would happen in 2 if it were treated as if it were of the 1 kind? If logical inference constitutes the rules of a language game (Benacerraf and Putnam, 1964, p. 481), then it might be said that the suggested experiments are attempts to change, rather arbitrarily, the rules of the language game in the situations. Empirical research may reveal that some language games are intimately related to the nature of the situation or task and others are not. Maybe in certain tasks and in certain situations, certain language games are more suitable than in others. Such research may reveal the realm of applicability of various rules concerning logical operators and inferences. It may be more fruitful than arguing from theoretical or philosophical points of view as to whether or not existing uses of logical operators and inferences are adequate to portray human thinking.

Truth: In Logic, Mathematics, and Empirical Sciences

Logic and Truth

When initially developed as a formal system, logic seemed inexorably bound to truth, for the Greek philosophers formulated the "theory of logic as the structure of knowledge and truth. . . . In its own intention the Aristotelian logic was a logic of truth" (Dewey, 1930, pp. 599–600). What about modern systems of logic? Have they discarded truth as an archaic concept? You have but to open at random many texts on modern logic, including texts on symbolic and mathematical logic, to see that this is not the case.

Take Quine's distinguished text on mathematical logic (1951a) as an example. It rejects as insufficiently informative the characterizations of logic as "the science of forms" or as "the science of necessary inference." Instead, it describes logic in terms of the truths with which it deals. To characterize "the truths of logic" (p. 1) Quine introduces the notion of a *logical vocabulary* (such words as *is, and, not, or, if-then,* and so on) and the notion of *essentially.* "A word may be said to occur essentially in a statement if replacement of the word by another is capable of turning the statement into a falsehood" (p. 2). Logical truths, then, are those in which only the words in the logical vocabulary occur essentially. Although mathematical logic differs so markedly from traditional formal logic "as to be generally and not unjustifiably regarded as a new science" (p. 1), nonetheless both are concerned with logical truths and with statements about these truths (p. 3).

Quine notes that in characterizing logical truths, he takes for granted the general notion of truth. Recognizing that it is fashionable to align oneself with the "hard-headed" by repudiating such a notion, Quine refuses to do so, maintaining that "in point of fact there is no denying that we know what it means to say that a given statement is true—absolutely True [truth with a capital T]—just as clearly as we understand the given statement itself. . . . Applied to any statement S, the word 'true' is no obscurer than the obscurest word in the statement S itself; for to say that S is true is simply to say S" (p. 4).

The notion of truth is central in many characterizations of the propositional calculus, also known as the *sentential* or *statement* calculus. Thus, in a chapter on the propositional calculus, Black writes: "Formal logic studies the rules which state the conditions under which the truth of a proposition . . . can be deduced from the truth of a set of propositions . . . by virtue of their logical form alone" (1934, p. 42). And Rosser writes: "The study of statement formulas, with especial reference to their truth or falsity, constitutes the statement calculus. . . . A statement formula which is true no matter what statements are taken in it is said to be 'universally valid'" (1953, p. 24).

Modern logic involves, in addition to the propositional calculus, other calculi, such as the predicate calculus and the number-theoretic calculus. These two are frequently characterized with reference to the notion of truth.

In Suppes' text on modern logic, a formula is defined to be "universally valid if and only if every interpretation of it in every non-empty domain of individuals [objects] is true" (1957, p. 67). Suppes notes: "The intuitive idea behind this definition is that universally valid formulas should be true in every possible world" (pp. 67–68). Similarly the notion of truth is involved in the definition of valid and invalid arguments. Thus, an argument is defined to be invalid "if and only if there is an interpretation in some non-empty domain which makes its premises true and its conclusion false" (p. 69). Truth is also involved in the definition of consistency: "A formula is consistent if and only if it has at least one true interpretation in some non-empty domain of individuals" (p. 68). Truth is also involved in definitions of theorems of logic. A formula is "a theorem of logic if and only if it is universally valid," that is, if it is "true independent of the truth or falsity of any particular factual premises" (p. 108).

Logical connectives such as *and, or, not,* and *implies* (*if-then*) are often referred to as *truth-functional connectives,* and the modes of composing formulas from them as *truth-functional modes of composition.* Tabular arrays that are used to determine the truth or falsehood of a statement by assigning truth values (truth or falsehood) to its ultimate components are *truth tables.* The set of those components of the statements which have the value of truth in, say, the kth row of a truth table has been called the kth *truth set of the function.* In short, the term *truth* has wide use in the terminology of modern logic.

It should be mentioned that there are n-valued logics, where n is greater than 2, which utilize such notions as probability and possibility or which recognize some "intermediate" values between truth and falsity. But these notions usually occur in addition to, and not in lieu of, the notions of truth and falsehood. There are some texts which prefer to use two symbols in place of truth and falsehood, such as T and F, or 1 and 0, or mumbo and jumbo, but the intuitive ideas that determine how these symbols are introduced and operated upon are still the notions of truth and falsehood. Even texts on metamathematics (see Kleene, 1952) may appeal to the notions of truth or falsity and to truth values (at least to motivate the presentation of metamathematics), particularly in dealing with the consistency of logical systems. However, there are some systems of logic, including the intuitionistic logic (see Heyting, 1930), which do not make explicit use of the notion of truth or of truth tables. On the whole, though, modern logic, including symbolic logic and mathematical logic, seems not to have divorced itself from the notion of truth. Thus, despite radical differences between modern logic and ancient Aristotelian logic, they are linked by the common core characteristic of logic throughout the ages: the notion of truth.

Mathematics and Truth

At one time mathematics was regarded as dealing with self-evident truths. But this is presumably an old fashioned notion. Yet, the notion of truth has not disappeared from mathematics. Consider what Bertrand Russell has to say on this matter. He notes that pure mathematics, in addition to considering propositions and their properties, "uses a notion which is not a constituent of the propositions which it considers, namely the notion of truth" (1938, p. 3). It was also Russell who wrote that "mathematics may be defined as the subject in which we never know what we are talking about nor whether what we are saying is true" (1918, p. 75). Since definitions in mathematics depend on undefined terms, we do not know what we are talking about; and since the theorems depend on unproved assumptions involving the undefined terms, we do not know whether what we are saying is true. What is it then that we do know in mathematics? And what is the nature of mathematical truth?

The major schools of foundational thought in mathematics have been regarded as constituting different approaches to the establishment of mathematical truths. Max Black tells us that if logicism or formalism were correct, "the assembly of mathematical truths preserved" in the first case would consist of those which can be deduced from the axioms logicism accepts, and, in the second case, "those which had been safeguarded by proofs of consistency" (1934, p. 170). Black also writes that Brouwer maintains "that existence in mathematics is synonymous with constructibility, and that the truth, and indeed significance, of mathematical theorems is conditional on the possibility of constructing the entities which occur in their formulation" (p. 198). Mathematicians,

Black believes, with the possible exception of some intuitionists, "willingly conceive of it as an unchangeable system of eternal truths" (p. 169).

Eternal or not, what are mathematical truths? How do they compare with logical truths and with the "empirical truths" dealt with by such sciences as physics or psychology? Let us consider some of the varied answers that have been given to these questions.

Preliminary survey

One answer is that mathematics is a collection of self-evident truths. Obvious difficulties with this answer are that what is self-evident to one person may not be self-evident to another and that what is self-evident, even to many, for many years, may turn out to be untrue (for example, the "self-evident fact" that the world is flat). Moreover, some of the propositions and even axioms of mathematics are not self-evident or at least not as self-evident as others. Thus, the famous parallel axiom of Euclidean geometry was suspect as an axiom, and attempts were therefore made to establish it as a theorem because it seemed less self-evident than the other axioms. Indeed, there are whole branches of higher mathematics, as many a graduate student will confess, which do not appear to be at all self-evident.

Another answer is that mathematical propositions are empirical propositions. For example, the famous physicist Isaac Newton (1642–1727) conceived of geometry as a branch of the empirical science of mechanics. The philosopher John Stuart Mill (1806–1873) regarded mathematics as an empirical science that differed from the other empirical sciences in that its subject matter was more general and its propositions far better established. From this point of view, mathematical propositions are empirical propositions, induced from experience, and repeatedly confirmed by experience.

Still another answer is that mathematical propositions, or at least certain mathematical axioms, are not induced from experience but are innately given to the human mind. This is illustrated by the views of the philosopher-mathematician Gottfried Leibniz (1646–1716) who claimed that geometric truths are "innate, and are in us virtually, so that we can find them there if we consider attentively and set in order what we already have in the mind" (1916 edition, p. 78). Probably the best-known proponent of this viewpoint is Immanuel Kant who conceived of Euclid's geometry as corresponding to our a priori knowledge, a priori in the sense of prior to experience. According to Kant, Euclid's geometry was a formulation of our a priori intuitions of the structure of space. Kant's views have been interpreted as meaning that Euclid's axioms and the consequences of the axioms are "apodictic truths concerning the spatial form of all possible experience" (Nagel, 1961, p. 218). Kant's view of geometry had a powerful impact on philosophers, mathematicians, and physicists, until the development and popularization of non-Euclidean geometries gradually showed it to be untenable.

The various conceptions discussed so far seem to have in common their connection with experience, with the world of facts. Mathematical propositions, as self-evident truths, may be considered to be truths about reality, about experience. Mathematical propositions, as empirical propositions, are considered to be derived from experience. Mathematical propositions, as a priori intuitions, may also be regarded as intuitive conceptions describing, or corresponding to, facets of experience, even though not derived from experience.

There is a view of mathematics which regards its propositions as neither self-evident truths nor as empirical propositions nor as a priori intuitions. This view of mathematics, which is held by many philosophers and mathematicians of the twentieth century, considers that mathematics asserts nothing whatsoever about experience or about the world of facts. This is the viewpoint of, for example, Bertrand Russell and Charles S. Peirce, who disagreed on the relationship between mathematics and logic. Peirce said that mathematics "asserts no matter of fact whatever" (1933, p. 191); it deals, not with actual state of things, but exclusively with hypothetical state of things. "Mathematics is the study of what is true of hypothetical state of things. That is its essence and definition" (p. 192).

Russell stated that mathematical knowledge is not empirical knowledge, induced from experience, and also that it is not in the nature of a priori intuition. Rather, he maintained that the study of the relationship between mathematics and logic shows that mathematical knowledge is "all of the same nature as the 'great truth' that there are three feet in a yard" (1945, p. 198).

But what kind of a "truth" is this "great truth"? Since a yard may be defined as consisting of three feet, the statement may be said to be "true by definition." Russell seems to be suggesting that mathematics, then, is true by definition. Statements that are true by definition, including the statement that there are three feet in a yard, are sometimes referred to as *analytic statements* or as *tautologies*. Probably the most popular contemporary view of mathematics is that it consists of tautologies or of analytic statements. Let us turn, therefore, to a discussion of such statements.

On Tautologies

The term *tautology* was used by Wittgenstein to refer to a statement of the traditional sentential calculus that is logically true for every possible distribution of values of "true" and "false" for its ultimate components. Thus, the method of a truth table would yield only the value "true" in the column corresponding to a statement that is a tautology. "If P and Q, then Q" is an example of a tautology, since it is logically true in the sentential calculus, regardless of whether each of the components (P, Q) is considered to be true or false. In other words, a statement formula is a tautology or is tautologous if and only if it is true no matter what statements are taken in it (substituted for the statement variables in it). Still other equivalent characterizations are that a tautology is a statement which is true solely by virtue of its truth-functional structure or mode of composition; that it is a true statement which involves *essentially* only the truth-functional connectives and not its ultimate constituent statements; that it is a statement which belongs to each of its truth sets, and so on. These equivalent characterizations coincide with the definition of a statement of the sentential calculus which is logically true (universally valid, or a theorem of logic). Therefore, a tautology may be characterized as a logical truth of the sentential calculus.

Some philosophers and logicians characterize as a tautology any logical truth or any theorem of logic (and even any theorem of mathematics). There are mathematicians, logicians, and philosophers who doubt the value of this extension of the term, considering it to be somewhat confusing and obscure (see Hilbert and Ackermann, 1950, under notes by the editor; Luce, 1960, p. 167; Suppes, 1957, p. 15n; Quine, 1951a, p. 55). The broader use of the term may have arisen because of Wittgenstein's doctrine that all logical and mathematical truths are tautologies. "This doctrine was intended by Wittgenstein as a thesis, not as a definition of tautology; and indeed it is a difficult thesis to defend" (Quine, 1951a, p. 55). Wittgenstein attempted to make the term *tautology* cover logical truths which involve quantification (such as "For all x . . ." and "There exists an x such that . . .") and which belong to what may be called the *predicate calculus*. But this attempt to include the "quantificationally true" statements as tautologies depended on "an effort to explain quantification as a sort of infinite mode of truth-functional composition" (Quine, 1951a, p. 55). This effort is rejected by Quine who refers to the tautologous statements as forming one class of logical truths, the "quantificationally true" statements as a broader class, and the theorems of logic as still a broader class.

There is an important difference among these classes. The method of truth tables constitutes an effective procedure (a mechanical, general procedure involving a finite number of steps) for deciding whether or not a given statement of the sentential calculus is logically true. There exist other decision procedures; a considerable portion of a contemporary text or course on symbolic logic may be devoted to these procedures (see Copi, 1953). For example, a question on an examination in such a course asked students to demonstrate that a given formula of the sentential calculus was a tautology by means of each of the following methods: shorter truth-table method; the method of truth-table analysis; derivation of various normal forms (used in Hilbert and Ackermann, 1950, in lieu of truth tables) such as the perfect disjunctive normal form, the conjunctive normal form, the simplest normal form, and so on; regular method of deduction; method of conditional proof; method of indirect proof; method of *reductio ad absurdum*, and so on. In short, there exist general, and even effective, decision procedures for demonstrating whether or not a given statement of the sentential calculus is a logical truth. But there exists not even one effective procedure for doing this for formulas involving quantification, for formulas of the predicate calculus. Nor is this due to any lack of ingenuity. The American logician Alonzo Church proved in 1936 that it is impossible to devise a general procedure for mechanically deciding whether or not a formula involving quantification is true. It is possible to single out quantificationally true statements by a procedure which is general, but not mechanical (Quine, 1951a, p. 81). However, for the third class of logical truth, the theorems, there is not even a general procedure for deciding whether or not a given statement belongs to it. In other words, we lack a general procedure for determining whether or not a given statement is a theorem of logic.

In short, some philosophers and logicians agree that "all tautologous statements are logically true, but not all logically true statements are tautologous" (Quine, 1951a, p. 50), whereas others use the term *tautology*, or *tautologous*, for any logical truth. Our own view is that the wider use of the term is unfortunate, both because its meaning is then obscure, and because some of the characteristics of tautology, in the narrow sense, may inadvertently be attributed to all logical truths. At least one property of tautology, in the narrow sense—that there is an effective procedure for deciding whether or not a given statement is a tautology—does not hold, we have seen, for broader classes of logical truths, and so would not hold for tautology in the wider sense.

Some who reserve the term *tautology* for truths of the sentential calculus prefer to use the term *analytic* for logical truths in general. Others use *analytic* and *tautology* interchangeably. Let us glance at the history of the term *analytic* and survey some of its varied uses in the contemporary scene.

Analytic Statements

Immanuel Kant (1724–1804) used the term *analytic* for statements having the subject-predicate form and the property that the meaning of the predicate is "contained in" the meaning of the subject (Kant, 1929, originally 1781). "White horses are white" is such a statement. Thus, an analytic statement, as Kant used the term, is one in which the predicate repeated part of what was contained in the subject or in which the meaning of the predicate is contained in the meaning or definition of the subject. It may be said that Kant used the word *analytic* to refer to statements of the subject-predicate form that are true by definition. The name *analytic* may stem from the notion that the truth of such a statement can be determined solely through *analysis* of the statement, without resource to other information. Kant applied the name *synthetic* to truths that are not analytic. He applied the term *a priori* to truths that are known innately in contrast to those that are induced from experience, which he called *a posteriori*.

There have been philosophers, a prominent one being David Hume, who recognized only two kinds of truths. Using the above terminology, these truths may be characterized as (1) those which are a priori and analytic, and (2) those which are a posteriori and synthetic. But Kant recognized still another kind of truth, a hybrid which was both a priori and synthetic. Thus, he regarded the postulates of Euclidean geometry as constituting both a priori and synthetic truths. Similarly, he considered an arithmetical statement such as 2 + 3 = 5 a priori and synthetic, a priori because he held that the truth of this statement is not induced from experience and synthetic because he held that the statement's truth cannot be established solely through analysis of the sentence (taking into account the meaning of the terms).

When Kant's views were more popular than they are today, the view that truths may be both a priori and synthetic was also more popular. Today Hume's views, as expounded by the logical positivists, once more hold sway. Nonetheless, even today there are some philosophers who believe in Kant's hybrid brand of truth. In short, today (as in years past) it is a matter of dispute as to whether statements can be both synthetic and a priori. A true a priori statement is often referred to as a necessary statement—that is, one that is necessarily true—as one whose truth is independent of the world of facts, and whose truth therefore cannot be called into question by any facts or experiences. Sometimes the label of *rationalist* is attached to those who hold that a statement may be both necessary (a priori true) and synthetic, and the label of *empiricist* to those who claim that this cannot be the case. Further subdivisions are possible. For example, the *logical empiricist* maintains that all analytic (but no synthetic) statements are necessary or a priori truths, whereas the traditional empiricist hold that even many analytic statements are not necessary or a priori truths.

Semantic Variations

There have been some variations since Kant's time in the meanings of such terms as *a priori*, *analytic*, and *synthetic*. A priori usually refers to a statement whose truth is independent of experience, independent of any empirical information. Currently, the use of the term *analytic* often includes the concept of a priori, and the term *synthetic* often includes the concept of a posteriori. Thus, the term *analytic* is now often applied to statements that are "true a priori" in the sense that their truth or validation is independent of or is logically prior to factual evidence, and the term *synthetic* is often reserved for a statement whose truth or validation requires factual evidence. Hence, analytic statements are not factually informative and their truth or validation is independent of empirical evidence. "An analytic statement conveys no factual information . . . it has no factual implications, no empirical content; and it is precisely for this reason that the statement can be validated without recourse to empirical evidence" (Hempel, 1953, p. 150).

It may be recalled that Kant limited the term *analytic* to statements, true by definition, which have the subject-predicate form. Currently, the term is limited to the subject-predicate form by some writers, while others do not adhere to this restriction. Thus, some writers (for example, Hospers, 1953) restrict the term *analytic* in this manner, apply the term *tautology* to statements having all characteristics of an analytic statement except the subject-predicate form, and characterize a statement as *synthetic* if it is not analytic or a tautology. On the other hand, there are those (for example, Hempel, 1953) who divide statements into analytic and synthetic ones (and do not introduce the term *tautology*), characterizing a statement as analytic if it conveys no factual information and if it is true independently of empirical evidence, and otherwise characterizing it as synthetic.

As an illustration of still further variations in the meaning of the terms, note that the term *analytic* has also been applied to statements that may be logically false. Thus, some writers (for example, Hochberg, 1959) characterize as analytic any statement that, conveying no factual information, is true or false independently of the facts, and they designate true analytic statement as tautologies and false analytic statements as contradictions. *Analytic* is used here in a broader sense than in the preceding paragraphs (since here such a statement may be true or false and it need not have the subject-predicate form); the term *tautology* is used here as the term *analytic* was used in the preceding paragraphs, when it was not restricted to the subject-predicate form.

In short, there is considerable variation in the meaning of such terms as *analytic, synthetic,* and *tautology,* an invitation for semantic confusion.

Criticisms of Characterizations

Let us consider now some criticisms that may be made of attempts to characterize tautologies or (true) analytic statements. Recall Kant's definition of an analytic statement as one in which the meaning of the predicate is "contained in" the meaning of the subject. The philosopher, Georg W. F. Hegel (1770–1831) regarded this definition as paradoxical, since, if the meaning of the subject completely contains the meaning of the predicate, then the latter would no longer be predicate. A related, more comprehensive objection is that the meaning of the phrase "contained in" is insufficiently specified. Still a more comprehensive objection may be worded as follows: What is the meaning of "the meaning of the subject," "the meaning of the predicate," and the meaning of "contained in"? More generally speaking, what is the meaning of meaning? See Ogden and Richards (1923) for illustrations of the many issues and controversies centered around the "meaning of meaning."

The problem of the meaning of meaning is clearly not circumvented by those who do not restrict analytic statements to the subject-predicate form but regard as analytic any statement whose truth can be established solely through analysis of the meaning of the terms it contains. Nor is the problem ruled out by those who characterize as analytic a true statement that conveys no factual information and/or requires no empirical evidence for its verification. On what basis is it determined that a given statement is devoid of empirical content, that it offers no factual information? Why, for example do "White horses are white" and "All bachelors are unmarried" fall into this category, whereas "Some horses are white" and "Some bachelors are unhappy" do not? An answer we can anticipate is that the latter sentences require observation or empirical data for their verification, whereas the former can be verified solely by considering the *meaning* of the terms—but this takes us right back to the problems attendant on meaning.

Characterization in terms of logical form

It may seem that such problems are avoided if one characterizes analytic statements in terms of their logical form or logical structure rather than in terms of the meaning of the terms they involve. For example, there are logicians and philosophers who prefer to characterize as analytic those statements, and only those statements, which can be logically deduced from the principles of logic. In other words, analytic may be so defined that it coincides with what (some) logicians call a logical truth or a universally valid formula or a theorem of logic. This characterization brings in its wake a host of problems to which various answers have been given. What are the principles of logic? What definition should be accepted of a logical truth or of a universally valid formula or of a theorem of logic? These problems aside, this characterization of analytic makes it imperative, in order to establish that a statement is analytic, to show that it can be deduced from the principles of logic, that it is a theorem of logic. But we saw that there is no decision procedure available for determining whether or not a given statement is a theorem of logic. Hence we would have no way of knowing for many statements whether they are analytic or not.

Moreover, if the definition of analytic does not refer to the meaning of terms, may one continue to describe as analytic those statements whose truth is established on the basis of such meaning? It seems to us that sufficient attention has not been paid to the consequence that such statements as "all bachelors are unmarried" or "all bachelors are males" could no longer be characterized as analytic since their truth depends on the meaning of the terms and, specifically, on the meaning of the predicate in relation to the meaning of the subject. Thus, if analytic is defined in terms of logical truth or universal validity, and if logical truth and universal validity are defined solely in terms of logical structure, without attention to meaning, then a statement whose truth is dependent on meaning should not be characterized as analytic.

Such a point is explicitly made by Suppes (1957, p. 68), when he writes that his definition of a universally valid formula, based solely on the "bare logical structure" of the formula, would "deny the universal validity of certain sentences of ordinary language which would seem to be true in every possible world. A typical example is 'all bachelors are unmarried.'" Suppes notes that the logical analysis of sentences where truth depends on the meaning of the predicate is "a subtle and complicated matter." Yet just such sentences—"All bachelors are unmarried" or "All bachelors are males"—are frequently cited as clear-cut examples of statements that are universally valid, analytic, and tautologies, since "unmarried" or "male" is a part of the very meaning or definition of the word *bachelor*. Moreover, some writers, unlike Suppes, cite such examples, although they accept definitions, based solely on logical structure, of such terms as *universally valid, analytic*, and *tautology*. It seems to be a case of wanting both the advantages of abstraction from meaning and content provided by such definitions and the advantages of the richness of ordinary language with its dependence on meaning.

Self-contradiction
or logical impossibility

Another characterization of analytic statements and tautologies is that their negation or denial constitutes a self-contradiction and describes a logically impossible state of affairs. Thus, Hospers writes that to deny analytic statements or tautologies "*is to contradict oneself;* in other words *their denial results in a self-contradictory statement*" (1953, p. 91). In contrast, a synthetic statement, defined as one which is neither analytic nor a tautology, "can be denied without self-contradiction" (p. 91), regardless of whether it is true or false. The same text connects statements with states of affairs through the notions of logical possibility and impossibility. "A state-of-affairs is said to be *logically possible* whenever the *statement* that this state-of-affairs exists is not a self-contradictory one, and logically *im*possible when the statement *is* self-contradictory" (p. 94). Logical possibility is distinguished from empirical possibility and technical possibility. A state of affairs is said to be empirically possible when it is not contrary to the laws of nature. Technical possibility involves not only the laws of nature, which are assumed not to change, but also our knowledge of these laws and our ability to utilize them to produce certain conditions, where this knowledge and ability may change from one time to another. What is logically impossible is also empirically impossible and technically impossible. What is empirically impossible is technically impossible. Thus the order is: logical, empirical, and technical impossibility, with one kind of impossibility encompassing a successor. On the other hand, it need not encompass a predecessor—that is, what is empirically impossible need not be logically impossible, and what is technically impossible (at any given time) need not be empirically or logically impossible.

Thus, "what is logically impossible could not be the case in any universe (at least not in any universe conceivable by the human mind); what is only empirically impossible might be the case in *some* universe, but does not happen to be the case in ours" (p. 96).

In short, it is held by some writers that to deny a tautology or an analytic statement results in a self-contradictory statement, one which describes a logically impossible state of affairs, a state of affairs that could not be the case in any universe conceivable by the human mind.

Let us attempt to apply this criterion. Consider the principle of the excluded middle. It is accepted as a tautology in many systems of logic but is not so regarded in intuitionistic logic, for example, in Heyting's system (1930). The intuitionists do not consider that to deny the principle of the excluded middle is self-contradictory. Rather, Brouwer suggests that those who regard the principle of the excluded middle as unconditionally true or as universally valid may be confusing truth or correctness with a lack of contradictions.

It is important not to confuse the denial of a statement with the acceptance of the negation of this statement. Intuitionists do not accept the negation of the principle of the excluded middle. (Actually they accept the negation of its negation which in their system is not equivalent to the excluded-middle principle.) To deny the principle of the excluded middle is only to omit one of the postulates of systems that accept it, and hence to build what may be considered a subsystem of such systems. This subsystem could not be contradictory without introducing such contradictions into the larger system, based also on the excluded-middle principle. It is true that Heyting's logical calculus introduces other changes too, besides the dropping of the principle of the excluded middle. But these are irrelevant for the point under consideration, which is that denial of the principle of the excluded middle is not any more contradictory than its acceptance. On the basis of the above criterion of self-contradiction, is the principle of the excluded middle a tautology? It was said above that denial of a synthetic statement does not result in a self-contradiction. Is the excluded-middle principle then synthetic?

Moreover, intuitionists apparently can conceive of a universe in which the unqualified principle of the excluded middle does not hold, namely, a universe that includes general statements and infinite sets. They regard the principle as an abstraction from finite sets. Thus, the denial of the excluded-middle principle may not amount to a description of a state of affairs that could not be the case in any universe conceivable by the human mind. Is the statement of this principle then analytic or synthetic?

As another illustration from logic, note that tautologies in a 2-valued logic may not be tautologies in a many-valued logic—that is, in an n-valued logic, n greater than 2. For example, of the tautologies in a 2-valued system, such as that in *Principia Mathematica*, some remain tautologies, whereas others are not tautologies in Lukasiewicz's 3-valued system (see Tarski, 1956, Chapter IV); for example, no longer tautologies are the principles of excluded middle, of contradiction (not both P and not-P), of *modus ponens* (law of detachment: P and P implies Q imply Q), of *modus tollens* (not-Q and P implies Q imply not-P). Yet one can conceive of a universe (possibly our own) that might more appropriately be described by a 3-valued system (for example, truth, falsehood, and an intermediate value) than by a 2-valued system in which absolute truth and falsehood are the only values. In any event, to deny certain tautologies would not result in self-contradictory statements within the framework of the 3-valued logic but would result in such statements within the framework of the 2-valued logic. Hence, it is not quite accurate to say that to deny a tautology or an analytic statement is to engage in a self-contradiction; one may also have to specify the system of logic or other frame of reference from which the statement is viewed as being tautologous or as being analytic and as having the property that its denial is a self-contradiction.

Thus, the attempt to characterize a tautology or an analytic statement as one whose denial involves a self-contradiction raises a number of problems. What is a self-contradiction? Can a self-contradiction be defined independently of a system of logic? It would seem that it cannot. For example, it is presumably a self-contradiction to deny the law of the excluded middle in nonintuitionistic 2-valued logic; but it is *not* a contradiction to do so in intuitionistic systems of logic or in certain many-valued systems of logic. Famous antinomies of set theory, such as Russell's paradoxes, constitute contradictions in classical 2-valued systems but not in intuitionistic logic or in many-valued logic. Yet, there are certain paradoxes, involving contradictions within the system, which can appear even in many-valued logic (for example, Curry's paradox—see Curry, 1942; Fraenkel and Bar-Hillel, 1958, pp. 191–194). But whether or not a given collection of statements involves a contradiction may depend on the particular logical system in the context of which it is considered. The term *self-contradictory* seems to us to be misleading because it suggests that it is simply the "self" or the speaker who is introducing the contradiction or that the collection of statements *in vacuo* involves a contradiction. What seems to be overlooked is that a collection of statements which involves a contradiction in the context of one logical system may not involve a contradiction in the context of another logical system.

Similarly, the claim that the denial of a tautology or of an analytic statement constitutes a logical impossibility raises the question: What is a logical impossibility? Clearly what is "logically impossible" in one logical system may be logically possible in another system. For example, the denial of the law of contradiction would not constitute a logical impossibility in the context of a many-valued system of logic where this law is not a tautology or a theorem, but the denial might be regarded as a logical impossibility in the context of those systems of logic (including both classical and intuitionistic systems) where the law of contradiction does hold.

In order to attempt to preserve the notion that the denial of a tautology or of an analytic statement involves a self-contradiction or involves a logical impossibility, one would, at minimum, have to mention the logical system which serves as the frame of reference. But even this would not suffice to conserve the notion that to deny a tautology or analytic statement is to describe a state of affairs that is logically impossible in any universe conceivable by the human mind. The broadness of this notion—logical impossibility in any universe conceivable by the human mind—suggests that the tautology as well as the logical impossibility of its denial would remain a tautology and a logical impossibility in any logical system whatsoever. But, as we have seen, this may be a misleading conception.

Let us turn now to some illustrations of statements in which the denial of a tautology is described as self-contradictory or as a logical impossibility. As an illustration from mathematics, consider the claims: "Statements of arithmetic are tautologies because their denial is self-contradictory" (Hospers, 1953, p. 112) and "the postulates—and therefore also the theorems—of arithmetic are unconditionally true" (Hempel, 1953, p. 161). But there are those who hold that the statements of arithmetic are not tautologies and are not unconditionally true. We shall refer to several such viewpoints in a later section. Here we content ourselves with quoting a vigorous spokesman of the antitautology outlook, Friedrich Waismann, who maintains that mathematics in general, and arithmetic in particular, "does not consist of tautologies" (1959, p. 118). He regards the basic laws of arithmetic as arbitrary assumptions that can be changed. He can conceive of these laws denied and of new ones accepted. He can imagine a new arithmetic in which the number series and the operations with the numbers are changed from the customary ones. Thus, to deny the basic laws of arithmetic may not be to describe a logically impossible situation, for it has been said that "if a state of affairs is really logically *im*possible, it is not imaginable by anybody" (Hospers, 1953, p. 98).

Cultural Factors and Tautologies

A point that seems to us to have received insufficient attention is the role that cultural factors may play in determining what constitutes logical impossibility, logical truth, a tautology, an unconditional truth, and so on. For example, what was regarded as logically impossible in the context of traditional Aristotelian logic is not regarded as logically impossible in the context of some modern systems of logic. Aristotelian logic has been described as a product of Greek culture (see Dewey, 1930). Are modern systems of logic also influenced by cultural factors? More generally, do the logical systems that exist in a culture reflect linguistic and thought processes of that culture? Some anthropological studies suggest that even primitive peoples have certain logical systems. To describe such systems as more primitive than our own is beside the point here. The point that is relevant is that what constitutes logical impossibility in logical systems of one culture may not play this role in logical systems of another culture. What then does it mean to describe what is logically impossible as incapable of being imagined by anyone, as inconceivable to the human mind? Similarly, to describe a certain statement as a tautology, as unconditionally true, may be to overlook the possibility that its truth may be dependent on certain conditions, including the logical system which perhaps in itself is a cultural product, as well as on certain other cultural conditions.

We have cited descriptions of arithmetical statements as tautologies, as unconditionally true, as true in all possible worlds. The question may be raised: Are arithmetical statements cultural products? Of interest here are studies (altogether too few) which anthropologists and psychologists have made of arithmetical concepts among primitive peoples. Consider, for example, Max Wertheimer's report (1938a) on number concepts among primitive peoples, which was discussed in Chapter 14. It is widely believed (at least in our culture) that the natural numbers constitute the simplest structural properties that can be abstracted from objects. For example, formalists are said to see in "mathematics the science of the structure of objects" and to consider that numbers "are the simplest structural properties of objects" (Black, 1934, p. 8). But a different point of view is suggested by some studies of the number concept among primitive peoples. Thus, Wertheimer's report suggests that our numbers may not be the simplest or the least abstract structural properties of objects. "There are structures [*Gebilde*] which, less abstract than our numbers, nevertheless . . . can be used in place of numbers. These structures do not abstract from their natural context and natural relationships" (1938a, p. 265). If mathematics is truly the science of the structure of objects, then the "science" of these structures that serve some primitive peoples as numbers could constitute a mathematics or at least an arithmetic. Consider some of the differences between such an arithmetic and our own.

"*Numbers* are applicable to anything and everything, to any arbitrary objects, arrangements, or groups, and they themselves are in all cases the same. *Structures*, on the other hand, are relevant only to natural groupings or relationships between parts and their whole" (p. 266).

Thus there are primitive people who will speak of two eyes or two warriors or a thumb and forefinger as pair structures or as pairs, but not of a man and horse, or of a mother and child, or of two mothers. Wertheimer notes that there is a certain kind of thinking in which concepts are not formed so as to function in an abstract logical operation, but are formed with regard to the concrete or biological relevance of the concepts. On the other hand, there are concepts which seem to be conceived in such a way that any one of them may appear in any operation of formal logic.

What we are trying to bring out here is that our way of thinking and our logic may itself influence our number concepts and our way of dealing with numbers. Can it be that the possible influence of our thinking and our logic are overlooked in saying that arithmetical statements are tautologies or analytic, that they are universally valid, unconditionally true, that their denial constitutes a logically impossible state of affairs, a state of affairs not imaginable by anyone, and so on? Perhaps those with a different way of thinking or with a different system of logic might think of arithmetical statements that are quite different than ours, not only of different number concepts but also of different operations with them. Even the conception of the genesis of numbers in terms of counting, which we seem to accept as natural and which is the intuitive notion underlying Peano's axioms and operations with the number series, is not the only factor that can give rise to numbers and to number series. To quote Wertheimer again:

Counting, for example, in the sense of repeated additions of unity does not constitute the only factor in the genesis of numbers. (p. 265)

Our numerical system is constructed . . . from the multiple application of one unique quantity. This is not, however, an absolute necessity, for cases may be cited where the various factors operative in the construction of number-analogues are also operative in determining numerical series. . . . The conditions and functions already discussed apply not only to the formation of quantitative structures but also to *operations* upon and with structures. This is shown in progressions towards larger structures analogous to those attained by our own abstract methods of addition and multiplication. Thus several specific structures combined together yield specific (not arbitrary) larger structures. Similarly with division. (p. 270)

The number-analogue tends to be related to material objects and their properties as do the results of operating with the number-analogues.

Even where higher numbers are reached by multiplicational operations, their relations to material objects nevertheless remain relevant. . . . Certain South Sea languages, for example, have different ways of counting fruit, money, animals, and men. . . . Different monetary materials are sometimes used for purchasing different articles, and indeed there are even cases where three non-exchangeable kinds of money exist side by side. (p. 270)

Division also, as well as counting, addition, and multiplication, is related to material objects and their properties. Thus, "the material itself is divisible only in such a way as to conform with its natural properties and natural requirements. Certain arrangements predetermine through their form *certain* divisions" (p. 270). Here we see that the distinction between arithmetical propositions and empirical objects is not drawn as sharply as it is in our culture.

In short, certain primitive people have "quantified structures," which serve the same ends as our numbers or can be used in place of our numbers and which, with some justification, may be referred to as number-analogues or even as numbers. Similarly, their operations with these numbers may be referred to as arithmetical operations and the system of their number concepts and operations as an arithmetic. Their arithmetical statements do not correspond to ours and yet are "true" or "valid" in their arithmetic and their logic. Moreover, the extent to which their number system is tied to material objects suggests that their arithmetical statements are more "synthetic" in the sense of being dependent on empirical data and in the sense of referring to the world of facts.

(Wertheimer used the previously cited examples in his lectures to demonstrate the need to develop a logic to represent Gestalt concepts. Grelling and Oppenheim (1938a, 1938b) have reported on a logic which attempts to deal with structures in the sense of *Gestalten*. Moreover, Grelling was developing these ideas when he was felled by the Nazi tyranny.)

Tautologies in the Natural Sciences

Are certain propositions of the natural sciences tautologies? It has been asserted that certain fundamental hypotheses of the natural sciences are incapable of being refuted by experimentation because they are true by definition. In challenging this assertion, Duhem (1953) notes that it was first stated by Milhaud (1896) in connection with chemistry, was then developed by Poincaré (1902) in reference to principles of mechanics, and was very clearly formulated by LeRoy (1901) in the following manner: "Certain fundamental hypotheses of physical theory cannot be contradicted by any experiment, because they constitute in reality *definitions*, and because certain expressions in the physicist's usage take their meanings only through them." One of the examples offered by LeRoy is the following: "When a heavy body falls freely, the acceleration of its fall is constant. Can such a law be contradicted by experiment? No, for it constitutes the very definition of what is meant by falling freely." He continues by noting that if, while studying the fall of a heavy body, physicists found that the body did not fall with uniform acceleration, they would conclude, not that the stated law is false, but that the body did not fall freely, that there were factors obstructing its motion. More generally, LeRoy concludes that "laws are not verifiable, taking things strictly . . . , because they constitute the very criterion by which we judge appearances as well as the methods that it would be necessary to utilize in order to submit them to an inquiry" (pp. 143–144).

Duhem doubts these contentions. Referring to the example, he notes that the words "free fall of a heavy body" have two distinct meanings: the common-sense meaning to the layman and the symbolic meaning in physical theory, where the words denote uniformly accelerated motion. There is approximate agreement between the two meanings. Physicists who study the fall of a heavy body and find it does not fall with uniform acceleration have various alternatives: (1) To declare that the fall studied was a free fall and to reject, not the observations, but the theoretical definition of "free fall." This would call for construction of new hypotheses and of a new system of mechanics in which the words "free fall" would not signify "uniformly accelerated motion" but "fall whose acceleration varies according to a certain law" (Duhem, 1953, p. 249); (2) A second alternative is to accept the theoretical definitions and to assume that errors in observation account for the discrepancy.

These two alternatives, Duhem points out, are available to the physicist whenever he is faced with a "disagreement between the concrete facts constituting an experiment and the symbolic representation which theory substitutes for this experiment" (p. 249). Generally, the physicist takes the second alternative rather than the first alternative which might call for changes in a vast theoretical system. In the particular example considered, the physicist would place his confidence in the theoretical formulation rather than in his observations. "But in this confidence accorded the law of fall of weights, we see nothing analogous to the certainty that a mathematical definition draws from its very essence, that is, to the kind of certainty we have when it would be foolish to doubt that the various points on a circumference [of a circle] are all equidistant from the center" (p. 249). The physicist is not forced to select the second alternative. What impels him to select it "is *not* logical necessity"; it might be awkward to choose the first alternative "but it would not be doing something logically absurd; he would not, for all that, be walking in the footsteps of the mathematician foolish enough to contradict his own definitions" (p. 250). Indeed, it may happen that by refusing to invoke errors in observation to reestablish agreement between observed facts and the theoretical scheme and instead drastically revising the theoretical hypotheses, the physicist may be laying the ground for a new and more comprehensive theory.

In summary, LeRoy asserts that certain fundamental hypotheses of physics cannot be verified or refuted by experiment, since they are, so to speak, "true by definition." Duhem denies this, pointing out that the hypotheses do not really constitute definitions, that their acceptance is not through logical necessity, that they are not independent of experimental findings, and that they can be changed through theoretical reformulation. As an example of a principle that was abandoned, Duhem gives the principle of the rectilinear propagation of light—the principle that light travels in straight lines.

> Was there, for instance, a clearer or more certain principle for thousands of years than this one: In a homogeneous medium, light is propagated in a straight line? Not only did this hypothesis carry all former Optics, Catoptrics, and Dioptrics . . . but it had become, so to speak, the physical definition of a straight line. It is to this hypothesis that any man wishing to make a straight line appeals, the carpenter who verifies the straightness of a piece of wood, the surveyor who lines up his sights, the geodetic surveyor who obtains a direction with the help of the pinholes of his alidade, the astronomer who defines the position of stars by the optical axis of his telescope. However, the day came when physicists tired of attributing to some cause of error the diffraction effects observed by Grimaldi, when they resolved to reject the law of the rectilinear propagation of light and to give Optics entirely new foundations; and this bold resolution was the signal of remarkable progress for physical theory. (1953, p. 250)

Toulmin (1960) also makes the point that experience may suggest the need to reject certain scientific principles and that such rejection would mean the overthrow, not just of the principle, but of the whole system in which it is the keystone. Interestingly enough, the principle of the rectilinear propagation of light, which the quotation from Duhem describes as one that physicist abandoned, happens to be offered by Toulmin as an illustration of a principle that physicists still adhere to and would be most unlikely to abandon.

> . . . the principle that light travels in straight lines seems to be almost indefeasible; certainly it is hard to imagine physicists abandoning completely the idea of light as something traveling in straight lines, for to give up this principle would involve abandoning geometrical optics as we know it. If we question the principle of rectilinear propagation, the whole subject is at stake; that is why the principle is not open to falsification in any straightforward way.
>
> It is not that, for physicists, the principle ceases to be empirical and becomes tautologous or conventionally true. They might, in circumstances sufficiently unlike the present one, decide to give it up entirely, but they would do so only if they were ready to *write off* geometrical optics as a whole. What the circumstances would have to be, in order for physicists to decide that the methods of geometrical optics were no longer any use, is something that is open to discussion, but this would clearly require changes in the world far more drastic than those which are needed to falsify any naive interpretation of "Light travels in straight lines," e.g., as an empirical generalization. (1960, pp. 83–84)

Thus, one writer tells us that the principle of the rectilinear propagation of light was abandoned, resulting in a new foundation for optics and bringing about remarkable progress in physical theory, whereas a later writer finds it hard to imagine that physicists would ever abandon it and tells us that this principle is still the keystone of optics and is most unlikely to be abandoned. Yet, note that Toulmin says that this does not make the principle lose its empirical character and become a tautology.

In summary, Duhem disagrees with LeRoy's contention that some scientific propositions or laws are tautologies. Claiming that they are not true by definition, that they are not independent of experimental findings, and that they can be abandoned or modified through theoretical formulation, he offers as an example of a principle that was rejected, the law of the rectilinear propagation of light. Ironically, another physicist, Toulmin, offers this as an example of a principle that physicists have not abandoned and would be hard pressed to reject. The question remains: Are certain scientific principles tautologies or not? We leave it to the reader to form his own opinion.

Conventionalism

One way of supposedly avoiding the problem of truth is to claim that the axioms which scientists accept are neither true nor false but simply conventions. Axioms are sometimes referred to as conventionally true, to indicate that it is only by convention that they are regarded as true. The physicist Henri Poincaré vigorously expounded conventionalism.

Poincaré held, for example, that whether physical space was to be considered to be Euclidean or non-Euclidean in nature was a matter of convention, and that it was convenient to preserve the convention that it was Euclidean, even at the cost of changing principles of physics. More generally, he held that scientists presuppose certain rules or laws, which may therefore be considered as a priori; but they are not a priori intuitions. Rather, they are conventions, and hence arbitrary in the sense that they could be changed. But why are certain rules selected? They are selected on the basis of the scientist's convenience and because they permit laws of nature to be given a simple formulation. And why is it necessary to have any a priori rules or laws? Because "for Poincaré, no observations can be made without presupposing certain laws; the facts of experience are meaningless unless interpreted in a presupposed space-time framework, and the best presuppositions are those that provide the simplest and most convenient interpretations" (Churchman, 1948, p. 139).

We already referred to Poincaré's view that it is convenient to consider space to be Euclidean in nature. His views on the question of time are illustrated by the following quotations drawn from a passage dealing with the notion of simultaneity.

> We do not have a direct intuition of simultaneity, no more a direct intuition of the equality of two durations. . . . We gain the idea of simultaneity by means of certain rules which we employ continuously without explaining why. . . . These rules are not forced on us and we can amuse ourselves by inventing others; however, we cannot deny the rules without complicating to a large extent the formulation of the laws of physics, of mechanics, of astronomy.
>
> We choose these rules, then, *not because they are true, but because they are the most convenient,* and we could sum them up by saying: "The simultaneity of two events, or the order of their succession, the equality of two durations, ought to be defined in such a manner that the formulation of the natural laws is as simple as possible. In other words, all these rules, all these definitions, are only the fruits of an unconscious opportunism." (Poincaré, 1913, p. 136)

The supposed a priori character of these laws has been criticized on the grounds that the meaning of simplicity and convenience, and the determination that given laws are simple and convenient, depend on other information and call for considerable scientific experience. "Hence, the verification of an a priori law on the basis of convenience must depend upon other information, and the a priori has lost its priority" (Churchman, 1948, p. 144).

Poincaré's brand of conventionalism may be criticized on other grounds, as we shall soon see. First, though, let us pause to note that conventionalism has its adherents not only in the physical sciences but also in mathematics. Some hold that not only the statements of geometry but those of all branches of mathematics, including arithmetic, constitute conventions. For example:

> We will say that the propositions of arithmetic are neither true nor false, but only compatible or non-compatible with certain conventions. . . . the basic laws of arithmetic are arbitrary assumptions . . . arithmetic is a calculus which starts only from certain conventions but floats as freely as the solar system and rests on nothing. . . . Only the convention is the ultimate. (Waismann, 1959, p. 121)

Waismann regards logic as another branch of mathematics, which starts not from any "truths" but only from certain conventions. He considers it inappropriate to characterize as true (or false) the propositions of any branch of mathematics, including logic and arithmetic. He is strongly opposed to the opinion that logic or mathematics consists of tautologies, in the sense of propositions which are true merely because of their form. The equation $2 + 2 = 4$, he notes, is not a tautology, but a direction or a rule "similar to a rule of moving in chess" (p. 119), a rule established by convention. The equation is a rule that serves as a transition between propositions, so that, given certain propositions, others can be formed. For example, from the proposition that I have 2 pennies in my left hand and 2 pennies in my right hand, I can conclude that I have 4 pennies in both hands. Thus, the equation is just a rule that can guide our behavior and with which we will comply or not. "If the equation were a tautology, all this would be impossible. For what should it mean to comply with or to infringe a tautology?" (p. 120).

There are several points of interest. For one thing, note the distinction that is drawn between a tautology and a rule established by convention. The term *tautology* has been applied (perhaps misapplied) to statements that are "true by definition," such as the statement that there are three feet in a yard. In fact, in support of the opinion that $2 + 2 = 4$ is a tautology the argument is often raised that the statement that $2 + 2 = 4$ is true by definition, by virtue of the definitions of addition of natural number, either explicit definitions or the implicit ones involved in an axiomatic development. If a statement is true by definition, what determines the definition? This question, too often left unanswered, has been answered in terms of conventionalism. Definitions are conventions. Hence a statement that is true by definition may be regarded as true by convention. In short, it seems to us that the thesis that the propositions of a discipline are true by definition need not differ essentially from the thesis that they are regarded as true by convention. Further evidence of similarity between the two is the fact that in a formal system it is often a relatively simple matter to interchange the roles of definitions and postulates so that what was "true by definition" becomes "true by convention" or vice versa.

It is also of interest to note how closely this view of mathematical propositions parallels the view of propositions of the natural sciences held by Moritz Schlick, who wrote that they are not "propositions which are true or false but rather set forth instructions for the formation of such propositions . . . [being] directions, rules of behavior, for the investigator to find his way about in reality" (cited in Toulmin, 1960, pp. 91–92). This illustrates once more how difficult it is to differentiate conceptions of mathematical propositions from conceptions of physical propositions.

Recall also the similarity that Waismann indicated between the arithmetical equation and a rule of chess. It is just such a thesis—that the axioms and principles of science and mathematics are but arbitrary rules of a game—that is distressing to some scientists and mathematicians. For example:

> A serious threat to the very life of science is implied in the assertion that mathematics is nothing but a system of conclusions drawn from definitions and postulates that must be consistent but otherwise may be created by the free will of the mathematician. If this description were accurate, mathematics could not attract any intelligent person. It would be a game with definitions, rules, and syllogisms, without motive or goal. The notion that the intellect can create meaningful postulational systems at its whim is a deceptive half-truth. Only under the discipline of responsibility to the organic whole, only guided by intrinsic necessity, can the free mind achieve results of scientific value. (Courant and Robbins, 1941, p. xvii)

Often associated with conventionalism (but not necessarily intrinsic to it) is a lack of concern with the problem of truth as well as the belief that conventionalism somehow eliminates this problem. Criticizing this viewpoint, Churchman wrote that "it is assumed that if a given proposition can be designated as a 'convention' of the science, then one has automatically removed all problems concerning its truth . . . the scientist should always beware of basing truth on convention, beware, that is, of using a definition to resolve a problem" (1948, pp. 143–144). For to say that scientific propositions are conventions neither removes nor answers the problem of truth (see Schlick, 1953). Poincaré asserted that scientists choose certain rules not because they are true but because they are convenient. However, he did not define *convenience* other than in terms of simplicity of formulation of rules, which is itself in need of definition. What are the criteria of convenience and of simplicity in scientific work? One might say that all natural laws are determined by Superman or that they are all expressed by the equation $e^0 = 1$. But what would be the value of such formulations? Given various formulations of natural laws, would the scientist not prefer the one that most comprehensively fits experimental and other empirical findings and that allows for more and better predictions that are confirmed by experience? Would such factors not be used in determining the convenience and simplicity of the rules and in assessing the scientist's search for truth? Thus, criteria and methods used to ascertain convenience and simplicity may be the very ones used in ascertaining the effectiveness of the search for truth (see Churchman, 1948, p. 140). But then where is the borderline between truth or a search for truth, on the one hand, and convention, based on convenience and simplicity, on the other?

Even if some or all laws of nature are not appropriately described by such terms as true or false or by such terms as probable or improbable, this is not by itself incompatible with scientists engaging in a search for truth. As Toulmin words it:

> Suppose one says that laws of nature are not true, false, or probable; that these terms are indeed not even applicable to them; and that scientists are accordingly not interested in the question of the "truth" of laws of nature—all of which might fairly be said; one does not thereby deny the obvious, namely, that scientists search for the truth. (1960, p. 79)

Incidentally, Toulmin considers that laws of nature or physical principles resemble other kinds of laws, rules, and regulations in that they are not themselves true or false, although statements about their range of application can be true or false. Rather than asking of an hypothesis or of a law, "Is it true?" he suggests that at least in some cases it may be more appropriate to ask, "When does it hold?" Nonetheless, Toulmin points out that to consider that laws of nature are neither true nor false does not force one to conclude that they are true by convention or that they are tautologies.

Conventionalism, as an explanation of how axioms of scientific systems are selected, does not explain enough. Granted momentarily that scientists (including mathematicians) are free to select their axioms, so that the axioms are conventions, why is it that certain axioms are selected rather than others? Why is it that axioms and even whole theories are sometimes altered or rejected? Conventionalism does not tell what the requirements are for axioms, why some axioms are more suitable (or more "convenient") than others. In particular, conventionalism does not stipulate that axioms and the consequences derived from them are of value in the natural sciences to the extent to which they fit certain facts or experiences and allow for verifiable predictions. One can accept conventionalism, in the sense of recognizing that scientists are free to select axioms, and yet at the same time recognize that the problem of truth or of the "fittingness" of the axioms has (or is still) to be faced. This opinion is clearly illustrated in Einstein's writings.

> The essential thing [in science] is the aim to represent the multitude of concepts and theorems, close to experience, as theorems, logically deduced and belonging to a basis, as narrow as possible, of fundamental concepts and fundamental relations which themselves can be chosen freely (axioms). The liberty of choice, however, is of a special kind; it is not in any way similar to the liberty of a writer of fiction. Rather, it is similar to that of a man engaged in solving a well-designed word puzzle. He may, it is true, propose any word as the solution; but there is only *one* word which really solves the puzzle in all its forms. (1950, p. 64)

Similarly, Einstein is quoted by Wertheimer as saying that scientists are entirely free in choosing axioms but that the "only virtue of axioms is to furnish fundamental propositions from which one can derive conclusions that fit the facts" (Wertheimer, 1945, p. 179).

Speaking of the diverse directions taken in the search for theoretical foundations for physics, Einstein wrote: "It is open to every man to choose the direction of his striving; and also every man may draw comfort from Lessing's fine saying, that the search for truth is more precious than its possession" (p. 110).

Even in discussing principles of ethics, Einstein advanced a similar thesis, recognizing axioms as arbitrary and yet as having to stand the "truth-test" of experience:

> For pure logic all axioms are arbitrary, including the axioms of ethics. But they are by no means arbitrary from a psychological and genetic point of view. . . .
> It is the privilege of man's moral genius . . . to advance ethical axioms which are so comprehensive and so well founded that men will accept them as grounded in the vast mass of their individual emotional experiences. Ethical axioms are found and tested not very differently from the axioms of science. Truth is what stands the test of experience. (Einstein, 1950, p. 115)

Note how similar the intent of this passage from Einstein is to what the "great conventionalist" himself, Henri Poincaré, wrote: "Experiment is the sole source of truth" (1913, p. 131).

In mathematics, too, there are those who believe that unless axioms are selected with an eye to truth, with an eye to their relationship to some reality or actuality outside of mathematics, mathematics becomes but a meaningless game (see Kleene, 1952, p. 41). For example, intuitionists do not regard axioms as conventions. When a spokesman for classical mathematics asks whether or not intuitionism accepts Peano's axioms, the reply is: "While you think in terms of axioms and deductions, we think in terms of evidence; that makes all the difference. I do not accept any axioms which I might reject if I chose to do so" (Heyting, 1956, p. 13). In other words, axioms are required by the evidence rather than being arbitrary conventions.

In summary, we have seen that there are different points of view with regard to whether or not scientific and mathematical axioms are conventions. Conventionalism may be correct that there is freedom of choice in selection of axioms or principles and that by themselves these have nothing to do with truth or falsehood. But the test of the value to science or mathematics of these principles and of the system into which they are incorporated, may call for concern with experience or other "actuality" outside of the system. It may call for study of the extent to which the axioms "fit" or are true for these experiences or for this "actuality" or "reality." And one may undertake such study without having to decide whether or not to embrace phenomenalism or realism or another philosophy concerning the nature of experience or reality (see Braithwaite, 1960; Burt, 1963).

Other Conceptions of Mathematical Truth

Let us now continue our discussion of the diverse conceptions of mathematical truth. It is sometimes said that until the nineteenth century mathematical axioms were regarded as empirical propositions, whereas in the twentieth century they are no longer so regarded. Such a summary is an overgeneralization on two distinct grounds: firstly, from ancient times there have been men who distinguished between mathematical and empirical propositions; secondly, even today some mathematicians and philosophers do not regard mathematical propositions as basically different from empirical propositions. The logician Charles Sanders Peirce wrote:

> For all modern mathematicians agree with Plato and Aristotle that mathematics deals exclusively with hypothetical states of things, and asserts no matter of fact whatever; and further, that it is thus alone that the necessity of its conclusions is to be explained. . . . Mathematics is the study of what is true of hypothetical states of things. That is its essence and definition. (1933, p. 191)

That mathematicians ever agreed on the nature of mathematics is very doubtful; that modern mathematicians agree at present on the nature of mathematics is certainly not the case. But, that the writings of even the ancient philosophers may be interpreted as supporting a distinction between mathematical and empirical truths is of interest, since this distinction is, at times, traced back only as far as the time of the philosopher, David Hume (1711–1776), who emphatically differentiated between mathematical and empirical propositions.

Distinctions among propositions

A distinction drawn between the propositions of logic and mathematics on the one hand, and the propositions of the empirical sciences (such as chemistry, physics, psychology) on the other hand, is sometimes worded as follows. The propositions of logic and mathematics are logically necessary in the sense that their truth is independent of facts or of experience. In contrast, the propositions of the empirical sciences are logically contingent in the sense that experience is relevant to their truth or falsity; in other words, their truth is contingent on certain conditions that happen to prevail, their truth "is contingent upon what the universe happens to be like" (Hospers, 1953, p. 104). Hence, mathematical and logical propositions are often described as logically necessary truths, as unconditional truths, or as absolutely certain, whereas propositions of the empirical sciences are described as logically contingent or as conditional truths. This has been regarded as the chief distinction between the propositions of mathematics (and logic) and those of the empirical sciences. To cite a few examples:

> The irreducible difference between the propositions of logic and mathematics and those of a natural science are that the former are logically necessary and the latter logically contingent. (Braithwaite, 1960, p. 353)
> The most distinctive characteristic which differentiates mathematics from the various branches of empirical science, and which accounts for its fame as the queen of the sciences, is no doubt the peculiar certainty and necessity of its results. No proposition in even the most advanced parts of empirical science can ever attain this status. (Hempel, 1949, p. 238)
> [The statements of arithmetic] are fundamentally different from those of the natural sciences. The statements of arithmetic are *necessary* (truths), while those of the sciences are not. They would hold true in all possible worlds, the laws of the sciences need not do so at all. (Hospers, 1953, p. 110)

Quite varied terminology is employed in the differentiation of mathematical and logical propositions from those of the empirical sciences. In addition to or in lieu of referring to the former as logically necessary (or as necessary truths or as necessary statements) some writers refer to them as analytic, or tautologous, as true by definition, and so on. In contrast, they refer to statements of the empirical sciences as nontautologous, as nonanalytic, or as synthetic, as not true by definition, and so on. Without becoming bogged down in a mire of terminological variety, we point to two grounds which seem to underlie the various distinctions, regardless of the particular semantic guise they assume.

1. Mathematical propositions do not require empirical or experimental evidence for their verification.
2. Mathematical propositions are empty of factual content and do not refer to matters of fact.

In contrast, propositions of the empirical sciences are frequently considered to require empirical or experimental evidence for their verification and to convey information, to have factual content, to refer to matters of fact.

It is property 1 that seems to underlie the notion that mathematical propositions are logically necessary, whereas propositions of the empirical sciences are logically contingent. Whether it is property 2 that leads to property 1 or vice versa is not of concern here. Certainly property 2 has frequently been attributed to mathematical propositions. For example: "The propositions of mathematics are devoid of factual content; they convey no information whatever on any empirical subject matter" (Hempel, 1953, p. 159).

The distinction is often drawn in terms of the analytic-synthetic dichotomy. It is a basic tenet of logical positivism that propositions of logic and mathematics are analytic (or tautological in the sense of verbally self-evident), whereas those of the empirical sciences are synthetic (Bergmann, 1954). Moreover, logical positivists hold that if a proposition is neither analytic nor synthetic it is perforce meaningless. Convinced that the statements often made in traditional epistemology, metaphysics, and ethics are neither analytic nor synthetic, logical positivists have shrugged them off as cognitively meaningless, as nonsense, as having no sense, and as not of proper concern either for science or for the philosophy of science. Rudolph Carnap, a leader of contemporary logical positivists, wrote:

> Metaphysical propositions are neither true nor false, because they assert nothing, they contain neither knowledge nor error, they lie completely outside the field of knowledge, of theory, outside the discussion of truth or falsehood. . . . The danger lies in the *deceptive* character of metaphysics [as compared to the arts]; it gives the illusion of knowledge without actually giving any knowledge. This is the reason why we reject it. (Carnap, 1935, pp. 29–31)

In their rejection of metaphysical propositions, logical positivists are following Hume. Carnap acknowledged the debt to Hume in the following words:

> The opinion that metaphysical propositions have no sense because they do not concern any facts, has already been expressed by *Hume*. He writes in the last chapter of his "Enquiry Concerning Human Understanding" (published in the year 1748) as follows: "It seems to me, that the only objects of the abstract sciences or of demonstration, are quantity and number. . . . All other enquiries of men regard only matter of fact and existence; and these are evidently incapable of demonstration. . . . When we run over libraries, persuaded of these principles, what havoc must we make? If we take in our hand any volume, of divinity or school metaphysics, for instance; let us ask, Does it contain any abstract reasoning concerning quantity or number? No. Does it contain any experimental reasoning concerning matter of fact and existence? No. Commit it then to the flames: for it can contain nothing but sophistry and illusion." We agree with this view of Hume, which says—translated into our terminology—that only the propositions of mathematics and empirical science have sense, and that all other propositions are without sense. (Carnap, 1935, pp. 35–36)

Parenthetically, we note that on the basis of Hume's criterion, which Carnap said he accepted, some modern mathematical volumes (for example, on abstract set theory and on topology) would have to be committed to the flames, since they do not necessarily contain abstract reasoning concerning quantity or number.

What about the propositions of the philosophy of science and in particular, those of logical analysis? Carnap recognized that the objection may be raised that his own writings "would be without sense, for they are neither mathematical nor empirical, that is, verifiable by experience" (p.

224). He tried to overcome this objection. In this respect he differs from a predecessor, Wittgenstein, who, in his *Tractatus Logico-Philosophicus* of 1922, developed the thesis that metaphysical propositions are without sense and agreed that his own propositions, as all his writings of philosophy, are senseless (Wittgenstein, 1961, p. 189). (For a diverging opinion see Weinberg, 1960.)

The logical positivists have been severely criticized. Consider, for example, Hill's evaluation:

> . . . the pure Logical Positivists' position in ethics really amounts to a very unempirical rejection of the data that moral philosophy should explain. . . . so complete and astonishing a denial of so large a segment of what has every appearance of being one of the most rational parts of man's life and one of the sanest aspects of his discourse is such a radical break with that very human experience to which the Logical Positivists appeal that, if it is to be sustained, the evidence must be overwhelmingly convincing. But the evidence presented by the Logical Positivists has no such convincing character.
>
> In the first place, the Logical Positivists' criteria of meaningful statements— that they must be either tautologies or else verifiable in terms of sense experience—are useful for certain purely scientific purposes but, when applied to all statements whatever, are arbitrary and so unduly restrictive as to exclude along with moral judgments many other statements that seem to most men to be significant. The purpose for which the Logical Positivists propose their tests of significant statements, that of preventing undue interference of moral, metaphysical, and sentimental considerations in the work of exact science, is, to be sure, commendable enough. However, since exact science may be protected equally well by insisting only that the judgments of such science be verified by the methods in question, without insisting that all statements that do not conform to these methods are nonsense, this worthy purpose provides no adequate justification for the demand that the criteria of verifiability in terms of tautology or sense experience be applied to all statements. Indeed, to insist upon such universal applicability of these tests is an infringement of strict science upon other legitimate kinds of inquiry which is quite as objectionable as the infringement of these other inquiries upon exact science. (1950, p. 27)

It seems to us of interest to contrast Carnap's rejection of metaphysical propositions with his plea for a principle of tolerance (1937, p. 51). Should the principle of tolerance be extended to propositions other than those of mathematics, logic, and the empirical sciences? Some psychologists have pointed out that the strictures of logical positivism have a flavor of dogmatic dictates rather than of scientific tolerance (Burt, 1960, 1963). (See Weinberg, 1960, for a critical evaluation of logical positivism.)

Pure and applied mathematics

Mathematics is sometimes regarded as consisting only of so-called pure mathematics, while applied mathematics is viewed as part of the empirical sciences. However, the term *mathematics* is sometimes so construed that it covers both pure and applied mathematics. From the latter point of view, the distinction may be made that mathematics, in the sense of pure mathematics, gives no information about the world, that it does not refer to reality, and that it consists of statements that are universally valid, which are necessary, unconditional truths. On the other hand, mathematics, in the sense of applied mathematics, may refer to matters of fact or reality and consist of conditional truths or probabilities. For example, pure geometry says nothing about reality; applied geometry, where the undefined terms such as *point* and *line* are interpreted so as to be correlated with aspects of physical or experiential reality, may be related to matters of fact. But the axioms of geometry are only approximately satisfied in such concrete interpretations. For example, if *point* is interpreted to be a dot on the blackboard and *line* a streak on the blackboard, then it is possible to have more than one line through two points. Since the axioms are only approximately satisfied, the theorems of geometry are at best approximately true when applied to the world of reality. Hence, it has been said that the statements of pure geometry are absolute and certain truths, whereas those of applied geometry are only approximately true or are probability statements. It has also been said that the statements of pure geometry may be considered to be true by definition (with the postulates regarded as offering implicit definitions of the undefined terms), whereas the statements of applied geometry are true or probable only to the extent to which they fit or are confirmed by empirical facts. Many controversial discussions about geometry and geometric truths have been said to "confound issues concerning matters of *empirical fact* with issues regarding matters of *definition*" (Nagel, 1961, p. 217). In particular, it has been charged that pure and applied geometry seem to be confounded in Newton's view of geometry as a branch of the empirical science of mechanics, in Leibniz's view of geometric truths as innate, and in Kant's view of Euclid's geometry as a formulation of our a priori intuitions of the structure of space.

In short, the absolute certainty of the statements of pure geometry is not characteristic of the statements of applied geometry. More generally, what has been called the *characteristic certainty* of mathematics is limited to pure mathematics and is not characteristic of applied mathematics in which mathematics and reality are related. To quote an often-cited remark by Einstein: "As far as the laws of mathematics refer to reality, they are not certain; and as far as they are certain, they do not refer to reality."

Validity and truth

Some mathematicians prefer the concept of validity to that of truth. They are concerned with whether a statement in a mathematical system is valid in the sense that it is derivable from the axioms through valid (logically correct) reasoning. They are not concerned with whether the statement is true. In fact, they may not admit that the problem of truth is a matter of concern to the mathematician *qua* mathematician. The problem of truth they leave to the speculative philosophers and the problem of approximate truth, as to whether systems of mathematics can be interpreted as approximate models of reality, they leave to physicists and other empirical scientists. In short, they are concerned only with the statements of pure mathematics which they describe as logically valid or universally valid.

But does the use of the concept of validity really eliminate the problem of truth? It seems to us that it does not, since the concept of logical validity or universal validity is usually defined in terms of the notion of truth. There were examples of this in the beginning of this chapter and many others could be cited. Hence, it may be an illusion to think that one has dispensed with the notion of truth in mathematics simply by replacing it with the notion of validity since the latter, in turn, is usually linked, explicitly or implicitly, with the notion of truth.

Pure mathematics as a branch of empirical knowledge

The view of John Stuart Mill that mathematics is an empirical science has never entirely disappeared from the mathematical scene. That it is still alive in recent years is illustrated by Mostowski's belief that "the source and ultimate *raison d'être* of the notion of number, both natural and real, is experience and practical applicability" (Mostowski et al., 1955, p. 16). It is also illustrated in the conviction, held by the psychologist Rignano (1928) and others, that all mathematics is the performance of imagined experiments, with the mental performance recorded and represented in symbols which we call *mathematical symbols*. Whatever may be the shortcomings of such views, they are presented here to illustrate that even in conceptions of mathematics held in the twentieth century, mathematical propositions are not always sharply differentiated from empirical propositions.

There is still another way in which attempts are made to weaken the boundary between mathematics and empirical sciences. Rather than claiming that mathematics is an empirical science, there are some who claim that the empirical sciences are less empirical and more mathematical and formal than is usually recognized. This viewpoint is given forceful expression by Quine (1951b).

Those who refuse to draw a sharp distinction between mathematical propositions and empirical propositions may object to the differentiation between the *absolute truth* or *absolute certainty* of (pure) mathematics, on the one hand, and the *approximate truth* or *conditional truth* of the empirical sciences. Some regard the difference to be a matter of degree rather than quality or kind. They hold that the propositions of mathematics may be better confirmed by experience, but that their truth does not differ in kind from that of the empirical propositions.

That mathematics is not really independent of the world of experience is a view which finds expression in any conception of mathematics that recognizes the psychological and sociological factors that influence it. To the extent that such factors are also regarded as influencing the empirical sciences, there is again a weakening of the distinctions between them. That there is a psychological foundation for mathematics and the empirical sciences is suggested in the writings of Ernst Mach (1838–1916), and of G. Heymans (1857–1930). In Chapters 12 and 14, we noted that Brouwer also stresses the psychological and sociological factors that influence the communication and exposition of mathematics. The school of philosophical analysis known as *Significs* holds that *mathematical thought* is itself partly linguistic in nature, and hence is subject to the psychological forces that influence language. Significs tends to view language as an emotionally charged tool which men use to influence others. The meaning of language is considered to depend on the purpose for which it is used. Some members of the school of Significs, including Mannoury (1934, 1947), hold that even mathematical language has, to some extent, an emotional, purposeful character. Discussing such views, Fraenkel and Bar-Hillel wrote that Mannoury maintains that not even in the symbolic language of mathematics

> is the subjective, persuasive, emotional character of language altogether lacking. A mathematical formula would then, not have a meaning *per se* but according to the purpose for which it is used. . . . The emotional and psychological moment, and this alone, is apt to explain the choice of principles (axioms) underlying mathematics and is still more perceptible in mathematical models of the external world as constructed in theoretical physics. Yet, even Mannoury admits that the assertions of mathematics are independent of sentiments of like and dislike to a higher degree than those of any other science. (1958, p. 207)

Here, again, the difference between mathematical and empirical proposition is regarded as one of degree rather than of kind.

Ontology and mathematics

There are diverse metaphysical or ontological views with regard to the reality to which mathematical propositions refer and with regard to the nature of existence of mathematical entities. A survey and thought-provoking discussion of ontological views of mathematics are presented by Fraenkel and Bar-Hillel (1958, pp. 332–347). We can only touch on some of these views. There is an ontological viewpoint, sometimes called *empirical realism,* which considers that the world with which pure mathematics deals is as real as the world with which, say, zoologists or physicists deal, and that at least some mathematical entities exist in about the same sense in which animals or atoms exist. There are members of this school who hold that natural numbers and arithmetic exist in about the sense that animals do, and others who go even further and agree with Mostowski (1955) that this is the case even for sets and set theories.

It is somewhat ironical that at one time Bertrand Russell expressed a similar view with reference to logic, stating: "Logic is concerned with the real world just as truly as zoology, though with its more abstract and general features" (see Fraenkel and Bar-Hillel, 1958, p. 345n). He soon changed this outlook to one that sees logic (and mathematics too, of course) as not concerned with the world of existence. Russell (1918, p. 156) has characterized the world of existence as containing all thoughts and feelings, and as being "fleeting, vague," without sharp boundaries, and without clear plan or arrangement; he has contrasted the world of existence with the "world" with which logicians and mathematicians deal where everything is "unchangeable, rigid, exact, delightful to the mathematician, the logician, the builder of metaphysical systems, and all who love perfection more than life." This last point of view has been interpreted as indicative of a kind of modern Platonism (Ogden and Richards, 1923, p. 30).

Platonic and quasi-Platonic ideas (or ideals) seem to have influenced a number of modern mathematicians. There is a viewpoint, sometimes described as Platonic realism, which considers that numbers and their arithmetic exist not as empirical entities but as Platonic ideals. Since there are also Platonic conceptions of the world of reality—in which, for example men and animals and atoms are regarded as existing as Platonic ideals—this Platonic view is again one that is not incompatible with a basic similarity between mathematical and empirical entities and propositions. There is also a viewpoint, which may be called *quasi*-Platonic, that seems to conceive of mathematics as dealing with entities that are somewhere between empirical entities and Platonic ideals.

It is of course not easy to pigeonhole any given individual into any one of these ontological classifications. For example, Kurt Gödel has been called a quasi-Platonist and yet his ideas may be interpreted as in line with the Platonic or the empirical-realist outlook. Gödel wrote, with reference to objects such as classes and concepts, "that the assumption of such objects is quite as legitimate as the assumption of physical bodies and there is quite as much reason to believe in their existence" (1944, p. 137). Similarly, Gödel considered that the concepts and axioms of set theory describe some well-determined reality and that, in this reality, any given conjecture about sets must be either true or false. That a certain famous conjecture (Cantor's conjecture of the generalized continuum hypothesis) cannot be shown to be either true or false on the basis of known axioms of set theory—a result established by Gödel—is interpreted by him to indicate that the known axioms of set theory do not completely or adequately characterize the aforementioned reality.

In short, even this cursory sketch suffices to show that there are some metaphysical or ontological views that do not draw a clear-cut distinction between mathematical and empirical statements or between the reality with which pure mathematics is concerned and the reality with which the empirical sciences are concerned.

The question might be raised: Are there any mathematical or metamathematical theorems that support certain philosophical or ontological views of mathematics at the expense of others? Attempts have been made to interpret in this way some metamathematical theorems, such as Gödel's incompletability theorem. Attempts of this nature, with regard to Gödel's theorem, have been criticized by Myhill (1952). Fraenkel and Bar-Hillel (1958, pp. 109, 344) do not believe that any of the attempts to exploit metamathematical findings to support one or another philosophy of mathematics has been successful. They conclude:

> On the contrary, we believe it to be unlikely that any new mathematical or metamathematical results will ever definitely refute any ontological standpoint, though they might conceivably have some influence on the readiness to adopt such a standpoint, for reasons which are extra-rational. Should one want to go on from here and conclude that all ontological views on mathematics, since irrefutable, are thereby also irrelevant for mathematics, though not necessarily for mathematicians, we see no good reasons against such a conclusion. (pp. 344–345)

CHAPTER 17

Reductionism
and Related Issues

Reductionism is a term that has been applied to two related approaches to research and theory. One approach attempts to explain a complex whole in terms of its parts or elements. The second approach attempts to "reduce" the concepts and propositions of one science or discipline to those of another discipline, for example, the logicists' attempts to reduce mathematics to logic. The history of science offers examples of both approaches as well as controversies over reductionism. This chapter is devoted to discussions of the approaches to reductionism and to issues involved in the controversies.

Atomism versus Holism

Reductionism has been characterized as involving "the attempt to explain a complex interrelated whole in terms of its simpler elements or parts or in terms of elements belonging to a lower level of phenomena" (Sloane, 1945, p. 217). In all sciences there are theorists who set this as the goal of their science. It is therefore not surprising that some psychologists, too, consider it desirable or essential that a scientific explanation of a psychological phenomenon should reduce it to its simpler elements or parts. But other psychologists have protested that such a reduction may overlook important characteristics and aspects of the phenomenon. This dispute is related to what has been called the *atomistic versus holistic controversy*, or the *microscopic versus macroscopic controversy*.

Gestalt psychology is generally regarded as representing an holistic approach and opposing an atomistic approach. It is probably well known that Gestalt psychology was launched largely as a protest against the prevailing belief that science called for the reduction of a complex into components and for study of these parts. For example, in 1922 Wertheimer questioned the prevailing hypothesis that "scientific comprehension of a mental phenomenon required the discovery of its 'elements' and then, by laws applicable to these elements, a reconstruction of the phenomenon" (1938c, p. 12). He criticized the hypothesis that "every 'complex' consists of a sum of elementary contents or pieces (e.g., sensations)" (p. 12). In contrast to these hypotheses Wertheimer held:

> Only rarely, only under certain characteristic conditions, only within very narrow limits and perhaps never more than approximately do we find purely summative relationships. It is inappropriate to treat so special a case as typical of all mental events. (p. 13)
> The given is itself in varying degrees "structured" ("Gestalted"), it consists of more or less definitely structured wholes and whole-processes with their whole-properties and laws, characteristic whole-tendencies and whole-determination of parts. . . . we are dealing here with wholes and whole-processes possessed of specific inner, intrinsic laws; we are considering structures with their concrete structural principles. (pp. 14–15)

Instead of the prevailing approach to science, Gestalt psychology proposed a different approach or "formula," as expounded by Wertheimer in 1925:

> It has long seemed obvious—and is in fact, the characteristic tone of European science—that "science" means breaking up complexes into their component elements. Isolate the elements, discover their laws, then reassemble them, and the problem is solved. All wholes are reduced to pieces and piecewise relations between pieces.
> The fundamental "formula" of Gestalt theory might be expressed in this way: There are wholes, the behavior of which is not determined by that of their individual elements, but where the part-processes are themselves determined by the intrinsic nature of the whole. It is the hope of Gestalt theory to determine the nature of such wholes.
> With a formula such as this, one might close, for Gestalt theory is neither more nor less than this. (1938d, p. 2)

Implicit in the above quotations from Wertheimer is the distinction between a Gestalt and an and-summation which is nothing more than the sum of its parts. It is also instructive here to refer to Köhler's remarks. He wrote: "When spatial, visual, auditory, and intellectual processes are such as to display properties other than could be derived from the parts in summation, they may be regarded as unities illustrating what we mean by the word 'Gestalten'" (1938b, p. 17). Köhler wrote that a summation (sum or and-summation) "is that kind of togetherness from which any one or more units may be removed without any effect either on the ones remaining or on the ones removed" (p. 25). A summation also has the property that its constituents (parts or pieces) "may be added together one after another without thereby causing any alteration in any of them" (p. 25).

In summary, the fundamental question, Wertheimer saw, could be simply stated: "Are the parts of a given whole determined by the inner structure of that whole, or are the events such that, as independent, piecemeal, fortuitous and blind the total activity is a sum of the part-activity?" (1938d, p. 7). The answer given by Gestalt theory was that while there are some wholes of the latter type (and-summations), others are of the former type (Gestalten), and these cannot be adequately understood by arbitrarily dividing or reducing them to parts and then combining what is learned about the parts.

A melody is an example of a Gestalt. Wertheimer wrote: "Is it really true that when I hear a melody I have a *sum* of individual tones (pieces) which constitute the primary foundation of my experience? . . . What I really have, what I hear of each individual note . . . is a *part* which is itself determined by the character of the whole" (p. 5). Experiments on threshold phenomena reveal, for example, that "when I see two colors the sensations I have are determined by the whole-conditions of the entire stimulus situation" (p. 5). Indeed, experiments, mainly on vision, suggest that "perhaps any part depends upon the particular whole in which it occurs" (p. 5). Physiological theory requires "the assumption of whole processes . . . cells of an organism are *parts* of the whole and excitations occurring in them are thus to be viewed as part-processes functionally related to whole-processes of the entire organism" (Wertheimer, 1938c, p. 15). Similarly, Köhler wrote that organic functions participate in and exhibit "essentially Gestalt characteristics" so that "central physiological processes cannot be regarded as sums of individual excitations, but as configured whole-processes" (1938b, p. 18). Köhler also gave examples of physical Gestalten, whole-phenomena which occur in physics. A physical system reaches a state independent of time (a so-called stationary state or state of equilibrium) when the system as a whole satisfies a certain condition, for example, that the potential energy is a minimum. "The state or process at any place therefore depends in principle on the conditions obtaining in all other parts of the system" (p. 19). If "laws of equilibrium or stationary states for the individual parts can be formulated separately, then these parts do not together constitute a *single* physical system, but each part is a system in itself" (p. 19). Indeed, what is characteristic of a physical system is that "the conditions prevailing at any given point are determined by those obtaining in all the other parts" (p. 19). Consequently an attempt to derive a law of the physical system "additively from parts of a system would necessarily fail. The law of the system prescribes what must take place in the parts, not the reverse" (p. 27).

The above should not be taken to mean that in dealing with Gestalten, Gestalt theory is opposed to reduction or analysis of the whole into parts or that it regards the parts as insignificant or that it insists that only the whole and not the parts be studied. Köhler pointed out: "The concept of parts, of summations, etc., do not lose their important significance when we deal with Gestalt phenomena. One must be clear, however, about *what* it is to which the concepts are applied" (1938b, p. 31). Wertheimer wrote that "elements" in Gestalten "are determined as parts by the intrinsic conditions of their wholes and are to be understood, 'as parts' relative to such wholes" (1938c, p. 15). As Wertheimer phrased it:

> *"Pieces"* almost always appear *"as parts"* in whole processes. . . . To sever a *"part"* from the organized whole in which it occurs—whether it itself be a subsidiary whole or an *"element"*—is a very real process usually involving alterations in that *"part."* Modifications of a part frequently involve changes elsewhere in the whole itself. Nor is the nature of these alterations arbitrary, for they *too* are determined by whole-conditions. . . . The role played here by the parts is one *of* "parts" genuinely *"participating"*—not of extraneous, independent and-units. (p. 14)

Study of wholes and parts

Gestalt theory does not object to the study of pieces or parts; what *"is* repudiated is the piecewise handling of psychological data" (p. 15), where pieces are viewed as independent parts and their processes are treated from a "purely summative" point of view rather than as "part-processes functionally related to whole-processes" (p. 15). Although Gestalt psychology is not opposed to analysis of a whole into parts, it holds that not just any division into parts is suitable for comprehension of the parts of the whole. As Wertheimer put it: "the comprehension of whole-properties and whole-conditions *must* precede consideration of the real significance of parts" (p. 15). Hence Wertheimer advocated a method of analysis "from above," from the whole to the parts, rather than a procedure "from below upwards," from the parts to the whole (p. 15). A method "from below" may lead to arbitrarily reducing a complex to parts and may lead to descriptions and explanations based on and-summations of the findings resulting from study of the parts in isolation.

One objection to reductionism is that it does violence to the whole to reduce it to parts. But a method "from above" can be used to analyze a whole and to study its parts, without "violating" the whole. Such a method can lead to comprehension of whole-properties and to awareness of the "natural" parts of the whole and of the roles these parts play. In short, the method "from above" is not restricted to study of the whole but may involve analysis of the whole into parts and study of the parts.

It is of interest that Gestalt theory is opposed to an extreme holistic doctrine. The holistic doctrine might be described as follows: A whole is itself part of a larger whole, which in turn is part of a larger whole, and so on; since only wholes and not parts must be studied, in order to study any complex it is necessary to study the whole universe. This extreme viewpoint is also related to the doctrine of universal interaction, which maintains that since everything interacts with everything else, to study any one object or system it is necessary to study the whole universe. Köhler criticized both this position and the other extreme, that everything is an and-summation, when he wrote:

> *One* point of view would be that nature is composed of independent elements whose purely additive total constitutes reality. *Another* that there are no such elements in nature, that all states and processes are real in a vast universal whole, and hence that all "parts" are but products of abstraction. The first proposition is completely wrong; the second hinders comprehension of the Gestalt principle more than it helps. . . . The hypothesis of universal interaction [gives] a picture of nature that is completely misleading. . . . The doctrine appears to be a complete acceptance of the Gestalt principle; in point of fact it only corrupts that principle. (1938b, p. 30)

The case of radioactive substances whose disintegrations take place according to their own laws, regardless of the surroundings, is cited by Köhler as a justification for rejection of the hypothesis of universal interaction. This does not mean that all states and processes are indifferent to events around them. "The *size* of an area beyond which interaction between a process and its surroundings may be ignored is a matter for specific determination" (p. 30), and the first step in physical experimentation consists in making this determination.

Köhler pointed out that the doctrine of universal interaction means that there are no parts that can be studied and that "the whole world" must be studied in each investigation. Since this cannot be done, the doctrine leads, on the one hand, to defeatism, or romantic skepticism, which rules out all possibility of science. On the other hand, it may lead to the view that we must overlook universal interaction and deal only with the abstracted parts or pieces of nature which would mean a "return in practice to the assumption of independent elements and and-summations" (p. 30). Both the universal interaction and the and-summation viewpoints, Köhler stressed, miss the important point: ". . . the existence of self-enclosed, finitely extended Gestalten with their scientifically determinable, natural laws (*Eigengesetze*). . . . Whereas the doctrine of universal interactionism results in no responsible scientific inquiry, but leads in practice to a purely additive point of view, consideration of finite structures deals instead with definite non-additive properties" (p. 31).

In short, the extreme holistic viewpoint regards a whole either as an and-summation or, if we may attempt a pun, as a "hole" in which to bury science. Instead, Gestalt psychology recognizes finite structures, not necessarily and-summations, which can be studied scientifically. Such study does not rule out the "reduction" or analysis of a whole into parts but calls for analysis "from above," which takes into account the nature of the whole and the real significance of the parts.

Structural and functional
analysis

It is instructive to consider a distinction that has been made between two kinds of analysis by Wheeler and Perkins (1932).

There are in general two kinds of analysis, each of which has its value as well as its limitations. The first of these methods is *structural analysis*, which is the reduction of a whole to its parts. (p. 239)

The second procedure is called *functional analysis*, and is the method of varying the conditions under which a given event takes place, for the purpose of ascertaining the conditions necessary for its existence. . . . Functional analysis *need not* reduce a whole to its parts. It tells us what happens to the whole under sets of conditions that modify but preserve it. (p. 241)

For example, structural analysis of water "divides" it into hydrogen and oxygen; functional analysis studies the properties of water under various conditions, such as variations in temperature or with different substances in solution. Structural analysis is considered to have two important limitations. One limitation is that the parts "are *new* events, different from anything that occurs in the complex process before the analysis is made; thus, description of the parts gives artificial data concerning the original process" (p. 239). Second, the complex process determines the properties of the parts and "cannot be explained by combining the parts after they have been obtained by analysis" (p. 239). Structural analysis, however, has two assets. Where it is impossible to study the whole at one time, because of the complexity of the event or because the conditions it depends on are too numerous, structural analysis permits the segregation of parts for study. For example, in biology a part of the body rather than the whole body may be studied at one time, in an extreme case by dissection of the part. "The study of anatomy is structural analysis *par excellence*" (p. 241). Moreover, a description obtained by structural analysis may lead to clues about the whole from which the part came.

Functional analysis may lead to clues which allow prediction and control of a phenomenon. It has the limitation that an event or object may be too complex to allow it to be studied as a whole. Nonetheless, Wheeler and Perkins prefer to carry out their investigation of the learning process mainly by methods of functional analysis because "the process of learning is a unit in space and in time [and] cannot therefore be treated as a sum of so many elements or skills, derived by structural analysis, but as a total, unified process, operating under a given *set* of conditions" (p. 241).

It seems to us that the dichotomy between structural and functional analysis is not equivalent to the atomistic-holistic dichotomy. An investigator may attempt an holistic approach, with or without varying the conditions under which the whole is studied, that is, with or without functional analysis. Thus he may or may not investigate what happens to the whole under various conditions or how different variables affect the roles of certain parts of the whole or how they affect the relationship of the whole to certain other complexes. The investigator may use an atomistic approach, by studying a part of a whole in isolation from this whole, with or without varying the conditions under which the part is studied. To vary such conditions combines an atomistic approach or structural analysis with a kind of functional analysis.

As we mentioned previously, an argument against reductionism is that it does violence to the whole to reduce it to parts. However, it seems to us that to do justice to the whole does not necessarily require that it be studied "as a whole" or from an holistic point of view. Neither the holistic nor the atomistic approach and neither functional nor structural analysis guarantees that justice is done to the studied phenomenon. One may use any of these approaches and be blinded to important aspects of a complex whole or arrive at considerable understanding of the whole. For example, an atomistic approach, even if it involves study of arbitrarily selected parts of a whole, may yield clues that foster understanding of the whole, particularly if the approach is combined with systematic variation of the parts that are studied and the conditions under which they are studied. An approach is not good in and of itself but must be assessed in terms of the context in which it is used, the manner in which it is applied, and the information it yields.

In any event, it has not been proved that one approach (for example, holistic) yields everything that the other approaches (for example, atomistic, structural, and functional analysis) yield and hence that one approach can be used to the exclusion of the others. An investigator who is interested in a thorough study of a particular whole might do well to apply various approaches or combinations of approaches to it, holistic as well as atomistic, functional as well as structural analysis.

It should also be kept in mind that certain problems for investigation are artifacts of the methods of investigation, not only in psychology but in any discipline. For example, in his lectures Wertheimer pointed out that an atomistic approach to perception led to certain problems which took on different meaning or disappeared or were resolved when a method "from above" was applied to the study of perception. While such an approach resolved certain perplexities in perception, it raised other problems for research. It is not known whether the problems that are raised by (or are artifacts of) a particular approach are encompassed by the problems associated with the other approaches. This is another justification for a variety of approaches.

Reductionism in Psychological
Research

A reductionistic outlook has had considerable influence on psychological research. Research has often focused on the discovery, isolation, and manipulation of what are considered to be simple, "basic" elements. Another facet of the reductionistic viewpoint is the tendency to focus on what is purportedly the simplest case of a given class of phenomena. Consider, for example, investigations of learning. From Ebbinghaus' classical experiments involving the learning of nonsense syllables to Skinner's experiments on lever pressing by a rat, often the endeavor has been to study simple examples of learning rather than more complex, more complicated instances. Apropos of this, Hilgard remarked: ". . . even the experiment which Hull has adapted from Skinner as the source of most of his quantitative statements—lever pressing by a rat-in-a-box—is a very complicated segment of behavior. Hull sometimes forgets this, and writes as though he were down to bedrock when using this experiment as a reference source" (Hilgard, 1948, p. 109). Discussing Hull's almost exclusive concern with classical and instrumental conditioning in the *Principles of Behavior* (Hull, 1943), Spence wrote: "Because of the simplicity of these experimental situations he (Hull) believes that they provide the best means of revealing the basic learning principles. It is his intention to employ the basic constructs and hypothetical laws discovered there, plus whatever additional ones are necessary to explain more complex learning phenomena" (1950, pp. 162–163). Theoretical constructs for visual discrimination learning have been based largely on learning in a situation where only two differing visual stimuli are presented, "it being assumed that this is a 'simple' situation and therefore better adapted for theoretical manipulation" (Krechevsky, 1937, p. 113). We are not concerned here with whether these actually represent simple learning situations but only with indicating that theoretical principles are being derived from these presumably simple situations.

Some psychologists claim that the principles governing a simple case of, say, learning, need not necessarily be identical with, or even included in, the principles of a more complex case. There are those who believe that the so-called simple cases may be highly artificial. The degree of simplicity or complexity which is considered essential sometimes becomes a serious point of contention. For example, in the continuity-discontinuity controversy of learning theory, an adherent of one position may reject the experimental evidence offered by the other side on the grounds that the learning involved is too simple (or too complex) to allow for the study of basic processes.

Reductionism in psychology seems to rest on the following assump-

tions: (1) that it is easier to work first with a more restricted, less complex case, with "simple elements" or with part of a larger whole rather
than with the complex whole itself; (2) that it is essential to isolate, study,
and explain the "basic elements" or the simpler cases before proceeding
to the study of the whole or of the more complex case; (3) that the principles of the part or of the simpler cases are necessarily identical with or
included in those governing the whole or the more complex case; and (4)
that the theory of the simpler case is necessarily identical with or simpler
than the theory governing the more complex case.

Some Mathematical Illustrations

Let us turn to mathematics for some illustrations which may be pertinent to the four points just enumerated. The natural numbers have been
regarded as a basis of mathematics. "Number is the basis of modern
mathematics . . . it has become the modern guiding principle that all
mathematical statements should be reducible ultimately to statements
about the *natural numbers*, 1, 2, 3, · · ·" (Courant and Robbins, 1941,
p. 1). The history of the study of natural numbers does not support the
four previously mentioned points. Mathematicians did not clear up all
the mysteries about natural numbers before dealing with other aspects of
mathematics. The theory of numbers, which is the discipline specifically
concerned with natural numbers, has been called "the last great uncivi-
lized continent of mathematics. . . . If any young Alexander is weeping
for a new world to conquer, it lies before him" (Bell, 1951, p. 221). The
theory of numbers abounds with unsolved problems which have taxed
the ingenuity of brilliant mathematicians. Many problems in this discipline are easily formulated and understood but they resist solution. "A
characteristic of number theory not possessed by other mathematical
disciplines [is that many of its problems] are extremely difficult but the
concepts involved are so elementary that the very young student can
understand the problem" (Hayden and Finan, 1961, p. 49). While the
natural numbers may be the elements to which mathematical statements
should be reducible, the theory of natural number is certainly not identical with, included in as a recognizable component, or simpler than every
remaining mathematical discipline.

It may be more instructive to consider a subdivision of the natural
numbers, the *prime* numbers. A prime number is a natural number other
than 1 whose only factors among the natural numbers are itself and 1.
The unique factorization theorem establishes that every integer greater
than 1 can be factored into a product of primes in one and only one way
(except for arbitrariness in the order of occurrence of the factors). The
prime numbers, therefore, represent the "simple elements" in terms of

which every natural number can be uniquely expressed. If every mathematical statement is regarded as ultimately reducible to statements about natural numbers and the natural numbers as "reducible" to unique products of prime numbers, then the latter may be considered as the basic mathematical elements. Yet, mathematics did not deal exhaustively with prime numbers before dealing with more "complex" mathematical statements. Many a problem about prime numbers still challenges mathematicians. Among these is the famous Goldbach conjecture (1742), set forth in a letter to Euler, that every even number (except 2, which is itself a prime) can be represented as a sum of two primes; for example, $4 = 2 + 2$, $6 = 3 + 3, 8 = 5 + 3, \cdots$. Neither Euler nor any other mathematician has proved this conjecture to be true nor provided a contradictory example. Not until 1931 was a first step taken toward establishing a proof of Goldbach's conjecture and this step was still far from the original conjecture for it consisted in the proof by the Russian mathematician Schnirelmann (1905–1938) that every positive integer can be represented as the sum of not more than 300,000 primes.

Proofs of some of the theorems about prime numbers are extremely difficult. Thus, the prime number theorem, concerning the distribution of primes in the number series, has been proved by using advanced mathematical analysis. "To prove this theorem, concerned only with the most elementary concepts, it is necessary to employ the most powerful methods of modern mathematics" (Courant and Robbins, 1941, p. 30). Available proofs of some of the theorems pertaining to prime numbers— to the "simple elements" from which other integers can be constructed— rank among the most complicated in mathematics. Here again we see that study of "basic elements" need not be easier to accomplish than the study of complexes built up of such elements. Moreover, the principles and theory of prime numbers are not identical with the principles and theory of natural numbers nor have the former principles been able to be used as a basis for deriving all properties of natural numbers. Thus we see that the four assumptions concerning the relation between the study and principles of simpler elements and complexes which seem to underlie a reductionistic trend in psychology do not have counterparts in the discipline of natural numbers.

To take another illustration further along the hierarchy of number concepts, consider the relationship between complex numbers and real numbers. A complex number may be represented as $a + bi$, where i is the positive square root of -1 and a and b are real numbers. Thus the complex numbers include the real numbers as a special case (when $b = 0$); that is, real numbers belong to the domain of complex numbers. The algebra of complex numbers, however, is in some respects simpler than the algebra of real numbers. In part, this is because every polynomial equation with complex coefficients has a complex number as a root (which follows from the fundamental theorem of algebra) and in fact has as many roots as its degree, but there are equations with real coefficients that do not have any real number as a root, for example, $x^2 + 1 = 0$. Here again is an illustration that the study of the "complex" or "whole" may be simpler than the study of a more restricted case or a "part" of the "whole."

Finally, we consider a problem in topology which may be given a concrete interpretation in terms of the coloring of geographical maps. In order to distinguish two countries which have a part of their boundary in common, it is usual to employ different colors for them. When this is done, it has been found in practice that all known maps can be colored by using only four colors. This has led to the conjecture that four colors will always suffice to color a map in a plane or on a sphere. Originally proposed in 1840, the problem has still not been solved, notwithstanding the efforts of many famous mathematicians. But the corresponding problem has been solved for some other surfaces—for instance, the problem of the minimum number of colors required to color a map on the surface of a torus (a surface with the shape of a doughnut or an inflated inner tube). "A remarkable fact connected with the four color problem is that for surfaces more complicated than the plane or the sphere the corresponding theorems have actually been proved, so that, paradoxically enough, the analysis of more complicated geometrical surfaces appears in this respect to be easier than that of the simplest cases" (Courant and Robbins, 1941, p. 248).

Admittedly, these examples may be completely devoid of relevance so far as psychological problems are concerned. But they at least serve to illustrate that in a discipline other than psychology, it is not always simpler to work with a more restricted, less complex case or with part of a larger whole and that it is not necessary to solve the former in order to be able to work adequately with the latter. Allow that the examples have a suggestive value for psychology and the moral for psychological research is evident: The development of psychology as a science need not depend upon the discovery of the "basic simple units" of behavior or on their prior study; the degree of difficulty of dealing scientifically with phenomena is not necessarily commensurate with the degree of complexity of the phenomenon, and the principles or theories of the part or of the less complex case are not necessarily identical with nor a basis on which to build up the principles and theories of the whole or of the more complex instance.

As we have seen, the ultimate aim in mathematics has been considered to be that of reducing all concepts to the natural numbers and all propositions in each branch of mathematics to propositions about the natural numbers. This aim, of course, has not been achieved. Not all mathematical activity is directed toward its achievement. Much mathematical work is done without specific consideration of how it can be reduced to concepts and propositions about the natural numbers. And such work is not regarded as less mathematical or less important than work that aims to reduce a branch of mathematics to the natural numbers. Analogously, even if an ultimate aim in psychology is to reduce it to some other discipline or to another branch of psychology, work that is not directed toward this aim is not necessarily less scientific or less important than work that is so directed.

Reduction to Another Discipline

The term *reductionism* has also been applied to the belief that the concepts of a science should be expressed in terms of the concepts of a "more fundamental science." "Psychology, it has long been felt, becomes scientific in so far as it is reduced to physiology, neurology, biochemistry, or physics" (Sloane, 1945, p. 217). Strict reductionists, Preston pointed out (1951, p. 10), would require reduction to concepts of physics and mathematics on the grounds that these are the most fundamental sciences. An opposing viewpoint, sometimes referred to as nonreductionism, contends that the concepts of one science need not be reducible to those of any other science. Preston characterizes the two points of view as follows:

> Reductionists regard the important objective of their science to be the explanation of their data in the language of sciences of a more fundamental character. This view may be held so strongly as to exclude any other kind of work as being scientific in nature. On the other hand, there are psychologists who . . . believe that the most fruitful mission which psychology can accept is the working out of the relationships of the concepts within the science . . . without regard to whether they will or will not ultimately reduce to the concepts of other sciences. (p. 12)

The school in philosophy of science known as *logical positivism* or *logical empiricism* advocates *physicalism* in psychology: "Physical concepts are taken to be basic and irreducible. On this foundation, the concepts of chemistry, biology, psychology, and the social sciences are taken to be developed in this order" (Ackoff, 1952, p. 158).

There are those who would go beyond the physicalism urged by logical positivism. Davis advocates that instead of seeking the ideal of a science *like* physics, "we might do well to try making psychology a *part* of physics, or more precisely, a part of the body of general science which regards reducibility as an obvious requirement of a good theory" (1953, p. 7). Among the criteria proposed for *physical psychology* is the following: "Only those constructs would be tolerated which could be reduced to those of physical science" (p. 8).

The assumptions underlying this conception of reductionism would seem to be that the more fundamental the science, the more scientific are its concepts. "Scientific" may here conceivably refer to lack of contradiction among concepts, objectivity in definitions of concepts, the use of operational definitions, and, possibly, to nearness to irreducible concepts, with the concepts of mathematics and physics regarded as being the ultimate irreducibles, or at least as being relatively irreducible, the final independent variables in terms of which all other scientific concepts may be expressed. Indeed, it has been said that many scientists believe that the fundamental concepts of all the remaining sciences will, "under sufficiently intense investigation, be shown to be nothing more than complex functions of mathematical and physical concepts" (Preston, 1951, p. 10). One may ask: Why this belief? And what mathematical and physical concepts will turn out to be involved in these functions? The use of reducibility to the concepts of a more "fundamental science" as the gauge of the *scientific nature* of a concept, suggests that the concepts of this "fundamental science" are well established. For example, it suggests that the criterion that a concept must meet in order to be fundamental to mathematics or physics is already well established. There seems to be implied the idea that the foundations of physics and mathematics have been established and with them a set of fundaments or fundamental concepts. But are such assumptions justified by the state of affairs in mathematics or physics?

We have already seen that there is no established foundation for all of mathematics or for set theory or for other branches of mathematics. With time there have been changes in the meanings of certain mathematical concepts, for example, the concept of number. At present there is disagreement among mathematicians as to the nature and acceptability of certain concepts, for example, real number, mathematical existence, infinity, set. Let us turn now to a survey of some aspects of physics to see whether its concepts can serve as the fundaments to which to reduce psychological concepts.

Concepts of Physics

What are the concepts of physics? Clearly the answer will depend on what is meant by the term *physics?* Does it include the earliest attempts of man to gain some control or understanding of physical phenomena? Does it include only those concepts which belong to physics as a science? If so, just when did physics attain its scientific statehood? Did it begin with the Greeks, before them, after them?

To avoid such issues, which are themselves pregnant with problems and implications for one who wishes to use *the* concepts of physics as "irreducibles," let us restrict ourselves to relatively recent times and, in particular, to the main attempts to lay a foundation for physics, for in so doing we may gain some understanding of what constitute "the fundamental concepts" of physics. These attempts have been characterized as the search for a unifying theoretical basis for all of the various branches of physics, "consisting of a minimum of concepts and fundamental relationships, from which all the concepts and relationships of the single disciplines might be derived by logical process" (Einstein, 1950, p. 99). Illuminating accounts of these attempts to establish the foundations of physics are contained in several papers by Einstein (1936, 1940, 1948, 1949) all of which are included in a collection of his works (1950); the page references that follow are to the 1950 volume, which may itself serve as a ready reference source in the formulations of our brief allusions to classical mechanics, to field theory including the special and general theory of relativity, and to quantum physics.

Foundations of theoretical physics

If there were a well-established foundation for physics, one unifying theoretical basis, then the concepts invoked therein might presumably serve as the elements in terms of which other scientific concepts could be expressed. But as of the date of writing, no one unifying basis has yet been determined which is acceptable to all physicists. Classical mechanics of Newton, which may be considered as the first systematic attempt at laying a uniform theoretical foundation for physics, although highly successful in other branches of physics (for example, celestial mechanics, theory of heat), did not seem to account adequately for the phenomena of electricity and light. Increasing knowledge about the phenomena of interference, diffraction, and polarization of light argued against Newton's corpuscular theory of light and in favor of a wave theory. During the nineteenth century the dispute was settled in favor of the wave theory, which was quite unsuitable for Newton's theoretical foundation. Although a search for a mechanical foundation for physics still continued, gradually the search turned to field theory.

The field concept had been developed by Faraday in an attempt to account for electromagnetic effects. The precise formulation of the time-space laws of electromagnetic fields was the contribution of Maxwell whose differential equations revealed that these fields spread in the form of polarized waves and with the speed of light. It was only after Hertz's experiments demonstrated the existence of such electromagnetic waves that resistance to the field theory broke down.

For several decades most physicists clung to the conviction that a mechanical substructure would be found for Maxwell's theory. But the unsatisfactory results of their efforts led to gradual acceptance of the new field concepts as irreducible fundamentals—in other words, physicists resigned themselves to giving up the idea of a mechanical foundation. . . . [and] held to a field-theory program. But it *could not be called a foundation,* since nobody could tell whether a consistent field theory could ever explain on the one hand gravitation, on the other hand the elementary components of matter. (p. 103, italics ours)

Developments in field theory, culminating in Einstein's restricted and general theory of relativity, yielded a new theory of gravitation that diverged widely from that of Newton with respect to basic principles but which was close to Newton's theory in most practical applications. But Einstein recognized that "it cannot be claimed that those parts of the general relativity theory which can today be regarded as final have furnished physics with a complete and satisfactory foundation" (p. 106). In the first place, the general principle of relativity has been applied satisfactorily only to gravitational fields, but not to the total field (p. 48). And in the second place, the general relativity theory, like the earlier field theories, has not yet supplied an explanation of the atomistic or molecular structure of matter or of quantum phenomena.

But what of quantum mechanics? Can it not serve as a basis for all of physics? Quantum theory is criticized by Einstein on the grounds that, operating as it does with a totality of systems, it leaves entirely unclarified what happens to the single system or to the individual happening; it yields no "inside view of these important alterations in the single systems, in their structure and their causal connections" (p. 91). He concludes that "in my opinion the quantum theory does not seem likely to be able to produce a usable foundation for physics" (p. 97). While "translation of the field theory into the scheme of quantum statistics" might yield a basis, no one can venture to say whether this can actually be done in a satisfactory manner (p. 11). While the quantum theory and the theory of relativity do not directly contradict one another, they are "essentially independent of each other . . . [and] seem little adapted to fusion into one unified theory" (p. 104).

What is to be concluded? According to Einstein's writing in 1936, a conclusion confirmed in his later writings (for example, in 1948): "For the time being, we have to admit that *we do not possess* any general theoretical basis for physics, which can be regarded as its logical foundation" (1950, p. 110, italics ours).

But if there is no one general theoretical or logical basis, with its corresponding concepts, what does reductionism refer to when it speaks of reduction to *the* concepts of physics. Is this a reference to, say, the concepts of classical mechanics, or is it a generous and hospitable inclusion of all physical concepts? If the concepts of each theory were compatible with those of the other theories, such hospitability might be in place.

But we shall see that the principles and concepts of one theory may dramatically contradict those of another theory so that the set consisting of all their concepts is ridden with contradictions. In particular, since there is no foundation established for all of physics, the reductionist is theoretically at liberty to employ the concepts from any of the *attempts* at a foundation as his "irreducibles." This would constitute no difficulty if the concepts of one system were equivalent to or merely additions to the concepts of another. But we shall see that there prevail marked discrepancies, even incongruities among these concepts.

Classical Mechanics

Consider Newton's classical mechanics which has the following basic concepts: mass points with invariable mass; action at a distance between any pair of mass points; law of motion for the mass point. Also, time and space were recognized by Newton as "essential elements, as physically effective factors, of his system, if only by implication" (Einstein, 1950, p. 100).

Space is characterized by a coordinate system; that is, a bodily object is considered as described, with regard to its position, as being a point with place coordinates X, Y, Z relative to a particular coordinate system. Motion is described by giving X, Y, Z as functions of time. The system of coordinates in mechanics is called an *inertia* (inertial) *system* where this term denotes that the only motion which the coordinate system may undergo is motion that is free from twisting and acceleration—rectilinear (straight) and uniform. Any coordinate system that moves at the same rate and in the same direction as an inertia system is itself an inertia system. Laws of motion, as formulated in classical mechanics, held good (only) for all inertia systems.

Time is regarded as independent of space, as independent of any coordinate system. Each event may be characterized by its place coordinates and by a time value t, which is considered measurable by a clock (ideal periodic process). The clock is considered at rest at one point of the coordinate system. The time of an event taking place at any point is defined as the time shown on this clock simultaneously with the event. It is significant that the term *simultaneous* is not defined, but is assumed to be physically meaningful since with the help of light, whose velocity is regarded as practically infinite, simultaneity of events that are spatially distant from one another can apparently be determined immediately.

In addition to these fundamental concepts there are secondary ones; for example, the potential energy of a system, which is described as a function of the system's configuration.

The Field Concept

We have already mentioned the difficulties encountered in applying Newtonian mechanics to electric and magnetic phenomena. It had been customary to conceive of these phenomena as involving masses of a special kind of electrical particles and to assume the existence of forces acting at a distance. Faraday conceived of the electric particles together creating a condition in the surrounding space (a spatial state, now referred to as a field), which in turn produced a certain order in the iron filings. After the work of Maxwell and Hertz, it was recognized that the electromagnetic field could exist as a wave independent of the material source. But if this was so, physicists began to wonder, why should an appeal be made to action-at-a-distance to account for electrostatic interaction or even for gravitation? The field concept was invoked to account for these and other phenomena for which there had hitherto been recourse to forces mysteriously acting at a distance. "Everywhere Newton's actions-at-a-distance gave way to fields spreading with finite velocity" (Einstein, 1950, p. 102). Thus, one of the major concepts in Newtonian mechanics was replaced by the field concept. To be sure, at first a kind of mechanical interpretation was attempted for the field concept. Indeed, for several decades physicists sought for a mechanical substructure for Maxwell's theory, but the lack of fruitfulness of these attempts "led to gradual acceptance of the new field concepts as irreducible fundamentals" (p. 103).

The Restricted Theory of Relativity

The restricted or special theory of relativity has been described as a systematic extension of the electrodynamics developed by Maxwell and Lorentz. In the equations of electrodynamics, the velocity of light is taken to be a constant. Moreover, Maxwell's equations, pertaining to the law of propagation of light in empty space, are converted into equations of the same form when they are subjected to mathematical transformations of a certain kind known as Lorentz transformations. The two principles (postulates) on which the special relativity theory is based are the following:

1. The velocity of light is a definite constant c in empty space.
2. All systems of physical equations that express general laws are invariant with regard to the Lorentz transformation; that is, a law of nature does not change its form if one introduces into it a new inertial system by means of a Lorentz transformation on x, y, z, t.

The Lorentz transformation is a linear mathematical transformation characterized by invariance of the expression $dx^2 + dy^2 + dz^2 - c^2\,dt^2$

which is formed from the coordinate differences dx, dy, dz, dt of two "infinitely close events," where c represents the speed of light; that is, through the transformation this expression goes over into the same kind of expression formed from the coordinate differences in the new coordinate system.

The achievements of the special theory of relativity have been characterized in the following manner: "it has shown generally the role which the universal constant c (velocity of light) plays in the laws of nature and has demonstrated that there exists a close connection between the form in which time on the one hand and the spatial coordinates on the other hand enter into the laws of nature" (p. 45). These achievements have had radical consequences for the concepts of classical mechanics.

Time and space

Time, which was of an absolute character in Newton's system, independent of space (of the coordinate system), loses this absolute nature and is included with the (other) spatial coordinates in a four-dimensional description. The space-time continuum is introduced. In particular, the meaning of simultaneity is operationally defined and its absolute or invariant character destroyed. Since the velocity of light is assumed to be a constant (rather than infinite), it can no longer be assumed, as was done prior to relativity physics, that "simultaneously seen" and "simultaneously happening" are equivalent or that the time of propagation of light can be neglected. The special theory of relativity defines the time t of the event at a point P as the reading on a clock C at the time of arrival of a light signal emitted from the event, corrected for the time required for the light signal to travel the distance. "This definition reduces the concept of simultaneity of spatially distant events to that of the simultaneity of events happening at the same place (coincidence), namely the arrival of the light signal at C and the reading of C" (p. 43). There is no absolute simultaneity since a statement of the coincidence of two events has meaning only in relation to a system of coordinates. Similarly, the mass of bodies, the dimensions of bodies, and the speed of clocks are not invariant but are dependent on their state of motion with regard to the coordinates.

Actions-at-a-distance and motion

While the concept of forces interacting at a distance was threatened by the field concept, its final breath of life was (or should have been) removed by the change in the meaning of simultaneity. "Once it was shown that simultaneity was relative and depended on the frame of reference, every possibility of retaining actions-at-a-distance within the foundation of physics disappeared, since that concept presupposed the abso-

lute character of simultaneity (it must be possible to state the location of
the two interacting mass points 'at the same time')" (p. 105). The field,
as determined by differential equations, takes the place of the concept of
the force of interaction; in place of interaction of forces at a distance,
the relativity theory "allows interaction only by fields" (p. 80).

A new law of motion was derived for rapidly moving mass points, those
whose motions are not negligibly small as compared with the velocity of
light, which was verified soon afterward for the motion of electrically
laden particles.

Mass, energy, and material point

The most important result of the special relativity theory has been
described as the demonstration of the equivalence of the concepts of mass
and energy which were distinct, independent concepts in Newton's system. The inert mass (resistance to acceleration) of a system was found to
depend on its energy content so that "we were driven to the conception
that inert mass was nothing else than latent energy" (p. 56). Somewhat
inexactly, the relation may be expressed as $E = mc^2$, in which c represents the velocity of light, about 186,000 miles per second, E the energy
contained in a stationary mass, and m its mass. While the principle of
conservation of energy and the principle of conservation of mass had
previously been regarded as independent, now the latter lost its independence and became merged with the former.

Classical mechanics' concept of *potential energy* of a system is meaningless in relativity theory, since this concept is dependent on the characterization of various configurational variables "at the same time"; that is,
it rests on the idea of absolute simultaneity or absolute instantaneousness.

The notion of "material point" or particle is fundamental for mechanics. Einstein believed that "in the foundations of any consistent field
theory, there shall not be, in addition to the concept of field, any concept
concerning particles" (p. 78). Since the concept of particle is intimately
related to the concept of material point, this statement is significant in
the present context as illustrating possible incompatability of basic concepts of two theories in physics.

General Theory of Relativity

In both classical mechanics and the special theory of relativity, it is
assumed that the laws of nature are valid only with respect to inertial
systems. The only transformations for the coordinates, which leave un-
altered the form of the laws, are the Lorentz transformations that carry

one inertial system into another. Einstein raised the question of whether this restriction to inertial systems, to systems of coordinates in uniform movement of translation with reference to one another, is a restriction founded on physical facts. "What has nature to do with the coordinate systems that we propose and with their motions?" (p. 56). That the restriction was an arbitrary one was demonstrated by considering a curious situation in classical mechanics.

The same mass constant plays two different roles in classical mechanics, as inertial mass (resistance to acceleration) and gravitational mass (which determines the weight of the body in a given gravitational field). Since the same constant measures both the inertia and the weight of a body, it follows that it is impossible to discover by experiment whether the motion of a given system of coordinates is straight and uniform (that is, whether it is an inertia system) and the observed effects are due to a gravitational field, or, on the other hand, whether the system of coordinates is uniformly accelerated. Recognition of an equivalence between the two cases constitutes the equivalence principle of the general relativity theory. In other words, the principle is a statement of the equivalence of motion in a gravitational field in relation to an inertia system of coordinates and motion in the absence of a gravitational field in a coordinate system that is accelerated. Whether the same property appears as weight or inertia depends on which description (of coordinate systems) is employed. Here, then, is a key to a fact known since Galileo's time but for which there had previously been offered no satisfactory theoretical interpretation.

Moreover, the equivalence principle "shatters the concepts of the inertial system" (p. 105); the inertial system "loses its meaning" (p. 46). Why limit the motion of coordinate systems to rectilinear and uniform motion? And why limit the permissible transformations to the Lorentz transformations which are linear? ". . . the admission of a coordinate system which is accelerated with respect to the original 'inertial' coordinates means the admission of non-linear coordinate transformations. . . . After one has found oneself forced to admit non-linear coordinate systems . . . the simplest demand appears to admit all continuous coordinate transformations (which form a group)" (p. 46). The general theory of relativity admits all transformations of the coordinates so long as the transformations are free from mathematical singularities. It regards as general laws of nature only those equations which remain invariant under such transformations. Formulation of laws so that they meet this criterion is a task of the general theory of relativity. In simpler words, the task is to so formulate natural laws that "their form is identical for coordinate systems of any kind of states of motion" (p. 105).

Here again we see rejected concepts of Newton's system and even of the special relativity theory. In the latter theory space was considered to be an inertia system, the only admissible coordinate systems were considered to be inertia systems—that is, systems whose motions were rectilinear and uniform (nonaccelerated), and the only permissible transformations (those which leave laws of nature invariant) were considered to be the linear (Lorentz) transformations. The general relativity theory does *not* consider space to be an inertia system, admits all arbitrary curvilinear coordinate systems in which the fields are described by regular functions, and allows as permissible transformation of the coordinates all continuous transformations which are free from singularities.

Summary statement

Concepts in Newton's system included (1) mass point with invariant mass, (2) forces interacting at a distance, (3) certain laws of motion, (4) time, (5) space, (6) inertia system, and (7) potential energy. Special relativity theory brought about a radical reinterpretation of the concept of time and of its relation to space, with consequent reverberations, either major modifications or outright rejections, of most of the other concepts. General relativity theory ruled out the exclusive claim of inertia systems to serve as coordinate systems in physics.

Quantum Theory

Quantum physics arose out of the realization that there are functions in physics that are not continuous but that take on only certain discrete states or values, with discontinuous transitions between these states or values. Mathematical expression of those discrete states has been found to be connected with another universal constant, Planck's constant h. Attempts to explain these discrete states led to descriptions that could not be interpreted as actual mathematical descriptions of an event taking place in time and space but rather that served "only to make statistical statements and predictions of the results of all measurements which we can carry out upon the system. . . . Instead of a model description of actual space-time events, it gives the probability distributions for possible measurements as functions of time" (pp. 108–109). In the sense that its laws are of a statistical (probability) nature, quantum physics differs fundamentally from all previous theories of physics. The crucial difference between quantum mechanics and Einstein's or Newton's system, F. S. C. Northrop pointed out in the introduction to Heisenberg's book (1958, p. 7), "centers in the definition of a mechanical system at any moment of time, and this difference is that quantum mechanics introduces the concept of probability into its definition of state," with the result that whereas previously probability and chance had entered only in the theory of errors, in the verification of what the scientist knew, now it enters "into the theoretical statements of what he knows."

What are the concepts of quantum theory? In addition to probability, it employs as fundamental concepts those of force and material point; these, however, are to be understood differently than in classical mechanics, since, for example, they involve "quantum corrections" to the corresponding concepts of classical mechanics. Its conception of matter and atomic structure, based on probability distributions, differs from classical conceptions as does its conception of causality, of cause and effect. It also employs the concepts of absolute time and potential energy. Indeed, one of Einstein's main arguments against the likelihood of quantum mechanics serving as a useful basis for the whole of physics is that in one of the fundamental equations of quantum theory, the Schrödinger equation, "absolute time, and also the potential energy, play a decisive role, while these two concepts have been recognized by the theory of relativity as inadmissible in principle" (1950, p. 92). To escape from this difficulty, Einstein believed that one must base quantum theory upon field and field laws instead of upon forces of interaction. This means that one must transpose the methods of quantum mechanics (which have been applied to systems with a finite number of degrees of freedom) to fields that are systems of infinitely many degrees of freedom. While this may not be impossible in principle, attempts to do so even in the restricted case of linear equations have resulted in "terrifying" complications; and these complications "certainly will rise sky high if one wishes to obey the requirements of the general theory of relativity [not to be restricted to linear equations], the justification of which in principle nobody doubts" (p. 92).

On the other hand, it has been argued that it is relativity theory which should change its concepts to agree more with quantum concepts. The success of methods used in quantum physics may point to a "purely algebraic method of description of nature, that is to the elimination of continuous functions from physics" (p. 92). Then one would have to give up, on principle, the space-time continuum which is basal to present formulations of nonquantum theories in physics (as well as in most other sciences).

A summary of the very different character of the concepts employed in quantum physics as compared with those in field theory (including relativity theory) is contained in Einstein's remark: "The theoretical physicists of our generation are expecting the erection of a new theoretical basis for physics (quantum theory) which would make use of fundamental concepts greatly different from those of the field theory considered up to now" (p. 85).

Heisenberg, famous for the "indeterminacy principle" of quantum mechanics, considers that the major contribution of modern physics has been the change it wrought in concepts.

> Coming back now to the contributions of modern physics, one may say that the most important change brought about by its results consists in the dissolution of this rigid frame of concepts of the nineteenth century. Of course, many attempts had been made before to get away from this rigid frame which seemed obviously too narrow for an understanding of the essential parts of reality. But it had not been possible to see what could be wrong with the fundamental concepts like matter, space, time, and causality that had been so extremely useful in the history of science. Only experimental research itself, carried out with all the refined equipment that technical science could offer, and its mathematical interpretation, provided the basis for a critical analysis— or, one may say, enforced the critical analysis—of these concepts, and finally resulted in the dissolution of the rigid frame.
>
> This dissolution took place in two distinct stages. The first was the discovery, through the theory of relativity, that such fundamental concepts as space and time could be changed and in fact must be changed on account of new experience. . . . The second stage was the discussion of the concept of matter enforced by the experimental results concerning the atomic structure. (1962, pp. 198–199)

Heisenberg seems to warn against the reductionistic trend when he concludes that these new results of modern physics

> had first of all to be considered as a serious warning against the somewhat forced application of scientific concepts in domains where they did not belong. The application of the concepts of classical physics, e.g., in chemistry, had been a mistake. Therefore, one will nowadays be less inclined to assume that the concepts of physics, even those of quantum theory, can certainly be applied in biology or other sciences. (p. 199)

Reduction of Psychology

We have seen that there are conflicting opinions as to whether the most famous attempt at reductionism, the *Principia Mathematica*, achieved its aim. The present writers believe that it was not achieved and that the logistic thesis has not been established. In the present context we are interested in what this might mean for reductionism in the empirical sciences. If the task of reducing mathematics to logic has proved so difficult, then the task of reducing all of psychology to mathematics or to logic may seem to some to be even more formidable. It will be recalled that the propositions of the empirical sciences are often differentiated from those of mathematics and logic, for example, on the grounds that the latter do not give factual or empirical information. One might reasonably expect that the difficulties encountered in reducing propositions of mathematics to those of logic would be compounded in reducing propositions of one kind (empirical science) to those of another kind (mathematics or logic). Of course reductionists in psychology could simplify their task by not requiring standards that are as rigorous and precise as those of logicism. Reductionism could also restrict itself to those aspects of psychology that lend themselves to reduction to mathematics and logic and await the development of new logic and mathematics to deal with aspects that have as yet not been reduced. The reductionists in psychology might eschew mathematics and logic and instead turn to one of the empirical sciences, such as biology or physics. Even then the psychologist might encounter some of the difficulties that confront logicism. For example, just as logicists modified the ordinary definition of logic (for example, by introducing the axiom of infinity) in order to encompass parts of arithmetic, so reductionists in psychology might have to modify the definitions of biology or physics in order to encompass significant parts of psychology. This need not be the case if the reductionist would instead modify the definition of psychology and reject concepts and portions of psychology that are not reducible. He might justify this by saying that they are not (or not as yet) amenable to scientific study, but such a decision might raise protests from those who consider that what was rejected belongs to psychology and is amenable to a scientific approach other than reductionism.

In a seminar on methodology which had been devoted to reductionism, some students proposed, apropos of the idea that the concepts and propositions of psychology could be reduced to those of other disciplines, that the various topics and problems of psychology could be studied in other departments. They pointed out that much of comparative-physiological psychology could be studied in the biology department, statistical methods in the mathematics department, culture and personality in the anthropology department, social psychology in the sociology department, and history and systems of psychology in the history and philosophy departments. As the group got going, specific topics and problems of psychology were distributed among the departments of physics, chemistry, political science, and economics; the applied and clinical aspects of psychology were assigned to schools of social work, education, medicine, engineering, and business. Someone commented that if psychology was nothing but certain concepts and propositions of other disciplines, then it might be more honest for professors in psychology departments to send their students to other departments. Before long, some members of the group concluded that the topics and problems of psychology could be studied best in other departments and that there was no need for a separate discipline or separate department of psychology.

The instructor remarked that this was not reducing psychology but dismembering it. One of the students who had remained quiet during the session up to this point now asked: "Is it better to dismember the human spirit than an academic field? Why is the unity of an institution more sacred than the unity of a human being and the claim to uniqueness of a discipline more valid than the claim to uniqueness of a human being?"

This rather emotional statement resembles somewhat the objections to reductionism made by some humanistic psychologists. They see reductionism as somehow neglecting the peculiarly human characteristics of a person. This point is rather succinctly made by J. Cohen in his objections to the neurological model of mental functioning used by some reductionists. "The basic flaw in reductionism and the neurological model of man which it entails is, in my view, its impersonal character. . . . The reductionist view-point in asserting that the mental life of man can be *wholly* represented in neural terms denies to him those very qualities which distinguish him from a robot" (1961, p. 6).

The Principle of Parsimony

An argument for reductionism is scientific economy, or parsimony. Reduction of the concepts and assumptions of several sciences to one science, it has been said, eliminates unnecessary concepts, avoids redundancies, and is in keeping with the principle of parsimony or of scientific economy and simplicity. Although economy and simplicity in scientific explanations were advocated before the fourteenth century, the principle of parsimony is often equated with a maxim known as *Occam's razor*. The maxim is attributed to William of Occam (Ockam, or Ockham, England, about 1280–1349), sometimes called the last of the Scholastic philosophers. His philosophical views (see Cushman, 1946; Jones, 1952; Windelband, 1958) were close to nominalism or, more precisely, to terminism. He maintained that reason should be separated from revelation, that knowledge belongs to the world of senses, and that explanatory concepts should be kept as close as possible to the observable data. In discussing various conceptions of the nature of the soul, William of Occam wrote, "And in favor of these there is this to be said: What can be explained on fewer principles is explained needlessly by more" (see Jones, 1952, Vol. I, p. 520). This maxim, which is Occam's razor, has been formulated in various ways. For example: "Entities are not to be multiplied beyond necessity (except by necessity, more than is necessary)" and "It is vain to do with more what can be done with fewer" (Mason, 1962, p. 118).

The principle of parsimony, or Occam's razor, is not a description of what actually happens in science but a prescription for science. It has served as a guiding principle in science but, as we shall see, has met with some resistance. It has been applied with reference to the quantity and quality of explanatory concepts in a scientific theory, suggesting a preference for fewer and simpler concepts. It has been used as justification for avoiding the postulation of unverifiable entities for what can be explained more directly. Where there are alternative hypotheses, both of which account for a given phenomenon, it has been used to decide in favor of the simpler. In the analysis of data or experience, it has been used to justify the dictum that the analysis should be carried no further than is necessary to obtain a desired result. It has been also pointed out that these varied applications of Occam's razor are not related or connected. Thus, Ritchie notes that "the application of any rule such as Occam's razor to . . . the analysis of experience is not necessarily connected in fact or in logic with the applicability of a similar rule . . . to other problems, e.g., the value of hypotheses" (1960, p. 115).

The principle of parsimony has been described as a rule of nature that mirrors the parsimony of nature. But it has also been said that the principle of parsimony is not a law of nature nor a law of logic nor a rule that should have any special philosophical or methodological sanction or prestige.

> Occam's Razor however, cannot, so far as I can see, be considered as a law of nature. Some of the older physicists used to consider it as axiomatic that "Nature is always simple." Unfortunately the evidence is all the other way, that Nature is very complicated. . . . Occam's Razor, then, must be taken as being at most a methodological rule and not as a law having any special philosophical prestige. . . . In any case the rule is not a law of logic, but in the proper sense of the words a law of thought. That is to say, it professes to be a maxim for correct or at least successful reasoning on certain problems, but can be neglected without contradiction if desired and does not by itself provide any guarantee as to the correctness of the conclusions. (Ritchie, 1960, pp. 114–115)

The meanings of the terms that appear in Occam's razor have also been questioned. "In its most frequently quoted form it (Occam's Razor) asserts that entities are not to be multiplied more than is necessary. But, first, what is an entity; and second, necessary for what?" (p. 114). Chein makes a similar point: "The principle states that explanatory concepts should not needlessly be multiplied. . . . But how is needlessly to be assessed" (1963, p. 5n). What are the criteria for determining the nature of the "entities" and how far should they be "multiplied"? For example, how does one determine that the analysis of data or experience is carried out as far as is necessary and no further? The principle of parsimony has been hedged in with the stipulation that the entities (concepts, principles, or analysis) be sufficient in quantity or quality. There is the danger that Occam's razor may cut off too much. Ritchie describes it as "rather an unhandy instrument and reminiscent of the kind of razor that cuts more off your chin than just your beard" (1960, p. 114).

Offhand, it might seem that the meaning of Occam's razor can be clarified by saying that if there are two alternatives (in concepts, hypotheses, procedures, and so on), and if all other things are equal, then the simpler alternative should be selected. Aside from raising the questions of what it means for all other things to be equal and how it can ever be determined if such a state of affairs exists, the attempt at clarification shifts the problem to the meaning of *simpler*. Who is to determine what is simpler, and on what basis is the determination to be made? What is judged to be simpler is partly a function of the particular judge and of his times. The history of physics is replete with illustrations of changes in the conception of what is simpler.

> There was a time when, in physics, laws that could be expressed without using differential calculus were preferred, and in the long struggle between the corpuscular and the wave theories of light, the argument was rife that the corpuscular theory was mathematically simpler, while the wave theory required the solution of boundary problems of partial differential equations, a highly complex matter. (Frank, 1961b, p. 14)

Just as the corpuscular theory was favored on the grounds that it was mathematically simpler, so an argument once given for favoring Newton's theory over Einstein's theory was that it was mathematically simpler. Newton's theory requires only the ordinary calculus while Einstein's theory requires more advanced mathematics. Ironically, the calculus was mathematically "too complex" in the argument about the corpuscular and wave theories but was mathematically "simple" in the argument about Newton's and Einstein's theories. This well illustrates that a "mathematical estimation of simplicity depends upon the state of culture of a certain period" (p. 14). It also depends on the mathematical knowledge of a particular person within that period. People with the training to understand the mathematics involved in Einstein's theory will find that it is "of incredible beauty and simplicity," whereas others may find it "of immense complexity, and this low degree of simplicity will not be compensated by a great number of observed facts" for which the theory accounts (p. 14).

The meaning of simplicity becomes even more complicated if a purely mathematical estimation of simplicity is replaced by other criteria. For example, criteria of simplicity (or of acceptance) of a theory may be the extent to which it is compatible with the existing state of knowledge or with other theories about observable phenomena or with common-sense experiences. It seems to us that Occam's razor, particularly when interpreted to tell us "to stay as close as we can to available data" (Chein, 1963, p. 5n), and not to invoke unverifiable entities, might be construed to mean that a theory should be as compatible as possible with everyday observations, with the common-sense experiences of our daily life. While the Copernican (heliocentric) theory was mathematically simpler than the Ptolemaic (geocentric) theory, it was less compatible with common-sense experiences and it was on this basis that it was rejected by Francis Bacon.

The principle of parsimony has been used as justification for the practice of assuming that functions and relationships are linear (first degree, straight line relationships). This has been done even when it was known that the system in question is not subject to a linear relationship.

> Everybody would agree that a linear function is simpler than a function of the second or higher degree . . . For this reason, physics is filled with laws that express proportionality, such as Hooke's law in elasticity or Ohm's laws in electrodynamics. In all these cases, there is no doubt that a non-linear relationship would describe the facts in a more accurate way, but one tries to get along with a linear law as much as possible. (Frank, 1961b, pp. 13–14)

A preference for linear laws and relationships is not limited to physics. We shall see that it plays a part in the description of functional relationships in psychology. In general, there is a tendency to formulate and adhere to relatively simple relationships, although not necessarily linear ones. An example occurs in quality control where samples of manufactured products (for example, radio tubes or flashbulbs), are tested in order to determine whether or not the supply from which the samples were taken meet acceptable standards. It is generally assumed that an exponential relationship is involved here, even though studies by the Bureau of Standards in Washington, D.C., as well as other evidence suggests that the relationship is less simple than an exponential or a logarithmic relationship. Of course parsimony may not be the only reason for adherence to the exponential, linear, or other simplified relationships. Convenience and tradition undoubtedly play their parts.

We previously noted that the principle of parsimony (Occam's razor) has been used in defense of reductionism. However, it should be pointed out that its use for such purposes has been questioned. Occam's razor, it is claimed, is not generally applicable when one discipline or language system is reduced to another, for example, when psychological, humanistic or mentalistic concepts and models are "reduced" to physiological concepts or machine models. MacKay claims: "It is not even possible to defend reductionism by the principle of Ockham's Razor, for this refers to a choice between alternative descriptions in the same language-system, and not to a choice between descriptions in alternative language-systems" (1954, p. 267).

We leave it to the reader to decide for himself whether or not the principle of parsimony is applicable as a defense of reductionism and just how strong a defense it is.

Parsimony in Mathematics

In mathematics there is seldom explicit reference to Occam's razor. Parsimony, however, is involved in an axiomatic presentation of a mathematical theory in the sense that independence of axioms is usually desirable. An axiom is independent if it is not a consequence of the other axioms in the system. If it is nonindependent (if it can be derived as a theorem from the other axioms), then it is redundant to include it as an axiom. In other words, it is unparsimonious to assume it as an axiom, since it can be proven from the other axioms.

The problem of whether or not a particular axiom is independent can be difficult. To show that the axiom is nonindependent, one tries to prove that it can be derived as a theorem from the other axioms. To show that it is independent, one might consider the system that results when the axiom in question is deleted and a contradictory axiom (such as the negation of the axiom) is substituted for it. If the resulting system can be shown to be consistent (that is, not to imply any contradictory statement), then the conclusion is that the original axiom is independent. The underlying reasoning may be worded in this way: If the original axiom, call it A, were a logical consequence of the remaining axioms, then when to these there was adjoined an axiom contradictory to A, which may be called not-A, the resulting system would yield a contradiction, A and not-A, and therefore would not be consistent.

A famous problem concerned the independence or nonindependence of the parallel line axiom in Euclidean geometry. Centuries of efforts devoted to the problem led to the (erroneous) conclusion that the parallel line axiom was nonindependent because substitution of a contradictory axiom led to apparent contradictions, that is, results that contradicted those of Euclidean geometry. It took the mathematical sophistication of Gauss, Boylai, and Lobachevski to recognize that the resulting system was a non-Euclidean geometry which turned out to be as consistent as Euclidean geometry. Therefore, it was concluded that the axiom of parallels is independent of the other axioms in Euclidean geometry. This example illustrates not only how difficult the problem of independence of an axiom can be but also how difficult it may be to know whether or not a contradiction has been found.

A more recent problem is the independence of the axiom of choice, that is, whether or not it can be derived from other axioms of set theory. Beginning in 1904, when Zermelo first explicitly formulated the axiom, many attempts were made to establish its independence. In 1958, the independence of the axiom of choice was still *"an open problem:* the central problem of independence for which, for the time being, no method of possible solution is in sight"* (Fraenkel and Bar-Hillel, 1958, p. 52). In 1963, however, Paul J. Cohen reported that the axiom of choice is independent of an axiom system for set theory.

There have been well-known axiom systems that, unknown to their founders, contained axioms that were not independent. One example is Hilbert's set of axioms for geometry (1899) in which two axioms were later discovered to be consequences of the other axioms. Another example is the system of "primitive propositions" for the propositional calculus of the *Principia Mathematica* (1910–1913) of Whitehead and Russell; Bernays (1926) showed that one of the axioms was nonindependent. Still another example is R. L. Moore's (1916) set of eight axioms for plane topology, which was shown by Wilder (1928) to contain an axiom that was implied by the others.

Thus, while independence of axioms is in line with parsimony, it may be difficult to know whether or not it has been attained. If a system is found to have a nonindependent axiom, this in no way invalidates the system. One simply characterizes the axiom in question as a theorem and supplies the proof of its derivability from the other axioms. Independence of the axioms of a mathematical system is "aesthetically desirable, although not logically important" (Richardson, 1941, p. 455). Independence of an axiom system is generally regarded as less important and less desirable than, for example, the consistency of the system.

> Actually, however, we do not place the same emphasis on independence as we do on consistency. Consistency is *always* desired, but there may be cases where independence is *not* desired. Examples of this arise in the teaching of mathematics. (Wilder, 1952, p. 30)

In teaching geometry as an axiomatic system to high school students or younger students, it may be pedagogically advisable to accept as an axiom a theorem that is very difficult to prove, particularly if it occurs in the early part of the course. Sometimes it may be revealed to the students, when they are more familiar with the subject matter and the methods of proof, that the axiom is really a theorem. It seems to us that, in all honesty, this should be disclosed to the students at the time the axiom is accepted. This may help them to realize that there is no inherent dichotomy between axioms and theorems. What is a theorem might be accepted as an axiom; what is an axiom in one system might be a theorem in another.

Moreover, in teaching it is not always desirable to use the smallest number of axioms from which the theory could be developed, even if this is in the interest of parsimony. For example, Hilbert's axiomatic system of geometry uses fewer axioms than does ordinary high school geometry and proves as theorems what are taken to be postulates in high school. Yet it is perhaps pedagogically wiser to adhere to the less rigorous high school geometry. Even in college and graduate mathematics it is not always advisable, from the point of view of pedagogy or because of considerations of time, to start with the smallest number of axioms which are known to be possible. The problem of the number of axioms is a superficial problem, since arbitrary combinations of the axioms can join any number into one grand axiom. On the other hand, it may make the system clearer and simpler to understand if one axiom is broken into two. Thus the number of axioms "is no measure of simplicity" (Wilder, 1952, p. 31).

Parsimony is implicitly appealed to and unnecessary steps are avoided in proofs. Actually, however, it is possible to have a precise characterization of proof, as in symbolic logic or metamathematics (Kleene, 1952), which does not rule out the possibility of intervening steps that are superfluous and in no way contribute to the desired conclusion. Although fewer steps are aesthetically desirable, the most "natural" proof may not be the shortest in terms of number of steps. Here, again, it is in part a question of to whom the presentation is directed. In a mathematical journal a proof may be abbreviated to the point where it is immediately understood only by mathematicians working in the particular area. Such a proof, though "simple" in terms of number of steps, might not appear simple even to a professional mathematician if it were outside his area of specialization. Thus the mere number of steps is not an indication of simplicity.

Parsimony in Psychology

The principle of parsimony, or Occam's razor, has had a pervasive influence on psychology. It has been said that there is perhaps no better example of consistency in the behavior of the psychologist as a scientific investigator than in his acceptance of the principle of parsimony (Battig, 1962). In psychology, Occam's razor has been associated with Lloyd Morgan's canon (1894) against the use of anthropomorphic explanations of animal behavior. Early experimental studies of animal behavior used anthropomorphic concepts, for example, endowed animals with the capacity to think. Since the time that psychologists began to take Morgan's canon seriously, they have apparently been able to explain animal behavior without resorting to such assumptions. Perhaps because of this apparent success in explaining the behavior of animals, some psychologists began to apply terms used in these explanations to human beings, stating that there is no need to assume cognition and thinking in man. Since cognitive concepts are not necessary, the argument runs, it is more parsimonious to dispense with them and to explain human behavior on the basis of concepts that have been successfully used to explain animal behavior, for example, conditioning. This argument has been challenged. To be rat-centered in explaining human behavior, it has been said, may be as inappropriate as to be human-centered or anthropomorphic in explaining rats' behavior. Without necessarily denying that good research work and significant findings have resulted in the study of animal and human behavior from application of the "simple" concepts and the rejection of assumptions of cognitive concepts, some critics point out that using them may result in overlooking essential aspects of human behavior. The very simplicity of the concepts makes for an oversimplified and impoverished view of man. Moreover, the animal-oriented studies cannot lead to knowledge about the existence or the nature of the overlooked aspects. Chein (1963) makes this point when he states that he has no objections to psychologists determining whether there are any dependable S-R relationships when cognitive processes are disregarded but he does object to their pretending that what was disregarded does not exist or is not a concern of science, or to their remaining oblivious to the fact that they are in no position to say anything about the variation of the ignored factors under the conditions of observation and, in particular, in no position to judge how these factors affect the relationships that they discovered. Chein continues: "The principle of parsimony was never intended as a license to achieve *simplicity* by ignoring the *un*parsimoniousness of nature. The *simplicity* demanded by the principle is of the *explanation*, not of the *explicandum*" (p. 6n). In other words, the simplicity of S-R learning theories may represent a misuse of the principle of parsimony. Moreover, the allocation made in some noncognitive theories of learning, such as conditioning theory, in order that they account for complex aspects of human learning "introduces such complications into the theoretical model as to bring into serious question its greatest alleged virtue, the parsimonious explanation that it offers" (p. 5). Ironically, the advantage of greater parsimony is claimed both by noncognitive as well as by cognitive theorists (Chein, 1963; R. K. White, 1943).

Parsimony and number of variables

Factor analysis provides another example of the influence of the principle of parsimony. The basic premise of factor analysis is that the phenomenon under investigation may be represented as a linear function of a finite (preferably a small) number of independent variables or factors. It has been recognized that the assumption that the function is linear may be an undue simplification. As we previously noted, the assumption of linearity may be due in part to the influence of parsimony. What we are concerned with here is the assumption that there are involved a finite number of independent variables or factors (the fundamental factors or abilities). A reason for this assumption is suggested by Guilford:

> The data with which we begin our task of factor analysis consist of a table of intercorrelations . . . We could be content to assume as many variables as there are tests and to let the question of abilities rest just there. That is what testers have had to do in the past. But there is an infinite number of possible tests, and to assume an infinite number of abilities is *poor scientific economy.* (1936, p. 471, italics ours)

In other words, to assume an infinite number of abilities when a finite number will suffice represents poor scientific economy and may be considered to violate the principle of parsimony. More generally, to assume that the number of underlying numerical variables is infinite when it is actually finite goes against the principle of parsimony. But suppose it is not known whether or not the number of underlying independent variables is finite. To assume that it is, may lead to difficulties. To illustrate this let us suppose that a test performance or other psychological phenomenon (or a dynamic physical system) actually involves only a finite number, n, of independent numerical variables. Then the degrees of freedom of the phenomenon or of the system are n in number. Suppose further that it is assumed at the onset that an infinite number of independent numerical variables (degrees of freedom) is involved. If the subsequent mathematical treatment is adequate, then some of the infinitely many variables which have been assumed will be found to be superfluous and dependent, and the treatment will ultimately result in the reduction of the infinitely many variables to the n independent ones. On the other hand, if the phenomenon or system actually involves infinitely many independent numerical variables or degrees of freedom, then the mathematical treatment can yield only an inadequate account and cannot yield the proper (infinitely many) degrees of freedom.

The point under discussion may become clearer in the terminology of functions and functional. A *functional* may be regarded as a function of infinitely many independent numerical variables or, equivalently, as a function of functions, that is, the independent variables are themselves functions. Suppose that the phenomenon under investigation is actually a function of a numerical variable x, with the function expressed as $u = f(x)$, but that this is unknown and it is assumed to be a function of functions, $u = g(h(x))$; that is, $h(x)$ is assumed to be the independent variable. What will happen? The mathematical treatment, if adequate, should yield the information that $h(x)$ is identically equal to x; that is, $h(x)$ will reduce to x. On the other hand, suppose that the phenomenon under investigation is actually a function of a function but instead it is assumed to be a function of the numerical variable x. Then the mathematical treatment cannot be adequate because there is no way in which x can be "reduced" or "raised" to $h(x)$. Hence, to assume more variables than are actually needed or to assume that the independent variable is a function when it is actually a numerical variable may represent poor scientific economy but it does not prevent the proper solution. To assume fewer variables than is required, to assume a function of numerical variables when a function of functions is actually required, represents imprudent economy since it rules out the possibility of attaining the solution. It is therefore safer, as a general rule, when we do not know if the number of numerical variables or degrees of freedom is finite or infinite, to assume the latter; similarly, when we do not know if the independent variable is a numerical variable or a function, then it is safer to assume the latter. In short, in so far as the number and kind of variables are concerned, it is more in the interest of adequate mathematical treatment to assume more than is needed than to adhere too closely to a principle of parsimony.

Controversy over parsimony in psychology

In a critical evaluation of the role of parsimony in psychology, Battig pointed out that its predominant application by psychologists has been to theory, where it has been invoked with regard to number, quality, and independence of concepts. Parsimony has favored theories based on a single, central concept and has contributed to some fruitless controversies over dichotomous issues, such as heredity versus environment, absolute versus relational choice, reinforcement versus contiguity and "other over-simplified 'either-or' theoretical issues, most of which eventually become resolved only through a somewhat less parsimonious theory incorporating elements of both the original antagonistic positions" (Battig, 1962, p. 558). Parsimony has also favored single-factor theories of learning (for example, that all learning can be explained by conditioning) in contrast to multiple-factor theories which recognize several kinds of learning (see, for example, Tolman, 1949). Parsimonious considerations applied to functional relationships have served as justification for a preference for a linear relationship even when it was inappropriate for the data. For example, coefficients of correlation are usually restricted to the Pearson product-moment correlation coefficient (r), which describes the extent to which a functional relationship between variables corresponds to a linear relationship. This is the case, according to Battig, even though the Pearson product-moment correlation coefficient is known to be inappropriate for nonlinear relationships and even though there are available correlation coefficients (for example, *eta*) for nonlinear relationships. In research design parsimony has favored single-factor designs, in which only one factor or one relationship is varied or studied, in contrast to multifactor designs. Battig notes that the seemingly greater economy of single-factor research designs may be largely illusionary since a multifactor design, by giving an equivalent amount of information as several single-factor studies, may actually be more economical in terms of time and effort. Moreover, a single-factor design cannot give information about possible interactions involving the variable, whereas multifactor studies, where variables can be systematically varied, can do so. "Contrary to popular opinion, the single-factor approach is usually inappropriate, misleading, and a major source of fruitless controversy when unknown interactions are present" (Battig, 1962, p. 565). Parsimony also "plays an important and not always appropriate role" in observation and measurement where its "most obviously unfortunate result has been a limitation on the total amount of observation or number of different measures which are taken" (p. 567). There is a tendency to focus on those aspects of behavior which can be readily observed and measured and to overlook other and perhaps equally significant aspects. Moreover, parsimony has favored unduly simplified procedures in the analysis of data. Battig also mentioned the difficulties involved in psychology in determining whether those conditions hold which are prerequisite for application of the principle of parsimony—namely, that conditions are "otherwise equivalent" except for the alternatives under consideration. He concluded (p. 571) that "psychologists are presently working at a far too simple level, well below the actual level of complexity of our behavioral phenomena," that "psychological research has been significantly retarded by the largely inappropriate use" of criteria pertaining to the principle of parsimony and to simplicity and economy, and that "under conditions where they can be meaningfully applied [such criteria] are also unnecessary." He advocates that "psychologists throw off the yokes of parsimony in any shape or form as a basis for making research decisions . . . [and] ignore considerations of parsimony and simplicity entirely in their choice of research strategy" (p. 571).

As might have been expected, Battig's critique of parsimony has not gone unchallenged. Ressler (1963) disputes Battig's suggestion that psychologists should ignore considerations of simplicity. In its defense he cites the arguments of Kemeny (1953), Feuer (1957), Harre (1959), and Popper (1959). For the problem of selecting an hypothesis to describe a functional relationship between two variables, Kemeny proposed the following approach: "Select the simplest hypothesis compatible with the observed values. If there are several, select anyone of them" (1953, p. 397). Harre (1959) wrote that if the hypotheses were polynomials which corresponded to the observations (data points), then the simplest might be taken as the one of lowest order, degree, and coefficient. Ressler contends that Kemeny's analysis of the problem "makes it clear that an appeal to a simplicity criterion is essential in selecting an hypothesis to describe a functional relationship" (1963, p. 645). Ressler points out the epistemological justification for simplicity given by Popper who claims that simplicity is closely related to the falsifiability of a theory, that is, the ease with which it is possible to test its possible falsehood. A smaller number of measurements or determinations is needed to test the falsehood of a simple theory; the more complex theory is more resistant to such tests. If auxiliary hypotheses are added whenever a theory is in danger of being shown to be false, then the theory "must be described as complex in the highest degree. . . . For the degree of falsifiability of

THE PRINCIPLE OF PARSIMONY

a system thus protected is equal to zero" (Popper, 1959, p. 145). Similarly, Feuer regards Occam's razor as a special case of the verifiability principle and believes that the principle of simplicity "discriminates between motives which welcome experimental test in contrast to those which . . . evade a decision by factual evidence. The principle of simplicity is a warning against the psychological repression of fact by recourse to indefinitely extensible systems of hypotheses" (1957, pp. 113–114). Moreover, Ressler argues that a lack of precision goes hand in hand with a lack of simplicity. An imprecise theoretical statement, he claims, is necessarily a lengthy disjunction (that is, simple statements connected by *or*). The length of the disjunction and the complexity of the statement increase as its degree of imprecision increases. Since a disjunction is true as long as one of its components is true and is false only if all of its components are false, it follows that a "vague, imprecise statement is exceedingly difficult to falsify. . . . The more the statement is imprecise, with the accompanying complexity of the disjunction, the less falsifiable it becomes, until the last vestiges of simplicity disappear simultaneously" (Ressler, 1963, p. 646).

In contrast to Battig's point of view Ressler contends that "the principle of simplicity is essential to any scientific enterprise, that it is fundamentally related to most basic and well-accepted rules of science, and that failure to observe it . . . would severely hamper the progress of psychology . . . [and] would make it exceedingly difficult to answer any questions about nature scientifically" (p. 643).

Although some psychologists would side with Battig and others with Ressler, there are still others who would be reluctant to take either position. Some of these psychologists would tend to agree with Burt's (1963) formulation regarding the use of Occam's razor in psychology:

Now I am heretic enough to plead unashamedly for what Voltaire has called *le superflu—chose très nécessaire*. It is as necessary in science as it is elsewhere. Certainly, so long as the scientist's aim is merely to *prove* things—that is, to reach verifiable conclusions which can be asserted with the highest degree of confidence—Occam's maxim, I willingly grant, provides a sound methodological canon: the fewer assumptions we include in our initial basis, the more we increase the probability of the inferences deduced from them, and the smaller the target we offer for our opponents to attack. Hence if . . . all the psychologist sets out to do is just to "construct operationally testable predictions of human behavior—forecasts which shall have a maximum degree of accuracy", then *a priori* concepts and unproved postulates should be reduced to a minimum. But surely the scientist aspires to something more than this; he wants not only to *prove* things, but also to *understand* things. And for this second purpose a far larger array of initial concepts and postulates will nearly always be essential. In other fields, science is, and always has been, full of such speculative postulates—many, if not most of them, little more than refined versions of the familiar notions of common sense. Why then should the psychologist be forbidden the natural wish to explain and to understand as

well as to prove and to predict? There is just one needful precaution. Inferences based on the two types of interpretative model—the "economical model"
and the "explanatory model," as they may be called—must always be sharply
distinguished, so that the reader should not be misled into attaching to the
latter the same amount of assurance that belongs solely to the former. (p. 61)

Reductionism and Unification
of Sciences

One motivation for reductionism is the belief that it will integrate or
unify the sciences. "Obviously, an inherent attraction of reductive explanation is its implications for possible ways of unifying the separate
scientific disciplines . . . an ultimate aim of many scientific workers"
(Jessor, 1958, p. 170). Integration of the sciences has traditionally been
a goal of philosophy. It is also a goal of those logical positivists who
realize that it is not enough to aim at logical analysis of science. To logical positivists the unification can be achieved only through a unified or
common language of science. The same belief can be traced back to Ernst
Mach, a physicist who was considered a forerunner of logical positivists.
Mach, who believed that all the sciences ultimately form a whole (1886,
cited in Frank, 1961b, p. 88) advocated that all scientific propositions be
expressed in terms of perception. He used perception in the wide sense of
the term, for example, perception of space, time, form, color, warmth.
He held that since every experiment involves observation every scientific
proposition can be established or refuted only by the observer's perceptions. To be acceptable, a proposition had to be reducible to a proposition that contains as predicates only perception terms. Any sentence
that was not so reducible was considered by Mach to be metaphysical
and had to be eliminated from scientific discourse.

Neurath, an economist and a leading logical positivist, although agreeing with Mach that a unified language was necessary, maintained that its
basic concepts should not pertain to perception but to "physical things."
He applied the term *physicalism* to such a language. In physicalism sense
impressions would be derived concepts, that is, reduced to "physical
things." For example, a sensation of warmth or warmth perception is a
perceptual or "phenomenal" concept and does not belong in physicalism,
whereas a chair, for example, is a physical thing.

In his early writings, Carnap tried to use perception as a basis of a
logical language of science, developing a so-called phenomenal language
(1928). In his later writings, he shifted from Mach's to Neurath's viewpoint and sought to construct a physicalistic language of science. Not
only Carnap but the Vienna School of logical positivism shifted readily
from a language based on perception to physicalism. That such a shift
could occur has puzzled many people. Frank, one of the founders of logi-

cal positivism, offered the following explanation: "What is of essential importance is only the question whether we believe that it is possible to comprehend all fields in one and the same language. . . . it is of secondary importance whether this unification be achieved in terms of perception . . . or whether the physical language is to be introduced" (1961b, p. 93). Moreover, the shift does not represent a change in basic philosophy from idealism, which some interpret as Mach's philosophy, to materialism, which some interpret as Neurath's philosophy. Neither idealism nor materialism, both with metaphysical attachments, was of concern to either man. The problem of whether the "real world" consists of perception or of matter is irrelevant. It is, rather, a question of whether the phenomenal language or the physical language is more suitable or more convenient as the language of unified science. It is perhaps comparable, Frank suggested, to the question of what system of symbols is most suitable or most convenient for introducing a unified symbolism in logic.

A unified language may be regarded as consistent with (or perhaps even as a consequence of) a desire for economy or parsimony in science. If a unified body of concepts can serve for all the sciences, then it may result in fewer concepts and in a simpler system of propositions than having separate concepts and propositions for each science. A unified science seems to be in keeping with a principle of economy or parsimony. Thus, this principle may constitute a motivation for the unity of science and, indirectly, for reductionism.

Reductionism has been closely linked with achievement of a unified language, but the two are not inextricably linked. In particular, not all attempts at a unified language have involved the same reductionistic tendency or the hierarchy of sciences that is associated with reductionism. For example, physicalism, which regards physical things as the basic concepts, in a sense suggests that physics is the basic science. But Mach, a scientist with some renown as a physicist, philosopher, and psychologist, believed that even in physics one has to use a language that is applicable to other sciences. Mach wrote: "I want only to take, in physics, a standpoint that does not have to be abandoned immediately when we look over into the field of another science" (1886, cited in Frank, 1961b, p. 88). He did not advocate a language based on physical things or matter, but chose as basic concepts terms from perception. There resulted a phenomenal language somewhat akin to the terminology of certain psychologists, ranging from William James to contemporary Gestalt psychologists. Thus, the basic concepts in Mach's attempt at a unified language are psychological in nature. The concepts of other sciences are to be expressed in terms of the phenomenal or the psychological concepts. From a reductionistic point of view, this may be considered by some to put psychology, rather than physics, in the role of the most basic science. Our concern here is not with whether physics or psychology is the more basic science. We are interested only in showing that attempts at a unified language have not always been concomitant with the traditional hierarchy of the sciences associated with reductionism.

It seems to us that discussions about a unified science and a unified language have tended to confound or at least have not distinguished sufficiently between two issues or propositions: (1) a unified or common language will result in or contribute toward a unified science; and (2) a unified science can be achieved only through a unified language.

These two issues are not equivalent. One may, for example, accept the first issue and yet not accept the second on the grounds that there are other ways to achieve a unified science. Yet the second is often found in discussions of a unified science; for example, Frank wrote, apropos of the introduction of such words as *soul* and *matter*, that they are probably not reducible to the same terms and that "the introduction of an expression of this kind renders impossible the representation of our experiences by a unitary system of terms; in other words, it renders the unification of science impossible" (1961b, p. 90). Note that the intent here is that if a unified system of terms is impossible, then the unification of science is impossible, which is equivalent to the second issue. A modification of it is that a unified science can be achieved only through a specific unified language. "According to Mach, the unification of science is possible, but only by forming all scientific propositions as propositions about complexes of perception" (p. 90).

Propositions 1 and 2 both involve moot issues. There is the question of whether or not a unified language has as yet been attained and whether or not it has resulted or will result in the attainment of a unified science. We are particularly interested here in proposition 2 and in whether the unity of science may be achieved by means other than a unified language (and by means other than reductionism). It is noteworthy that there have been varied approaches to unification of the sciences and that still other approaches are conceivable.

1. The history of human thought reveals various attempts to unify the existing sciences through a unifying idea or theme. Included might be the *Organum* of Aristotle, the writings of St. Thomas Aquinas and other Thomistic philosophers, as well as Hegel's metaphysical system which was intended to encompass all the sciences. Although each of these attempts has been criticized and rejected for various reasons, what is of interest to us is that they represent attempts at unification of the sciences other than through a unified language. Still another approach to integration is through analysis of the history of the sciences and other intellectual thought, in order to find some common trend that can serve to unify the diversity of activities that take place in the name of science. Unification has also been attempted in terms of a common method or methodology. This is sometimes referred to as the *scientific method*. But the scientific method does not have a unique characterization; it has meant different things at different times and to different men (see Chapter 15). Other attempts to unify the sciences are in terms of a common form or structure. This need not be synonymous with a common

language, even though the logical structure of the sciences has been closely related to a unified language in the writings of the logical positivists. The form or structure might be abstracted from the content and language of each science (akin to what formalism did for parts of mathematics) and then a common core or unifying structure sought, without the introduction of a common language or a common body of basic concepts.

2. Unity may be in terms of social institutional organizations, for example, the American Association for the Advancement of Science, wherein all kinds of scientists participate in the exchange of ideas through meetings and publications. The nature of the integration obtained by such social institutions may depend upon the organization's structure and upon how its constitution regulates eligibility for membership which may result in including or excluding various fields of intellectual endeavor.

3. It may be desirable, as some people have suggested (see Bronowski, 1959; Nicolson, 1963), to unify the sciences with those intellectual activities which have been relegated to the humanistic disciplines. The kind of integration achieved may depend on the specific scientific and humanistic activities under consideration and on the mode of approach to their unification.

4. Unity may be approached through an interdisciplinary attack on specific problems of a theoretical or practical nature. These problems can bring together people from different disciplines, each viewing the problems from his orientation and attempting to contribute to their solution. Thus, scientists can be united by the common goal of solving specific problems. Different kinds of problems may result in bringing together different scientists and may also result in different relationships among the scientists. Space research programs, for example, bring together people from different fields. Working together in such programs may be physicists, mathematicians, chemists, aeronautical engineers, electrical engineers, mechanical engineers, each perhaps having received the designation of "space engineer" or some other such title. Moreover, also working in the space program one may find psychologists, biologists, physicians, and so on. Here, integration is brought about by diverse aspects of a common problem and goal.

5. Universities and research centers can work toward integration of the sciences and of the sciences with humanities. In addition to the cooperative interdisciplinary attack on problems mentioned previously, interdisciplinary courses and programs of study may be used. Instructional techniques can be utilized not only to integrate various specialties within one discipline but also to integrate different disciplines (see Luchins, 1955, 1959). Here, the integration is in terms of the scientist himself in that his training and experience acquaint him with different fields. We consider such a scientist a *generalist*, much like a general practitioner in medicine. The generalist in science is produced by interdisciplinary interest and training and experience, in contrast to the specialist in a particular science. History provides us with giants of intellectual thought who were generalists, from Aristotle to da Vinci to Mach. Illustrative of contemporary interest in producing a generalist in science is the bachelor of science degree, with major field of study undesignated, so that the student need not have a major concentration of credit in any one science but can take courses in all of them. Space research programs, industries of various kinds, and computer design and operation can provide a place for a student with such an "unspecialized" degree in science. Also illustrative of an interdisciplinary outlook are the radical modifications in recent years in engineering programs, particularly in their integration with the humanities. The biomedical programs being developed at present are based on interdisciplinary training in the sciences and in medicine. There is also interest in biomedical-engineering programs to turn out a physician who has the

engineering skill to deal with the complex computers and other machines now used in medical diagnosis, research, and practice, and who can participate in the development of new machines.

In brief, attempts at unification of the sciences (and of the sciences with the humanities) need not be limited to attempts to develop a unified language. Such attempts may be in terms of a unifying idea or theme, an underlying trend, common methods or methodology, common form or structure, an integrating organization or group of scientists, an inter-disciplinary attack on a problem or phenomenon, interdisciplinary courses or training that make for unification within the scientist himself, and possibly still other approaches. The question then becomes one of whether this or that proposal to unify the sciences or to unify all intel-lectual activities is adequate. This is, more or less, a pragmatic question, quite distinct from the problem of whether or not the sciences should remain separate and distinct. For certain purposes it may be advisable to consider the sciences as distinct and for other purposes to regard them as unified. In any event, the pursuit of unification is not the same as the attainment of actual unity. If unity of the sciences is achieved, it need not detract from the uniqueness of each science. To consider a trivial example, one of the questions on the Wechsler-Bellevue test asks how a tree and a fly are alike; they are alike, for example, in that they are alive and this concept of "aliveness" can serve as a unifying concept or unifying point of view without eliminating the differences between a tree and a fly. Analogously, a point of view that unifies the sciences need not detract from the unique characteristics that distinguish a particular science. Unification or integration of the sciences does not remove the differences between them but catalogues their concepts in different ways for different purposes.

Finally, it should be noted that there is no general agreement on the desirability of unification of all the sciences, or all the natural sciences, or all the behavioral sciences. For example, Sacksteder (1963) argues in favor of pluralism rather than monistic unification of the behavioral sciences.

Reinterpretation of Reductionism

Reductionism is customarily regarded as involving a relationship that may be described as antisymmetrical rather than symmetrical. A rela-tionship R is said to be symmetrical if when A has the relationship R to B (denoted symbolically by ARB) then B has the relationship R to A, that is, ARB implies BRA. A relationship R is said to be antisym-metrical if when A has the relationship R to B then B does not have the relationship R to A (except in the case when A equals B); in other words,

ARB implies BRA only if A and B are equal but if A and B are not equal, then ARB does not imply BRA. Reductionism, as customarily viewed, involves an antisymmetrical relationship in the sense that if discipline A is reduced to discipline B, B is not considered to be reduced to A. In particular, reductionism is usually regarded as involving a one-directional dependency relationship. If A is reduced to B, then A is considered dependent on B but not the other way around. From this point of view, logicism attempts to establish the dependency of mathematics on logic or, more precisely, the dependency of concepts and propositions of mathematics on those of logic; and physicalism in psychology seeks to establish the dependency of concepts and principles of psychology on those of the physical sciences. Yet it is possible to regard reductionism as involving a two-directional, symmetrical relationship. To approach this conceptualization, let us think of reductionism as an interpretation or reinterpretation of the concepts and propositions of one discipline in terms of the concepts and propositions of another discipline. From this point of view, logicism is an attempt to interpret or reinterpret concepts and propositions of mathematics in terms of those of logic and physicalism is an attempt to interpret or reinterpret concepts and principles of psychology in terms of those of the physical sciences. An example that will prove illuminating is Descartes' analytic geometry, which has been considered to be a reduction of geometry to arithmetic or algebra. Descartes coordinated concepts of geometry with those of arithmetic and algebra. He introduced a coordinate system of perpendicular axes called *rectangular*, *orthogonal*, or *Cartesian* (which is the Latinized form of Descartes' name), with the point of intersection of the axes constituting the origin and the same scale used on all axes to measure directed distances from the origin, denoted by positive and negative numbers. A point is considered to correspond to its set of coordinates with respect to the given coordinate system (a set of real numbers), and a curve or other geometric figure is considered to correspond to the algebraic equation satisfied by the coordinates of the points on the curve or figure and by the coordinates of no other points. It is, therefore, understandable that the name *coordinate geometry* has been considered more appropriate for this discipline than analytic geometry (Brumfiel, Eicholz, and Shanks, 1960, p. 252).

In short, analytic geometry, which has been regarded as reducing geometry to arithmetic or algebra, may be considered to involve coordination or correspondence. Other cases of reductionism can also be regarded as involving coordination or correspondence. From this point of view, logicism seeks to coordinate certain concepts and propositions of logic with those of mathematics; physicalism seeks to coordinate concepts and principles of psychology with those of the physical or natural sciences.

Reductionism, considered as involving a coordination or correspondence, is a symmetrical rather than an antisymmetrical relationship and is not a one-directional dependency relationship. If points are coordinated with numbers or sets of numbers, then the latter are coordinated with points and are just as dependent on the points as the points are on them.

Reductionism, considered as a one-directional dependency relationship, tends to be associated with a notion of a hierarchy of disciplines, wherein the disciplines at the higher levels in the hierarchical ordering are regarded as dependent on, and even as less basic or less fundamental than, those at the lower levels. For example, logical positivism is said to advocate physicalism in psychology as well as "the doctrine of the 'hierarchy of the sciences' in which it is asserted that there is a one-directional conceptual dependence of the various scientific disciplines" (Ackoff, 1952, p. 158). The essence of reductionism has been described as contained in the following related propositions:

> The several disciplines or sciences may be considered as hierarchically ordered from, e.g., physics at the base through chemistry, biology, and psychology, to the social and historical disciplines at the top. . . . The terms or concepts and the relations or laws of one discipline may fully and without loss of meaning be translated into or deduced from those of another discipline. . . . Such deductions or derivability proceeds only in one direction [so that] terms and laws of the higher discipline are "reduced" to those of a lower one. . . . The lower the level of terms employed to explain a given phenomenon, the more causal or fundamental or basic the explanation. (Jessor, 1958, p. 171)

One of the objections to reductionism is the implicit or explicit assumption of a hierarchy of sciences. For one thing, the hierarchical concept, or the concept of levels, of science is not a clear concept (Kroeber, 1952; Jessor, 1958). For another, it tends to be accompanied by value judgments as to the relative "basicness" or scientific character of disciplines in various positions in the hierarchy.

A symmetrical conception of reductionism as involving coordination or correspondence is not concomitant with (and may work in the direction of eliminating) the concept of a hierarchy of sciences and the accompanying value judgments. The discipline of analytic geometry does not, in and of itself, make geometry more or less scientific or at a higher or lower level than algebra or arithmetic. Similarly, if logicism is regarded as a coordination of concepts and principles of mathematics and logic, then it does not impute to either discipline a lower or higher level or the character of a more fundamental discipline. In the same vein, if physicalism is regarded as a coordination of concepts and principles of psychology and of the physical sciences, then it does not impute a lower or less fundamental level or status to psychology.

The conception of reductionism as a one-directional dependency relationship has also been accompanied by the assumption that the concepts of the reduced discipline are somehow made irrelevant, or disappear, or are eliminated or become "nothing but" concepts of the discipline to which it has been reduced. An extreme form of the assumption is that the reduced discipline loses its autonomous character and becomes "nothing but" part of the discipline to which it has been reduced. Such assumptions may be germane to disputes concerning the autonomous nature of various disciplines, such as anthropology, psychology, and biology (L. A. White, 1949; von Bertalanffy, 1951; Jessor, 1958). They may also underlie or add fuel to the controversy between vitalism and mechanism.* Vitalists fear that if biological concepts are reduced to those of the physical sciences, then biological concepts will be eliminated or will be nothing but mechanistic concepts; all that is alive and vital will be accounted for sheerly in terms of machines and mechanics. Vitalists find such consequences untenable and therefore insist that biological concepts cannot or should not be reduced to physical ones. That mechanists find the consequence agreeable may help to account for their insistence that biological concepts be reduced to physical ones. Yet, reduction of the concepts of discipline A to those of discipline B does not necessarily make the former irrelevant or nothing but the latter; nor does it mark an end to the concepts of discipline A or an end to its autonomous nature. For example, reduction of concepts of thermodynamics to mechanics did not make for the disappearance from science of thermodynamic concepts or of thermodynamics itself. To return to the example of analytic geometry. The reduction (coordination) of points to numbers, or sets of numbers, did not eliminate from mathematics either the concept of point or the subject of geometry; geometry retains its autonomous character notwithstanding analytic geometry which has neither displaced nor replaced it. It is not the case that a point on a line is "nothing but" a real number just because there is a one-to-one correspondence between the points on the line and real numbers. Similarly, a point in the plane may be coordinated with (or interpreted as) a pair of real numbers, (a, b), which, appropriately enough, are called its coordinates. The same point may also be coordinated with (or interpreted as) the complex number $a + bi$. In turn, this complex number may be variously coordinated with (or interpreted as) the pair of real numbers (a, b), the given point, or a vector whose initial end is at the origin of the coordinate system and whose terminal end is at the given point. Such coordination or interpretation does not make a complex number nothing but a vector in the plane nor does it make such a vector nothing but a complex number. Moreover, this correspondence between complex numbers and vectors has not eliminated either concept from mathematics, has not made either irrelevant, and has not led to the

---

* We are indebted to Dr. Norman Greenfeld for suggesting this point and the accompanying formulation.

disappearance or loss of autonomy of the subject matter pertaining to complex numbers or the subject matter pertaining to vectors.

What we have been trying to bring out is that reduction of one discipline to another need not bring in its wake the disappearance of the reduced discipline or of its concepts. If psychology is reduced to biology, biology is reduced to chemistry, or anthropology is reduced to psychology, then there seems to be little reason to fear the loss of the autonomy of the reduced discipline or the disappearance of its concepts or their resolution into nothing but concepts of another discipline. At least such fears seem baseless if reductionism is considered to involve coordination between two disciplines or interpretation of one in terms of another.

The coordination or correspondence that underlies the suggested conception of reductionism is similar to what is done when a system A is established as isomorphic to a system B or when a set of elements is shown to be a model for, or an interpretation of, an axiomatic system. This suggests that various activities which have not generally been placed under the rubric of reductionism may belong there if reductionism is regarded as involving a coordination, correspondence, or interpretation.

In short, the suggested symmetrical conception of reductionism seems to be a useful one. Unlike the antisymmetrical conception of reductionism, it does not tend to evoke the controversial notion of a hierarchy of sciences. It may help to dispel the fear that reductionism leads to loss of autonomy of a discipline. The suggested conception reveals the inadequacy of (or, at least, the lack of necessity for) certain assumptions that have been made about reductionism (for example, that the reduced concepts disappear or become nothing but concepts of another discipline) and it may help to eliminate some of the controversy to which these assumptions have contributed. Furthermore, the suggested conception covers not only the activities usually included under reductionism but also includes other activities, such as establishment of an isomorphism or of a model for a system.

Analytic geometry is an elegant and beautiful discipline that is of interest in its own right as well as being of value in other branches of mathematics, such as geometry, algebra, and calculus. Yet, as has been stressed, it has not replaced or devalued geometry, which is sometimes called *synthetic* to distinguish it from analytic geometry. Each discipline is studied for its own merits. For certain purposes or for certain problems it may be better or more suitable to use synthetic rather than analytic geometry. Often one does not know whether a given problem will yield more readily to an analytic or synthetic approach, so that the mathematician tries one approach after the other or a combination of the two. If he is interested in a synthetic (analytic) proof, the mathematician may nonetheless use analytic (synthetic) geometry for suggestions on how to proceed in the proof. It is of interest at times to provide both an analytic and a synthetic proof. Thus, analytic and synthetic geometry complement and supplement each other.

It should be pointed out that there are some mathematicians who do not consider that geometry belongs to mathematics, but perhaps to physics, to geography, or to some earth science. Some go so far as to refuse to use the concepts of geometry. This brings to mind the mathematics professor, "a pure algebraist," who refuses to use the word *point* or to draw a dot on the blackboard or on a paper in order to represent it. Instead, he refers to a point in two-dimensional space (the plane) as an ordered pair of real numbers (a, b) and he refers to a point in n-dimensional space as an ordered n-tuple of real numbers. For this mathematician and others with an antigeometric outlook, the reduction of concepts of geometry to those of arithmetic or algebra makes them more acceptable. They prefer the "reduced concepts" to the original ones. These mathematicians (apparently few in number) resemble the psychologists (who seem to be relatively more numerous) who want psychological concepts reduced to concepts of biology or physics or physiology or mathematics and who prefer the "reduced concepts" to the original ones.

It seems to us that there are suggestions here for psychology. Reduction of psychology to, say, physics would constitute an extremely interesting exercise in reasoning and would yield a discipline that would probably be of interest in its own right as well as of value to psychology as a whole and perhaps of value to physics and other disciplines. But such a reduction need not replace psychology any more than analytic geometry has replaced synthetic geometry. For certain purposes and certain problems it may be more suitable to use the reductionistic approach and the "reduced" discipline, but for other purposes and problems, these may be less suitable than a nonreductionistic outlook and discipline. A reductionistic and a nonreductionistic approach may complement and supplement each other. There is no need to restrict psychologists exclusively to one approach or the other. Of course, some psychologists may have personal preferences for a reductionistic approach or a "reduced discipline" just as some mathematicians prefer analytic geometry to synthetic geometry. But this does not mean that all psychologists must abide by the preference of the few.

Foundations of Psychology

Historical Background

Academic psychology's history since the time of Wilhelm Wundt (1832–1920) suggests that it has been concerned with foundational problems from its very beginning. This concern may stem in part from the philosophical roots from which academic psychology sprang. Of course, all of the sciences may be regarded as having arisen from philosophy if we use its broad meaning of *science in general* or *Wissenschaft*.

> According to this meaning philosophy in general is the methodical work of thought through which we are to know that which "is"; individual "philosophies" are the particular sciences in which individual realms of the existent are to be investigated and known.
>
> With this first *theoretical meaning* of the word "philosophy" a second was very early associated . . . philosophy in the Hellenistic period received the *practical meaning* of an *art of life, based upon scientific principles*. . . . In consequence of this change, purely theoretical interest passed over to the particular "philosophies," which now in part assumed the names of their special subjects of research, historical or belonging to natural science, while mathematics and medicine kept all the more rigorously that independence which they had possessed from the beginning with relation to science in general. (Windelband, 1958, p. 2)

That mathematics kept its independence from philosophy may be a reason why foundations of mathematics is a relatively recent discipline. Whereas mathematics was independent of philosophy, academic psychology was intimately interwoven with philosophy and was one of the last of the sciences to sever its ties with philosophy. In the 1930s, and even later, psychology was sometimes taught in philosophy departments. Perhaps one reason for the interest in foundational problems in psychology may be this long association with philosophy.

Perhaps another reason why foundational problems are in the fore in academic psychology is that its origin and development show less dependence on the craftsman or technological, tradition than do some of the other sciences. For example, metallurgy and chemistry were more steeped in the craftsman tradition than was psychology. About the sixteenth century, the scholarly and craftsman traditions began to interact, contributing to the development of the "new sciences" in the seventeenth century (Mason, 1962). It has been said that problems of the craftsman contributed to the development of the new scientific theories (Conant, 1952; Mason, 1962). For example, Galileo was stimulated by problems in engineering as before him were Leonardo da Vinci, Nicola Tartaglia, Simon Stevin, and others (Mason, 1962, p. 153). In this respect, academic psychology resembles "pure mathematics," which also did not arise from a craft tradition. It would be hard, for example, to make a case for the thesis that Euclid's geometry grew out of the techniques of Egyptian "rope stretchers," or out of Egyptian surveying techniques, or that the theory of numbers arose merely out of counting or computational work.

Some of the problems of early academic psychology were more directly related to issues in scholarly discussions of traditional philosophy than to the problems of people involved in shaping, controlling, and predicting behavior of actual individuals and groups. The fountains that fed the streams of academic psychology were the Lyceum and the Académe and not the market place, home, political state, army, church, clinic, and so on. For example, some academic psychologists were interested in developing a scientific approach to the philosophical problems of how man gains knowledge from the world and in what is the basis of knowledge. It might not be inappropriate to refer to them as experimental epistemologists. In seeking a scientific approach to these and other philosophical problems, psychologists became concerned not only with traditional philosophical problems but also with such questions as what is science and what constitutes the scientific method. Such issues did not concern the average worker in the natural sciences to the same extent as they did in psychology. The natural sciences had developed their experimental methods in conjunction with their craftsman techniques and even while dealing with technical problems. Psychologists turned to the natural sciences to get hints for experimental procedures and became concerned with scientific methodology in general. Interested in a scientific approach to the study of man, psychologists did not begin with the folk wisdom or practical knowledge about man, which had accumulated through the ages, nor did they turn to the "behavior technologists" and their rules of thumb, techniques, and attempts at explanations of behavior. The "mundane" problems that interested the "behavior technologists" were not particularly interesting to academic psychology, which was concerned not so much with the behavior of a particular individual as with obtaining laws of behavior in general. In this respect, academic psychology resembled the conception of psychology in Aristotle's *De Anima*. Generally speaking, it did not start with actual ways in which men in daily life learn, think, and behave and with man's actual needs. It tended to substitute for the problems of real life other problems that lent themselves to experimental investigation in the laboratory. In short, it might be said that early academic psychology tended to reject the problems of real life along with the "know-how" of the nonacademic individuals. At a later date, the functionalists (for example, Dewey) and particularly the Watsonian behaviorists and the Gestalt psychologists criticized the psychology of their time because of its separation from real life and practical problems. These protests did not result in a focus on such problems or in a union of academic psychology with the existing practical or behavior technology.

A few decades ago it was not unusual for students to be told that the practical problems that brought them to psychology were not the concern of academic psychology. Moreover, such courses as social, personality, educational, testing, mental hygiene, and clinical psychology were not taught in some psychology departments. Today these courses are taught in psychology departments, but they may still be regarded as the practical or applied courses in contrast to the pure or academic psychology courses. Some psychologists consider the latter to be the foundational courses and believe that the practical areas, such as clinical and social psychology, depend on knowledge in these courses. But, it has been pointed out (Kelly, 1955) that many psychologists see little relation between the academic courses and the applied areas.

Perhaps it is incorrect to assume that a so-called foundational course in psychology will necessarily be helpful in or basic to the applied areas. A course in foundations of mathematics, concerned with the various foundational schools and their problems, is not likely to be helpful in or basic to the applied mathematical areas. But this is not to say that foundational courses, whether in mathematics or in psychology, should be shunned by students who expect to work in the applied areas. Perhaps it would be best not to try to justify the foundational courses on the grounds that they may be useful for applications. We could try to develop an interest in foundational issues for their own sake. Appeal to the student's curiosity and imagination may help him to see foundational problems as tantalizing issues concerning the nature of man, the nature of society, the nature of knowledge, the nature of science, and so on. Foundational courses could be justified on the grounds that they may make the student wonder and help to enhance characteristics of man as Homo sapiens instead of man as tool user. They could also be justified on the grounds that the Ph.D. degree is a doctor of philosophy degree and indicates an interest in foundational issues. These approaches may be more frank ways of justifying the study of foundational problems than to say that they will make one a better clinician or other kind of applied psychologist. Just what transfer of training effect there is from such academic courses to the applied areas is a matter for research instead of speculative justification.

In addition to foundations in the sense in which we have been using the term, there are also empirical foundations in the sense of fundamental knowledge and skills of a particular area; for example, the empirical foundations of clinical and social psychology. The term *foundations* has these varied meanings in mathematics also. One may open a text entitled *Foundations of Mathematics* without knowing beforehand that it is concerned with the foundational schools and various philosophical and logical problems or that it deals with certain fundamental mathematical knowledge and skills of the kind taught in courses for college freshmen who are not majoring in mathematics. One text or one course is not a substitute for the other and the two meanings of foundations are not interchangeable. In psychology, also, empirical foundations are not a substitute for foundations in the sense of philosophical and logical issues and vice versa. Attempts to substitute one for the other, and failure to distinguish between these two meanings of *foundations*, create some confusion and may contribute to some of the controversy between academic and applied psychology. We shall discuss further the various meanings of foundations of psychology in the next section. In order to concretize the discussion, we shall focus mainly on clinical psychology, where interest in foundations runs high and students often have to take a course or courses in foundations in order to meet their Ph.D. requirements. Sometimes the student expects *empirical* foundations but is presented with *philosophical* foundations and vice versa. Texts on foundations in this area also confound the two meanings.

Foundations of Clinical Psychology

In clinical psychology, as is true of experimental-theoretical psychology and of science on the whole, there is considerable concern with foundations. Despite the popularity of the term *foundations*, there are wide differences of opinion as to the importance of foundations for psychology in general or for clinical theory and practice in particular. Some clinicians regard foundations as rather esoteric, as properly of concern only to philosophers, and as having little or no importance either for a science of psychology or for clinical practice. At the other extreme are those who believe that concern with foundations is advisable and even essential for sound theory and effective practice.

There are also diverse views on how firmly foundations are established for psychology in general or for clinical psychology in particular. Some believe that the foundations already exist, but others consider that not even a good start has been made in this direction. Moreover, divergent opinions exist with reference to the source of foundations. For some clinicians the source is a philosophy or theory of psychotherapy, for example, a particular theory of psychoanalysis. Foundations are sought by others in a theory of personality, motivation, perception, learning, and so on. For example, attempts have been made to found clinical concepts, theory, and practice on concepts and principles of a particular theory of learning (Dollard and Miller, 1950, and Mowrer, 1950).

There is a tendency to attempt to use so-called academic psychology as a foundation for clinical psychology and to relate or reduce clinical concepts to concepts of the academic discipline. Thus, psychoanalytic concepts have been related to and in some cases reduced to learning concepts (for instance, drive-reduction concepts, as in the work of Miller and Dollard and of Mowrer). This may be a part of a trend toward reductionism throughout psychology, evinced in the attempts to reduce concepts and principles of psychology to those of a "more fundamental" discipline. Academic psychology, or a particular branch of it, has been regarded as the more fundamental discipline to which clinical practice should be reduced.

What Are Foundations?

The term *foundations* has been used with a variety of modifiers as well as without. One hears not only about foundations of psychology or of clinical psychology but also about its logical foundations, its methodological foundations, its epistemological and philosophical foundations, and its empirical foundations, with the distinctions among these usually not spelled out. It seems to us that foundations have been used in psychology with at least the three following meanings:

1. *Foundations* may refer to the formal or logical structure of psychology or a branch of psychology. Efforts to establish the formal or logical foundations of a discipline often involve attempts to set up the (informally given) discipline as a formal theory or as an axiomatic or a hypothetico-deductive system. They may also involve attempts to study the relation of the discipline to the findings in the so-called science of science, or philosophy of science. Methodological, epistemological, and philosophical foundations are sometimes (but not always) used as synonymous with one another and with formal or logical foundations.

2. The term also has been used with a referent analogous to that of the foundation upon which a building rests. In this sense, foundations of psychology refer to facts, concepts, knowledge, and techniques that can serve as grounding for theory and practice. Foundation in this sense also refers to ethics, values, means, and ends that should underlie the science and practice of psychology.

3. *Foundations* sometimes refers to descriptions of psychology in terms of professional organization (for example, the structure and function of the American Psychological Association) and in terms of descriptions of the various positions that engage psychologists.

Incidentally, this trichotomy is reminiscent of the three approaches to the study of life that have been attributed to certain Greek philosophers of antiquity.

1'. Psychology, considered the most general science, attempted to arrive at principles which held for life in general. An example is furnished by Aristotle's *De Anima*.

2'. In contrast to this broad philosophical approach was an approach concerned with what used to be called the *doctrines of man*. The concern here was with how people should behave and what should be the nature of interpersonal relationships. Aristotle's *Politics* and *Ethics* may be used as examples, since these books may be interpreted as representing discourses on doctrines of man in contrast to *De Anima* which represents a discussion of principles independent of practical applications.

3'. Still another approach was concerned primarily with descriptions of actual behavior, akin to a naturalist's account of his observations or to a journalist's report of an event.

Examination of 1', 2', and 3' reveals their analogies to 1, 2, and 3, respectively, in the threefold division of referents of the term *foundations*.

Contemporary interest in foundations seems to center on 1, that is, on logical or formal foundations. This interest is reflected in attempts to formalize, to axiomatize, and to "mathematize" psychology. There are some who believe that foundations in the sense of 1 necessarily encompass 2 and 3. They consider that the problems of the logical foundations include the problems of foundations in the sense of 2 and 3 and that establishment of the logical foundations would solve, or help to solve, the problems involved in 2 and 3. They see logical foundations as leading to a unification of the diverse aspects of a discipline, as a means of establishing unity in place of the apparent multiplicity of phenomena and concepts in psychology. Some even regard logical foundations as the progenitor of both sound theory and effective practice. They consider that formalization of a discipline helps to make explicit the bases for building theories and gives the guides for conceptualizing practice so that their effectiveness can be more readily tested. For these and other reasons, some consider that the primary fundament should be in terms of 1.

We do not entirely share the above described view. It seems to us that foundations in terms of 1, 2, and 3 are all important and that one is not an adequate replacement for the other. Those who are interested in foundations in terms of 1 tend to be primarily concerned with formalizing and systematizing the welter of concepts and phenomena in clinical psychology. Those who are interested in foundations in terms of 2 and 3 tend to be primarily interested in guides for clinical practice. But, both motives have a place in the development of foundations. Nor are they mutually exclusive; rather, they complement each other. Concomitantly, foundations in terms of 1, 2, and 3 can complement each other. A logically elegant and abstract scheme to formalize, for example, clinical theory is of interest in itself and, in addition, may be of practical value if it is capable of interpretations that are relevant for clinical theory and practice. Knowledge of existing theories and practices, as well as consideration of issues pertaining to what theories and practices *should* be or *should* do, can be of value in the development of logical foundations. This is not to say that in a search for logical foundations one has to be restricted to, or blinded by, existing theories and practices.

It may be worthwhile again to distinguish between logical and empirical foundations. Empirical foundations of a discipline may be regarded as encompassing certain facts, concepts, principles, and skills; in brief, as encompassing certain (basic) empirical knowledge of the discipline. The empirical knowledge can be used to suggest and to support informal and formal theories, theorettes, hypotheses, speculations, and conjectures. Problems of the logical foundations may have to be distinguished from problems of the empirical foundations of a discipline. They need not be identical. Just such a distinction was made by Carnap in a discussion of the foundations of physics. "Much has been said in recent times," he noted, "about the problem of the so-called philosophical or logical foundations of the individual sciences, by which are understood . . . certain problems of the logic of science in relation to the domains of the sciences" (1937, pp. 322–323). He then distinguished between the problem of the logical foundations of physics and the problem of its "empirical foundation (problem of verification)" (p. 323). In short, in physics, logical foundations and their problems are not a substitute for empirical foundations and their problems. The same distinction may be of value in psychology.

A search for logical foundations is not a substitute for observation and research to discover empirical knowledge, for example, facts, principles, concepts, and techniques (possibly, but not necessarily, implicit or explicit in contemporary psychological theory and practice) that may be able to yield some understanding or rationale of existing practices and to serve as guides or bases for the construction of both theory and practice. A search for formal foundations cannot guarantee that it will lead to the discovery of—and hence does not free us from a search for—empirical knowledge on which to base theory and practice. Moreover, logical foundations by themselves cannot produce all needed empirical knowledge. They may be able to serve as a means of tracing subtle implications of already discovered empirical knowledge. This in turn may allow for extension of results obtained through empirical research. But logical foundations do not necessarily replicate all existing empirical information or all information that may be discovered via observation and learning.

The point may be made that in the development of empirical foundations one is narrowed and tied down by limitations and errors of observational methods and experimental techniques. However, it may be countered that in the development of logical foundations one is narrowed and tied down by limitations and errors of the particular assumptions or postulates with which one starts.

It may not be too farfetched to say that some who regard formal foundations as the primary fundament believe, like some ancient philosophers (to paraphrase Hull, 1959, with some liberties), that one can discover all the secrets of nature by himself, without assimilating existing information, that one does not necessarily have to be well versed in the existing knowledge about a discipline when one plunges into formulation of its foundations. They consider that such formulations will yield existing knowledge and predict new information, that the formulation will itself generate needed empirical knowledge in the discipline. For example, some who regard a particular theory or a particular area of psychology as the source of its formal foundations (for example, a theory of learning or of motivation or a particular mathematical model) sometimes imply that the intensive training they have in this theory or in this area automatically gives them the training, knowledge, and tools needed to deal confidently with actual problems of clinical practice.

Relationship between Discipline and Foundations

At the risk of expressing the obvious, we stress that a discipline and its foundations are not necessarily one and the same. Study of scientific and mathematical foundations has not replaced study of the various branches of these disciplines and their applications. For example, the study of foundations of mathematics is not a substitute for the study of algebra, geometry, topology, analysis, or other branches of mathematics. There are those who consider that foundations of set theory might serve as foundations for mathematics as a whole and even for logic. Yet, the study of foundations of set theory is not a replacement for the study of other branches of mathematics. It is not even a replacement for the study of set theory itself. A text on foundations of set theory is not an adequate substitute for a text on set theory, even when both are on an abstract level (compare *Foundations of Set Theory* by Fraenkel and Bar-Hillel, 1958, with *Abstract Set Theory* by Fraenkel, 1961). A course on foundations of set theory does not generally take the place of a course on set theory any more than a course on foundations of geometry takes the place of a traditional course on geometry.

As it is the case in mathematics, so it is the case in psychology that foundations of psychology do not coincide with psychology as a whole. For example, courses in foundations of clinical psychology are not necessarily adequate replacements for courses in clinical psychology. Moreover, knowledge of foundations of clinical psychology is not a substitute for actual knowledge and skills of clinical psychology and clinical practices.

The problems and goals of a discipline are not exhausted by its foundational problems. For example, foundational problems of mathematics do not include all the problems or all the types of problems found throughout mathematics. Similarly, foundational problems of clinical psychology do not exhaust the problems of clinical psychology, either theoretical or practical problems. The goals of those interested in establishing foundations for clinical psychology do not include the professional goals of all clinical psychologists. Solution of foundational problems of clinical psychology and achievement of foundational goals will not necessarily solve all the problems of clinical psychology or make for the attainment of all the professional objectives of clinical psychologists. In particular, acquaintance with foundations (logical, empirical, or both) of clinical psychology and with foundational problems will not necessarily help the clinician to solve concrete problems that confront him in therapeutic and other clinical situations. But this in no way lessens the importance of studying and investigating foundations and foundational problems of clinical psychology.

Are Foundations Essential?

A foundation, acceptable to all or most mathematicians, has not been developed either for mathematics as a whole or for certain branches of mathematics, such as number theory or set theory. As recently as 1946, an outstanding mathematician wrote: "we are less certain than ever about the ultimate foundations of (logic and) mathematics. Like everybody and everything in the world today, we have our 'crisis.' We have had it for nearly fifty years" (Weyl, 1946, p. 13).

Even more recently, authors of a text on foundations of set theory wrote that "attitudes on how set theory might be given a satisfactory foundation are as yet widely divergent, and a host of problems connected herewith are far from being solved" (Fraenkel and Bar-Hillel, 1958, p. 347). Concluding that foundations of set theory are still somewhat shaky, they point out that, nonetheless, concepts, methods, and results of set theory are widely and successfully utilized throughout mathematics. More generally, although there is no acceptable foundation for mathematics, mathematics is a thriving discipline with many branches and with diverse applications. We stress this point in view of the assumption, implicit in certain contemporary discussions of psychology, that it is essential to develop and to secure a foundation for psychology and, in particular, that a foundation for clinical psychology is a prerequisite for sound clinical theory and practice.

The analogue has not been the case for mathematics and its applications. As Black (1934, p. 4) warns, it is "a fallacy . . . to imagine that the mathematical edifice is in danger through weak foundations" and that philosophy—or, we might add, that the logic of science or the science of science—"must be invited like a newer Atlas to carry the burden of the disaster on its shoulders." Similarly, it may be a fallacy to consider that clinical psychology is in danger of collapsing unless a foundation is erected for it.

This is not to say that foundations and their investigations are unimportant. Rather, it is important to keep them in their proper place and to recognize that foundational investigations can be concomitant with— and need not be prerequisites for—the development of a discipline and its applications.

Despite the interest in foundations of mathematics, there are relatively few mathematicians who are doing research on foundations. Moreover, "it is probably safe to say that the average present-day worker in the foundations [of mathematics] is more interested in the problems to which they have given rise than in the choice or validity of an underlying philosophy" (Wilder, 1952, p. 265).

Analogously, important as are foundations of psychology, not all psychologists have to be working to establish it. Moreover, the problems to which the study of foundations give rise should perhaps be at least of as much interest as concern over the choice or validity of a particular viewpoint or philosophy concerning the nature of foundations or the nature of psychology.

Tolerance of a Variety of Foundations

One reason for investigations of the foundations of a discipline is the hope or belief that they may reveal the relative adequacy of theories concerning the discipline. Thus it may be believed that investigations regarding the foundations of clinical psychology may reveal which of several competing clinical theories is most adequate or may pave the way for development of a new and more adequate theory. Investigations of mathematical foundations seem not to have served such purposes to any large extent. Set theory, where foundational investigations have probably been at least as numerous and intense as in any branch of mathematics, still abounds with competing theories. Discussing this point, Fraenkel and Bar-Hillel wrote:

> But so far we don't see any reason compelling us to believe that there will be a unique solution to the foundational problems of set theory which will induce all mathematicians to accept one such theory as *the* Set theory. . . . The

existence of many competing set theories . . . is hardly harmful enough to justify the imposition of some *credo* or other in this respect . . . there is often only one step from the belief in the existence of an objective criterion that would uniquely determine the issue between competing theories and the belief that one has found this criterion and is therefore entitled to disqualify all these theories, except possibly one. . . . There are many authors who prefer perturbation out of freedom to tranquility out of external coercion. (1958, p. 346)

We do not see any reason compelling us to believe that there will be a unique solution to foundational problems of clinical theory or clinical psychology which will induce all or most psychologists to accept one theory as *the* clinical theory. Existence of many competing clinical theories is not harmful in and of itself and may be preferable to the imposition of some credo or other form of external coercion.

More generally, we think that there should be no tyranny of one conception of foundations of psychology. This means, for example, that logical foundations need not be regarded as the only conception, at the expense of empirical foundations, or vice versa. Furthermore, it means that one approach to logical or empirical foundations (for example, via psychoanalysis, a theory of learning, a theory of perception) need not, on a priori grounds, be regarded as the only approach or as the best possible approach.

Rather than a restriction to any particular conception of foundations on one ground or another, it may be advisable to have more discussions of various conceptions of foundations. These discussions should include attempts at explicit formulations of the nature of foundations as well as formulations of problems that arise from, and within, various conceptions of foundations. They should also include attempts at formulating the objectives of foundations as well as consideration of how the objectives are being achieved and of how they might be achieved.

In this connection it may be of interest to invoke Carnap's advocacy of a *principle of tolerance*, in the study of the logical syntax of languages: *"It is not our business to set up prohibitions, but to arrive at conventions"* (1937, p. 51). A similar principle seems to underlie Curry's plea for tolerance (1951, p. 64), with reference to acceptability of views on the nature or philosophy of mathematics. Discussing Curry's plea, Fraenkel and Bar-Hillel wrote: "Any author who . . . insists that only mathematical systems of a certain kind have a *raison d'être* would do well to ponder once more whether his intolerance does not hamper the progress of science rather than channel it into the only promising road" (1958, p. 343). The implication for psychologists is patent. Consider constructibility (which intuitionists and certain other mathematicians regard as an essential criterion of legitimate mathematics). Fraenkel and Bar-Hillel reason (p. 343) that while constructibility may be a necessary condition for the acceptability of a mathematical theory *for certain purposes*, so that "theories of the constructible" deserve to be studied by mathematicians of any philosophical convictions (and indeed have been studied by people with diverse convictions as well as by those with no known philosophical allegiance), the claim that constructible mathematics is the only *legitimate* mathematics has little chance of convincing anyone who does not share the intuitionist's convictions. By the same token, a particular criterion may be a necessary condition for acceptance of a psychological theory *for certain purposes*. For example, for a given purpose it may be necessary, or at least advisable, that a theory be expressed in traditional psychoanalytic terminology. While theories of psychoanalysis deserve to be studied, and indeed have been studied, by psychologists with diverse convictions, the claim that psychoanalysis is the only *legitimate* clinical theory or therapy warrants careful evaluation and may convince only those who share the psychoanalyst's convictions. The same can be said for those who espouse a certain kind of learning theory, perceptual theory, or other theory, as the basis for clinical practice.

Metaphysics: Theory and Practice

There are diverse metaphysical beliefs implicit in orientations to mathematics. Some of these have been classified as realism, nominalism, and conceptualism. Discussing the various beliefs, Fraenkel and Bar-Hillel note that nominalists, for example, "have a healthy respect for those parts of mathematics which are used in the sciences and many would rather renounce their philosophical intuitions than curtail the useful mathematics" (1958, p. 334). Similarly, many other mathematicians do not allow their philosophical beliefs to place undue restrictions on useful mathematics.

Although metaphysical considerations *are* relevant to the problem of providing a secure foundation for mathematics, nonetheless, in actual applications of mathematics, metaphysical views are often of little concern.

> Metaphysical convictions certainly make no difference—with the possible exception of some very tough-minded intuitionists—for the application of mathematics to science and technology. No director of research in some industrial outfit would inquire into the metaphysical beliefs of the mathematician he is about to hire. There seems to exist no correlation between these beliefs and the performances in which the director of research is interested. In the attempt to solve some set of differential equations, all mathematicians will peacefully cooperate though they might thereafter, during a lunch hour conversation, disagree violently about the "nature of mathematics." We make these commonplace observations, not in order to disparage discussions about the nature of mathematics—this whole book is dedicated to the discussion of one aspect of this problem—but to put them in their right place. (p. 160)

It is our impression that there are directors of psychological institutes who, in hiring a psychologist, would behave quite differently than the director of research just mentioned; they would be interested in his metaphysical beliefs or, at least, in his theoretical preferences. Moreover, there are psychologists who do not reserve their theoretical beliefs for lunchroom conversations but allow them to permeate their applications of psychology, their views of problems, and their reactions to others who hold different beliefs. It seems to us that different views on the nature of psychology or on the nature of a specific branch of psychology really influence the application of psychology. It has been said that experienced therapists, despite their different theoretical convictions, all tend to do about the same things in therapy. We do not concur with this generalization. We have repeatedly seen (in two countries, in four states of the United States, and in many public and private hospitals, clinics, and university psychology departments) that differences in theoretical orientations or convictions can give rise to, or be concomitant with, considerable differences in actual practices of therapy. A conviction concerning the nature of clinical psychology or of psychotherapy may influence not only the approaches to therapy and the choice of methods but also the choice of patients and even the formulation of a patient's problems. We have seen theoretical convictions used to change the nature of the problem and used as justification for particular approaches to a given problem.

It has been said that many mathematicians would rather curb their metaphysical beliefs than curtail useful mathematics. We wonder whether the analogue holds in psychology. The case comes to mind of the student, in need of treatment for a serious emotional disturbance, who agreed to go for treatment to a nearby clinic provided that his counselor would accompany him. The counselor, oriented to nondirective therapy, refused to do so on the grounds that it was not in accordance with this orientation. He was ready to admit that it would be "useful" to the student if he would accompany him to the clinic but contended that to do so was counter to his own theoretical views. Underlying this and similar cases may be the thesis that "useful psychotherapy" or "useful psychology" does not exist independently of theoretical convictions. This thesis, in turn, may be related to the notion that the difference between a trained clinician and a layman, both of whom are involved in therapeutic activity, is that the former can offer theoretical justification for what he does, whereas the layman may be unable to do so but does what he thinks is useful or fitting in a particular situation. Some psychologists may be primarily concerned with the theoretical bases of their psychotherapeutic procedures rather than with their usefulness. In fact, some psychologists consider that the training of psychologists is superior to that of medical doctors because the aim is to train theorists rather than technicians (this, on the questionable assumption that medical doctors are technicians when they do what they consider is required in a situation without necessarily having a clear theoretical basis for their actions).

There tends to be little cooperation among psychotherapists with diverse theoretical convictions (with the exceptions of some institutions where there may be cooperation among the various therapists who take part in a given patient's therapeutic program, sometimes because they all share the same theoretical orientation and at times because the institution insists on cooperation). In private practice, it is unusual for psychotherapists of different theoretical convictions to work cooperatively to help one patient or one group of patients. A therapist might treat a patient after the latter has left a therapist with different theoretical convictions, but it is a rarity for therapists with diverse theoretical orientations to work jointly on a treatment program. For example, a nondirective therapist would not be likely to work jointly with a directive therapist, or a traditional Freudian with an Adlerian, and so on. It is true that therapists with diverse convictions may get together during a case conference in a clinic. But even then it is not unusual for each to give his own interpretation of the case, based on his theoretical convictions, and even to assume that his interpretation, his formulation of the problem, his proposals for treatment, and his evaluations of treatment are the correct ones. What we would like to see is a situation wherein psychotherapists would forget (or overlook or hold in abeyance) their convictions and their metaphysical beliefs in order to work together to help the patient.

In summary, it is difficult to find a counterpart, in psychotherapy, of the situation wherein mathematicians of diverse metaphysical beliefs might work together on the solution of a set of differential equations. But, in all fairness, it should be said that there is little in psychotherapy—or, for that matter, in psychology in general—that corresponds to differential equations in mathematics. For the problems to be solved in psychotherapy, or in psychology in general, there usually is not (despite the popularity of mathematical models) as clear-cut a formulation as for a differential equation and not as much accord on what constitutes a solution as there is usually (but not always) with reference to a mathematical solution of a differential equation. This raises some questions concerning the nature of a problem and the nature of a solution. Answers to such questions may not be solely matters for a priori or theoretical speculations. Some light on these questions may be shed by finding out what psychologists and nonpsychologists mean and to what they refer when they speak of psychological problems and of their solutions. One of the important tasks, as we see it, is to discover specific characteristics of actual problems and their actual solutions in the workday world of psychologists. Of course, a theoretical taxonomy to help classify the problems might also be of value. But we think that naturalistic observation of what constitutes a psychological problem and a solution to it should precede an attempt at theoretical classification. In fact, naturalistic observation may suggest some of the variables and categories to be used in a taxonomy of psychological problems and solutions.

Reasons for Foundational
Preferences

That a given individual holds one or another view toward the foundations of mathematics or the foundations of psychology or any other discipline may be partly a question of personal inclination. This poses some interesting problems for the psychology and sociology of knowledge. What are some of the psychological and sociological factors that incline a person toward one or another view with reference to foundations of mathematics or foundations of psychology or, more generally, one or another philosophical or metaphysical orientation? Moreover, what are some of the psychological and sociological factors that lead scholars to change from one to another orientation? One may say with Fraenkel and Bar-Hillel:

> There are very few contemporary logicians and mathematicians who consistently and unflinchingly have adhered all their lifetime to one philosophical view. . . . Most authors who occupy themselves with the foundations of mathematics have exhibited a curious unsteadiness in matters philosophical. It was only natural for them to ascribe these changes of mind to their increasing maturity of thinking and to regard their later positions as better justified than their earlier ones, in whatever direction the shift might have gone. (1958, p. 338)

A problem for research is to determine the specific factors that contributed to a given change in foundational preference. Was the change made on the basis of objective evidence? Were social pressures involved and, if so, what kinds of pressures? Was the change due to a change in personal attitudes or in one's philosophy of life? Although these are admittedly difficult problems, the difficulties involved should not be considered inherently insurmountable.

Psychology and the Philosophy
of Science

Contemporary psychology has rediscovered philosophy. Even behaviorists among psychologists seriously study philosophy. Whereas it was said of Watson that he would not be found in the same woods with a philosopher, modern behaviorists are interested in philosophers and philosophies, particularly in the philosophical analysis of science. Logical positivism, in particular, seems to have been received with open arms by many psychologists.

Analysis of the various conceptions of science and its foundations offered by different schools of thought in philosophical analysis reveals that clear-cut decisions among them are not the case. We question the value to psychology of accepting one or another conception of science or of the foundations of science, as a dogma to which psychology should conform.

Admittedly, we may be able to gain many worthwhile suggestions from the attempts at philosophical analysis of the sciences and of their foundations. One suggestion we can garner from the history of the natural sciences is that a large amount of work is involved in collecting data on which to build a science. The natural sciences did not emerge out of an academy concerned with philosophy of science or logic or metamathematics; these disciplines emerged after sciences and mathematics were already well under way.

In discussions of the philosophy of science we come across various assertions as to what science is or is not. Interestingly enough, most discoveries in science were made without first securing rules from philosophers of science with reference to the meaningfulness of ideas and principles or with reference to the validity and fruitfulness of methods. That some outstanding logical positivists (for example, Schlick) decided that certain statements of empirical sciences were meaningless and had to be classed with those of ethics and other metaphysical assertions, apparently did not halt scientific discoveries or induce scientists to stop making their "meaningless" statements. In the 1930s, some logical positivists (for example, Carnap) considered that all of philosophical analysis—and hence all that was needed for the study of deductive systems—could be subsumed under *syntax*, the study of the calculi of formal or abstract systems of symbols without reference to the meaning of the symbols. Since then, some, Carnap for example, have come to the point of view that syntax must be supplemented by *semantics*, which is concerned with the meaning of symbols and the relationship of signs to objects outside of the formal system. But neither mathematics nor the natural sciences seemed to wait for the decision as to whether or not syntax sufficed for their study. Nor did the decision seem to affect in any decisive way the concrete activities of mathematicians or the physical scientists.

We do not wish to depreciate the value of the philosophy of science or of philosophical analysis as an intellectual discipline, but wish only to point out that it should not be, and has not been, a dictator or policeman of the activities of mathematicians and natural scientists. Contemporary psychologists who regard the writings of philosophical analysis as dictates as to the form science should take—and who are perhaps concerned with whether or not they are conforming to these dictates—may be able to take comfort in realizing that mathematicians and natural scientists do not seem to be afraid of violating the canons promulgated by philosophical analysis.

We are told both by certain philosophers of science and by certain behavioristically inclined psychologists that the hallmark of a science is that is deals with observable facts and hence its data must be public data open to observation by all rather than private data of immediate experience. On the other hand, we are told that it is the hypothetico-deductive method applied to empirical material which is the essential feature of a science and that certain private data are deducible from general hypotheses in the same way in which public data are deducible. From this second point of view, psychology is a science if it uses the hypothetico-deductive method to produce empirically testable hypotheses, whether or not the consequences of the hypotheses are private and incommunicable (Braithwaite, 1960, p. 9). But if psychology does not use the hypothetico-deductive method, is it really unscientific? Is a given study in psychology which does not use this method outside the pale of science anymore than one which does not use public data? Why should one or another view of science determine whether or not psychology, and the activities of psychologists, are scientific?

With all due respect for the importance of the philosophical or logical analysis of science, it seems to us regrettable that many psychologists are interested only in this aspect of philosophy. We do not agree with Russell's contention that logical analysis is "the main business of philosophy" (1945, p. 202). Philosophy traditionally has had, and still has, other concerns. Some of these can also be of interest to psychologists. Philosophy can provide us with an abundance of hypotheses and even insightful conceptions of the nature of man, the nature of society, and the nature of the relationship between the two. Here too, as in logical analysis, disputes rather than clear-cut answers prevail. But psychologists may be able to examine those ideas for research suggestions and even for possible suggestive solutions to their problems. For example, they may examine the various philosophical doctrines of the nature of man and study their implications for the study of learning, thinking, perception, and motivation. Here, psychologists can get suggestions for new problems toward which to direct their scientific curiosity rather than look to philosophy for restrictions on the form research or theory must take in order to be considered scientific.

Physical scientists do not seem to wait for philosophers to tell them how to go about the business of scientific research and theorizing. May not psychologists do likewise? Contemporary psychologists may see in philosophy of science a chance to bring order and control into a growing discipline. Self-conscious about its status as a science, eager to allay possible doubts about its worthiness to deserve the name of science, psychology seems unduly eager to conform to what philosophical analysis says scientists are supposed to do. It is tempting to draw an analogy to the newly rich, eager to be accepted in high society, who eagerly devour handbooks on etiquette and rules of social protocol, while those already well established in society assume a more casual attitude. Perhaps mathematics and the physical sciences are sufficiently well established to be able to take a casual, even if interested, attitude toward philosophical analysis. If some philosophers should decide that accepted concepts of the natural sciences are meaningless and belong with metaphysics, physicists can afford to shrug their shoulders at their ouster from the philosophical analysis "social register" of science. But it may seem that psychology, eager to prove that it is a science, may have to conform to one or another canon of what constitutes a science. There are several dangers in this. For one thing, philosophical analysis provides diverse answers as to what constitutes mathematics, empirical sciences, and mathematical or scientific propositions (Luchins and Luchins 1963c). If psychology tries to please all logical analysts, it will find the task no more rewarding than did the man with the donkey who tried to please all bypassers and ended up carrying the donkey. A serious issue is involved here. To allow philosophy of science to dictate the form or nature of science and of scientific statements seems to be antithetical to the spirit of science. Science could not have grown had it not rejected certain dictates (see Hull, 1959). Are dictates regarding the nature and form of science any more tolerable than dictates regarding the content of specific scientific propositions? If authority and tradition should not be allowed to dictate that the sun revolves around the earth rather than vice versa, should they be allowed to dictate the form of scientific research and theorizing, even in the name of philosophical or logical analysis?

It has been said that the scientific attitude is that of putting question marks where periods once occurred. It is not known in advance where questions will be placed and where periods will remain. The forms of mathematical and scientific inquiry and theorizing have defied precise description and programming. We cannot program a man or a machine to turn out new mathematical or scientific ideas. To prescribe canons for mathematics or science or to prescribe the form these take may be to put periods where question marks belong.

This does not mean that it is unscientific to try to remove the question marks. Rather it seems to us that it is fully in line with the scientific spirit—which itself has defied precise description—to attempt to characterize science, provided that these attempts are searches for truth, and that a given attempt is regarded as a search and not dictated as *the* means which scientists must use to approach truth. In short, it seems to us that the writings of logical analysis are of most value to science if we recognize that here and there question marks may replace periods.

Psychology's concern with what logical analysis has to say about methodology of science seems to be reflected in the curriculum, particularly the graduate curriculum. It is of interest to compare the number of courses on methodology and experimental design required of and taken by the graduate student of psychology with the number required of and taken by the graduate student of physics. Psychology students (and their instructors) may protest, as they sometimes do, that physicists are naïve with regard to methodological questions of experimental design and lack the sophistication that the courses in question can produce. The question then arises: How does it happen that the naïve methodologists of physics produce fruits, alongside of which psychologists are often ashamed to place the products of their sophisticated methodological thought?

A rather brutish sort of analogy is to compare philosophers of science with librarians seeking for efficient methods to classify and group together books. The library system may affect the availability of information or the ease of access to it, but it does not dictate which books scholars may read. The library system may have much to say about the concepts on the basis of which books are to be placed together on the shelves as well as which books should or should not have similar markings on their spines, but it does not dictate the content of the books. Library classification requires some knowledge of the content of the book and knowledge of the classificatory system; but the author, in writing his book, does not have to take into account the existing classificatory systems.

We are raising the question of whether or not (apart from heuristic and suggestive values) philosophy of science should be expected or should be permitted, to tell us what methods to use in psychology or how to organize our data so that it will be scientific. It makes little difference if these dictates come from philosophers of science who are also psychologists, that is, the methodologists of the department. A librarian may turn author and write a book extolling the virtues of a particular library classificatory system. But this very book may be classified in diverse ways under different systems. Moreover, authors writing books need not be unduly concerned about any of the classificatory systems, certainly not to the extent of influencing what they think and write.

It seems to us that some psychologists anticipate a short cut to a systematic scientific psychology via the pathway of the logic of science, the science of science, or the philosophy of science. Some try to take, as a model for psychology, logical foundations of theoretical physics and mathematics as discussed by logicians and philosophers of science. Perhaps it is believed that such a model may obviate some of the mistakes made and some of the detours taken in attempts to develop foundations for physics. By beginning with a sound formulation of a science, as provided in the science of science, some psychologists hope to build psychology on a firm foundation via the logic of science.

What may be overlooked in these attempts is that logical foundations, as read into a particular science by logicians or philosophers of science, are not necessarily isomorphic to empirical foundations of the science and are not likely to be the bases on which the science was actually built. The science of physics, for example, has not developed historically in accordance with the structures and strictures that have been ascribed to it by logicians or philosophers. (A point could even be made that physics, as we know it today, might never have developed if it had to await the establishment of logical foundations. Indeed, it is doubtful that such foundations have as yet been established. Moreover, in the historical development of physics there have been apparent violations of some of the formal tenets and principles which are sometimes regarded as basal to a science.) Attempts at obtaining logical foundations of physics constitute relatively late developments, representing attempts to formalize and systematize already existing informal theories. The same is the case for foundations of mathematics. Perhaps even in psychology there is no short cut, no royal road to foundations, which eliminates or cuts down considerably the need for empirical knowledge and research and for informal formulations.

Bibliography

Ackermann, W. 1954 *Solvable cases of the decision problem.* Amsterdam: North-Holland Pub.

Ackoff, R. L. 1952 Scientific method and social science—East and West. *Sci. Monogr.*, **75**, 155–160.

Adler, I. 1960 *The new mathematics.* New York: New American Library.

Adler, I. 1961 *Thinking machines.* New York: New American Library.

Aléksandrov, A. D. 1951 Ob idéalizmé v matématiki (on idealism in mathematics). *Priroda* (Leningrad), **7**, 3–11; **8**, 3–9.

Alexander, P. 1956 Complementary descriptions. *Mind,* **65**, 145–165.

Alexander, P. 1958 Theory-construction and theory-testing. *Brit. J. Phil. Sci.*, **10**, 29–38.

Alston, W. P. 1958 Ontological commitments. *Phil. Stud.*, **9**, 8–17.

Andree, R. V. 1959 *Selections from modern abstract algebra.* New York: Holt, Rinehart and Winston.

Apostle, H. G. 1952 *Aristotle's philosophy of mathematics.* Chicago: Univer. of Chicago Press.

Aristotle 1920 *Collected works.* (Oxford translation) New York: Oxford Univer. Press.

Armer, P. 1963 Attitudes towards intelligent machines. In E. A. Feigenbaum and I. Feldman (Eds.), *Computers and thought.* New York: McGraw-Hill.

Artin, E. 1957 *Geometric algebra.* New York: Interscience.

Ashby, W. R. 1952 *Design for a brain.* New York: Wiley.

Ashby, W. R. 1956 *An introduction to cybernetics.* New York: Wiley.

Atkinson, R. C. (Ed.) 1963 *Studies in mathematical psychology.* Vol. 1. Stanford, Calif.: Stanford Univer. Press.

Attneave, F. 1954 Some informational aspects of visual perception. *Psychol. Rev.*, **61**, 183–193.

Attneave, F. 1959 *Application of information theory.* New York: Holt, Rinehart and Winston.

Audley, R. J. 1960 A stochastic model for individual choice behavior. *Psychol. Rev.*, **67**, 1–15.

Ayer, A. J. 1946 *Language, truth and logic.* New York: Oxford Univer. Press.

Ayer, A. J. 1953 Truth. *Rev. int. Phil.*, **7**, 183–200.

Bacon, F. 1878 (1620) *Novum organum.* (Ed. T. Fowler) New York: Oxford Univer. Press.

Banach, S., & A. Tarski 1924 Sur la décomposition des ensembles de points en parties respectivement congruentes. *Fund. Math.*, **6**, 244–277.

Barber, B. 1961 Resistance by scientists to scientific discovery. *Science,* **134**, 596–602.

Bar-Hillel, Y. 1957 Husserl's conception of a purely logical grammar. *Phil. Phenomem. Res.*, **17**, 362–369.

Barker, S. F. 1961 The role of simplicity in explanation. In H. Feigl and G. Maxwell (Eds.), *Current issues in the philosophy of science.* New York: Holt, Rinehart and Winston.

Barnett, L. 1957 *The universe and Dr. Einstein.* New York: New American Library.

Bartlett, Sir F. 1959 Some problems of scientific thinking. *Ergonomics*, **2**, 229–238.

Battig, W. F. 1962 Parsimony in psychology. *Psychol. Rep.*, **11**, 555–572.

Beck, L. W. 1950 Constructions and inferred entities. *Phil. Sci.*, **17**, 74–86.

Becker, O. 1954 *Grundlagen der Mathematik in geschichtlicher Entwicklung.* Freiburg: K. Alber.

Bell, E. T. 1951 *Mathematics: queen and servant of science.* New York: McGraw-Hill.

Benacerraf, P., & H. Putnam (Eds.) 1964 *Philosophy of mathematics.* Englewood Cliffs, N.J.: Prentice-Hall.

Bergmann, G. 1951 The logic of psychological concepts. *Phil. Sci.*, **18**, 93–110.

Bergmann, G. 1954 *The metaphysics of logical positivism.* New York: McKay.

Bergmann, G., & K. W. Spence 1941 Operationism and theory in psychology, *Psychol. Rev.*, **18**, 1–14.

Bernays, P. 1926 Axiomatische Untersuchung des Aussagen-Kalküls der "Principia mathematica." *Math. Z.*, **25**, 305–320.

Bernays, P. 1935 Quelques points essentiels de la métamathématique. *L'Ens. Math.*, **34**, 52–69.

Bernstein, A., & M. deV. Roberts 1958 Computers vs. chess-players. *Scientif. Amer.*, **198**, 96–105.

von Bertalanffy, L. 1951 Problems of general systems theory. *Human Biol.*, **23**, 302–312.

Beth, E. W. 1959 *The foundations of mathematics.* Amsterdam: North-Holland Pub.

Beth, E. W. 1962 *Formal methods.* Dordrecht-Holland: D. Reidel.

Bharucha-Reid, A. T. 1960 *Elements of the theory of Markov processes and their applications.* New York: McGraw-Hill.

Birkhoff, G. D. 1933 *Aesthetic measure.* Cambridge, Mass.: Harvard Univer. Press.

Birkhoff, G., & S. MacLane 1944 *A survey of modern algebra.* New York: Macmillan.

Bitterman, M. E. 1960 Towards a comparative psychology of learning. *Amer. Psychologist*, **15**, 704–712.

Black, M. 1934 *The nature of mathematics.* New York: Harcourt, Brace & World. (A paperback edition was published in 1959 by Littlefield, Adams.)

Black, M. 1948 The semantic definition of truth. *Analysis*, **8**, 49–63.

Blair, G. S. 1949 Some aspects of the search for invariants. *Brit. J. Phil. Sci.*, **1**, 1–16.

Blair, G. W. S. 1950 *Measurements of mind and matter.* London: Dennis Dobson.

Blake, R. R., G. V. Ramsey, & L. V. Moran 1951 Perceptual processes as basic to an understanding of complex behavior. In R. R. Blake and G. V. Ramsey (Eds.), *Perception: an approach to personality.* New York: Ronald.

Bocheński, I. M. 1951 *Ancient formal logic.* Amsterdam: North-Holland Pub.

Boole, G. 1854 *An investigation of the laws of thought.* London: Macmillan.

Borel, É. 1926 *Space and time.* London: Blackie.

Borel, É. 1947 *Les paradoxes de l'infini.* Paris: Gallimard.

Borel, É., & R. Deltheil 1931 *La géométrie et les imaginaires.* Paris: A. Michel.

Borgers, A. 1949 Development of

the notions of set and the axioms of sets. *Synthese*, **7**, 374–390.

Boring, E. G. 1961 The beginning and growth of measurement in psychology. In H. Woolf (Ed.), *Quantification: a history of the meaning of measurement in the natural and social sciences.* Indianapolis, Ind.: Bobbs-Merrill.

Borko, H. 1962 *Computer application in the social sciences.* Englewood Cliffs, N.J.: Prentice-Hall.

Bourbaki, N. 1949 Foundations of mathematics for the working mathematician. *J. symbol. Log.*, **14**, 1–8.

Braithwaite, R. B. 1960 *Scientific explanation.* New York: Harper & Row.

Brentano, F. C. 1930 *Wahrheit und Evidenz.* Leipzig: F. Meiner.

Bridgman, P. W. 1954 Science and common sense. *Scientif. Mon.*, **79**, 32–39.

Broadbent, D. E. 1959 Information theory and older approaches in psychology. *Proc. 15th int. Congr. Psychol.*, 111–115.

Bronowski, J. 1959 *Science and human values.* New York: Harper & Row.

Brouwer, L. E. J. 1907 *Over de Grondslagen der Wiskunde.* Amsterdam-Leipzig: Mass & van Suchtelen.

Brouwer, L. E. J. 1908 De onbetrouwbaarheid der logische principes. *Tijdschrift voor Wijsbegeerte*, **2**, 152–158.

Brouwer, L. E. J. 1913 *Intuitionisme en formalisme.* English trans. in *Bull. Amer. Math. Soc.*, 1913, **20**, 81–96.

Brouwer, L. E. J. 1918–1919 *Begründung der Mengenlehre unabhängig vom logischen Satz vom ausgeschlossenen Dritten.* Amsterdam: J. Muller.

Brouwer, L. E. J. 1919a Intuitionistische Mengenlehre. *Proc. Akad. Amsterdam*, **23**, 949–954.

Brouwer, L. E. J. 1919b *Wiskunde, waarheid, werkelijkheid.* Groningen: P. Noordhoff.

Brouwer, L. E. J. 1920 Besitzt jede reele Zahl eine Dezimalbruchentiwicklung? *Proc. Akad. Amsterdam*, **23**, 955–965.

Brouwer, L. E. J. 1923 Begründung der Funktionenlehre unabhängig vom logischen Satz vom ausgeschlossenen Dritten. *Verh. Akad. Wet. Amsterdam*, **13**, No. 2.

Brouwer, L. E. J. 1924 Zur Begründung der intuitionistischen Mathematik, I. *Math. Ann.*, **93**, 244–258.

Brouwer, L. E. J. 1925 Intuitionistische Zerlegung mathematischer Grundbegriffe. *Jahresbericht Deutsch. Math. Ver.*, **33**, 251–256.

Brouwer, L. E. J. 1927 Intuitionistische Betrachtungen über den Formalismus. *Proc. Akad. Amsterdam*, **31**, 374–387.

Brouwer, L. E. J. 1929 Mathematik, Wissenschaft und Sprache. *Monat. Math. Phys.*, **36**, 153–164.

Brouwer, L. E. J. 1950a Remarques sur la notion d'ordre. *C. R. Acad. Sci., Paris*, **230**, 263–265.

Brouwer, L. E. J. 1950b Sur la possibilité d'ordonnes le continu. *C. R. Acad. Sci., Paris*, **230**, 349–350.

Brouwer, L. E. J. 1952 Historical background, principles and methods of intuitionism. *South African J. Sci.*, **49**, 139–146.

Brouwer, L. E. J. 1954 Points and spaces. *Canadian J. Math.*, **6**, 1–17.

Brown, H. C. 1911 The logic of Mr. Russell. *J. Phil.*, **8**, 85–99.

Brumfiel, C. F., R. E. Eicholz, & M. E. Shanks 1960 *Geometry.* Reading, Mass.: Addison-Wesley.

Bruner, J. S. 1960 Individual and collective problems in the study of thinking. *Ann. N.Y. Acad. Sci.*, **91**, 22–37.

Buchwald, A. M. 1961 Verbal utterance as data. In H. Feigl and G. Maxwell (Eds.), *Current issues in the philosophy of science.* New York: Holt, Rinehart and Winston.

Burt, C. 1958 Definition and scientific method in psychology. *Brit. J. statist. Psychol.*, **11**, 31–70.

Burt, C. 1960 Logical positivism

and the concept of consciousness. *Brit. J. statist. Psychol.*, **13**, 55–77.

Burt, C. 1963 The psychology of value. *Brit. J. statist. Psychol.*, **16**, 59–104.

Burtt, E. A. 1932 *The metaphysical foundations of modern physical science*. (rev. ed.) New York: Harcourt, Brace & World.

Burtt, E. A. 1939 *English philosophers from Bacon to Mill*. New York: Random House.

Bush, R. R. 1963 Estimation and evaluation. In R. D. Luce, R. R. Bush, and E. Galanter (Eds.), *Handbook of mathematical psychology*. New York: Wiley.

Bush, R. R., & F. A. Mosteller 1951 A mathematical model for simple learning. *Psychol. Rev.*, **58**, 313–322.

Bush, R. R., & F. A. Mosteller 1955 *Stochastic models for learning*. New York: Wiley.

Caldwell, W. E. 1953 The mathematical formulation of a unified field theory. *Psychol. Rev.*, **60**, 64–72.

Cantor, G. 1952 (1895–1897) *Contributions to the foundation of the theory of transfinite numbers*. (Trans. P. E. A. Jourdian) La Salle, Ill.: Open Court.

Carmichael, R. D. 1930 *The logic of discovery*. La Salle, Ill.: Open Court.

Carnap, R. 1928 *Der logische Aufbau der Welt*. Leipzig: Meines.

Carnap, R. 1935 *Philosophy and logical syntax*. London: Routledge and Kegan Paul.

Carnap, R. 1937 *The logical syntax of language*. (Trans. A. Smeaton) New York: Harcourt, Brace & World.

Carnap, R. 1939 *Foundations of logic and mathematics*. Chicago: Univer. of Chicago Press.

Carnap, R. 1951 *The nature and applications of inductive logic*. Chicago: Univer. of Chicago Press.

Carnap, R. 1954 *Einführung in die symbolische Logik*. Vienna: Springer-Verlag.

Carnap, R. 1956 *Meaning and necessity*. Chicago: Univer. of Chicago Press.

Carroll, J. B. (Ed.) 1956 *Language thought, and reality*. New York: Wiley.

Cartwright, D., & F. Harary 1956 Structural balance: a generalization of Heider's theory. *Psychol. Rev.*, **63**, 277–293.

Cautela, J. R., & H. Mikaelian 1963 A machine capable of being conditioned. *Amer. J. Psychol.*, **66**, 128–134.

Caws, P. 1959 The functions of definitions in science. *Phil. Sci.*, **26**, 201–228.

Chapanis, A. 1961 Men, machines, and models. *Amer. Psychologist*, **16**, 113–131.

Chein, I. 1963 The image of man. *J. soc. Issues*, **18**, 1–35.

Cherry, C. 1957 On the validity of applying communication theory to experimental psychology. *Brit. J. Psychol.*, **48**, 176–188.

Church, A. 1928 On the law of excluded middle. *Bull. Amer. Math. Soc.*, **34**, 75–78.

Church, A. 1936 An unsolvable problem of elementary number theory. *Amer. J. Math.*, **58**, 345–363.

Church, A. 1956 *Introduction to mathematical logic*. Princeton, N.J.: Princeton Univer. Press.

Churchman, C. W. 1948 *The theory of experimental inference*. New York: Macmillan.

Churchman, C. W., & R. L. Ackoff 1950 *Methods of inquiry*. St. Louis, Mo.: Educational Pub.

Chwistek, L. 1924–1925 The theory of constructive types. (Principles of logic and mathematics) *Ann. Soc. Polon. Math.*, **2**, 9–48; **3**, 92–141.

Chwistek, L. 1948 *The limits of science*. (Trans. H. C. Brodie and A. P. Coleman) New York: Harcourt, Brace & World.

Cofer, C. N. 1957 Reasoning as associative process: III. The role of verbal responses in problem solving. *J. gen. Psychol.*, **57**, 55–68.

Cohen, J. 1955 Can there be artificial minds? *Analysis*, **16**, 36–41.

Cohen, J. 1961 The concept of mind. *J. psychol. Res.*, **5**, 1–7.

Cohen, P. J. 1961 A note on constructive methods in Banach algebras. *Proc. Amer. Math. Soc.*, **12**, 159–163.

Cohen, P. J. 1963 *The axiom of choice*. Stanford, Calif.: Stanford Univer. Press. Multilithed report.

Cohen, P. J. 1963–1964 The independence of the continuum hypothesis: I and II. *Proc. Nat. Acad. Sci., U.S.A.*, **50**, 1143–1148; **51**, 105–110.

Cohen, M. R., & E. Nagel 1934 *An introduction to logic and scientific method*. New York: Harcourt, Brace & World.

Conant, J. B. 1951 *On understanding science*. New York: New American Library.

Conant, J. B. 1952 *Modern science and modern man*. Garden City, N.Y.: Garden City.

Coolidge, J. L. 1940 *A history of geometrical method*. New York: Oxford Univer. Press.

Coombs, C. H., H. Raiffa, & R. M. Thrall 1954 Some views on mathematical models and measurement theory. *Psychol. Rev.*, **61**, 132–144.

Copi, I. M. 1950 The inconsistency or redundancy of Principia mathematica. *Phil. Phenomen. Res.*, **11**, 190–199.

Copi, I. M. 1953 *Introduction to logic*. New York: Macmillan.

Cotton, J. W. 1955 On making predictions from Hull's theory. *Psychol. Rev.*, **62**, 303–314.

Courant, R., & H. Robbins 1941 *What is mathematics?* New York: Oxford Univer. Press.

Cramér, H. 1946 *Mathematical methods of statistics*. Princeton, N.J.: Princeton Univer. Press.

Culbertson, J. T. 1963 *The minds of robots: sense data, memory images and behavior in conscious automata*. Urbana, Ill.: Univer. of Illinois Press.

Curry, H. B. 1942 The inconsist-

ency of certain formal logics. *J. symbol. Log.*, **7**, 115–117.

Curry, H. B. 1951 *Outlines of a formalist philosophy of mathematics*. Amsterdam: North-Holland Pub.

Curry, H. B. 1963 *Foundations of mathematical logic*. New York: McGraw-Hill.

Cushman, H. E. 1946 *A beginner's history of philosophy*. Boston: Houghton Mifflin.

van Dantzig, D. 1947 On the principles of intuitionistic and affirmative mathematics. *Proc. Akad. Amsterdam*, **50**, 918–929.

van Dantzig, D. 1948 Significs and its relation to semiotics. *10th int. Congr. Phil., Amsterdam*, **2**, 176–189.

Dantzig, T. 1956 *Number: the language of science*. New York: Doubleday.

Davenport, H. 1960 *The higher arithmetic*. New York: Harper & Row.

Davis, M. (Ed.) 1965 *The undecidable*. Hewlett, N.Y.: Raven Press.

Davis, R. C. 1953 Physical psychology. *Psychol. Rev.*, **60**, 7–14.

Dedekind, R. 1872 *Stetigkeit und irrationale Zahlen*. Braunschweig: F. Vieweg.

Dedekind, R. 1888 *Was sind und was sollen die Zahlen?* Braunschweig: F. Vieweg.

Dedekind, R. 1901 *Essays on the theory of number*. (Trans. W. W. Beman) Chicago: Open Court.

De Morgan, A. 1847 *Formal logic*. London: Taylor and Walton.

Descartes, R. 1931 (1637) *Discourse on method*. (Trans. E. S. Haldane and G. R. T. Ross) New York: Cambridge Univer. Press.

De Sua, F. 1956 Consistency and completeness: a résumé. *Amer. Math. Mon.*, **63**, 295–305.

Deutsch, K. W. 1951 Mechanism, teleology and mind. *Phil. Phenomen. Res.*, **12**, 185–223.

Dewey, J. 1909 *How we think*. London: Heath, Cranton.

Dewey, J. 1929 The sphere of the excluded middle. *J. Phil.*, **26**, 701–705.

Dewey, J. 1930 Logic. In E. R. A.

Seligman & A. Johnson (Eds.), *Encyclopedia of the social sciences.* New York: Macmillan.

Dienes, Z. P. 1952 Sulla definizione dei gradi di rigore. *Univer. Torino Rend. Sem. Mat.*, **11**, 223–253.

Dinneen, G. P. 1955 Programming pattern recognition. *Proc. WJCC*, 94–100.

Dirac, P. 1947 *The principles of quantum mechanics.* (3d ed.) New York: Oxford Univer. Press.

Dollard, J., & N. E. Miller 1950 *Personality and psychotherapy.* New York: McGraw-Hill.

Dubos, R. 1961 *The dreams of utopia.* New York: Columbia Univer. Press.

Duhem, P. 1953a *Aim and structure of physical science.* (Trans. P. P. Wiener) Princeton, N.J.: Princeton Univer. Press.

Duhem, P. 1953b Physical theory and experiment. In H. Feigl and M. Brodbeck (Eds.), *Readings in the philosophy of science.* New York: Appleton-Century-Crofts.

Duncker, K. 1945 On problem solving. (Trans. L. S. Lees) *Psychol. Monogr.*, **58**. Whole No. 270.

Dunham, B. 1960 Symbolic logic and computing machines: a survey and summary. In *Summaries: summer institute for symbolic logic, Cornell Univer., 1957.* (2d ed.) Princeton, N.J.: C.R.D., Institute for Defense Analysis.

Eberlein, W. F. 1963 The geometric theory of quaternions. *Amer. Math. Mon.*, **70**, 952–954.

Eddington, A. S. 1924 *The mathematical theory of relativity.* (2d ed.) New York: Cambridge Univer. Press.

Edwards, W. 1954 The theory of decision making. *Psychol. Bull.*, **51**, 380–417.

Edwards, W., H. Lindman, & L. J. Savage 1963 Bayesian statistical inference for psychological research. *Psychol. Rev.*, **70**, 193–242.

Einstein, A. 1950 *Out of my later years.* New York: Philosophical Library.

Einstein, A. 1953 (1923) Geometry and experience. In H. Feigl and M. Brodbeck (Eds.), *Readings in the philosophy of science.* New York: Appleton-Century-Crofts.

Ellis, E. 1951 Notes on the symbolic process. *Mind*, **60**, 62–79.

Ellis, W. D. (Ed.) 1938 *A source book of Gestalt psychology.* New York: Harcourt, Brace & World.

Enriques, F. 1929 *The historic development of logic.* (Trans. J. Rosenthal) New York: Holt, Rinehart and Winston.

Estes, W. K. 1950 Toward a statistical theory of learning. *Psychol. Rev.*, **57**, 94–107.

Estes, W. K. 1961 Growth and function of mathematical models for learning. In *Current trends in psychological theory.* Pittsburgh, Pa.: Univer. of Pittsburgh Press.

Evans, E. 1954 On some semantic illusions. *Mind*, **63**, 203–218.

Farber, M. 1930 A review of recent phenomenological literature. *J. Phil.*, **27**, 337–349.

Feferman, S. 1964 *The number systems.* Reading, Mass.: Addison-Wesley.

Feibleman, J. K. 1956 Mathematics and its application in the sciences. *Phil. Sci.*, **23**, 204–215.

Feibleman, J. K. 1959 The logical structure of the scientific method. *Dialectica*, **13**, 208–225.

Feigenbaum, A. E. 1961 The simulation of verbal learning behavior. *Proc. WJCC*, 121–132.

Feigenbaum, A. E., & J. Feldman (Eds.) 1963 *Computers and thought.* New York: McGraw-Hill.

Feigl, H. 1949 Logical empiricism. In H. Feigl and W. Sellars (Eds.), *Readings in philosophical analysis.* New York: Appleton-Century-Crofts.

Feigl, H. 1955 Functionalism, psychological theory, and the unity of the sciences: some discussion remarks. *Psychol. Rev.*, **62**, 232–235.

Feigl, H. 1959 Philosophical embarrassments of psychology. *Amer. Psychologist*, **14**, 115–128.

Feigl, H., & M. Brodbeck (Eds.) 1953 *Readings in the philosophy of science.* New York: Appleton-Century-Crofts.

Feigl, H., & G. Maxwell (Eds.) 1961 *Current issues in the philosophy of science.* New York: Holt, Rinehart and Winston.

Feigl, H., & W. Sellars (Eds.) 1949 *Readings in philosophical analysis.* New York: Appleton-Century-Crofts.

Festinger, L. 1957 *A theory of cognitive dissonance.* New York: Harper & Row.

Feuer, L. S. 1957 The principle of simplicity. *Phil. Sci.,* **24,** 109–122.

Fisher, G. L., Jr., et al. (Eds.) 1962 *Optical character recognition.* Washington, D.C.: Spartan Books.

Fitch, F. B., & G. Barry 1950 Towards a formalization of Hull's behavior theory. *Phil. Sci.,* **17,** 260–265.

Fitts, P. M. 1951 Engineering psychology and equipment design. In S. S. Stevens (Ed.), *Handbook of experimental psychology.* New York: Wiley.

Fitts, P. M., M. Weinstein, & M. Rappaport 1956 Stimulus correlates of visual pattern recognition. *J. exp. Psychol.,* **51,** 1–11.

Flavell, J. H. 1963 *The developmental psychology of Jean Piaget.* Princeton, N.J.: Van Nostrand.

Fraenkel, A. A. 1961 *Abstract set theory.* Amsterdam: North-Holland Pub.

Fraenkel, A. A., & Y. Bar-Hillel 1958 *Foundations of set theory.* Amsterdam, North-Holland Pub.

Frank, P. 1957 *Philosophy of science.* Englewood Cliffs, N.J.: Prentice-Hall.

Frank, P. 1961a *Modern science and its philosophy.* New York: Collier.

Frank, P. (Ed.) 1961b *The validation of scientific theories.* New York: Collier.

Frazer, R. A., W. J. Duncan, & A. R. Collar 1938 *Elementary matrices and some applications to dynamics and differential equations.* New York: Cambridge Univer. Press.

Frederiksen, H., & H. Gulliksen (Eds.) 1964 *Contributions to mathematical psychology.* New York: Holt, Rinehart and Winston.

Frege, G. 1879 *Begriffsschrift eine der arithmetischen nachgebildete Formelsprache des reinen Denkens.* Halle: Louis Nebert.

Frege, G. 1884 *Die Grundlagen der Arithmetik.* Breslau: M. & H. Marcus.

Frege, G. 1893–1903 *Grundgesetze der Arithmetik.* Vols. I and II. Jena: H. Pohle.

Frege, G. 1960 *The foundations of arithmetic.* (Trans. J. L. Austin) New York: Harper & Row.

Freudenthal, H. 1960 *Lincos: a design of a language for cosmic intercourse.* Amsterdam: North-Holland Pub.

Freytag-Löringhoff, G. 1951 *Philosophical problems of mathematics.* (Trans. A. Zepelin) New York: Philosophical Library.

Friedburg, R. M. 1960 An experiment in mechanical learning. In *Summaries: summer institute for symbolic logic, Cornell Univer., 1957.* (2d ed.) Princeton, N.J.: C.R.D., Institute for Defense Analysis.

Gagné, R. M. 1962 The acquisition of knowledge. *Psychol. Rev.,* **69,** 355–365.

Gagné, R. M. (Ed.) 1962 *Psychological principles in system development.* New York: Holt, Rinehart and Winston.

Galanter, E. 1963 Contemporary psychophysics. In R. Brown, E. Galanter, E. H. Hess, and G. Mandler (Eds.), *New directions in psychology.* New York: Holt, Rinehart and Winston.

Galanter, E., & M. Gestenhaber 1956 On thought: the extrinsic theory. *Psychol. Rev.,* **63,** 218–227.

Galileo, G. 1914 (1632) *Dialogues concerning two new sciences.* (Trans. H. Crew and A. de Salvio) New York: Macmillan.

Gardner, M. 1958 *Logic machines and diagrams*. New York: McGraw-Hill.

Garner, W. R. 1958 Symmetric uncertainty analysis and its implications for psychology. *Psychol. Rev.*, **65**, 183–196.

Garner, W. R. 1962 *Uncertainty and structure in psychological concepts*. New York: Wiley.

Garner, W. R., H. F. Hunt, & E. W. Taylor 1959 Education for research in psychology. *Amer. Psychologist*, **14**, 167–179.

Gauss, K. F. 1863–1903 *Werke*. 9 vols. Leipzig: Teubner.

Gauss, K. F. 1937 *Inaugural lecture on astronomy and papers on the foundations of mathematics*. (Trans. and ed. G. W. Dunnington) Baton Rouge: Louisiana State Univer. Press.

Geach, P. T. 1955 On insolublia. *Analysis*, **15**, 71–72.

Gelernter, H. L. 1960 Theorem proving by machine. In *Summaries: summer institute for symbolic logic, Cornell Univer., 1957*. (2d ed.) Princeton, N.J.: C.R.D., Institute for Defense Analysis.

Gelernter, H. L., J. R. Hansen, & D. W. Loveland 1960 Empirical explorations of the geometry theorem machines. *Proc. WJCC*, 143–149.

Gelernter, H. L., & N. Rochester 1958 Intelligent behavior in problem solving machines. *IBM J. Res. Develpm.*, **2**, 336–345.

Gelfond, A. O. 1960 *Transcendental and algebraic numbers*. New York: Dover.

George, F. H. 1953 Formalization of language systems in behavior theory. *Psychol. Rev.*, **60**, 232–240.

George, F. H. 1956 Logical networks and behavior. *Bull. Math. Biophys.*, **18**, 337–348.

George, F. H. 1959 Models and theories in social psychology. In L. Gross (Ed.), *Symposium on sociological theory*. New York: Harper & Row.

Gibson, J. J. 1950 The visual world. Boston: Houghton Mifflin.

Gilmore, P. C. 1962 Some forms of completeness. *J. symbol. Log.*, **27**, 344–351.

Gleason, H. A. 1961 *An introduction to descriptive linguistics*. New York: Holt, Rinehart and Winston. (The first ed. was published in 1955 as *Descriptive linguistics*.)

Goddard, L. 1958 "True" and "provable." *Mind*, **67**, 13–31.

Gödel, K. 1930 Die Vollständigkeit der Axiome des logischen Funktionenkalküls. *Monat. Math. Phys.*, **37**, 349–360.

Gödel, K. 1931 Über formal unentscheidbare Sätze der *Principia Mathematica* und verwandter Systeme. I. *Monat. Math. Phys.*, **38**, 173–198.

Gödel, K. 1932 Über Vollständigheit und Widerspruchsfreiheit. *Erg. Math. Kollog.*, **3**, 12–13.

Gödel, K. 1933 Zur intuitionistischen Arithmetik und Zahlentheorie. *Erg. Math. Kollog.*, **4**, 35–38.

Gödel, K. 1940 *The consistency of the axiom of choice and the generalized continuum hypothesis with the axioms of set theory*. Princeton, N.J.: Princeton Univer. Press. (A rev. ed. was published in 1951.)

Gödel, K. 1944 Russell's mathematical logic. In P. A. Schlipp (Ed.), *The philosophy of Bertrand Russell*. Evanston, Ill.: Northwestern Univer. Press.

Gödel, K. 1947 What is Cantor's continuum problem? *Amer. Math. Mon.*, **54**, 515–525.

Goldstein, K., & M. Scheerer 1941 Abstract and concrete behavior. *Psychol. Monogr.*, **41**, No. 239.

Goldstine, H. H. 1961 Information theory. *Science*, **133**, 1395–1399.

Goodman, M. 1951 *The structure of appearance*. Cambridge, Mass.: Harvard Univer. Press.

Goodstein, R. L. 1939 Mathematical systems. *Mind*, **48**, 58–73.

Goodstein, R. L. 1950 The formal structure of a denumerable system.

Trans. Amer. Math. Soc., **68**, 174–182.

Goodstein, R. L. 1957 *Recursive number theory*. Amsterdam: North-Holland Pub.

Götlind, E. 1961 Two views about the function of models in empirical theories. *Theorie*, **27**, 58–69.

Gottschaldt, K. 1938 (1926) Gestalt factors and repetition. In W. D. Ellis (Ed.), *A sourcebook of Gestalt psychology*. New York: Harcourt, Brace & World.

Green, B. F. 1961 Using computers to study human perception. *Educ. psychol. Measmt*, **21**, 227–233.

Green, E. J. 1962 *The learning process and programmed instruction*. New York: Holt, Rinehart and Winston.

Grelling, K. 1936 The logical paradoxes. *Mind*, **45**, 481–486.

Grelling, K., & P. Oppenheim 1938a Der Gestaltsbegriff im Lichte der neuen Logik. *Erkenntnis*, **7**, 211–225.

Grelling, K., & P. Oppenheim 1938b Supplementary remarks to the concept of Gestalt. *Erkenntnis*, **7**, 357–359.

Griss, G. F. C. 1948 Logique des mathématiques intuitionists sans négation. *C. R. Acad. Sci., Paris*, **227**, 946–947.

Griss, G. F. C. 1950 The logic of negationless intuitionistic mathematics. *Proc. Akad. Amsterdam*, **53**, 456–463.

Griswell, J., H. Solomon, & P. Suppes 1962 *Mathematical methods in small group processes*. Stanford, Calif.: Stanford Univer. Press.

Gross, L. (Ed.) 1959 *Symposium on sociological theory*. New York: Harper & Row.

Grünbaum, A. 1952 A consistent conception of the extended linear continuum as an aggregate of unextended elements. *Phil. Sci.*, **19**, 288–306.

Grzegorczyk, A. 1959 Some approaches to constructive analysis. In A. Heyting (Ed.), *Constructivity in mathematics*. Amsterdam: North-Holland Pub.

Guilbaud, G. T. 1960 *What is cybernetics?* (Trans. J. MacKay) New York: Grove.

Guilford, J. P. 1936 *Psychometric methods*. New York: McGraw-Hill.

Gulliksen, H. 1958 *Mathematical solutions for psychological problems*. Tech. Report. U.S. Naval Res., Princeton Univer. (Also published in *Amer. Scientist*, 1959, **47**, 178–201.)

Haag, V. H. 1964 *Structure of algebra*. Reading, Mass.: Addison-Wesley.

Hadamard, J. 1945 *The psychology of invention in the mathematical field*. New York: Dover.

Haire, M. (Ed.) 1959 *Modern organizational theory*. New York: Wiley.

Hake, H. W. 1957 *Contributions to the study of pattern vision*. Wright-Patterson AFB, Ohio: ASTIA Document No. AD 142035.

Halmos, P. R. 1950 *Measure theory*. Princeton, N.J.: Van Nostrand.

Halmos, P. R. 1956 Algebraic logic, II. *Fund. Math.*, **43**, 255–325.

Halmos, P. R. 1960 *Naive set theory*. Princeton, N.J.: Van Nostrand.

Hanson, N. R. 1961 Is there a logic of discovery? In H. Feigl and G. Maxwell (Eds.), *Current issues in the philosophy of science*. New York: Holt, Rinehart and Winston.

Hare, A. P. 1961 Computer simulation of interaction in small groups. *Behav. Sci.*, **6**, 261–265.

Harman, W. W. 1962 The humanities in an age of science. *IRE Trans. Educ.*, E-4, 118–126.

Harre, R. 1959 Simplicity as a criterion of induction. *Philosophy*, **34**, 229–234.

Hartung, F. E. 1951 Science as an institution. *Phil. Sci.*, **18**, 35–53.

Hausdorff, F. 1957 (1927) *Set theory*. New York: Dover.

Hayden, D., & E. J. Finan 1961 *Algebra one: teacher's supplement*. New York: Allyn and Bacon.

Heath, T. L. 1912 *The method of Archimedes, recently discovered by Heiberg*. New York: Cambridge Univer. Press.

Heath, T. L. 1921 *A history of Greek mathematics*. New York: Oxford Univer. Press.

Hegel, G. W. F. 1927 *Sämtliche Werke*. Stuttgart: F. Frommann.

Heider, F. 1946 Attitudes and cognitive organization. *J. Psychol.*, **21**, 107–112.

Heisenberg, W. 1962 *Physics and philosophy*. New York: Harper & Row.

Hempel, C. G. 1949 Geometry and empirical science. In H. Feigl and W. Sellars (Eds.), *Readings in philosophical analysis*. New York: Appleton-Century-Crofts.

Hempel, C. G. 1953 On the nature of mathematical truth. In H. Feigl and M. Brodbeck (Eds.), *Readings in the philosophy of science*. New York: Appleton-Century-Crofts.

Henkin, L. 1956 Two concepts from the theory of models. *J. symbol. Log.*, **21**, 28–32.

Herbrand, J. 1931–1932 Sur la non-contradiction de l'arithmétique. *J. Reine angew. Math.*, **166**, 1–8.

Hermes, H. 1951 Zum Bergriff der Axiomatisierbarkeit. *Math. Nachr.*, **4**, 343–347.

Heyting, A. 1930 Die formalen Regeln der intuitionistischen Logik. *Sitz. Preuss. Akad. Wiss. Berlin*, 42–56.

Heyting, A., 1934 *Mathematische Grundlagenforschung. Intuitionismus. Beweistheorie*. Ergebnisse der Math. und Grenzgebiete, 3, No. 4. Berlin: Springer.

Heyting, A. 1935 Intuitionistische Wisskunde. *Math. B.*, **4**, 72–82.

Heyting, A. 1954 Logique et intuitionnisme. *Actes 2e Coll. int. Log. Math.*, 75–82.

Heyting, A. 1955 *Les fondements des mathématiques*. Paris: Gauthier-Villars.

Heyting, A. 1956 *Intuitionism: an introduction*. Amsterdam: North-Holland Pub.

Heyting, A. (Ed.) 1959 *Constructivity in mathematics*. Amsterdam: North-Holland Pub.

Hilbert, D. 1902 *The foundations of geometry*. (Trans. E. J. Townsend.) La Salle, Ill.: Open Court.

Hilbert, D. 1922 Neubegründung der Mathematik. Erste Mitteilung. *Abh. Hamburg Univer.*, **1**, 157–177.

Hilbert, D., 1923 Die logischen Grundlagen der Mathematik. *Math. Ann.*, **88**, 151–165.

Hilbert, D. 1925 Über das Unendliche. *Math. Ann.*, **95**, 161–190.

Hilbert, D. 1928 Die Grundlagen der Mathematik (Mit Diskussionsbemerkungen von H. Weyl und einem Zusatz von P. Bernays). *Abh. Hamburg Univer.*, **6**, 65–92.

Hilbert, D. 1931 Beweis des Tertium non datur. *Nachr. Ges. Wiss. Göttingen Math. Phys. Klasse*, 120–125.

Hilbert, D. 1956 (1899) *Grundlagen der Geometrie*. (Rev. P. Bernays) Stuttgart: Teubner.

Hilbert, D., & W. Ackermann 1928 *Grundzüge der theoretischen Logik*. Berlin: J. Springer.

Hilbert, D., & W. Ackermann 1950 *Principles of mathematical logic*. (Trans. L. M. Hammond, G. G. Leckie, and F. Steinhardt. Ed. R. E. Luce) New York: Chelsea Publishing Company.

Hilbert, D., & P. Bernays 1944 *Grundlagen der Mathematik*. Vols. 1 and 2. Ann Arbor, Mich.: Edwards. (Originally published in Berlin: J. Springer, 1934–1939.)

Hilbert, D., & S. Cohn-Vessen 1952 *Geometry and the imagination*. (Trans. P. Nemenyi) New York: Chelsea Publishing Company.

Hilgard, E. R. 1948 *Theories of learning*. New York: Appleton-Century-Crofts.

Hill, T. E. 1950 *Contemporary ethical theory*. New York: Macmillan.

Hille, E., & R. S. Phillips 1957 *Functional analysis and semi-groups*. Providence, R.I.: Amer. Math. Soc. Publ.

Hinshaw, V., Jr. 1950 Levels of analysis. *Phil. Phenomen. Res.*, **11**, 213–220.

Hobson, E. W. 1957 (1907) *The theory of functions of a real variable and the theory of Fourier's series.* Vols. I and II. New York: Dover.

Hochberg, H. 1959 Axiomatic systems, formalization, and scientific theories. In L. Gross (Ed.), *Symposium on sociological theory.* New York: Harper & Row.

Hochberg, J. E. 1962 Nativism and empiricism. In L. Postman (Ed.), *Psychology in the making.* New York: Knopf.

Hochberg, J. E. 1964 *Perception.* Englewood Cliffs, N.J.: Prentice-Hall.

Hochberg, J. E., & E. A. McAlister 1953 A quantitative approach to figural "goodness." *J. exp. Psychol.*, **46**, 361–364.

Hoffman, K., & R. Kunze 1961 *Linear algebra.* Englewood Cliffs, N.J.: Prentice-Hall.

Hook, S. 1961 *Dimensions of mind.* New York: Collier.

Hooper, A. 1948 *Makers of mathematics.* New York: Random House.

Horst, P. 1963 *Matrix algebra for social scientists.* New York: Holt, Rinehart and Winston.

Hospers, J. 1953 *An introduction to philosophical analysis.* Englewood Cliffs, N.J.: Prentice-Hall.

Hovland, C. I. 1960 Computer simulation of thinking. *Amer. Psychologist*, **15**, 687–693.

Hovland, C. I., et al. 1957 *The order of presentation in persuasion.* New Haven, Conn.: Yale Univer. Press.

Hull, C. L. 1943 *Principles of behavior.* New York: Appleton-Century-Crofts.

Hull, C. L. 1951 *Essentials of behavior.* New Haven, Conn: Yale Univer. Press.

Hull, C. L., et al. 1940 *Mathematico-deductive theory of rote learning.* New Haven, Conn.: Yale Univer. Press.

Hull, L. W. H. 1959 *History and philosophy of science.* New York: McKay.

Hume, D. 1896 *A treatise of human nature.* New York: Oxford Univer. Press.

Humphrey, G. 1951 *Thinking: an introduction to its experimental psychology.* New York: Wiley.

Huntington, E. V. 1955 (1917) *The continuum and other types of serial order.* New York: Dover.

Husserl, E. 1913 *Logische Untersuchungen.* Halle: Louis Nebert.

Husserl, E. 1931 *Ideas: general introduction to pure phenomenology.* New York: Macmillan.

Jacobson, N. 1951 *Lectures in abstract algebra.* Vols. I and II. Princeton, N.J.: Van Nostrand.

Jaśkowski, S. 1936 Recherches sur le système de la logique intuitioniste. *Actual. Sci. Industr.* **393**, 58–61.

Jessor, R. 1958 The problem of reductionism in psychology. *Psychol. Rev.*, **65**, 170–178.

Johansson, I. 1936 Der Minimalkalkül, ein reduzierter intuitionistischer Formalismus. *Compositio Math.*, **4**, 119–136.

Johnson, D. M. 1955 *The psychology of thought and judgment.* New York: Haper & Row.

Johnson, D. M. 1962 Main forms of thought. *Centennial Rev.*, **6**, 120–130.

Jones, W. T. 1952 *A history of Western philosophy.* Vols. I and II. New York: Harcourt, Brace & World.

Jorgensen, J. 1953 Some reflection on reflexivity. *Mind*, **62**, 289–300.

Jourdian, P. E. A. (Ed.) 1952 Introduction. In G. Cantor, *Contributions to the founding of the theory of transfinite numbers.* La Salle, Ill.: Open Court.

Kalmár, L. 1959 An argument against the plausibility of Church's thesis. In A. Heyting (Ed.), *Constructivity in mathematics.* Amsterdam: North-Holland Pub.

Kanger, S. 1957 Provability in logic. *Stockholm Stud. Phil.*, **1**, 1–47.

Kant, I. 1867–1868 *Sämtliche Werke.* Leipzig: L. Voss.

Kant, I. 1929 (1781) *Critique of pure reason.* (Trans. N. Kemp Smith) London: Macmillan.

Kantor, J. R. 1942 Preface to interbehavioral psychology. *Psychol. Rev.*, **5**, 173–193.

Kattsoff, L. 1948 *A philosophy of mathematics.* Ames, Iowa: Iowa State Coll. Press.

Kazemier, B. H., & D. Vuysje (Eds.) 1964 *The concept and the role of the model in mathematics and natural and social sciences.* New York: Gordon and Breach.

Kelly, G. A. 1955 I itch too. *Amer. Psychologist*, **10**, 172–174.

Kemeny, J. G. 1948 Models of logical systems. *J. symbol. Log.*, **15**, 16–30.

Kemeny, J. G. 1953 The use of simplicity in induction. *Phil. Rev.*, **62**, 391–408.

Kemeny, J. G. 1955 Two measures of complexity. *J. Phil.*, **52**, 721–734.

Kemeny, J. G. 1959a *A philosopher looks at science.* Princeton, N.J.: Van Nostrand.

Kemeny, J. G. 1959b Mathematics without numbers. *Daedalus*, **88**, 577–591.

Kemeny, J. G., & P. Oppenheim 1956 On reduction. *Phil. Stud.*, **7**, 6–17.

Kemeny, J. G., & L. Snell 1957 Markov processes in learning theory. *Psychometrika*, **22**, 221–230.

Kendler, H. H. 1951 Reflections and confessions of a reinforcement theorist. *Psychol. Rev.*, **58**, 368–374.

Kendler, H. H., & T. S. Kendler 1962 Vertical and horizontal processes in problem solving. *Psychol. Rev.*, **69**, 1–16.

Kershner, R. B., & L. R. Wilcox 1950 *The anatomy of mathematics.* New York: Ronald.

Kilpatrick, F. P. 1961 *Explorations in transactional psychology.* New York: New York Univer. Press.

Kleene, S. C. 1943 Recursive predicates and quantifiers. *Trans. Amer. Math. Soc.*, **53**, 41–73.

Kleene, S. C. 1945 On the interpretation of intuitionistic number theory. *J. symbol. Log.*, **10**, 109–124.

Kleene, S. C. 1950 A symmetric form of Gödel's theorem. *Indag. Math.*, **12**, 244–246.

Kleene, S. C. 1952 *Introduction to metamathematics.* Princeton, N.J.: Van Nostrand.

Kleene, S. C., & J. B. Rosser 1935 The inconsistency of certain formal logics. *Ann. Math.*, **36**, 630–636.

Klein, F. 1930 *Famous problems of geometry.* New York: Stechert.

Klein, F. 1932 *Elementary mathematics from an advanced standpoint.* Part 1. (Trans. E. R. Hedrick and C. A. Noble) New York: Macmillan

Koch, S. 1959–1964 *Psychology: a study of a science.* Vols. I through VI. New York: McGraw-Hill.

Koffka, K. 1925 *The growth of the mind.* New York: Harcourt, Brace & World.

Koffka, K. 1935 *Principles of Gestalt psychology.* New York: Harcourt, Brace & World.

Köhler, W. 1925 *Mentality of apes.* London: Routledge and Kegan Paul.

Köhler, W. 1929 *Gestalt psychology.* New York: Liveright.

Köhler, W. 1938a Simple structural functions in the chimpanzee and in the chicken. In E. D. Ellis (Ed.), *A source book of Gestalt psychology.* New York: Harcourt, Brace & World.

Köhler, W. 1938b Physical Gestalten. In E. D. Ellis (Ed.), *A source book of Gestalt psychology.* New York: Harcourt, Brace & World.

Köhler, W. 1938c *The place of value in a world of facts.* New York: Liveright.

Köhler, W. 1941 On the nature of associations. *Proc. Amer. Phil. Soc.*, **84**, 489–502.

Kolmogoroff, A. 1932 Zur Deutung der intuitionistischen Logik. *Math. Z.*, **35**, 58–65.

Körner, S. 1959 *Conceptual thinking.* New York: Dover.

Körner, S. 1962 *The philosophy of mathematics.* New York: Harper & Row.

Kovach, L. D. 1960 Life can be *so* nonlinear. *Amer. Scientist*, **48**, 218–225.

Krechevsky, I. 1937 A note concerning "The nature of discrimination learning in animals." *Psychol. Rev.*, **44**, 97–104.

Kreisel, G. 1951 Some remarks on the foundations of mathematics: an expository article. *Math. Gazette*, **35**, 23–28.

Kreisel, G. 1956–1957 Some uses of metamathematics. (Review of A. Robinson, *Complete Theories*) *Brit. J. Phil. Sci.*, **7**, 161–163.

Kreisel, G. 1959 Interpretation of analysis by means of constructive functionals of finite type. In A. Heyting (Ed.), *Constructivity in mathematics.* Amsterdam: North-Holland Pub.

Kreisel, G. 1962 On weak completeness of intuitionistic predicate logic. *J. symbol. Log.*, **27**, 139–158.

Kroeber, A. L. 1952 *The nature of culture.* Chicago: Univer. of Chicago Press.

Kuratowski, K. 1961 *Introduction to set theory and topology.* New York: Pergamon.

Landahl, H. D. 1962 The mathematical theory of the central nervous system. *Ann. N.Y. Acad. Sci.*, **96**, 1056–1070.

Landau, E. 1960 *Foundations of analysis.* New York: Chelsea Publishing Company.

Lang, S. 1958 *Introduction to algebraic geometry.* New York: Interscience.

Leibniz, G. 1916 *The philosophical works of Leibniz.* (Trans. G. M. Duncan) New Haven, Conn.: Tuttle, Morehouse, and Taylor.

Lejewski, C. 1954 Logic and existence. *Brit. J. Phil. Sci.*, **5**, 1–16.

Lemke, C. E. 1964 Bimatrix games and mathematical programming. AFOSR, Rensselaer Polytechnic Inst. *Math. Rep.*, No. 67.

Lemke, C. E., & J. T. Howson, Jr. 1964 Equilibrium points of bimatrix games. *J. Soc. industr. appl. Math.*, **12**, 413–423.

LeRoy, E. 1901 Un positivisme nouveau. *Rev. Metaphys. Morale*, **9**, 143–144.

Lévy-Bruhl, L. 1926 *How natives think.* London: G. Allen.

Lewin, K. 1936 *Principles of topological psychology.* New York: McGraw-Hill.

Lewin, K. 1951 *Field theory in social science.* New York: Harper & Row.

Lewis, C. I. 1912 Implication and the algebra of logic. *Mind*, **21**, 522–531.

Lewis, C. I. 1917 The issues concerning material implication. *J. Phil. Psychol. scientif. Meth.*, **14**, 350–355.

Lewis, C. I., & C. H. Langford 1932 *Symbolic logic.* New York: Appleton-Century-Crofts.

Lieber, L. R., & H. S. Lieber, 1947 *Mits, wits and logic.* New York: Norton.

Littlewood, D. E., 1960. *The skeleton key of mathematics.* New York: Harper & Row.

Löb, M. H. 1955 Solution of a problem of Leon Henkin. *J. symbol. Log.*, **20**, 115–118.

Löb, M. H. 1956 Formal systems of constructive mathematics. *J. symbol. Log.*, **21**, 63–75.

Löb, M. H. 1959 Constructive truth. In A. Heyting (Ed.), *Constructivity in mathematics.* Amsterdam: North-Holland Pub.

Locke, W. N., & A. D. Booth (Eds.) 1955 *Machine translation of languages.* New York: Wiley.

London, I. D. 1949 The role of the model in explanation. *J. genet. Psychol.*, **74**, 165–176.

Lorenzen, P. 1955 *Einführung in die operative Logik und Mathematik.* Berlin: J. Springer.

Łoś, J. 1954 Sur le théorème de Gödel pour les théories indénombrables. *Bull. Acad. Polon. Sci.*, **2**, 319–320.

Luce, R. D. 1960 *Developments in mathematical psychology.* New York: Free Press.

Luce, R. D. 1963 Detection and recognition. In R. D. Luce, R. R. Bush, and E. Galanter (Eds.), *Handbook of mathematical psychology.* New York: Wiley.

Luce, R. D. 1964 The mathematics used in mathematical psychology. *Amer. Math. Mon.*, **71**, 364–378.

Luce, R. D., R. R. Bush, & E. Galanter 1963a *Handbook of mathematical psychology*. New York: Wiley.

Luce, R. D., R. R. Bush, & E. Galanter 1963b *Readings in mathematical psychology*. New York: Wiley.

Luchins, A. S. 1942 Mechanization in problem solving. *Psychol. Monogr.*, **42**, No. 53.

Luchins, A. S. 1951 An evaluation of some current criticisms of Gestalt psychological work on perception. *Psychol. Rev.*, **58**, 69–95.

Luchins, A. S. 1955 Integration of clinical and experimental-theoretical psychology through core courses. *Psychol. Rep.*, **4**, 221–246.

Luchins, A. S. 1957a Primacy-recency in impression formation (Chap. 4); Experimental attempts to minimize the impact of first impression (Chap. 5). In C. I. Hovland et al., *Order of presentation in persuasion*. New Haven, Conn.: Yale Univer. Press.

Luchins, A. S. 1957b A variational approach to phenomena in social psychology. In M. Sherif and M. D. Wilson (Eds.), *Emerging problems in social psychology*. Norman, Okla.: Univer. of Oklahoma Press.

Luchins, A. S. 1957c A variational approach to empathy. *J. soc. Psychol.*, **44**, 11–18.

Luchins, A. S. 1959 *A functional approach to training in clinical psychology*. Springfield, Ill.: Charles C Thomas.

Luchins, A. S. 1960 On some aspects of the creativity problem. *Ann. N.Y. Acad. Sci.*, **91**, 128–140.

Luchins, A. S. 1961 Some aspects of Wertheimer's approach to personality. *J. indiv. Psychol.* **17**, 20–26.

Luchins, A. S., & E. H. Luchins 1947 A structural approach to the teaching of the concept of area in intuitive geometry. *J. educ. Res.*, **40**, 528–533.

Luchins, A. S., & E. H. Luchins 1953 *A phenomenon-centered varia-tional approach to psychology*. Mimeographed editions by McGill Univer., Univer. of Oregon, and State Univer. of New York.

Luchins, A. S., & E. H. Luchins 1954 Variables and functions. *Psychol. Rev.* **61**, 315–322.

Luchins, A. S., & E. H. Luchins 1959 *Rigidity of behavior: a variational approach to the effect of Einstellung*. Eugene, Ore.: Univer. of Oregon Press.

Luchins, A. S., & E. H. Luchins 1963a The problem of truth in the study of perception. *Psychol. Rec.*, **13**, 213–220.

Luchins, A. S., & E. H. Luchins 1963b The referent of the frame of reference. *Psychol. Rec.*, **14**, 293–304.

Luchins, A. S., & E. H. Luchins 1963c Two philosophies of science. *Synthese*, **15**, 292–316.

Luchins, A. S., & E. H. Luchins 1963d The meaning of real and unreal. (unpublished)

Luchins, A. S., & E. H. Luchins 1964a On the study of invariants. *J. gen. Psychol.*, **70**, 265–267.

Luchins, A. S., & E. H. Luchins 1964b Reactions to inconsistencies: phenomenal versus logical contradictions. *J. gen. Psychol.*, in press.

Luchins, A. S., & E. H. Luchins 1964c On awareness and denotation of contradictions. *J. gen. Psychol.*, **71**, 233–246.

Luneberg, R. 1947 *Mathematical analysis of binocular vision*. Princeton, N.J.: Princeton Univer. Press.

Maatch, J. L., & J. L. Behan 1955 A more rigorous theoretical language. *Psychol. Rev.*, **60**, 189–195.

Mach, E. 1886 *Beiträge zur Analyse der Empfindungen*. Jena: G. Fischer.

MacKay, D. M. 1954 On comparing brains with machines. *Amer. Scientist*, **42**, 261–268.

Madden, E. H. 1957 A logical analysis of psychological isomorphism. *Brit. J. Phil. Sci.*, **31**, 177–191.

Madden, E. H. 1960 *The structure of scientific thought*. Boston: Houghton Mifflin.

Madden, E. H. 1962 *Philosophical problems of psychology.* New York: Odyssey.

Maier, N. F. R. 1933 An aspect of human reasoning. *Brit. J. Psychol.,* **24,** 144–155.

Maier, N. F. R. 1964 *Problem solving.* New York: McGraw-Hill.

Mandler, G., & W. Kessen 1959 *The language of psychology.* New York: Wiley.

Mannoury, G. 1934 Die signifischen Grundlagen der Mathematik. *Erkenntnis,* **4,** 288–309, 317–345.

Mannoury, G. 1947 *Les fondements psychol-linguistiques des mathématiques.* Neuchatel: Griffon.

Margenau, H. 1950 *The nature of physical reality.* New York: McGraw-Hill.

Markov, A. A. 1947 On the impossibility of certain algorithms in the theory of associative systems. *Doklady Akad. Nauk SSSR,* **55,** 583–586.

Martin, R. M. 1959 *Toward a systematic pragmatics.* Amsterdam: North-Holland Pub.

Martin, R. M. 1962 On knowing, believing, thinking. *J. Phil.,* **59,** 586–600.

Marx, H. M., & W. A. Hillex 1964 *Systems and theories in psychology.* New York: McGraw-Hill.

Mason, S. F. 1962 *A history of the sciences.* New York: Collier.

Mays, W. 1962 *The philosophy of Whitehead.* New York: Collier.

McCoy, N. H. 1948 Rings and ideals. *Carus Math. Monogr.,* Math. Assoc. America, Baltimore, Md.: Waverly Press.

McCoy, N. H. 1960 *Introduction to modern algebra.* Boston: Allyn and Bacon.

McCulloch, W. S. 1949 The brain as a computing machine. *Elec. Engng,* **68,** 492.

McCulloch, W. S. 1952 *Finality and form.* Springfield, Ill.: Charles C Thomas.

McCulloch, W. S. 1954 Through the den of the metaphysician. *Brit.*

J. Phil. Sci., **5,** 18–31.

McCulloch, W. S., & J. Pfieffer 1949 Digital computers called brains. *Scientif. Mon.,* **69,** 368–376.

McCulloch, W. S., & W. Pitts 1943 A logical calculus of the ideas immanent in nervous activity. *Bull. Math. Biophys.,* **5,** 115–133.

McGill, V. J. 1939 Concerning the laws of contradiction and excluded middle. *Phil. Sci.,* **6,** 196–211.

McGuigan, E. J. 1953 Formalization of psychological theory. *Psychol. Rev.,* **60,** 377–382.

McGuire, W. J. 1960 A syllogistic analysis of cognitive relationships. In M. J. Rosenberg, C. I. Hovland, et al., *Attitude organization and change.* New Haven, Conn.: Yale Univer. Press.

McKinsey, J. C. C. 1939 Proof of the independence of the primitive symbols of Heyting's calculus of propositions. *J. symbol. Log.,* **4,** 155–158.

McKinsey, J. C. C. 1949 A new definition of truth. *Synthese,* **7,** 428–433.

McKinsey, J. C. C., & P. Suppes 1953 Philosophy and the axiomatic foundations of physics. *Actes XI Congr. int. Phil.,* **6,** 49–54.

McKinsey, J. C. C., & A. Tarski 1946 On closed elements in closure algebras. *Ann. Math.,* **47,** 122–162.

Menger, K. 1954 On variables in mathematics and natural science. *Brit. J. Phil. Sci.,* **5,** 136.

Merrifield, P. R., J. P. Guilford, P. R. Christensen, & J. W. Frich 1962 The role of intellectual factors in problem solving. *Psychol. Monogr.,* **76,** No. 529.

Mesthene, E. G. 1950 On the status of the laws of logic. *Phil. Phenomen. Res.,* **10,** 354–373.

Milhaud, G. 1896 The science rationnelle. *Rev. Metaphys. Morale,* **5,** 280.

Mill, J. S. 1950 (1843) *A system of logic.* In E. Nagel (Ed.), *J. S. Mill's philosophy of scientific method.* New York: Hafner.

Miller, G. A. 1951 *Language and communication.* New York: Mc-Graw-Hill.

Miller, G. A. 1964 *Mathematics and psychology.* New York: Wiley.

Miller, G. A., E. Galanter, & K. H. Pribram 1960 *Plans and the structure of behavior.* New York: Holt, Rinehart and Winston.

Minkin, J. S. 1957 *The world of Moses Maimonides.* New York: Thomas Yoseloff.

Minsky, M. 1961 Steps toward artificial intelligence. *Proc. IRE,* **48,** 8–30.

von Mises, R. 1951 *Positivism: a study in human understanding.* Cambridge, Mass.: Harvard Univer. Press.

Moody, E. A. 1953 *Truth and consequences in mediaeval logic.* Amsterdam: North-Holland Pub.

Moore, G. E. 1922 *Philosophical studies.* London: Routledge and Kegan Paul.

Moore, R. L. 1916 On the foundations of plane analysis situs. *Trans. Amer. Math. Soc.,* **17,** 131–164.

Moore, O. K., & S. B. Anderson 1954 Modern logic and tasks for experiments on problem solving behavior. *J. Psychol.,* **38,** 151–160.

Morgan, D. N. 1953 Creativity today. *J. Aesthet. Art Critic.,* **12,** 1–24.

Mostowski, A. 1959 On various degrees of constructivism. In A. Heyting (Ed.), *Constructivity in Mathematics.* Amsterdam: North-Holland Pub.

Mostowski, A., et al. 1955 The present state of investigations on the foundations of mathematics. *Rozprawy Mat., IX.*

Mowrer, O. H. 1950 *Learning theory and personality dynamics.* New York: Ronald.

Myhill, J. R. 1950a A complete theory of natural, rational, and real numbers. *J. symbol. Log.,* **15,** 185–196.

Myhill, J. R. 1950b A system which can define its own truth. *Fund. Math.,* **37,** 190–192.

Myhill, J. R. 1952 Some philosophical implications of mathematical logic. *Rev. Metaphys.,* **6,** 169–198.

Myhill, J. R. 1953 Criteria for constructibility of real numbers. *J. symbol. Log.,* **18,** 7–10.

Nagel, E. 1929 Intuition, consistency, and the excluded middle. *J. Phil.,* **26,** 477–489.

Nagel, E. 1939 The formation of modern conceptions of formal logic in the development of geometry. *Osiris,* **7,** 142–224.

Nagel, E. 1957 *Logic without metaphysics, and other essays in the philosophy of science.* New York: Free Press.

Nagel, E. 1961 *The structure of science.* New York: Harcourt, Brace & World.

Nagel, E., & J. R. Newman 1958 *Gödel's proof.* New York: New York Univer. Press.

Nagel, E., P. Suppes, & A. Tarski (Eds.) 1960 *Logic, methodology, and philosophy of science: proc. int. Congr.* Stanford, Calif.: Stanford Univer. Press.

Negley, G. 1942 *The organization of knowledge; an introduction to philosophical analysis.* Englewood Cliffs, N.J.: Prentice-Hall.

Nelson, D. 1949 Constructible falsity. *J. symbol. Log.,* **14,** 16–26.

Nelson, D. 1959 Negation and separation of concepts in constructive systems. In A. Heyting (Ed.), *Constructivity in mathematics.* Amsterdam: North-Holland Pub.

von Neumann, J. 1925–1926 Eine Axiomatisierung der Mengenlehre. *J. Reine angew. Math.,* **154,** 219–240; **155,** 128.

von Neumann, J. 1927 Zur Hilbertschen Beweistheorie. *Math Z.,* **26,** 1–46.

von Neumann, J. 1928 Die Axiomatisierung der Mengenlehre. *Math. Z.,* **27,** 669–752.

von Neumann, J. 1931–1932 Die formalistische Grundlegung der

Mathematik. *Erkenntnis*, **2**, 116–121.

von Neumann, J. 1947 The mathematician. In R. B. Heywood (Ed.), *The works of the mind*. Chicago: Chicago Univer. Press.

von Neumann, J. 1951 The general and logical theory of automata. In L. A. Jeffress (Ed.), *The Hixon Symposium*. New York: Wiley.

Neurath, O. 1931 Physicalism: the philosophy of the Viennese Circle. *Monist*, **41**, 418–423.

Newcomb, T. M. 1953 An approach to the study of communication acts. *Psychol. Rev.*, **60**, 493–504.

Newell, A. 1963 *The possibility of planning language in man-computer communication*. Pittsburgh, Pa.: Carnegie Press. Mimeographed report.

Newell, A., J. C. Shaw, & H. A. Simon 1958 Elements of a theory of human problem solving. *Psychol. Rev.*, **65**, 151–166.

Newell, A., & H. A. Simon 1959 *The simulation of human thought*. Santa Monica, Calif.: The Rand Corp. Paper P-1734.

Newell, A., & H. A. Simon 1961 Computer simulation of human thinking. *Science*, **134**, 2011–2017.

Newell, A., & H. A. Simon 1963 Computers in psychology. In R. D. Luce, R. R. Bush, and E. Galanter (Eds.), *Handbook of mathematical psychology*. New York: Wiley.

Nicolson, M. H. 1963 Two voices: science and literature. *Amer. Scientist*, **51**, 454–462.

Niven, I. 1961 *Numbers: rational and irrational*. New York: Random House.

Northrop, F. S. C. 1947 *The logic of the sciences and the humanities*. New York: Macmillan.

Ogden, C. K., & I. A. Richards 1923 *The meaning of meaning*. New York: Harcourt, Brace & World.

Olmsted, J. M. H. 1961 *Advanced calculus*. New York: Appleton-Century-Crofts.

Ortega y Gasset, J. 1932 *The revolt of the masses*. New York: Norton.

Osgood, C. E. 1953 *Method and theory in experimental psychology*. New York: Oxford Univer. Press.

Osgood, C. E. 1963 Psycholinguistics. In S. Koch (Ed.), *Psychology: a study of a science*. New York: McGraw-Hill.

Osgood, C. E., G. Suci, & P. Tannenbaum 1957 *The measurement of meaning*. Urbana, Ill.: Univer. of Illinois Press.

Palter, R. 1956 Philosophical principles and scientific theory. *Phil. Sci.*, **23**, 111–135.

Pap, A. 1949 *Elements of analytic philosophy*. New York: Macmillan.

Peano, G. 1894–1908 *Formulaire de mathématiques*. Vols. I through V. Turin: Bocra.

Peirce, C. S. 1933 *Collected papers of Charles Sanders Peirce*. C. Hartshorne and P. Weiss (Eds.). Cambridge, Mass.: Harvard Univer. Press.

Perry, R. B. 1916 *Present philosophical tendencies*. New York: McKay.

Péter, R. 1959 Rekursivität und Konstruktivität. In A. Heyting (Ed.), *Constructivity in mathematics*. Amsterdam: North-Holland Pub.

Piaget, J. 1947 Du rapport des sciences avec la philosophie. *Synthese*, **6**, 130–150.

Piaget, J. 1949 *Traité de logique*. Paris: Colin.

Piaget, J. 1953 How children form mathematical concepts. *Scientif. Amer.*, **189**, 74–79.

Piaget, J., B. Inhelder, & A. Szeminska 1960 *The child's conception of geometry*. New York: Basic Books.

Pitts, W., & W. S. McColloch 1947 How we know universals: the perception of auditory and visual form. *Bull. Math. Biophys.*, **9**, 127–147.

Pledge, H. T. 1959 *Science since 1500*. New York: Harper & Row.

Plutchik, R. A. 1963 Operationism as methodology. *Behav. Sci.*, **3**, 234–241.

Poincaré, H. 1902 Du rôle de l'intuition et de la logique en mathématiques. *C. R. 2e Congr. int. Math., Paris*, 115–130.

Poincaré, H. 1913 *The foundations of science*. (Trans. G. B. Halstead) New York: The Science Press.

Poincaré, H. 1963 *Mathematics and science: last essays*. (Dernières pensées) (Trans. J. W. Bolduc) New York: Dover.

Polanyi, M. 1946 *Science, faith and society*. New York: Oxford Univer. Press.

Polanyi, M. 1958 *Personal knowledge*. Chicago: Univer. of Chicago Press.

Polya, G. 1954a *How to solve it*. Princeton, N.J.: Princeton Univer. Press.

Polya, G. 1954b *Mathematics of plausible reasoning*. Princeton, N.J.: Princeton Univer. Press.

Popper, K. R. 1959 *The logic of scientific discovery*. New York: Basic Books.

Post, E. L. 1947 Recursive unsolvability of a problem of Thue. *J. symbol. Log.*, **12**, 1–11.

Postman, L. 1963 Perception and learning. In S. Koch (Ed.), *Psychology: a study of a science*. New York: McGraw-Hill.

Pratt, C. C. 1939 *The logic of modern psychology*. New York: Macmillan.

Preston, M. G. 1951 Methodological considerations. In H. Helson (Ed.), *Theoretical foundations of psychology*. Princeton, N.J.: Van Nostrand.

Quastler, H. (Ed.) 1955 *Information theory in psychology*. New York: Free Press.

Quine, W. V. 1951a *Mathematical logic*. Cambridge, Mass.: Harvard Univer. Press.

Quine, W. V. 1951b Two dogmas of empiricism. *Phil. Res.*, **40**, 20–43.

Ramsey, F. P. 1931 *The foundations of mathematics and other logical essays*. R. B. Braithwaite (Ed.), New York: Harcourt, Brace & World.

Randall, J. H., Jr. 1940 *The making of the modern mind*. Boston: Houghton Mifflin.

Raphael, B. 1964 *SIR: a computer program for semantic information retrieval*. Ph.D. Thesis. Cambridge, Mass.: Mass. Inst. Tech.

Rapoport, A. 1948 On the application of the information concept to learning theory. *Bull. Math. Biophys.*, **18**, 317.

Rapoport, A. 1956 A critique of stochastic models for learning. *Behav. Sci.*, **1**, 59–68.

Rapoport, A. 1961 In search of quantifiable parameters of group performance. In D. P. Eckmann (Ed.), *Systems: research and design*. New York: Wiley.

Rapoport, A., & C. Orwont, 1962 Experimental games: a review. *Behav. Sci.*, **7**, 1–37.

Rashevsky, N. 1938 *Mathematical biophysics*. Chicago: Chicago Univer. Press.

Rashevsky, N. 1946 The neural mechanism of logical thinking. *Bull. Math. Biophys.*, **8**, 29–40.

Rashevsky, N. 1951 *Mathematical biology of social behavior*. Chicago: Univer. of Chicago Press.

Rashevsky, N. 1956 The geometrization of biology. *Bull. Math. Biophys.*, **18**, 31–56.

Reichenbach, H. 1938 *Experience and prediction*. Chicago: Univer. of Chicago Press.

Reichenbach, H. 1948 *Philosophical foundations of quantum mechanics*. Berkeley, Calif.: Univer. of California Press.

Reid, C. 1959 *Introduction to higher mathematics*. New York: Crowell.

Reisser, O. L. 1939 Aristotelian, Galilean, and non-Aristotelian modes of thinking. *Psychol. Rev.*, **46**, 151–162.

Rescher, N., & P. Oppenheim 1955 Logical analysis of Gestalt concepts. *Brit. J. Phil. Sci.*, **6**, 89–106.

Ressler, R. H. 1963 Some justification for parsimony in psychology. *Psychol. Rep.* **13**, 643–646.

Restle, F. 1961 *Psychology of judgment and choice*. New York: Wiley.

Rice, H. G. 1954 Recursive real numbers. *Proc. Amer. Math. Soc.*, **5**, 784–791.

Richardson, M. 1941 *Fundamentals of mathematics*. New York: Macmillan.

Richardson, M. 1945 The place of mathematics in a liberal education. *Nat. Math. Mag.*, **9**, 1–10.

Rignano, E. 1928 *Psychology of reasoning*. New York: Harcourt, Brace & World.

Ritchie, A. D. 1960 (1923) *Scientific method*. Paterson, N.J.: Littlefield, Adams.

Robinson, A. 1956 *Complete theories*. Amsterdam: North-Holland Pub.

Robinson, A. 1957 Proving a theorem (as done by man, logician, or machine). In *Summaries: summer institute for symbolic logic, Cornell Univer., 1957*. (2d ed.) Princeton, N.J.: C.R.D., Institute for Defense Analysis.

Robinson, R. M. 1947 On the decomposition of spheres. *Fund. Math.*, **34**, 246–260.

Roby, T. B. 1959 An opinion on the construction of behavior theory. *Amer. Psychologist*, **14**, 129–134.

Rogers, C. R. 1959 A theory of therapy, personality, and interpersonal relationships, as developed in the client-centered framework. In S. Koch (Ed.), *Psychology: a study of a science*. New York: McGraw-Hill.

van Rootselaar, B. 1954 *Generalization of the Brouwer integral*. Thesis. Univer. of Amsterdam.

Rose, G. F. 1952 *Jaśkowski's truth tables and realizability*. Thesis. Univer. of Wisconsin.

Rosenblatt, F. 1958 The perceptron. *Psychol. Rev.*, **65**, 386–407.

Rosser, J. B. 1936a Constructibility as a criterion for existence. *J. symbol. Log.*, **1**, 36–39.

Rosser, J. B. 1936b Extensions of some theorems of Gödel and Church. *J. symbol. Log.*, **1**, 87–91.

Rosser, J. B. 1939a On the consistency of Quine's "New foundations for mathematical logic." *J. symbol. Log.*, **4**, 15–24.

Rosser, J. B. 1939b An informal exposition of proofs of Gödel's theorems and Church's theorem. *J. symbol. Log.*, **4**, 53–60.

Rosser, J. B. 1953 *Logic for mathematicians*. New York: McGraw-Hill.

Rosser, J. B., & A. R. Turquette 1952 *Many-valued logics*. Amsterdam: North-Holland Pub.

Rosser, J. B., & H. Wang 1950 Nonstandard models for formal logic. *J. symbol. Log.*, **15**, 113–129.

Rossman, J. 1931 *The psychology of the inventor*. Washington, D.C.: Inventors' Publ.

Roth, J. P. 1962 *A pragmatic theory of algorithms*. IBM Tech. Rep. 00.918.

Roth, J. P. 1963 The theory of algorithms. In J. G. Arken and C. M. Main (Eds.), *Switching theory in space technology*. Stanford, Calif.: Stanford Univer. Press.

Rozeboom, W. W. 1960 The fallacy of the null-hypothesis significance test. *Psychol. Bull.*, **57**, 416–428.

Rozeboom, W. W. 1961 Formal analysis and the language of behavior theory. In H. Feigl and G. Maxwell (Eds.), *Current issues in the philosophy of science*. New York: Holt, Rinehart and Winston.

Rubin, H., & J. Rubin 1963 *Equivalents of the axiom of choice*. Amsterdam: North-Holland Pub.

Rudin, W. 1953 *Principles of mathematical analysis*. New York: McGraw-Hill.

Russell, B. 1900 A critical exposition of the philosophy of Leibniz. New York: Cambridge Univer. Press.

Russell, B. 1902 On finite and infinite cardinal numbers. *Amer. J. Math.*, **24**, 378–383.

Russell, B. 1908 Mathematical logic as based on the theory of types. *Amer. J. Math.*, **30**, 222–262.

Russell, B. 1914 *Scientific method in*

philosophy. New York: Oxford Univer. Press.

Russell, B. 1918 *Mysticism and logic.* London: Longmans.

Russell, B. 1918–1919 The philosophy of logical atomism. *Monist,* **28,** 495–527; **29,** 32–63, 190–222, 345–380.

Russell, B. 1919 *Introduction to mathematical philosophy.* New York: Macmillan.

Russell, B. 1927 *Philosophy.* New York: Norton.

Russell, B. 1929 *Our knowledge of the external world.* La Salle, Ill.: Open Court.

Russell, B. 1938 (1903) *Principles of mathematics.* (2d ed.) New York: Norton.

Russell, B. 1940 *An inquiry into meaning and truth.* London: G. Allen.

Russell, B. 1945 *A history of western philosophy.* New York: Simon and Schuster.

Russell, B. 1948a *Human knowledge, its scope and limits.* New York: Simon and Schuster.

Russell, B. 1948b Whitehead and *Principia mathematica. Mind,* **57,** 137–138.

Russell, B. 1956a (1897) *An essay on the foundations of geometry.* New foreword by M. Kline. New York: Dover.

Russell, B. 1956b *Logic and knowledge: essays 1901–1950.* (Ed. R. C. Marsh) London: G. Allen.

Ryle, G. 1957 The theory of meaning. In C. A. Mace (Ed.), *British philosophy in the mid-century.* London: G. Allen.

Ryll-Nardzewski, C. 1953 The role of the axiom of induction in elementary arithmetic. *Fund. Math.,* **39,** 239–263.

Sacksteder, W. 1963 Diversity in the behavioral sciences. *Phil. Sci.,* **30,** 375–395.

Samson, E. W. 1954 Information theory: questions and uncertainties. AFCRC Tech. Rep. 54-1.

Sanin, N. A. 1954 On embeddings of

the classical logico-arithmetic calculus. *Doklady Akad. Nauk SSSR,* **94,** 193–196.

de Santillana, G. 1961 *The origins of scientific thought.* New York: New American Library.

Saporta, S. (Ed.) 1961 *Psycholinguistics: a book of readings.* New York: Holt, Rinehart and Winston.

Schaaf, W. L. 1948 *Mathematics, our great heritage: essays on the nature and cultural significance of mathematics.* New York: Harper & Row.

Scheffler, I. 1958 Inductive inference: a new approach. *Science,* **127,** 177–181.

Schiller, F. C. S. 1912 *Formal logic.* London: Macmillan.

Schiller, F. C. S. 1917 Scientific discovery and logical proof. In C. Singer (Ed.), *Studies in the history and the methods of the sciences.* Vol. 1. New York: Oxford Univer. Press.

Schiller, F. C. S. 1929 *Logic for use.* London: G. Bell.

Schlick, M. 1935 De la relation entre les notions psychologiques et les notions physique. *Rev. Synthèse,* **10,** 5–26.

Schlick, M. 1953 Are natural laws conventions? In H. Feigl and M. Brodbeck (Eds.), *Readings in the philosophy of science.* New York: Appleton-Century-Crofts.

Schröder, E. 1890–1905 *Vorlesungen über die Algebra der Logik.* Leipzig: Teubner.

Schrödinger, E. 1935 *Science and the human temperament.* New York: Norton.

Scott, D., & P. Suppes 1958 Foundational aspects of theories of measurement. *J. symbol. Log.,* **23,** 113–128.

Scriven, M. 1958 Definitions, explanations, and theories. *Phil. Sci.,* **2,** 99–195.

Sellars, R. W. 1925 *The essentials of logic.* Boston: Houghton Mifflin.

Shannon, C. E. 1938 A symbolic analysis of relay switching circuits. *Trans. Amer. Inst. elec. Engineers,* **57,** 713.

Shannon, C. E., & W. Weaver 1949 *A mathematical theory of communication.* Urbana, Ill.: Univer. of Illinois Press.

Shaw-Kive, M. 1954 Logical paradoxes for many-valued systems. *J. symbol. Log.,* **19,** 37–40.

Sherif, M. 1934 *Psychology of social norms.* New York: Harper & Row.

Shiraiski, S. 1954 The structure of the continuity of psychological experiences and the physical world. *Scientif. Thought, Tokyo,* **1,** 12–24.

Siegel, S. 1956 *Nonparametric statistics.* New York: McGraw-Hill.

Sierpiński, W. 1950a *Leçons sur les nombres transfinis.* Paris: Gauthier-Villars.

Sierpiński, W. 1950b *Cardinal and ordinal numbers.* New York: Hafner.

Simon, H. A. 1956 A comparison of game theory and learning theory. *Psychometrika,* **21,** 267–272.

Simon, H. A., & A. Newell 1964 Information processing in computer and man. *Amer. Scientist,* **53,** 281–300.

Singer, E. A. 1924 *Mind as behavior.* New York: Adams.

Skinner, B. F. 1958 Teaching machines. *Science,* **128,** 969–977.

Skolem, T. 1922–1923 Einige Bemerkungen zur axiomatischen Begründung der Mengenlehre. *Kongr. Skandinav. Math.,* 217–232.

Skolem, T. 1933 Über die Unmöglichkeit einer vollständigen Charakterisierung der Zahlenreine mittels eines endlichen Axiomensystems. *Norsk Mat. Forenings Skrifter,* Series 2, **10,** 73–82.

Skolem, T. 1934 Über die Nicht-Charakterisierbarkeit der Zahlenreihe mittels endlich oder abzählbar unendlich vieler Aussagen mit ausschliesslich Zahlenvariablen. *Fund. Math.,* **23,** 150–161.

Skolem, T. 1952 A remark on a set theory based on positive logic. *Norske Vid. Selsk. Forh.,* **25,** 112–116.

Skolem, T., G. Hasenjaeger, G. Kreisel,

A. Robinson, H. Wang, L. Henkin, & J. Łoś 1955 *Mathematical interpretations of formal systems.* Amsterdam: North-Holland Pub.

Sloane, E. H. 1945 Reductionism. *Psychol. Rev.,* **52,** 214–223.

Slobodkin, L. B. 1964 The strategy of evolution. *Amer. Scientist,* **52,** 342–357.

Sluckin, W. 1954 *Minds and machines.* Baltimore, Md.: Penguin.

Smith, D. E., & J. Ginsburg 1934 *A history of mathematics in America before 1900. Carus Math. Monogr.* No. 5, Buffalo: Math. Assoc. Amer.

Smullyan, R. M. 1957 Language in which self-reference is possible. *J. symbol. Log.,* **14,** 145–158.

Specker, E. 1949 Nicht konstruktive beweisbare Sätze der Analysis. *J. symbol. Log.,* **14,** 145-158.

Spence, K. W. 1936 The nature of discrimination learning in animals. *Psychol. Rev.,* **43,** 427–449.

Spence, K. W. 1940 Continuous versus non-continuous interpretations of discrimination learning. *Psychol. Rev.,* **47,** 271–288.

Spence, K. W. 1944 The nature of theory construction in contemporary psychology. *Psychol. Rev.,* **51,** 47–68.

Spence, K. W. 1948 The postulates and methods of "behaviorism." *Psychol. Rev.,* **55,** 67–78.

Spence, K. W. 1950 Cognitive versus stimulus-response theories of learning. *Psychol. Rev.,* **57,** 159–172.

de Spinoza, B. 1934 (1677) *Philosophy of Benedict de Spinoza.* (Trans. R. H. M. Elwes) New York: Tudor.

Stern, C. 1949 *Children discover arithmetic.* New York: Harper & Row.

Stevens, S. S. 1939 Psychology and the science of science. *Psychol. Bull.,* **36,** 221–263.

Stevens, S. S. 1958 Measurement and man. *Science,* **127,** 383–389.

Stroll, A. 1954 Is everyday language inconsistent? *Mind,* **63,** 219–225.

Summerfield, A., & D. Legge 1960 Perception and information theory.

Bull. Brit. Psychol. Soc., September, 1–6.

Suppes, P. 1960 A comparison of the meaning and use of models in mathematics and the empirical sciences. *Synthese*, **12**, 287–300.

Suppes, P. 1957 *Introduction to logic*. Princeton, N.J.: Van Nostrand.

Suppes, P. 1959 Measurement, empirical meaningfulness, and three-valued logic. In C. W. Churchman and P. Ratoosh (Eds.), *Measurement: definitions and theories*. New York: Wiley.

Sutton, O. G. 1960 *Mathematics in action*. New York: Harper & Row.

Székely, I. 1950 Knowledge and thinking. *Acta Psychol.*, **7**, 1–24.

Tarski, A., 1931 Sur les ensembles définissables de nombres réels, I. *Fund. Math.*, **17**, 210–239.

Tarski, A. 1933 Einige Betrachtungen über die Begriffe der ω Widerspruchsfreiheit und der ω Vollständigkeit. *Monat. Math. Phys.*, **40**, 97–112.

Tarski, A. 1941 On the calculus of relations. *J. symbol. Log.*, **6**, 73–89.

Tarski, A. 1946 *Introduction to logic*. New York: Oxford Univer. Press.

Tarski, A. 1949 Cancellation laws in the arithmetic of cardinals. *Fund. Math.*, **36**, 76–92.

Tarski, A. 1956 *Logic, semantics, metamathematics*. New York: Oxford Univer. Press.

Tarski, A., & J. C. C. McKinsey 1951 *A decision method for elementary algebra*. Berkeley, Calif.: Univer. of California Press.

Tarski, A., A. Mostowski, & R. M. Robinson 1953 *Undecidable theories*. Amsterdam: North-Holland Pub.

Taylor, A. E. 1936 *Plato*. New York: Dial.

Taylor, C. W. 1964 *Creativity: progress and potential*. New York: McGraw-Hill.

Taylor, D. W. 1958 *Decision making and problem solving*. Tech. Rep. 9. New Haven, Conn.: Yale Univer. Multilithed report.

Taylor, R. 1950 Comments on a mechanistic conception of purposefulness. *Phil. Sci.*, **17**, 310–317.

Ternus, J. 1938 (1926) The problems of phenomenal identity. In W. D. Ellis (Ed.), *A source book of Gestalt psychology*. New York: Harcourt, Brace & World.

Thayer, H. S. 1953 *Newton's philosophy of nature*. New York: Hafner.

Thorndike, E. L. 1932 *The fundamentals of learning*. New York: Columbia Univer. Press.

Thrall, R. M., C. H. Coombs, & R. L. Davis (Eds.) 1954 *Decision processes*. New York: Wiley.

Thurston, H. A. 1956 *The number-system*. New York: Interscience.

Thurstone, L. L. 1947 *Multiple-factor analysis*. Chicago: Univer. of Chicago Press.

Tolman, E. C. 1949 There is more than one kind of learning. *Psychol. Rev.*, **56**, 144–155.

Tomkins, S., & S. Messick (Eds.) 1963 *Simulation of personality processes*. New York: Wiley.

Toulmin, S. 1960 *The philosophy of science*. New York: Harper & Row.

Turing, A. M. 1936–1937 On computable numbers, with an application to the Entscheidungsproblem. *Proc. London Math. Soc.*, Series 2, **42**, 220–265.

Turing, A. M. 1963 Computing machinery and intelligence. In E. A. Feigenbaum and I. Feldman (Eds.), *Computers and thought*. New York: McGraw-Hill.

Uhr, L. 1959 Machine perception of printed and handwritten forms by means of procedures for assessing and recognition of Gestalts. In *Preprints of 14th Assoc. for Computing Machinery Meeting*, Boston.

Uhr, L. 1963 Pattern recognition computers as models for form perception. *Psychol. Bull.*, **60**, 40–73.

Underwood, B. J. 1952 An orientation for research on thinking. *Psychol. Rev.*, **59**, 209–219.

Vaught, R. L. 1954 Applications of

the Löwenheim-Skolem-Tarski theorem to problems of completeness and decidability. *Proc. Akad. Amsterdam*, **57**, 467–472.

Veblen, O. 1952 Opening address. *Proc. int. Congr. Math.*, **1**, 124–125.

Vinacke, W. E. 1952 *The psychology of thinking.* New York: McGraw-Hill.

Vossler, C., & L. Uhr 1962 Computer simulations of a perceptual learning model for sensory pattern recognition, concept formation, and symbol transformation. *Proc. IFIP Congr.*, **62**, 413–418.

Vredenduin, P. G. J. 1954 The logic of negationless mathematics. *Compositio Math.*, **11**, 204–270.

Vuysje, D. 1953 Significs, its tendency, methodology and applications. *Proc. Amer. Acad. Arts Sci.*, **80**, 223–270.

Waismann, F. 1959 *Introduction to mathematical thinking.* New York: Harper & Row. (Reprint of 1951 edition, New York: Unger.)

Walk, R. D., & E. J. Gibson 1963 A comparative and analytical study of visual depth perception. *Psychol. Monogr.*, **75**, Whole No. 15.

Walker, M. 1963 *The nature of scientific thought.* Englewood Cliffs, N.J.: Prentice-Hall.

Wang, H. 1952 Truth definitions and consistency proofs. *Trans. Amer. Math. Soc.*, **71**, 283–291.

Wang, H. 1953 Quelques notions d'axiomatique. *Rev. Phil. Louvain*, **51**, 409–443.

Wang, H. 1955 On formalization. *Mind*, **64**, 226–238.

Wang, H. 1960 Toward mechanical mathematics. *IBM J. Res. Develpm.*, **4**, 2–22.

Wang, H., & R. McNaughton 1953 *Les systèmes axiomatiques de la théorie des ensembles.* Paris: Gauthier-Villard.

Warner, R. 1958 *The Greek philosophers.* New York: New American Library.

Waters, R. H., & L. A. Pennington

1938 Operationism in psychology. *Psychol. Rev.*, **45**, 414–423.

Weaver, W. 1952 Information theory to 1951—a non-technical review. *J. speech hear. Disord.*, **17**, 166–174.

Webster, H. 1952 Dynamic hypothesis in psychology. *Psychol. Rev.*, **59**, 168–170.

Weinberg, J. R. 1960 *An examination of logical positivism.* Paterson, N.J.: Littlefield, Adams.

Weiss, P. 1928 The theory of types. *Mind*, **37**, 338–348.

Weitzenhoffer, A. N. 1951 Mathematical structures and psychological measurements. *Psychometrika*, **16**, 387–406.

Welch, L. 1960 Ideational reorganization of ideas in creative and noncreative thinking. *Ann. N.Y. Acad. Sci.*, **19**, 141–149.

Wells, R. 1961 Meaning and use. In S. Saporta (Ed.), *Psycholinguistics: a book of readings.* New York: Holt, Rinehart and Winston.

Werkmeister, W. H. 1940 *A philosophy of science.* New York: Harper & Row.

Werner, H. 1940 *Comparative psychology of mental development.* New York: Harper & Row.

Wertheimer, M. 1933 Zu dem Problem der Unterscheidung von Einzelinhalt und Teil. *J. Psychol.*, **129**, 353–358.

Wertheimer, M. 1934 On truth. *Soc. Res.*, **1**, 135–146.

Wertheimer, M. 1935 Some problems in the theory of ethics. *Soc. Res.*, **2**, 353–367.

Wertheimer, M. 1938a (1912) Number and numerical concepts in primitive people. In W. D. Ellis (Ed.), *A source book of Gestalt psychology.* New York: Harcourt, Brace & World.

Wertheimer, M. 1938b (1925) The syllogism and productive thinking. In W. D. Ellis (Ed.), *A source book of Gestalt psychology.* New York: Harcourt, Brace & World.

Wertheimer, M. 1938c (1922) The

general theoretical situation. In W. D. Ellis (Ed.), *A source book of Gestalt psychology*. New York: Harcourt, Brace & World.

Wertheimer, M. 1938d (1925) Gestalt theory. In W. D. Ellis (Ed.), *A source book of Gestalt psychology*. New York: Harcourt, Brace & World.

Wertheimer, M. 1938–1939 Unpublished lectures. New York: The New School for Social Research.

Wertheimer, M. 1945 *Productive thinking*. New York: Harper & Row.

Wertheimer, M. 1959 On discrimination experiments: I. two logical structures. (Ed. Lisa Wertheimer) *Psychol. Rev.*, **66**, 252–266.

Weyl, H. 1918 *Das Kontinuum: Kritische Untersuchung über die Grundlagen der Analysis*. Leipzig: von Veit.

Weyl, H. 1919 Über die neue Grundlagenkrise der Mathematik. *Math. Z.*, **10**, 39–79.

Weyl, H. 1926 Die heutige Erkenntnislage in der Mathematik. *Symposium* (Berlin), **1**, 1–32.

Weyl, H. 1928 Diskussionsbemerkungen zu dem zweiten Hilbertschen Vortrag über die Grundlagen der Mathematik. *Abh. Hamburg Univer.*, **6**, 86–88.

Weyl, H. 1931 *Die Stufen des Unendlichen*. Jena: G. Fischer.

Weyl, H. 1946 Mathematics and logic. *Amer. Math. Mon.*, **53**, 2–13.

Weyl, H. 1949 (1927) *Philosophy of mathematics and natural science*. (Rev. English ed.) Princeton, N.J.: Princeton Univer. Press.

Weyl, H. 1951 *Symmetry*. Princeton, N.J.: Princeton Univer. Press.

Wheeler, R. H., & F. T. Perkins 1932 *Principles of mental development*. New York: Crowell.

Whewell, W. 1858 *History of scientific ideas*. New York: Appleton-Century-Crofts.

White, L. A. 1949 *The science of culture*. New York: Farrar, Straus.

White, L. A. 1950 *The evolution of culture*. New York: McGraw-Hill.

White, M. 1955 *The age of analysis*. New York: New American Library.

White, R. K. 1943 The case for the Tolman-Lewin interpretation of learning. *Psychol. Rev.*, **50**, 157–186.

Whitehead, A. N. 1920 *The concept of nature*. New York: Cambridge Univer. Press.

Whitehead, A. N. 1929 *Process and reality*. New York: Macmillan.

Whitehead, A. N. 1948 (1925) *Science and the modern world*. New York: New American Library.

Whitehead, A. N., & B. Russell 1910–1913 Vols. I through III. *Principia mathematica*. New York: Cambridge Univer. Press.

Whorf, B. L. 1950 Language and logic. *Four articles on metalinguistics*. Washington, D.C.: Foreign Service Institute, U.S. Dep. State.

Whorf, B. L. 1956 Language, mind, reality. In J. Carroll (Ed.), *Language, thought, and reality*. New York: Wiley.

Wiener, N. 1948 *Cybernetics*. New York: Wiley.

Wiener, N. 1950 *The human use of human beings*. Boston: Houghton Mifflin.

Wiener, P. P. (Ed.) 1953 *Readings in philosophy of science*. New York: Scribner.

Wilder, R. L. 1928 Concerning R. L. Moore's axioms Σ for plane analysis situs. *Bull. Amer. Math. Soc.*, **34**, 258–271.

Wilder, R. L. 1950 The cultural basis of mathematics. *Proc. int. Congr. Math.*, **1**, 258–271.

Wilder, R. L. 1952 *Introduction to the foundations of mathematics*. New York: Wiley.

Wilder, R. L. 1953 The origin and growth of mathematical concepts. *Bull. Amer. Math. Soc.*, **59**, 423–448.

Wilder, R. L. 1959 The nature of modern mathematics. *Mich. Alum. Quart. Rev.*, **65**, 302–312.

Windelband, W. 1958 (1891) *A his-*

tory of philosophy. Vols. I and II. New York: Harper & Row.

Wisdom, J. 1952 Ludwig Wittgenstein, 1934–1937. *Mind*, **61,** 258–260.

Wisdom, J. 1953 *Philosophy and psychoanalysis*. New York: Oxford Univer. Press.

Wittgenstein, L. 1953 *Philosophical investigations*. (Trans. G. E. M. Anscombe) Oxford, England: Blackwell.

Wittgenstein, L. 1956 *Remarks on the foundations of mathematics*. (Ed. G. H. von Wright, R. Rhees, and G. E. M. Anscombe; Trans. G. E. M. Anscombe) New York: Macmillan.

Wittgenstein, L. 1961 (1922) *Tractatus logico-philosophicus*. (Trans. D. Pears and B. McGuinness) London: Routledge and Kegan Paul.

Wolff, W. 1943 *The expression of personality*. New York: Harper & Row.

Woodger, J. H. 1957 *The axiomatic method in biology*. New York: Cambridge Univer. Press.

Woodworth, R. S. 1938 *Experimental psychology*. New York: Holt, Rinehart and Winston.

Woodworth, R. S., & H. Schlosberg 1954 *Experimental psychology*. (Rev. ed.) New York: Holt, Rinehart and Winston.

Woolf, H. (Ed.) 1961 *Quantification: a history of the meaning of measurement in the natural and social sciences*. Indianapolis, Ind.: Bobbs-Merrill.

von Wright, G. H. 1951a *An essay in modal logic*. Amsterdam: North-Holland Pub.

von Wright, G. H. 1951b A treatise on induction and probability. London: Routledge and Kegan Paul.

Yuttings, S. 1956 Two semantical paradoxes. *J. symbol. Log.*, **20,** 119–120.

Zeller, E. 1955 *Outline of the history of Greek philosophy*. New York: Meridian.

Zermelo, E. 1904 Beweis, dass jede Menge wohlgeordnet werden kann. *Math. Ann.*, **5,** 514–516.

List of Journal
Abbreviations

Abh. Hamburg Univer. Abhandlungen aus dem Mathematischen Seminar der Universität Hamburg (Hamburg)
Acta Psychol. Acta Psychologia (Amsterdam)
Actes 2e Coll. int. Log. Math. Actes du 2e Colloque International de Logique Mathématique (Paris)
Actes XI Congr. int. Phil. Actes XI Congrès International de Philosophie (Brussels).
Actual. Sci. Industr. Actualités Scientifique et Industrielles (Paris)
AFCRC Tech. Rep. Air Force Cambridge Research Center Technical Reports
Amer. J. Math. American Journal of Mathematics
Amer. J. Psychol. American Journal of Psychology
Amer. Math. Mon. American Mathematical Monthly
Amer. Psychologist American Psychologist
Amer. Scientist American Scientist
Ann. Math. Annals of Mathematics
Ann. N.Y. Acad. Sci. Annals of New York Academy of Sciences
Ann. Soc. Polon. Math. Annales de la Société Polonaise de Mathématique (Warsaw)
Behav. Sci. Behavioral Science
Brit. J. Phil. Sci. British Journal for the Philosophy of Science
Brit. J. Psychol. British Journal of Psychology
Brit. J. statist. Psychol. British Journal of Statistical Psychology
Bull. Acad. Polon. Sci. Bulletin de l'Académie Polonaise des Sciences (Warsaw)
Bull. Amer. Math. Soc. Bulletin of the American Mathematical Society
Bull. Brit. Psychol. Soc. Bulletin of the British Psychological Society
Bull. Math. Biophys. Bulletin of Mathematics and Biophysics
Bull. Math. Phys. Bulletin of Mathematics and Physics
Canadian J. Math. Canadian Journal of Mathematics
Carus Math. Monogr. Carus Mathematics Monographs
Centennial Rev. Centennial Review
Compositio Math. Compositio Mathematica (Groningen)
C. R. Acad. Sci., Paris Comptes Rendus Hebdomadaires des Séances de l'Académie des Sciences (Paris)
C. R. 2e Congr. int. Math., Paris Comptes Rendus du 2e Congrès International de Mathématique
Doklady Akad. Nauk SSSR Doklady Akademii Nauk SSSR (Moscow)
Educ. psychol. Measmt Educational and Psychological Measurement

419

Elec. Engng   Electrical Engineering
Erg. Math. Kolloq.   Ergebnisse eines Mathematischen Kolloquiums
Fund. Math.   Fundamenta Mathematicae (Warsaw)
Human Biol.   Human Biology
IBM J. Res. Develpm.   IBM Journal of Research and Development
IBM Tech. Rep.   IBM Technical Report
Indag. Math.   Indagationes Mathematicae (Amsterdam)
IRE Trans. Educ.   International Review of Education, Transactions on Education
Jahresbericht Deutsch. Math. Ver.   Jahresbericht der Deutschen Mathematiker Vereinigung (Stuttgart)
J. Aesthet. Art Critic.   Journal of Aesthetics and Art Criticism
J. educ. Psychol.   Journal of Educational Psychology
J. educ. Res.   Journal of Educational Research
J. exp. Psychol.   Journal of Experimental Psychology
J. gen. Psychol.   Journal of General Psychology
J. genet. Psychol.   Journal of Genetic Psychology
J. indiv. Psychol.   Journal of Individual Psychology
J. Phil.   Journal of Philosophy
J. Phil. Psychol. scientif. Method.   Journal of Philosophy, Psychology, and Scientific Method
J. Psychol.   Journal of Psychology
J. psychol. Res.   Journal of Psychological Researches
J. Reine angew. Math.   Journal fur die reine und angewandte Mathematik (Berlin)
J. Soc. industr. appl. Math.   Journal of the Society of Industrial and Applied Mathematics
J. soc. Issues   Journal of Social Issues
J. speech hear. Disord.   Journal of Speech and Hearing Disorders
J. symbol. Log.   Journal of Symbolic Logic
Kongr. Skandinav Math.   Helsingfors Wissenschaftliche Vorträge gehalten auf dem Fünften Kongress des Skandinavischen Mathematiker in Helsingfors vom 4. bis 7. Juli 1922
L'Ens. Math.   L'Enseignement Mathématique (Geneva)
Math. Ann.   Mathematische Annalen (Berlin-Göttingen-Heidelberg)
Math. B   Mathematica B (Leiden)
Math. Gazette   Mathematical Gazette (London)
Math. Nachr.   Mathematische Nachrichten (Berlin)
Math. Rep.   Mathematics Reports of Rensselaer Polytechnic Institute
Math. Z.   Mathematische Zeitschrift (Berlin-Göttingen-Heidelberg)
Mich. Alum. Quart. Rev.   Michigan Alumni Quarterly Review
Monat. Math. Phys.   Monatshefte für Mathematik und Physik (Vienna)
Nachr. Ges. Wiss. Göttingen Math. Phys. Klasse   Nachrichten der Gesellschaft der Wissenschaften zu Göttingen Mathematisch-Physikalische Klasse (Göttingen)
Nat. Math. Mag.   National Mathematics Magazine
Norsk Mat. Forenings Skrifter   Norsk Matematisk Forenings Skrifter (Oslo)
Norske Vid. Selsk. Forh.   Det Kongelige Norske Videnskabers Selskabs Forhandlinger (Trondheim)
Phil. Phenomen. Res.   Philosophy and Phenomenological Research
Phil. Res.   Philosophical Research
Phil. Rev.   Philosophical Review
Phil. Sci.   Philosophy of Science

Phil. Stud. Philosophical Studies
Proc. Akad. Amsterdam Koninklijke Nederlandse Akademie van Wetenschappen (Amsterdam)
Proc. Amer. Acad. Arts Sci. Proceedings of the American Academy of Arts and Sciences
Proc. Amer. Math. Soc. Proceedings of the American Mathematical Society
Proc. Amer. Phil. Soc. Proceedings of the American Philosophical Society
Proc. 15th int. Congr. Psychol. Proceedings of the Fifteenth International Congress of Psychology
Proc. int. Congr. Math. Proceedings of the International Congress of Mathematicians (Cambridge, Massachusetts)
Proc. IFIP Congr. Proceedings of the International Federation for Information Processing Congress
Proc. IRE Proceedings International Review of Education
Proc. London Math. Soc. Proceedings of the London Mathematical Society
Proc. Nat. Acad. Sci. U.S.A. Proceedings of the National Academy of Sciences of the United States of America
Proc. WJCC Proceedings of the Western Joint Computer Conference
Psychol. Bull. Psychological Bulletin
Psychol. Monogr. Psychological Monographs
Psychol. Rec. Psychological Record
Psychol. Rep. Psychological Reports
Psychol. Rev. Psychological Review
Rev. int. Phil. Revue Internationale de Philosophie (Brussels)
Rev. Metaphys. Review of Metaphysics
Rev. Metaphys. Morale Revue de Métaphysique et de Morale (Paris)
Rev. Phil. Louvain Revue Philosophique de Louvain (Belgium)
Rev. Synthèse Revue de Synthèse (Paris)
Rozprawy Mat. Polska Akademia Nauk Instytut Matematyczny, Rozprawy Matematyczne (Warsaw)
Sci. Monogr. Science Monograph
Scientif. Amer. Scientific American
Scientif. Mon. Scientific Monthly
Scientif. Thought, Tokyo Scientific Thought (Tokyo)
Sitz. Preuss. Akad. Wiss. Berlin Sitzungsberichte der Preussischen Akademie der Wissenschaften, Physikalisch-Mathematisch Klasse (Berlin)
Soc. Res. Social Research
South African J. Sci. South African Journal of Science
Stockholm Stud. Phil. Stockholm Studies in Philosophy (Stockholm)
10th int. Congr. Phil., Amsterdam Library of 10th International Congress of Philosophy (Amsterdam)
Trans. Amer. Inst. elec. Engineers Transactions of the American Institute of Electrical Engineers
Trans. Amer. Math. Soc. Transactions of the American Mathematical Society
Univer. Torino Rend. Sem. Mat. Università e Politecnico di Torino, Rendiconti del Seminario Matematico (Turin)
Verh. Akad. Wet. Amsterdam Verhandelingen der Koninklijke Nederlandse Akademie van Wetenschappen (Amsterdam)

Name Index

Subject Index